# Fundamentals of QUALITATIVE CHEMICAL ANALYSIS
## *Semimicro Method*


**ROY K. McALPINE, Ph.D.**

and

**BYRON A. SOULE, Sc.D.**

*University of Michigan*


*FOURTH EDITION*


**D. VAN NOSTRAND COMPANY, INC.**

PRINCETON, NEW JERSEY

TORONTO LONDON

NEW YORK

D. VAN NOSTRAND COMPANY, INC.

120 Alexander St., Princeton, New Jersey
257 Fourth Avenue, New York 10, New York
25 Hollinger Rd., Toronto 16, Canada
Macmillan & Co., Ltd., St. Martin's St., London, W.C. 2, England

*All correspondence should be addressed to the principal office of the company at Princeton, N. J.*



Published simultaneously in Canada by
D. VAN NOSTRAND COMPANY (Canada), LTD.

Library of Congress Catalog Card No. 56-6886



***First Published, July 1936***
*Two Reprintings*

***Second Edition, September 1941***
*Five Reprintings*

***Third Edition, January 1949***
*Two Reprintings*

***Fourth Edition, January, 1956***

PRINTED IN THE UNITED STATES OF AMERICA

# Preface to the Fourth Edition

In the several revisions of this book there has been no change in the point of view that the main purposes of a course in Qualitative Analysis are to give the student direct contact with the chemical behavior of a number of common metals and acid radicals and to emphasize the necessity of working under controlled conditions in order to carry out desired reactions successfully. Further, in using the laboratory period essentially as a time for study, it is desirable that adequate time be allowed for work with known solutions where any irregularities may be recognized immediately. In the notes on analytical procedures those irregularities which are most commonly encountered by the student have been discussed in more than usual detail.

The main changes that have been introduced in this revision are:

1. The procedures have been rewritten to the semi-micro scale. In most cases this has involved changing quantities from milliliters to drops and the use of the centrifuge instead of filtering. In the few cases where, on the macro-scale, the reagent is added dropwise, it is necessary on the semi-micro scale to use a considerably diluted reagent for the final adjustment.

2. There has been added at the end of Chapter 3 a short discussion of activity of electrolytes, with particular application to solubility products and ionization constants.

3. The problems covering the application of ionization constants and solubility products to the group reagents (former Chapter 4) have been transferred to the chapters dealing with the individual groups and have been somewhat expanded to cover additional cases in the analysis of the groups.

4. The material on type questions (former Chapter 8) has been somewhat condensed and transferred to the appendix where it precedes the questions and equivalence problems for the individual groups.

5. The general review material in the appendix has been reorganized and divided into Equations, Problems (normal and empirical solutions, boiling and freezing points, ionization constants, pH, hydrolysis, solubility products, and chemical equilibrium) and Review Questions.

6. In the appendix has been placed a brief discussion of some mathematical relations, covering significant figures, useful approximations, some exponential relations, ratios and fractions, and the use of logarithms.

7. The emphasis on "net equations" in contrast to molecular or ionic equations has been increased. Thus the equations at the end of the chapters deal-

ing with the metallic groups have all been changed to this form. The same is true of most of the individual equations appearing throughout the text. In a few cases this involves a departure from formulas commonly used. Thus calculations based on ionization constants indicate that the metals lead, mercury, bismuth, cadmium, and iron (ferric) will be found after Group I chiefly as $PbCl^+$, $HgCl_4^{--}$, $BiCl_4^-$, $CdCl_2$, and $FeCl^{++}$. Similarly, in alkaline sulfide solution the major constituent is $HS^-$ rather than $S^{--}$, and the thio-anions $AsS_4^{---}$, $SbS_4^{---}$, and $SnS_3^{--}$ are derived from weak enough acids to be largely converted to $H_2AsS_4^-$, $H_2SbS_4^-$, and $HSnS_3^-$ in ammoniacal solutions. Further, in keeping with the modern trend, the dissolving of the amphoteric hydroxides in strong alkali is now explained as involving the formation of hydroxyl complexes rather than the neutralization of weak acids. However, since the titration curves for the dissolving processes do not show significant breaks, it has seemed adequate to add only a single hydroxyl ion to the formula of the hydroxide to represent the complex in solution. Thus, $Al(OH)_3$, $Sb(OH)_3$, $Sb(OH)_5$, $Sn(OH)_2$, $Sn(OH)_4$, $Pb(OH)_2$, and $Zn(OH)_2$ are considered to form $Al(OH)_4^-$, $Sb(OH)_4^-$, $Sb(OH)_6^-$, $Sn(OH)_3^-$, $Sn(OH)_5^-$, $Pb(OH)_3^-$, and $Zn(OH)_3^-$. Finally, equations formerly using $H^+$ have been changed to $H_3O^+$.

8. In balancing equations by the oxidation number method the change from $H^+$ to $H_3O^+$ has made it desirable to reverse the last two steps as usually given. Thus, in next to the last step, one now determines the number of molecules of $H_3O^+$ or $OH^-$ needed by checking the charges on the other reagents and products as already adjusted. The last step then inserts $H_2O$ as reagent or product in the amount necessary to account for the extra atoms of hydrogen and oxygen. For example, in the reaction $CuS + HNO_3 = Cu(NO_3)_2 + S + NO + H_2O$, after the stage is reached, $3CuS + 2NO_3^- + ?H_3O^+ = 3Cu^{++} + 3S + 2NO + ?H_2O$, the fact that there are 2 minus charges on the $2NO_3^-$ and 6 plus charges on the $3Cu^{++}$ shows that $8H_3O^+$ must be used as reagent to balance the charges. From this the coefficient 12 for $H_2O$ is easily obtained. Similarly, in the ammonia test for a nitrate, after the point is reached, $3NO_3^- + 8Al + ?OH^- = 8Al(OH)_4^- + 3NH_3$, the difference in negative charges on the two sides shows that $5OH^-$ must be used as reagent. After this, the extra atoms of H and O in the products show the need of $18H_2O$ as additional reagent.

In conclusion, we wish to acknowledge the assistance of Dr. P. F. Weatherill who pioneered in the use of the text in classes employing semi-micro procedures, and the friendly advice of Drs. P. J. Elving and J. H. Hodges with whom many of the changes were discussed.

R. K. M.
B. A. S.

# Contents

# I

# Introduction

**Qualitative Chemical Analysis** is the identification of elements, radicals, and pure substances in compounds and mixtures. This covers the whole realm of chemistry and is obviously more than could be attempted except after thorough acquaintance with the descriptive chemistry of both the inorganic and organic fields. Actually, the course given at the end of a semester's or a year's work in college chemistry is limited to the inorganic field—some twenty or less of the common metals and ten or twelve of the acid radicals.

The reason for thus restricting the ground to be covered is found in the fact that there are relatively few cases in which identifying tests are sufficiently characteristic and delicate to permit their use on the original materials without regard to other constituents present. Since other substances do interfere with the best available tests for most of the individual constituents, it becomes necessary to carry out a preliminary series of operations by which the metal or acid radical may be separated from interfering substances before it can be identified.

The operations thus used may, in individual cases, employ a wide range of chemical resources: precipitation, oxidation, reduction, complex formation, distillation, extraction, etc. The procedures as commonly worked out are limited so far as possible to operations that may be performed rapidly and effectively with simple apparatus. For this reason precipitation is the process most frequently employed, since it is generally possible to find a reagent that will form a precipitate with one metal or acid radical but not with another, so that the separation of the two may be effected (if the precipitate is sufficiently insoluble) by simply centrifuging and washing the precipitate. It may then be examined for such metals or acid radicals as form insoluble compounds with the reagent added, whereas the clear solution may be tested for those that do not.

A systematic procedure has been developed for the metals involving the use of reagents to divide the whole list into a series of smaller groups by precipitation reactions. The first reagent to be added is called the First Group

Reagent, and the metals thus separated from the rest by centrifuging and washing constitute Group I. To the clear solution, properly acidified, is added the Second Group Reagent, and the metals thus separated constitute Group II. This is continued until the metals forming precipitates with common reagents have been removed in their respective groups, the few remaining being classed as the last group in the series.

In such a procedure it is clear that preliminary experiments might be tried with various series of group reagents. The metals found in any one group would depend on the reagent used for the precipitation of that group and also on the reagents that had been used for the precipitation of previous groups. From this it might appear that there should be several schemes in common use. It is interesting, however, to note that, although other group reagents are suggested from time to time, the overwhelming majority of the procedures start with HCl as the first group reagent, then precipitate Group II with $H_2S$ in acid solution. For the precipitation of Group III the method presented in this book calls for $NH_4OH$ in slight excess in the presence of a large amount of $NH_4Cl$. The filtrate is treated with more $NH_4OH$ and then $H_2S$ is passed in to precipitate Group IV. Many other schemes use $NH_4OH + H_2S$ as the third group reagent, thus precipitating in Group III the metals which are here classed as Groups III and IV. This is the major variation in the group system as worked out for the common metals. The next group reagent is $(NH_4)_2CO_3$ in all the widely used procedures. It is evident from this that, while variations are suggested from time to time, none of the alternative plans show significant improvement over the present scheme in the two fundamental features of accuracy and convenience.

In the *selection of group reagents* four qualifications are of major importance. (1) The reagent should precipitate the metals of the given group completely enough so that the amount that remains in solution can be disregarded. (2) The reagent should form precipitates that are easy to work with in carrying out the further steps of separation and identification within the group. (3) The reagent should form precipitates that are reasonably free from contamination with later group metals. (4) The reagent should not interfere with later steps or should be easily removed.

None of the group reagents in the present scheme is satisfactory in the sense that it possesses fully the qualifications thus listed. In the discussions of the various groups, frequent suggestions of irregularities will be found which make it clear that the separations do not always proceed smoothly. Within recent years considerable interest has developed in the search for organic reagents that may be used in chemical analysis. In specific cases a number of important discoveries have been made, and it is entirely possible that as this work is extended a new set of group reagents will be discovered that will be free from many of the shortcomings of the ones in present use. It is possible even that specific reagents will be found for a sufficiently large number of the common metals so that the whole basis of the analytical procedure will be changed. Thus far, however, the systematic scheme in present use, with the necessity for reasonable attention to a number of specific details, remains as satisfactory as any available for general use.

## REVIEW MATERIAL

The following summary of certain parts of General Chemistry is given with a twofold purpose: (*a*) to furnish a basis for the explanations used in Qualitative Analysis, and (*b*) to indicate the topics that should be studied by those who need to supplement their previous training.

### Definitions

The use of descriptive words involves difficulties arising chiefly because the persons concerned are not in accord as to the precise meaning of the words. The scientist tries to avoid trouble of this sort by carefully defining his terms and then always using them in the strictly technical sense. The definitions given below are by no means flawless, but they will probably be satisfactory for present purposes.

*Acid.* An acid is a substance which in aqueous solution can furnish protons.

*Anion.* An anion is an ion bearing a negative charge.

*Base.* A base is a substance which in aqueous solution will combine with protons. (Is water an acid or a base?)

*Cation.* A cation is an ion bearing a positive charge.

*Concentration.* Concentration is the amount of solute per unit volume of solution.

*Empirical Solution.* An empirical solution is one made up so that one milliliter is equivalent to a unit amount (e.g., 0.1 g. or 0.01 g.) of some other substance. When using such a solution, calculation of results is avoided except for the shifting of a decimal point or multiplication by a simple factor. (Example: If 25.8 ml. of a certain solution of $AgNO_3$ were required to precipitate the $Cl^-$ from a sample of NaCl, and the $AgNO_3$ was made up so that 1 ml. was equivalent to 0.01 g. of NaCl, then the amount of NaCl in the sample was 0.258 g.)

*Equation.* An equation is a shorthand statement of the materials entering into a reaction, the products formed, and the ratio in which combination takes place. (Note that an equation merely tells what substances interact, the amount of each involved, the products formed, and the amount of each. An equation does not explain how or why the reaction indicated takes place, at what temperature or pressure, the equilibrium conditions, if an excess of one reagent is needed, etc., etc.)

*Formula.* A formula is a group of symbols used to represent the correct atomic composition of a compound.

*Ion.* An ion is an atom or group of atoms bearing an electric charge and usually (always in our work) found in aqueous solution.

*Molar Solution.* A molar solution is one that contains one gram molecular weight of solute per liter of solution. Such a solution is prepared by dissolving the molecular weight, in grams, of solute in less than a liter of water and then diluting to that volume. (In accurate work would the temperature be considered?)

*Normal Solution.* A normal solution is one that contains one gram equivalent of solute per liter of solution. In neutralization reactions one gram equivalent is the amount that will supply one gram atom of replaceable hydrogen or one gram molecule of replaceable hydroxyl radical; in oxidation or reduction reactions one gram equivalent is the amount that will carry out one unit of oxidation or reduction; in other cases the specific nature of the reaction involved must be taken into account (see p. 30).

*Precipitate.* A precipitate is a solid separating from solution. (Precipitates are described by giving their color and form, i.e., crystalline, gelatinous, curdy, flocculent, amorphous.)

*Radical.* A radical is an atom or group of atoms reacting as a unit.

*Reagent.* A reagent is anything added to set up desired conditions or to test the chemical behavior of a substance.

*Residue.* A residue is a remainder or surplus after a part has been removed, e.g., a precipitate becomes a residue upon centrifugation. A residue is not necessarily a solid.

*Salt.* A salt is a compound which contains a positive radical other than hydrogen and a negative radical other than hydroxyl. If the compound also contains hydrogen as a positive radical it is called an acid salt; if it contains hydroxyl (or oxygen) it is called a basic salt.

*Solute.* A solute is the substance dissolved. It may be a gas, liquid or solid.

*Solution.* A solution is a homogeneous mixture, mechanically inseparable and variable within limits. There are nine kinds of solutions of which a solid dissolved in water is only one.

*Solvent.* A solvent is the dissolving medium. In general it may be distinguished from the solute on the basis of the relative amount present, occasionally only by mutual agreement.

*Valence.* Valence is the combining power of an element or radical expressed in terms of the hydrogen atom.

## Nomenclature

*Hydroxides.* Name derived from the metal; e.g., NaOH is sodium hydroxide. In case the metal has more than one valence the stem of the metal with the suffix OUS, indicating the lower valence, or IC, indicating the higher valence, is used; e.g., $Fe(OH)_2$ is ferrous hydroxide and $Fe(OH)_3$ is ferric hydroxide.

*Acids.*

(*a*) Two-element acids are named by prefixing HYDRO to the stem of the negative element and adding the suffix IC; e.g., HCl is hydrochloric acid. ($H_2S$ according to this rule should be named hydrosulfuric acid but is usually called hydrogen sulfide.)

(*b*) Oxygen acids.

(1) One acid, usually the more common, is selected and named by adding the suffix IC to the stem of the non-metallic element; e.g., $HClO_3$ is chloric acid.

(2) The acid containing more oxygen (higher valence of the non-metal) is distinguished by the prefix PER; e.g., $HClO_4$ is perchloric acid.

(3) The acid containing less oxygen than in (1) (lower valence of the non-metal) is distinguished by adding the suffix OUS to the stem of the non-metallic element; e.g., $HClO_2$ is chlorous acid.

(4) The acid containing still less oxygen is distinguished by an additional affix, HYPO; e.g., HClO is hypochlorous acid.

*Salts.* (Normal.) The name of the positive ion of the hydroxide, without further modification, forms one part whereas the other is derived from the name of the acid.

(*a*) HYDRO acids yield IDE salts, HCl forms chlorides—with $Fe(OH)_2$, ferrous chloride; with $Fe(OH)_3$, ferric chloride.

(*b*) OUS acids yield ITE salts. Hypochlorous acid forms hypochlorites and chlorous acid forms chlorites.

(*c*) IC oxygen acids yield ATE salts. Chloric acid forms chlorates and perchloric acid forms perchlorates.

## Summary of Reactions

Whenever a reagent is added to a system in equilibrium the equilibrium is destroyed and a new one set up. This may be effected by the formation of a precipitate, gas, complex ion, or slightly ionized compound, or through oxidation and reduction. If any type of readjustment is sufficiently general in application it may be used to divide ions into classes or groups. The following is such a classification involving the extent to which the compounds indicated are soluble in water.

1. All normal nitrates are soluble.

2. All normal chlorides except AgCl and $Hg_2Cl_2$ are soluble, $PbCl_2$ slightly soluble.

3. All normal sulfates except $BaSO_4$, $SrSO_4$, $PbSO_4$, and $Hg_2SO_4$ are soluble, $CaSO_4$ and $Ag_2SO_4$ slightly soluble.

4. Carbonates of the alkalis (Na, K, $NH_4^+$) are soluble, all others, insoluble. ($Fe^{+3}$, $Al^{+3}$, $Cr^{+3}$ do not form carbonates in the presence of water. They form hydroxides.)

5. Sulfides of the alkalis are soluble; the others, insoluble. (Al and Cr do not form sulfides in the presence of water.) The sulfides of Ba, Sr, Ca, and Mg are largely hydrolyzed by water.

6. Oxides and hydroxides of the alkalis are soluble; the others, insoluble. (Ca, Sr and Ba form slightly to moderately soluble hydroxides. $As_2O_3$ is also only slightly soluble, but is better known in solution as arsenious acid, $H_3AsO_3$.)

Most reagents are capable of entering into several different kinds of reaction, such as double decomposition, displacement, oxidation, reduction, formation of complex compounds, etc. The following examples will help to make this point clearer:

1. **HCl** (*a*), as a strong acid, will neutralize bases and interact with metallic oxides and hydroxides with formation of salts and water; (*b*), as a mild oxidizing acid, will interact with metals above hydrogen in the electromotive series with liberation of hydrogen (the HCl is reduced to $H_2$); (*c*), as a soluble chloride, will form insoluble chlorides with silver, lead, and mercurous ions; (*d*), as a soluble chloride, will be oxidized in acid solution to chlorine by various strong oxidizing agents such as $HNO_3$, $K_2Cr_2O_7$, $Pb_3O_4$, $KMnO_4$, etc.; (*e*), as a soluble chloride, will combine with AgCl forming complex ions, $AgCl_2^-$, $AgCl_3^{--}$, etc., which increases the solubility of AgCl very appreciably.

2. **$HNO_3$** (*a*), as a strong acid, will neutralize bases including metallic oxides and hydroxides with formation of salts and water and will dissolve most of the insoluble salts of the weak acids, except that Sn and Sb are converted to $(H_2SnO_3)_x$ and $SbO(OH)_3$, respectively; (*b*), as a moderately strong oxidant, will dissolve all of the common metals except Cr, Al, Sb, and Sn (the latter two are readily attacked but form precipitates of $SbO(OH)_3$ and $(H_2SnO_3)_x$, respectively), and will oxidize Fe(ous), Sn(ous), Cu(ous), Hg(ous), $I^-$, $Br^-$, $Cl^-$, $S^{--}$ and $SO_3^{--}$ to Fe(ic), Sn(ic), Cu(ic), Hg(ic), $I_2$, $Br_2$, $Cl_2$, S°, and $SO_4^{--}$, respectively. In these reactions the nitric acid is reduced largely to NO. (*c*) Nitric acid will not precipitate nitrates except that in high concentration the solubility of several of the nitrates, especially $Ba(NO_3)_2$, is reduced considerably. In the case of alkaline solutions of hydroxy-complexes and most of the complex ammonia ions, partial neutralization with $HNO_3$ will usually cause precipitation of the corresponding hydroxide.

$$Pb(OH)_3^- + H_3O^+ = \underline{Pb(OH)_2} + 2H_2O$$

$$Cu(NH_3)_4^{++} + 2H_3O^+ = \underline{Cu(OH)_2} + 4NH_4^+$$

3. **$H_2SO_4$** (*a*), as a strong acid, will neutralize bases, including metallic oxides and hydroxides, with formation of salts and water; will dissolve most of the insoluble salts of weak acids, except that those metals will precipitate whose sulfates are insoluble; (*b*), as a mild oxidant in dilute solution, will dissolve metals above hydrogen in the electromotive series (see 10), the metal being oxidized to the lower salt-forming valence and the hydrogen ion reduced to $H_2$; (*c*), as a fairly strong oxidizing agent in hot concentrated solution, will dissolve even the common metals below hydrogen in the electromotive series, the metals being oxidized to their higher salt-forming valence (except Sb which forms $Sb_2(SO_4)_3$), and the acid being reduced to $SO_2$. Many of the other fairly strong reducing agents are oxidized by concentrated $H_2SO_4$, including $I^-$, $Br^-$, $S^{--}$, $Fe^{++}$, $Sn^{++}$, etc. With the strongest reducing agents some $S^\circ$ and $H_2S$ may be formed, with others not so strong the $H_2SO_4$ is reduced chiefly to $SO_2$; (*d*), as a soluble highly ionized sulfate, will form insoluble to slightly soluble sulfates with silver, lead, mercurous, barium, strontium and calcium ions. In concentrated sulfuric acid many of the common soluble sulfates are only slightly soluble, whereas most of the insoluble sulfates show marked increase in solubility. In the case of alkaline solutions of amphoteric hydroxides and most of the complex ammonia ions, partial neutralization with $H_2SO_4$ will usually cause precipitation of the corresponding hydroxide.

4. **HI** (or KI in acid solution) shows behavior similar to HCl, except that HI is a stronger reducing agent than HCl, being oxidized to $I_2$ by such mild oxidizing agents as $FeCl_3$, $CuCl_2$, etc., and enters more readily into the formation of complexes. Of the latter $BiI_4^-$ is important as a means of identifying Bi, and $HgI_4^{--}$ is important as the base of Nessler's reagent, used in testing for $NH_3$. Further, by formation of $HgI_4^{--}$, HI will dissolve Hg with evolution of $H_2$, contrary to the expectation from the electromotive series. The insoluble iodides are AgI, $PbI_2$, $Hg_2I_2$, $HgI_2$, $BiI_3$, CuI.

5. **NaOH** (and other strong alkalis such as KOH and $Ba(OH)_2$) (*a*), will neutralize acids; (*b*), will oxidize Al, Zn, and, less readily, Cr, to $Al(OH)_4^-$, $Zn(OH)_3^-$ and $Cr(OH)_4^-$ with evolution of $H_2$; (*c*), will precipitate oxides of Ag, $Hg_2^{++}$ and $Hg^{++}$, and hydroxides of the other common metals except the alkalis and alkaline earths. The following insoluble hydroxides are amphoteric: $Pb(OH)_2$, $Al(OH)_3$, $Cr(OH)_3$, $Zn(OH)_2$, $Sn(OH)_2$, $SnO(OH)_2$, $Sb_2O_3$, $SbO(OH)_3$. They dissolve in excess of strong alkali by formation of hydroxy-complexes, forming: $Pb(OH)_3^-$, $Al(OH)_4^-$, $Cr(OH)_4^-$, $Zn(OH)_3^-$, $Sn(OH)_3^-$, $Sn(OH)_5^-$, $Sb(OH)_4^-$, $Sb(OH)_6^-$. The failure of As to ppt. with NaOH is due to the high solubility of the hydroxides (acids) in water.

6. **$NH_4OH$** * (*a*), as a weak base, will neutralize the common acids, although the very weak acids—including the amphoteric hydroxides listed in (5)—are acted upon only to a slight extent; (*b*), as a mild reducing agent, will reduce (especially in the presence of NaOH, etc.) some of the stronger oxidizing agents such as $Cl_2$, $Br_2$, and $KMnO_4$ to $Cl^-$, $Br^-$, and $MnO_2$, the $NH_4OH$ being oxidized to $N_2$; (*c*), as a precipitating agent, will precipitate the oxide of silver and hydroxides of the other common metals except the alkalis, alkaline earths and mercury (in the latter case mercuric amino compounds are precipitated, e.g., $Hg_2Cl_2$ forms $Hg_2NH_2Cl$; $HgCl_2$ forms $HgNH_2Cl$); (*d*), as an unstable compound, supplies $NH_3$ which will combine with $Ag^+$, $Cu^{++}$, $Cd^{++}$, $Co^{++}$, $Ni^{++}$, and $Zn^{++}$ to form complex ions. This reaction takes place readily enough to dissolve the common precipitates of these metals, such as the oxides, hydroxides, carbonates, phosphates, etc., in fact, all but the most insoluble compounds such as the sulfides, AgI and $Ni(C_4H_7N_2O_2)_2$.

7. **$H_2S$** (*a*), as a weak acid, is neutralized by strong bases such as NaOH and $Ba(OH)_2$, but incompletely by $NH_4OH$; (*b*), as a fairly strong reducing agent, will reduce $HNO_3$, $K_2Cr_2O_7$, $KMnO_4$, $FeCl_3$, etc., being oxidized to S or even to $H_2SO_4$ by the stronger oxidizers; (*c*), as a precipitating agent, will precipitate sulfides of Ag, Hg ($Hg_2^{++}$ forms HgS + Hg), Bi, Cu, As, Sb, Sn, Pb, Cd, Zn, Fe, Co, Ni, and Mn. Of these, the sulfides of Ag, Hg, Bi, and Cu form readily in alkaline, neutral or even strongly acid solution; those of Pb, Cd, and Zn precipitate readily in alkaline, neutral or very slightly acid solution; those of Fe, Co, Ni, and Mn precipitate readily only in alkaline solution. The sulfides of As, $Sn^{+4}$, and $Sb^{+5}$ precipitate only in acid solution. In alkaline solution $H_2S$ will dissolve $As_2S_3$, $As_2S_5$, $SnS_2$, and $Sb_2S_5$ forming sulfo ions, e.g., $HAsS_4^{--}$, $HSnS_3^-$, and $HSbS_4^{--}$.

8. **NaCN** (*a*), as a salt of a very weak acid, will neutralize acid solutions, setting free HCN, which is extremely poisonous (*precaution:* do not add NaCN to an acid solution); (*b*), as a reducing agent, will reduce copper to the cuprous condition, permanganate and manganate to manganese dioxide, the cyanide being oxidized to cyanogen or a cyanate ($(CN)_2$ or NaCNO); (*c*), as a precipitating agent, NaCN will precipitate all the common metals except the alkalis, alkaline earths and mercury. With ferric iron, chromium and aluminium the precipitate is an hydroxide; in the other cases, a cyanide. The less soluble cyanides are Ag, Pb, Bi, Cu, Cd, Co, Ni, Zn, and Mn. Many

* A number of recent texts call this reagent "ammonia solution" and account for its alkalinity by the reaction, $NH_3 + H_2O = NH_4^+ + OH^-$. However, Sidgwick (Chemical Elements and Their Compounds, Oxford, 1950, pp. 659–60) believes that while the reagent does consist to a considerable extent of $NH_3$ dissolved in water, a moderate fraction is also hydrated to $NH_4OH$ (approx. 53% in 0.1 *M* solution at 25°C.) The ionization constant, $K_{NH_4OH} = 1.8 \times 10^{-5}$ dodges the question of equilibrium between the two forms by using $[NH_3] + [NH_4OH]$ in the denominator, $\frac{[NH_4^+] \times [OH^-]}{[NH_3] + [NH_4OH]} = 1.8 \times 10^{-5}$. For the precipitation of hydroxides the formula $NH_4OH$ will be used, but for the formation of complex ions the reagent will be regarded as $NH_3$.

of the metals form double or complex cyanides with excess of the reagent. Formulas for the more common of these are as follows: $NaAg(CN)_2$, $Na_2Cu(CN)_3$, $Na_2Cd(CN)_4$, $K_4Fe(CN)_6$, $K_3Fe(CN)_6$, $Na_4Co(CN)_6$, $Na_3Co(CN)_6$, $Na_2Ni(CN)_4$, and $Na_2Zn(CN)_4$. Potassium ferro- and ferricyanides are important reagents, both in analytical chemistry and elsewhere.

9. **$Na_2CO_3$** (or $K_2CO_3$) (*a*) will neutralize the common acids, with evolution of $CO_2$. With the very weak acids, including the amphoteric hydroxides (see 5), this takes place to only a very slight extent; (*b*) will dissolve Al and Zn slowly with formation of $Al(OH)_4^-$ and $Zn(OH)_3^-$ and evolution of $CO_2$ and $H_2$; (*c*), as a precipitating agent, will precipitate hydroxides of Sb, $Sn^{+4}$, $Fe^{+3}$, $Cr^{+3}$, and $Al^{+3}$, and normal or basic carbonates of the rest of the common metals except the alkalis and $NH_4^+$. The carbonates of Ag, Cu, and Hg form oxides on heating.

10. The **Electromotive Series** shows the order in which the metals displace each other from combination, the most electropositive metals placed first as follows: K, Na, Ba, Sr, Ca, Mg, Al, Mn, Zn, Cd, Cr, Fe, Co, Ni, Sn, Pb, H, Cu, As, Bi, Sb, Hg, Ag, Pt, Au.

## *LABORATORY EXERCISES*

1. *Reaction of* NaOH *with* $Cu(NO_3)_2$ *and* $Pb(NO_3)_2$.

Place 3–4 drops of $Cu(NO_3)_2$ and $Pb(NO_3)_2$ test solutions (10 mg. of metal per ml.) in separate test tubes and treat each with reagent NaOH, adding a drop at a time and shaking after each addition until the solution becomes alkaline (litmus paper test); then add 2–3 drops excess, mix thoroughly, and compare the results.

2. *Reaction of* $NH_4OH$ *with* $Cu(NO_3)_2$ *and* $Pb(NO_3)_2$.

Repeat Experiment 1 using $NH_4OH$ in place of NaOH.

3. *Effect of* $NH_4Cl$ *on the precipitation of* $Al(OH)_3$ *and* $Mg(OH)_2$ *with* $NH_4OH$.

Place 2–3 drops of $Al(NO_3)_3$ in each of two test tubes and dilute to 10 drops with distilled water. To one of the tubes add about 50 mg. of $NH_4Cl$ and shake until dissolved. Next add about 1 drop of $NH_4OH$ to each of the two tubes, shake thoroughly, and compare the amounts of $Al(OH)_3$ precipitated in the two cases.

Repeat the experiment using $Mg(NO_3)_2$ in place of $Al(NO_3)_3$. Result? Explain the difference noted.

4. *Effect of* $NH_4Cl$ *on a solution of sodium aluminate.*

Prepare a solution of $NaAl(OH)_3$ by placing 2–3 drops of $Al(NO_3)_3$ in a test tube and adding reagent NaOH 1 drop at a time, with shaking, until the solution is strongly alkaline and clear. Dilute to about 10 drops with distilled water, add 50 mg. of $NH_4Cl$ and shake until dissolved. Explain the reprecipitation of $Al(OH)_3$. Note that the precipitate is more opaque than that obtained in (3).

5. *Reaction of* $H_2S$ *in acid solution.*

Place 3–4 drops of $Cu(NO_3)_2$, $FeCl_3$, and $Ni(NO_3)_2$ in separate test tubes, add 1 drop of reagent HCl to each and then pass in $H_2S$ for about half a minute. (Rinse $H_2S$-tube after using in one solution before using in the next.) Compare the results obtained in the three cases.

6. *Reaction of* $H_2S$ *in alkaline solution.*

Place 3–4 drops of $Cu(NO_3)_2$, $FeCl_3$, and $Ni(NO_3)_2$ in separate test tubes, add 3–4 drops of reagent $NH_4OH$ to each tube, and note that both copper and nickel form clear solutions while the iron remains as a brown precipitate of $Fe(OH)_3$. Pass $H_2S$ into each of the three tubes for about half a minute and note the results. Compare the action of $H_2S$ on nickel in acid and in alkaline solution. Explain the difference. Which is less soluble in water, $Fe(OH)_3$ or $Fe_2S_3$? Justify your answer by reference to the experiment. Same for $Cu(OH)_2$ and CuS.

7. *Reaction of* KI *with* $Pb(NO_3)_2$, $BiCl_3$, *and* $FeCl_3$.

Place 1–2 drops of $Pb(NO_3)_2$, $BiCl_3$, and $FeCl_3$ in separate test tubes, add 1–2 drops of reagent KI to each, and note results. To the tubes containing Bi and Fe add 2 drops of carbon tetrachloride and shake to extract any free iodine.

## *HOME EXERCISES*

1. Tabulate the reaction of $AgNO_3$ with (*a*) HCl, (*b*) NaOH, (*c*) $NH_4OH$, (*d*) KI, (*e*) $H_2S$ in acid solution, (*f*) $H_2S$ in alkaline solution.
2. Same as Exercise 1 for $Pb(NO_3)_2$, $Cu(NO_3)_2$, $BiCl_3$, $FeCl_3$, $K_2Cr_2O_7$, $NiCl_2$, $ZnCl_2$, $KMnO_4$, $BaCl_2$, $SbCl_3$, $SnCl_4$.

# 2

# *Formulas and Equations*

The idea of chemical equivalence is fundamental. It has two aspects: equivalence in function and in combining capacity. The first meaning is involved when one considers the various reagents or reactions available for getting a particular result. In chemical shorthand the term is used in the other sense because symbols, formulas and equations imply valence, combining weights, etc. The present chapter is concerned with this latter meaning of the expression and assumes that chemical equivalence is measured using hydrogen as the basis, one atom of which represents unit valence or combining power. If one atom of another element will combine with or replace one atom of hydrogen, that element is univalent in the case under examination.

## WRITING CHEMICAL FORMULAS

The formula for a compound is a group of symbols indicating the elements combined and the proportions in which they are united. Obviously, a formula must be based primarily upon data obtained experimentally. We shall consider, however, only the problem of writing the formula when given the scientific name of the compound.

Positive and negative radicals combine in equivalent proportions, i.e., the same number of equivalents of positive and negative radicals will be associated in a compound. Since the valence of a radical shows how many chemical equivalents it represents, the student, for writing the simpler formulas of normal salts, needs to know only the symbols and valences to apply the following rule:

*The valence number of the positive radical is used as the subscript for the negative radical and the valence number of the negative radical is used as the subscript for the positive radical.* In case the two subscripts have a common factor it is removed unless there is evidence that the molecular weight corresponds to a more complex formula. Whenever the subscript is 1 it is omitted.

Suppose the formula for aluminum sulfate is desired. The symbols are Al and $SO_4$ respectively (see Table XIV, p. 309). The valence number of

Al is 3 and of $SO_4$, 2. Hence the formula is $Al_2(SO_4)_3$. The formula for sodium chloride is NaCl rather than $Na_1Cl_1$, and for barium sulfate, $BaSO_4$ instead of $Ba_2(SO_4)_2$.

When formulas for more complex substances are considered, the equivalence principle applies to acid and basic salts as $Na_2HPO_4$ and $Pb_3(OH)_2(CO_3)_2$; but, with addition compounds such as ammonia complexes, hydrates, etc., other factors enter which complicate the problem unless the formula is definitely described. The name *cupric sulfate pentahydrate* specifically indicates $CuSO_4 \cdot 5H_2O$ but $(NH_4)_3P(Mo_3O_{10})_4$ is not so readily deduced from the name *ammonium molybdiphosphate*. Potassium cyanide combines with a number of heavy metal cyanides to form compounds whose formulas are not revealed by their names. Potassium argenticyanide is $KAg(CN)_2$; potassium ferricyanide, $K_3Fe(CN)_6$; etc. Still more difficult from a valence standpoint are products such as $KCl \cdot PbCl_2$, $CaCl_2 \cdot PbCl_2$, $Fe_3C$, $Cu_2Zn_3$, and $MgZn_2$ obtained in equilibrium studies.

## CHEMICAL EQUATIONS

A balanced equation shows the products obtained when the indicated substances interact in a particular ratio. It focuses attention on the equivalence relations but is not concerned with any of the other factors essential to the progress of the reaction, such as temperature and pressure. Consequently, when writing an equation, the same principle is employed as in writing a formula, namely, that the reagents act in equivalent proportions.

When two substances interact, the coefficients required in the balanced equation must show that the reagents are used in the ratio of one equivalent of one to one of the other. If there is available a simple way to determine the number of equivalents represented by one molecule of one reagent, that number may be used as the coefficient of the other reagent and vice versa. Suppose one molecule of A contains two equivalents while one molecule of B contains three, then 3A:2B is the desired ratio. This method is based mathematically on the least common multiple principle. Once the combining ratio is found, the balancing may be completed by inspection. In order to facilitate a more detailed explanation of how to obtain the ratio, equations will be considered in two divisions: those not involving oxidation and reduction and those that do.

**Equations Not Involving Oxidation and Reduction.** These reactions may be placed in four classes: (1) simple decomposition, (2) direct combination, (3) double decomposition or metathesis, (4) other more complex interchanges. When calcium carbonate is heated above 650°C. it decomposes into CaO and $CO_2$. Conversely, at lower temperatures these two compounds form $CaCO_3$ by direct combination. The two equations are easily balanced by inspection

(1) $$CaCO_3 \rightarrow CaO + CO_2$$

(2) $$CaO + CO_2 \rightarrow CaCO_3$$

Equations involving metathesis are usually balanced without difficulty by taking care of the most complicated product first. In the reaction

$$AlCl_3 + Ag_2SO_4 \rightarrow Al_2(SO_4)_3 + AgCl$$

the compound $Al_2(SO_4)_3$ shows that two Al and three $SO_4$ radicals will be required. The ratio $2AlCl_3:3Ag_2SO_4$ reveals that six Cl and six Ag will be left to form six AgCl.

(3) $$2AlCl_3 + 3Ag_2SO_4 = Al_2(SO_4)_3 + 6AgCl$$

In reactions involving more complex interchanges it is usually not difficult to examine the formula of the main product, discover the ratio in which reagents must be used to supply the constituents, and then ascertain whether a substance supplies the same constituent to form some other product and add the needed amounts to get the correct coefficients.

If an excess of $NH_4OH$ is added to $CuSO_4$, cupric ammine sulfate is formed.

$$CuSO_4 + NH_4OH \rightarrow Cu(NH_3)_4SO_4 + H_2O$$

This product shows that four $NH_3$ are required by each Cu, hence the ratio, $1CuSO_4:4NH_4OH$, which results in $4H_2O$ as a by-product.

(4a) $$CuSO_4 + 4NH_4OH = Cu(NH_3)_4SO_4 + 4H_2O$$

If a solution of $PbCl_2$ is treated with NaOH until the precipitate first formed has dissolved, the reaction is

$$PbCl_2 + NaOH \rightarrow NaPb(OH)_3 + NaCl$$

Here the most complicated formula is $NaPb(OH)_3$. It shows that one NaOH will be required for every Pb, but each $PbCl_2$ furnishes two chlorine atoms which require an equal number of sodium atoms to form the NaCl. Hence a total of three molecules of NaOH will be needed, i.e., $1PbCl_2:3NaOH$. Inserting these coefficients gives the balanced equation

(4b) $$PbCl_2 + 3NaOH = NaPb(OH)_3 + 2NaCl$$

A yellow precipitate is obtained when a phosphate in nitric acid solution is treated with ammonium molybdate:

$$H_3PO_4 + (NH_4)_2MoO_4 + HNO_3 = (NH_4)_3P(Mo_3O_{10})_4 + NH_4NO_3 + H_2O$$

The complex molybdiphosphate formula shows that for each phosphorus atom (or $PO_4$ radical), twelve molybdenum atoms are needed; therefore, the two reagents must be used in the ratio $1H_3PO_4:12(NH_4)_2MoO_4$. Of the $24NH_4$ groups thus supplied, only 3 are used in the precipitate, leaving 21 to be accounted for. This requires $21HNO_3$ to form $21NH_4NO_3$. The H atoms supplied by the $H_3PO_4$ and $21HNO_3$ are found in the products as $12H_2O$. The balanced equation is, therefore,

(4c) $H_3PO_4 + 12(NH_4)_2MoO_4 + 21HNO_3$

$$= (NH_4)_3P(Mo_3O_{10}) + 21NH_4NO_3 + 12H_2O$$

The equations thus far have been written as molecular reactions. Actually, to the extent to which they represent reactions taking place in aqueous solution, they may be written in a simpler form as "net reactions." These show only the essential reagents and products. Strong electrolytes in aqueous solution are present as ions (more or less hydrated), while weaker electrolytes are largely in the molecular form. Thus the molecular formula will be used in net reactions only in the cases of weak electrolytes or precipitates. On this basis the above equations may be rewritten as follows:

(3) $$Cl^- + Ag^+ = AgCl$$

(4a) $$Cu^{++} + 4NH_3 = Cu(NH_3)_4{}^{++}$$

(4b) $$PbCl^+ + 3OH^- = Pb(OH)_3{}^- + Cl^-$$

(4c) $H_3PO_4 + 12HMoO_4{}^- + 3NH_4{}^+ + 9H_3O^+$

$$= (NH_4)_3P(Mo_3O_{10})_4 + 21H_2O$$

**Oxidation-reduction Equations.** Oxidation may be defined as an increase in active combining power for oxygen or its equivalent (which is the same as a decrease in combining power for hydrogen); reduction, a decrease in that function. Whenever oxidation takes place it is accompanied by a reduction of something else. Neither change can occur alone. This situation would be inferred from the conservation laws. As a simple analogy consider two pails attached one at each end of a rope hung over a pulley. If free suspension is assumed, raising one pail results in a lowering of the other and vice versa. The distance that one travels up or down is restricted to the space covered by the other and the total energy change of one equals that of the other except that the signs are opposite. The equivalence principle applies but the comparison should not be pushed too far.

A number of methods have been suggested for determining the ratio in which reagents interact but only two will be discussed here, namely, the oxidation number method first described by O. C. Johnson * in 1880 and the ion-electron method advocated by Jette and La Mer.†

**Oxidation Number Method.** An oxidation number is a number assigned to represent the state of oxidation of an element or radical in a particular substance. The numbers are based on the primary assumption that the state of oxidation of an uncombined element may be conveniently represented by the number zero. For every unit of oxidation involved in changing one gram atom of the element from the free state to that of a particular compound, the oxidation number is raised one numerical unit. For every unit of reduction involved in changing one gram atom of the element from the free state to that of a particular compound, the oxidation number is lowered by one numerical unit; hence a minus sign is attached.

In an actual oxidation-reduction reaction it frequently happens that the free state is not encountered among either the reagents or the products. In such cases, however, a comparison of the oxidation number of a particular element in the oxidizing agent with its oxidation number in the product will show how many units of reduction one gram atom of this element is undergoing. Similarly, a comparison of the oxidation number of a particular element in the reducing agent with its oxidation number in the product will show how many units of oxidation one gram atom of this element is undergoing. These changes in oxidation number furnish the basis for setting up the coefficients of the two reagents in such a way that the total number of units of oxidation represented will equal the total number of units of reduction. In balancing the equation after this stage has been reached the simple process of inspection is used.

The common rules for assigning oxidation numbers are:

1. The O.N. (oxidation number) of any element in the free state is zero.

2. The sum of the oxidation numbers of all elements in a compound is zero (each O.N. multiplied by the subscript of the element).

3. The O.N. of a positive or negative radical in a compound is the same as its valence and is positive for a positive radical and negative for a negative radical.

4. The O.N. of hydrogen in combination is $+1$, the chief exception being in hydrides of very electropositive metals such as NaH and KH, where the oxidation number of the Na or K is $+1$, whereas that of H is $-1$.

5. The O.N. of oxygen in combination is $-2$, the only exception being in $H_2O_2$ and related compounds where the O.N. of the oxygen is adjusted to that of the positive element in accordance with rule 2. Thus, in $H_2O_2$, $H = +1$ and $O = -1$.

6. In assigning O.N.'s to two elements forming a radical, usually one of them is known and the other is then derived by difference from the O.N. of the radical as a whole.

* O. C. Johnson, *Chem. News* **42,** 51 (1880).

† Jette and La Mer, *J. Chem. Education* **4,** 1021–30, 1158–67 (1927).

*Applications:*

| | | |
|---|---|---|
| $H_2O$ | $2H = +2$ | (Rule 4) |
| | $O = -2$ | (Rule 5) |
| | Sum $= 0$ | (Rule 2) |
| $H_2SO_4$ | $2H = +2$ | |
| | $4O = -8$ | |
| | $S = +6$ | (by difference) |
| | Sum $= 0$ | |
| $SO_4^{--}$ | $4O = -8$ | |
| | $S = +6$ | |
| | Sum $= -2$ | |
| $Na_2SO_4$ | $SO_4 = -2$ | |
| | $2Na = +2$ | |
| | Sum $= 0$ | |
| $NH_4Cl$ | $Cl = -1$ | |
| | $4H = +4$ | |
| | $N = -3$ | (by difference) |
| | Sum $= 0$ | |
| $NH_4^+$ | $4H = +4$ | |
| | $N = -3$ | |
| | Sum $= +1$ | |
| $CH_2O$ | $2H = +2$ | |
| | $O = -2$ | |
| | $C = 0$ | (by difference) |
| | Sum $= 0$ | |
| $H_2O_2$ | $2H = +2$ | |
| | $2O = -2$ | |
| | Sum $= 0$ | |

$$\begin{array}{lrl} Pb_3O_4 & 4O = & -8 \\ & 3Pb = & +8 \quad \text{(by difference)} \\ \hline & \text{Sum} = & 0 \end{array}$$

A study of the above examples will reveal three additional points: (*a*) the oxidation numbers consist of a sign (either plus or minus) and a number; (*b*) the oxidation number and valence number usually involve the same figure, but this is not always true (note the last three examples); (*c*) the oxidation number is not always a whole number (in $Pb_3O_4$ the Pb = +8/3).

Whenever an element is oxidized or reduced there is a change in its oxidation number. The difference between the value before and the value after the change is a measure of the oxidation or reduction and indicates the number of equivalents involved. This leads directly to the application in balancing equations which may be stated as follows:

*The total change in oxidation number for all atoms in one molecule of the oxidizing agent indicates the number of molecules of reducing agent to be used. The total change in oxidation number for all atoms in one molecule of the reducing agent indicates the number of molecules of oxidizing agent to be used.*

The two terms *oxidizing agent* and *reducing agent* may cause a slight amount of confusion at first. The former undergoes a *decrease* in oxidation number—it is reduced. The latter experiences an *increase* in oxidation number—it is oxidized. An oxidizing agent oxidizes a reducing agent and vice versa. If in any molecule one element is reduced and another oxidized, the decision regarding the classification of the compound rests upon the total change for the molecule; if negative, the compound is an oxidizing agent; if positive, a reducing agent. A few specific equations will help to explain the method further.

(*a*) In the oxidation of $H_2S$ by hot, fairly concentrated $HNO_3$, the skeleton net reaction may be shown as follows:

$$NO_3^- + H_2S + H_3O^+ = NO + HSO_4^- + H_2O$$

On checking the oxidation numbers of each element in both reagents and products, it is evident that *N* goes from +5 in $NO_3^-$ to +2 in NO and that S changes from −2 in $H_2S$ to +6 in $HSO_4^-$. Thus each atom of nitrogen undergoes 3 units of reduction and each atom of sulfur undergoes 8 units of oxidation. Therefore, the $NO_3^-$ and $H_2S$ must be used up in the ratio of $8NO_3^-:3H_2S$, and 8NO and $3HSO_4^-$ will be formed.

$$8NO_3^- + 3H_2S + ?H_3O^+ = 8NO + 3HSO_4^- + ?H_2O$$

The last step in balancing the equation is carried out in the simplest way by noting how many $H_3O^+$ must be added to balance the charges on the two sides of the equation, and then adjusting the coefficient of $H_2O$ to account for either the oxygen or the hydrogen atoms supplied. Thus, $8NO_3^-$ supply 8 minus charges, while $3HSO_4^-$ have only 3 minus charges; therefore, $5H_3O^+$ must be used to neutralize 5 of the negative charges.

$$8NO_3^- + 3H_2S + 5H_3O^+ = 8NO + 3HSO_4^- + ?H_2O$$

There are 21 atoms of H on the left side and only 3H in the $3HSO_4^-$; therefore 18H must be accounted for by $9H_2O$. One may then check the atoms of oxygen on the two sides to see that the equation is balanced.

$$8NO_3^- + 3H_2S + 5H_3O^+ = 8NO + 3HSO_4^- + 9H_2O$$

$$\text{Atoms of oxygen: } 24 + 5 = 8 + 12 + 9$$

Summarizing the steps in the process:

1. Find the elements that change in oxidation number.
2. Calculate the change per atom of each element.
3. Determine the total change per molecule of oxidant and per molecule of reductant.
4. Apply the ratio thus found.
5. Balance the elements thus oxidized and reduced.
6. Balance the charges on the ions with $H_3O^+$ in acid solution or with $OH^-$ in alkaline solution.
7. Balance the other elements by inspection.
8. Check the atoms on each side.

A convenient way to represent the calculations is to indicate the oxidation number of each element changing; then proceed as shown.

$$\overset{+5}{N}O_3^- + H_2\overset{-2}{S} + H_3O^+ = \overset{+2}{N}O + H\overset{+6}{S}O_4^- + H_2O$$

Oxidizing agent $= NO_3^-$

N changes from $+5$ to $+2 = -3$ (3 units of reduction per molecule).

Reducing agent $= H_2S$

S changes from $-2$ to $+6 = +8$ (8 units of oxidation per molecule).

Ratio = 3:8; therefore, use $8NO_3^-$ and $3H_2S$.

$$8NO_3^- + 3H_2S = 8NO + 3HSO_4^-$$

8 minus charges on left and only 3 on the right; therefore add $5H_3O^+$ on the left. Inspection then shows that the coefficient of $H_2O$ on the right is 9.

$$8NO_3^- + 3H_2S + 5H_3O^+ = 8NO + 3HSO_4^- + 9H_2O$$

(*b*) Metallic arsenic is soluble in hot, moderately concentrated nitric acid, forming $H_3AsO_4$ and NO.

$$\overset{0}{As_4} + \overset{+5}{N}O_3^- + H_3O^+ = \overset{+2}{N}O + H_3\overset{+5}{As}O_4$$

Oxidizing agent $= NO_3^-$

N changes from $+5$ to $+2 = -3$ (3 units of reduction per molecule).

Reducing agent $= As_4$

As changes from 0 to $+5 = +5$ (20 units of oxidation per molecule).

Ratio of ox. agt. to red. agt. $= 20{:}3$; therefore, use 20 $NO_3^-$ and $3As_4$.

$$3As_4 + 20NO_3^- + ?H_3O^+ = 12H_3AsO_4 + 20NO + ?H_2O$$

$20NO_3^- = 20$ minus charges, which require $20H_3O^+$ for neutralization since products are all molecular compounds. On checking H's, 20 $H_3O^+$ supply 60H of which only 36 are used in $12H_3AsO_4$, leaving 24 to be found as $12H_2O$.

$$3As_4 + 20NO_3^- + 20H_3O^+ = 12H_3AsO_4 + 20NO + 12H_2O$$

Atoms of oxygen: $(20 \times 3) + 20 = (12 \times 4) + 20 + 12$

(*c*) If one treats a nitrate with metallic aluminum in the presence of NaOH, the nitrate is reduced to $NH_3$ and the Al goes into solution as $Al(OH)_4^-$. If the nitrate used is $AgNO_3$, a second reaction will also occur—namely, reduction of the $Ag^+$ to Ag. Since the formula $AgNO_3$ indicates that the $Ag^+$ and $NO_3^-$ are present in equal amounts, the net reaction should keep these in the ratio of 1:1.

$$\overset{+1}{Ag^+} + \overset{+5}{N}O_3^- + \overset{0}{Al} + OH^- + H_2O = \overset{0}{Ag} + \overset{-3}{N}H_3 + \overset{+3}{Al}(OH)_4^-$$

Oxidizing agents $= Ag^+$ and $NO_3^-$

Ag changes from $+1$ to $0 = -1$

N changes from $+5$ to $-3 = -8$

Total reduction $= -9$

Reducing agent $=$ Al

Al changes from 0 to $+3 = +3$

Ratio of ox. agt. to red. agt. $= 3{:}9$ or $1{:}3$

$$Ag^+ + NO_3^- + 3Al + ?OH^- + ?H_2O = Ag + NH_3 + 3Al(OH)_4^-$$

$1^+ + 1^- = 0$ charges on left.
$3- = 3-$ charges on the right.
Therefore, add $3OH^-$ on the left to balance charges.
H supplied = 3, H in products = 3 + 12 = 15.
Add $6H_2O$ as reagent.

$$Ag^+ + NO_3^- + 3Al + 3OH^- + 6H_2O = Ag + NH_3 + 3Al(OH)_4^-$$

(*d*) Chromic sulfide heated with $H_2O_2$ in the presence of NaOH is oxidized to $Na_2CrO_4$ and $Na_2SO_4$ the $H_2O_2$ being reduced to $H_2O$.

$$\overset{+3\,-2}{Cr_2S_3} + \overset{-1}{HO_2^-} + OH^- = \overset{+6}{CrO_4^{--}} + \overset{+6}{SO_4^{--}} + \overset{-2}{H_2O}$$

Oxidizing agent = $HO_2^-$

O changes from $-1$ to $-2 = -1$ (2 units of reduction per molecule).

Reducing agent = $Cr_2S_3$

Cr changes from $+3$ to $+6 = +3$ (6 units of oxidation for 2 Cr).
S changes from $-2$ to $+6 = +8$ (24 units of oxidation for 3S).
Total change per molecule $Cr_2S_3 = +30$.

Ratio of ox. agt. to red. agt. = 30:2 or 15:1.

$$Cr_2S_3 + 15HO_2^- = 2CrO_4^{--} + 3SO_4^{--}$$

15− charges on the left, and 10− charges on the right. Add $5OH^-$ on the right to balance charges.

$$Cr_2S_3 + 15HO_2^- = 2CrO_4^{--} + 3SO_4^{--} + 5OH^-$$

Checking H's, 15 on the left, 5 on the right, add $5H_2O$ on the right.

$$Cr_2S_3 + 15HO_2^- = 2CrO_4^{--} + 3SO_4^{--} + 5OH^- + 5H_2O$$

Checking O's, $15 \times 2 = (2 \times 4) + (3 \times 4) + 5 + 5$.

(*e*) When copper sulfide is heated with 5 *N* $HNO_3$, it dissolves forming $Cu^{++}$, S and NO as main products.

$$Cu\overset{-2}{S} + \overset{+5}{N}O_3^- + H_3O^+ = Cu^{++} + \overset{0}{S} + \overset{+2}{N}O + H_2O$$

Oxidizing agent = $NO_3^-$

N changes from $+5$ to $+2 = -3$ (3 units of reduction per molecule).

Reducing agent = CuS

S changes from $-2$ to $0 = +2$ (2 units of oxidation per molecule).

Ratio of ox. agt. to red. agt. = 2:3.

$$3CuS + 2NO_3^- = 3Cu^{++} + 3S + 2NO$$

Charges on the left = 2−, on the right = 6+. Add $8H_3O^+$ on left to balance charges.

$$3CuS + 2NO_3^- + 8H_3O^+ = 3Cu^{++} + 3S + 2NO + ?H_2O$$

Checking H's = 24 on the left. Use $12H_2O$ on the right.

$$3CuS + 2NO_3^- + 8H_3O^+ = 3Cu^{++} + 3S + 2NO + 12H_2O$$

Checking O's: $(2 \times 3) + 8 = 2 + 12$.

(*f*) When chlorine is passed into a hot solution of KOH it is in part oxidized to $ClO_3^-$ and in part reduced to $Cl^-$. In this case it is acting as both an oxidizing agent and a reducing agent.

$$\overset{0}{Cl_2} + OH^- = \overset{+5}{Cl}O_3^- + \overset{-1}{Cl^-} + H_2O$$

Oxidizing agent = $Cl_2$

Cl changes from 0 to −1 = −1(× 2 = −2 per molecule of $Cl_2$).

Reducing agent = $Cl_2$

Cl changes from 0 to +5 = +5(× 2 = +10 per molecule of $Cl_2$).

Ratio of ox. agt. to red. agt. = 10:2 or 5:1.

$$6Cl_2 + ?OH^- = 2ClO_3^- + 10Cl^- + ?H_2O$$

Checking charges: left = 0, right = 2− + 10− = 12−.
Therefore, add $12OH^-$ on the left to balance charges.
Checking H's: left = 12, right = 0.
Therefore, add $6H_2O$.
Coefficients can all be reduced to lower terms.

$$3Cl_2 + 6OH^- = ClO_3^- + 5Cl^- + 3H_2O$$

Checking atoms of O shows equation is balanced.

**Ion-Electron Method.** This method * is an outgrowth of the idea that oxidation and reduction involve an exchange of electrons; that oxidation may best be defined as a loss, reduction a gain of electrons. Because the mechanism of reactions in the dry state is little known or understood, the scheme is applied only to changes taking place in solution, i.e., ionic reactions. An interesting experiment concerning such reactions in aqueous solu-

* For a more detailed discussion see Jette and La Mer, *J. Chem. Education* **4,** 1021–30, 1158–67 (1927).

tions may be carried out as follows: Place a solution of the oxidizing agent in one of two adjacent beakers and a solution of the reducing agent in the other (Fig. 1). Connect the two solutions by means of a salt-bridge (a U-tube stuffed with absorbent material, filled with a saturated solution of KCl

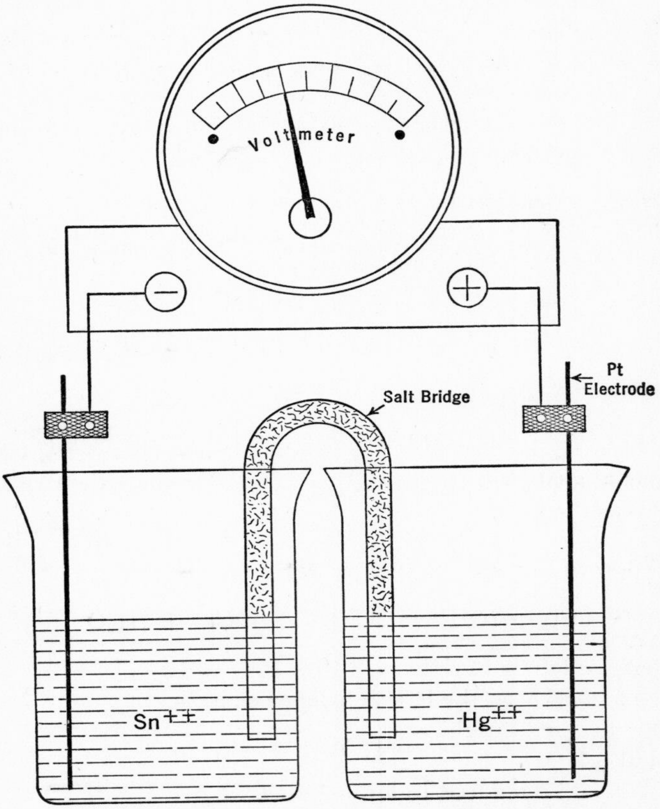


FIG. 1. Oxidation-Reduction Half-Cell Arrangement.

and then inverted in such a way that one arm dips into the solution in one beaker and the other arm dips into the solution in the other). Insert a platinum electrode into each of the two solutions and then connect the two electrodes in an external circuit by means of a copper wire. Note that as soon as this external circuit is completed the same chemical reaction will take place as if the two solutions had been mixed in a single beaker. Thus stannous chloride will reduce mercuric chloride, with precipitation of mercurous chloride; or ferric chloride will oxidize potassium iodide in acid solution to free iodine.

If a voltmeter is connected to the two electrodes, it will be found that the electrode dipping into the oxidizing agent is positive as compared with that in the reducing agent. In terms of electron transfer, this means that, as the reaction takes place, electrons leave the beaker containing the reducing agent and pass through the wire into the beaker containing the oxidizing agent. Using $e^-$ as the symbol for an electron, it is possible to write equations for the simple reactions occurring in the two beakers (half-cell reactions, as they are called), and then combine these two reactions in such proportions that the electrons supplied in the one beaker will just equal those used in the other, and thus arrive at a balanced equation for the reaction as it would occur if the two reagents were mixed directly.

**Example:** $SnCl_2 + HgCl_2$

Half-cell reaction for the oxidation of $SnCl_2$ in the one beaker.

$$2Cl^- + SnCl_4^{--} \rightarrow SnCl_6^{--} + 2e^-$$

Half-cell reaction for the reduction of $HgCl_2$ in the second beaker.

$$2HgCl_2 + 2e^- \rightarrow Hg_2Cl_2 + 2Cl^-$$

Since the first equation supplies 2 electrons as product and the second uses 2 electrons as reagent, the completed ionic equation may be written by adding the two together.

$$2Cl^- + SnCl_4^{--} + 2HgCl_2 + 2e^- = Hg_2Cl_2 + SnCl_6^{--} + 2Cl^- + 2e^-$$

Since 2 electrons and $2Cl^-$ appear both as reagents and as products, they may be cancelled, leaving the equation:

$$SnCl_4^{--} + 2HgCl_2 = Hg_2Cl_2 + SnCl_6^{--}$$

When writing these equations the reagents and products are given in the form in which they are considered to be chiefly present in the actual reaction. Thus several equations might be written for the half-cell reaction involving reduction of the $HgCl_2$.

$$2Hg^{++} + 2e^- = Hg_2^{++}$$

$$2Hg^{++} + 2Cl^- + 2e^- = Hg_2Cl_2$$

$$2HgCl_2 + 2e^- = Hg_2Cl_2 + 2Cl^-$$

Actually, however, it is known that $HgCl_2$ is slightly ionized and $Hg_2Cl_2$ is very slightly soluble; therefore, it is more in keeping with these facts to consider $HgCl_2$ as the reagent undergoing reduction and $Hg_2Cl_2$ as the product formed.

In more complex cases it is common practice to use $H_3O^+$, $OH^-$, and $H_2O$ as reagents or products when needed to account for the changes taking place in the half-cell reactions.

**Example:** $H_2S + HNO_3$

Half-cell reaction for the oxidation of $H_2S$

$$2H_2O + H_2S \rightarrow S^\circ + 2H_3O^+ + 2e^-$$

Half-cell reaction for the reduction of $HNO_3$

$$NO_3^- + 4H_3O^+ + 3e^- \rightarrow NO + 6H_2O$$

It will be noted that only simple inspection is needed to adjust the half-cell reactions so that the same amount of each element appears as reagent and as product, and that, if the formulas of the ions are properly written, it is then a very simple matter to add electrons as reagent or as product to balance the equation electrically. Thus, as $H_2S$ is oxidized to free $S^\circ$, the two $H_3O^+$ liberated show that two electrons must be liberated, since $H_2S$, the reagent, is a neutral molecule. In the same way, as $NO_3^-$ is reduced to NO, $4H_3O^+$ must be added to convert the extra two atoms of oxygen to $6H_2O$; but the products are all neutral molecules whereas $NO_3^-$ bears one negative charge and $4H_3O^+$ bear four positive charges. Thus 3 electrons must be added as reagents to neutralize the three extra positive charges supplied by the hydronium ions.

In completing the ionic equation for the oxidation of $H_2S$ by $HNO_3$, it is noted that the half-cell reaction for the oxidation of $H_2S$ liberates 2 electrons for each molecule of $H_2S$, whereas the reduction of $NO_3^-$ requires 3 electrons for each nitrate ion; therefore, the coefficients of the two half-cell reactions are multiplied by 3 and by 2, respectively, before adding.

$$6H_2O + 3H_2S \rightarrow 3S^\circ + 6H_3O^+ + 6e^-$$

$$2NO_3^- + 8H_3O^+ + 6e^- \rightarrow 2NO + 12H_2O$$

The final equation reads:

$$3H_2S + 2NO_3^- + 2H_3O^+ = 3S^\circ + 2NO + 6H_2O$$

**Example:** $CuS + HNO_3$

Half-cell reaction 1

$$CuS \rightarrow Cu^{++} + S^\circ + 2e^-$$

Half-cell reaction 2

$$NO_3^- + 4H_3O^+ + 3e^- \rightarrow NO + 6H_2O$$

Balanced equation

$$3CuS + 2NO_3^- + 8H_3O^+ = 3Cu^{++} + 3S^\circ + 2NO + 12H_2O$$

**Example:** $K_2Cr_2O_7 + HCl + CH_2O$

Half-cell reaction 1

$$CH_2O + 3H_2O \rightarrow CH_2O_2 + 2H_3O^+ + 2e^-$$

Half-cell reaction 2

$$Cr_2O_7^{--} + 14H_3O^+ + 6e^- \rightarrow 2Cr^{+3} + 21H_2O$$

Balanced equation

$$Cr_2O_7^{--} + 3CH_2O + 8H_3O^+ = 2Cr^{+3} + 3CH_2O_2 + 12H_2O$$

As review practice at the end of the course it is worthwhile to prepare a list of the oxidation-reduction reactions encountered during the semester. Write the half-cell reactions for the oxidizing agents and for the reducing agents. When these are examined, it will be found that many of these half-cell reactions are reversible, the system functioning as an oxidizing agent if there is a sufficiently strong reducing agent available to force electrons into the system, or as a reducing agent if there is a sufficiently strong oxidizing agent available to take electrons from the system.

**Net Reactions.** In connection with this system of writing equations it should be noted that in aqueous solution most of the simple ions are believed to exist in a hydrated condition; thus, hydrogen ion is $H \cdot H_2O^+$, cupric ion is $Cu \cdot 4H_2O^{++}$, ferric ion is $Fe \cdot 6H_2O^{+++}$, etc. Also, complex ions may be formed by the association of two simple ions of opposite charge in non-equivalent proportions. Some of these latter are well known, such as bismuth iodide ion, $BiI_4^-$, cuprocyanide ion, $Cu(CN)_3^{--}$, ferricyanide ion, $Fe(CN)_6^{---}$, etc., but there is evidence for the existence of many others which are not so well known, such as bismuth chloride ion, $BiCl_4^-$, lead chloride ions, $PbCl^+$ and $PbCl_3^-$, ferric chloride ions, $FeCl^{++}$, $FeCl_2^+$, $FeCl_4^-$, etc. To avoid making the equations unduly complex it will be the practice in this book to omit the hydration of ions (except $H_3O^+$ and the anions of the amphoteric hydroxides, which are now regarded as hydroxyl complexes in solution) and the formation of less common complex ions unless the particular reaction under consideration requires their use. As examples of this latter type two cases may be considered. First, when a solution of copper sulfate is treated with concentrated sulfuric acid and evaporated to fumes of $SO_3$, the final solution becomes practically colorless. The explanation is found in the dehydration of the $Cu \cdot 4H_2O^{++}$. Second, when a solution of ferric nitrate is treated with HCl, NaCl, or $NH_4Cl$, the solution turns yellow. This involves the formation of complex ferric chloride ions, the limiting case being $FeCl_6^{---}$. Equally interesting color differences are noted among the ions of trivalent chromium and bivalent cobalt.

## *PRACTICE EXERCISES IN WRITING EQUATIONS*

1. Write the molecular equations for the following reactions:

(*a*) $Pb(NO_3)_2 + NaOH$ (small amt.)
(*b*) $Pb(NO_3)_2 + NaOH$ (excess)
(*c*) $NaPb(OH)_3 + HNO_3$ (small amt.)
(*d*) $NaPb(OH)_3 + HNO_3$ (excess)
(*e*) $Pb(OH)_2 + NaOH$
(*f*) $Pb(OH)_2 + HNO_3$

2. Write the molecular equations for the following reactions:

(*a*) $Cu(NO_3)_2 + NH_4OH$ (small amt.)
(*b*) $Cu(NO_3)_2 + NH_4OH$ (excess)
(*c*) $Cu(NH_3)_4(NO_3)_2 + HNO_3$ (small amt.)
(*d*) $Cu(NH_3)_4(NO_3)_2 + HNO_3$ (excess)
(*e*) $Cu(OH)_2 + NH_4OH + NH_4NO_3$
(*f*) $Cu(OH)_2 + HNO_3$

3. Write the molecular equations for the following reactions:

(*a*) $AgCl + NH_4OH$
(*b*) $PbSO_4 + NaOH$
(*c*) $PbCrO_4 + HNO_3$
(*d*) $Sb_2S_5 + (NH_4)_2S$
(*e*) $Al(OH)_3 + NaOH$
(*f*) $CaCO_3 + HCl$

4. Write the molecular equations for the following reactions:

(*a*) $Ag(NH_3)_2Cl + HNO_3$
(*b*) $Ag(NH_3)_2Cl + KI$
(*c*) $HgCl_2 + NH_4OH$
(*d*) $Na_2Cd(CN)_4 + NH_4OH + H_2S$
(*e*) $NaAl(OH)_4 + HCl$ (small amt.)
(*f*) $NaZn(OH)_3 + H_2S$

5. Write the molecular equations for the following reactions:

(*a*) $PbS + HNO_3$
(*b*) $HgS + HCl + HNO_3$
(*c*) $As_2S_5 + HNO_3$
(*d*) $K_2Cr_2O_7 + HCl + KI$
(*e*) $Cr(OH)_3 + NaOH + H_2O_2$
(*f*) $KMnO_4 + HCl + H_2S$

6, 7, 8, 9, 10. Write the net equations for the reactions in Exercises 1, 2, 3, 4, 5.
11. Give the oxidation number method of balancing the equations in Exercise 5.
12. Give the ion-electron method of balancing the equations in Exercise 5.

13. Balance the following equations not involving oxidation and reduction:

(*a*) $HgCl_2 + NH_4OH = HgNH_2Cl + NH_4Cl + H_2O$
(*b*) $Fe_2(SO_4)_3 + Ba(OH)_2 = Fe(OH)_3 + BaSO_4$
(*c*) $Cu(NH_3)_4(NO_3)_2 + H_2S = CuS + NH_4NO_3$
(*d*) $Na_3AsO_4 + AgNO_3 + HNO_3$ (to neutral) $= Ag_3AsO_4 + NaNO_3$
(*e*) $Bi_2(C_2O_4)_3 + CaI_2 = CaC_2O_4 + Ca(BiI_4)_2$

(*f*) $NaH_2PO_4 + (NH_4)_6Mo_7O_{24} + HNO_3 = (NH_4)_3P(Mo_3O_{10})_4 + NH_4NO_3$
$+ NaNO_3$
(*g*) $AlCl_3 + NaOH = Na_3AlO_3 + NaCl + H_2O$
(*h*) $Pb_3(PO_4)_2 + Ba(OH)_2 = BaPbO_2 + Ba_3(PO_4)_2 + H_2O$
(*i*) $Cd(NH_3)_4SO_4 + NaCN = Na_2Cd(CN)_4 + Na_2SO_4 + NH_3$
(*j*) $NH_4OH + Na_2HgI_4 + NaOH = NH_2IHg_2O + NaI + H_2O$

14. Balance the following oxidation-reduction equations:

(*a*) $NaClO + H_2S = NaCl + H_2SO_4$
(*b*) $K_2Cr_2O_7 + FeCl_2 + HCl = CrCl_3 + FeCl_3 + KCl + H_2O$
(*c*) $Fe_3O_4 + KMnO_4 + H_2SO_4 = Fe_2(SO_4)_3 + K_2SO_4 + MnSO_4 + H_2O$
(*d*) $NaCrO_2 + NaOH + H_2O_2 = Na_2CrO_4 + H_2O$
(*e*) $Ag + HNO_3 = AgNO_3 + NO + H_2O$
(*f*) $Ag_2S + HNO_3 = AgNO_3 + NO + S + H_2O$
(*g*) $FeS + HNO_3 = Fe(NO_3)_3 + NO + S + H_2O$
(*h*) $AgNO_3 + NaClO = AgCl + AgClO_3 + NaNO_3$
(*i*) $Ca(OH)_2 + Cl_2 = CaCl_2 + Ca(ClO_3)_2 + H_2O$
(*j*) $CaS_5 + O_2 = CaS_2O_3 + S_2$
(*k*) $NH_4Cl + NH_4NO_3 = N_2 + Cl_2 + H_2O$
(*l*) $Bi(NO_3)_3 + Al + NaOH = Bi + NH_3 + NaAlO_2$
(*m*) $Cu_2As_2O_7 + Zn + H_2SO_4 = Cu + AsH_3 + ZnSO_4 + H_2O$
(*n*) $Fe(NO_3)_3 + FeSO_4 + H_2SO_4 = FeSO_4 \cdot NO + Fe_2(SO_4)_3 + H_2O$
(*o*) $Fe_3(AsO_3)_2 + K_2Cr_2O_7 + KHSO_4 = Fe_2(SO_4)_3 + H_3AsO_4 + Cr_2(SO_4)_3$
$+ K_2SO_4 + H_2O$

15. Complete and balance the following:

(*a*) $CuSO_4 + Fe$
(*b*) $SnS + (NH_4)_2S_2$
(*c*) $Ag_2C_2O_4 + NH_4OH$
(*d*) $NaH_2PO_4 + (NH_4)_2MoO_4 + HNO_3$
(*e*) $BiCl_3 + NaOH + Na_2SnO_2$
(*f*) $Sn + HNO_3$
(*g*) $HgCl_2 + NH_4OH$
(*h*) $KMnO_4 + FeSO_4 + H_2SO_4$
(*i*) $Bi_2(SO_4)_3 + FeI_2$
(*j*) $K_2Cr_2O_7 + H_2O_2 + H_2SO_4$ (cold)

# 3

# Chemical Arithmetic

The problems in chemical arithmetic, to be considered in this chapter, require an understanding of the quantitative significance of a chemical formula and a chemical equation. The facts involved may be summarized as follows: (*a*) The atomic weights of the elements in a compound, each multiplied by its subscript in the formula, give the ratio by weight in which the elements are combined in the compound. (*b*) The molecular weights of the reagents and products in a chemical reaction, each multiplied by its coefficient in the balanced equation, give the ratio by weight in which the reagents interact and the products are formed.

## TEST SOLUTIONS

In the laboratory two types of solutions are frequently used—test solutions and reagents. The test solutions are solutions of salts which supply convenient concentrations of the common metals and acid radicals for practice work in separation and identification. Such solutions make it easy to take a known amount of the metal or acid radical for examination of its behavior with various reagents. In most cases a solution of 1–2 mg. of the metal or acid radical is ample to recognize any initial reactions that may occur, and at the same time is small enough to permit typical secondary reactions to be carried out with only moderate amounts of the reagents; consequently, it has become common practice to make up these test solutions so that they will contain 10 mg./ml. of the significant metal or acid radical. On this basis, 2–5 drops of the solution in question will supply 1–2 mg. of the desired substance.

Problems involving the preparation of test solutions are solved by use of the quantitative composition of the compounds in question.

1. *Calculate the number of grams of* $AgNO_3$ *needed to prepare* 1 *liter of a test solution of* $Ag^+$.

Since the test solution should contain 10 mg. of $Ag^+$ per ml., and "mg./ml." is identical numerically with "grams/liter," one liter of the test solution will require 10 g. of $Ag^+$. But one must weigh the Ag as $AgNO_3$. Therefore, to supply 10 g. of Ag one must take 10 × (mol. wt. $AgNO_3$)/(at. wt. Ag) or

$$10 \times 170/108, \text{ or } 15.7 \text{ g. of } AgNO_3 \quad \textit{Ans.}$$

2. *Calculate the number of grams of* $Cu(NO_3)_2 \cdot 3H_2O$ *needed to prepare* 500 *ml. of a test solution of* $Cu^{++}$.

$$10 \text{ mg./ml.} = 5000 \text{ mg. in } 500 \text{ ml.} = 5.0 \text{ g. } Cu^{++} \text{ needed}$$

$$5 \times (\text{mol. wt. } Cu(NO_3)_2 \cdot 3H_2O)/(\text{at. wt. Cu}) = 5 \times 242/63.6 = 19.0$$

$$19 \text{ g. of } Cu(NO_3)_2 \cdot 3H_2O \text{ needed} \quad \textit{Ans.}$$

3. *Calculate the number of ml. of test solution of* $Hg_2^{++}$ *which could be prepared from* 12 *g. of* $Hg_2(NO_3)_2 \cdot 2H_2O$.

12 g. of $Hg_2(NO_3)_2 \cdot 2H_2O$ will contain 12 × (at. wt. Hg × 2)/(mol. wt. $Hg_2(NO_3)_2 \cdot 2H_2O$) or 12 × 401.2/561.2 or 8.58 g. Hg.

8.58 g. = 8580 mg. which would prepare 858 ml. of test solution *Ans.*

In all mathematical work one of the most important habits to form is that of checking the answer. This will insure the elimination of absurd results due to a misplaced decimal point or other error. The test should be simple and aim merely to approximate the correct figure. The above problem may be used to illustrate the method.

Using the values given, 858 ml. of the test solution should contain 8.58 g. of Hg.

$$8.58 \times 561.2/401.2 = 12 \text{ g. of } Hg_2(NO_3)_2 \cdot 2H_2O$$

Or, for a rough check,

$$8.58 = \text{approx. } 8.6$$

$$561.2 = \text{approx. } 560$$

$$401.2 = \text{approx. } 400$$

$$8.6 \times 560/400 = 8.6 \times 7/5 = 12.04$$

(Close enough to the original weight of the salt to indicate that the answer is in the right range.)

## REAGENTS

The term *reagent* is frequently used merely to distinguish a substance which enters into a reaction from the materials that are formed as products. In analytical chemistry, however, a special meaning is attached to this term to indicate something added to a system which has already been set up. In Qualitative Analysis a reagent is added for either of two purposes: (*a*) to explore the properties of the system, or (*b*) to carry out a desired reaction with materials suspected or known to be present.

For convenience in handling, most reagents are made available in the form of aqueous solutions when solubility permits. These reagents are commonly much more concentrated than the test solutions, and so it requires only a small volume to carry out the desired reactions with moderate amounts of the metals or acid radicals. Further, for ease of comparing the action of different reagents with a given amount of metal or acid radical, the concentrations of the reagents are usually worked out on the molar, or normal, basis rather than on the percentage basis, or as milligrams per milliliter.

**Molar Solution.** A molar solution contains one gram molecular weight (one mole) of the solute per liter of solution.

4. *How many grams of* $AgNO_3$ *would be required for* 250 *ml. of a* 0.5 *molar solution?*

$$\text{Molecular weight of } AgNO_3 = 170$$

$$250 \text{ ml.} = 0.25 \text{ liter}$$

$$170 \times 0.25 \times 0.5 = 21.25 \text{ g.} \quad \textit{Ans.}$$

(NOTE: If the equation is written $170 \times \frac{1}{4} \times \frac{1}{2} = ?$, it obviously is the same as $170/8 = ?$, which can be solved mentally. Such modifications materially reduce the amount of work involved, and hence should be used whenever possible.)

For purposes of neutralization a molar solution of NaOH is equivalent to a molar solution of KOH since equal volumes of the two reagents would supply equal amounts of $OH^-$. When the formulas of HCl and $H_2SO_4$ are compared, however, and it is realized that both hydrogen atoms of the sulfuric acid may enter into a neutralization reaction, it is obvious that a molar solution of HCl is not equivalent to a molar solution of $H_2SO_4$. Actually it takes twice as much of a molar solution of HCl as of $H_2SO_4$ to carry out a given amount of neutralization. To avoid the necessity of making allowance for the lack of equivalence of different molar solutions, it is common practice to adjust the concentrations so that equal volumes of the different reagents will contain equivalent amounts of reagent. In this system concentration is expressed in terms of the normal solution.

**Normal Solution.** A normal solution of a reagent contains one gram equivalent of the solute per liter of solution. Unfortunately, this definition is not always simple to apply because many reagents enter into more than one type of chemical reaction and the equivalent weight may be different in each case. It is necessary, therefore, in attempting to calculate the equivalent weight of a substance as compared with its molecular weight, to base this calculation on a specific reaction, either stated or clearly implied.

In the case of neutralization reactions the equivalent weight of a reagent will be its molecular weight divided by the number of reactive hydrogen or hydroxyl groups per molecule. In simple precipitation reactions the equivalent weight will be the molecular weight divided by the product of valence and subscript of the precipitating radical. In the case of oxidation or reduction the equivalent weight is the molecular weight divided by the number of units of reduction or oxidation per molecule of the reagent. In other more complex cases one of the materials in the reaction must be set up as a standard and the others compared with this in terms of the actual reaction.

To make these relations clearer, a number of specific cases may be considered. As neutralizing agents, $HCl$, $HNO_3$, $NaOH$, and $KOH$ would each effect one unit of neutralization per gram molecular weight of solute; therefore the equivalent weights of these substances would be their molecular weights. Such reagents as $Ba(OH)_2$ and $H_2SO_4$ would carry out two units of neutralization per gram molecular weight; therefore the equivalent weight of each would be half the molecular weight. As a precipitating agent one gram molecular weight of $HCl$ would supply one equivalent of chloride ion, one gram molecular weight of $FeCl_3$ would supply three equivalents of ferric ion, and one gram molecular weight of $Al_2(SO_4)_3$ would supply six equivalents of sulfate ion; therefore for these reactions the equivalent weights of $HCl$, $FeCl_3$, and $Al_2(SO_4)_3$ would be the molecular weight, one-third the molecular weight, and one-sixth the molecular weight, respectively.

As a neutralizing agent the equivalent weight of $HNO_3$ is identical with its molecular weight, but $HNO_3$ may also act as an oxidizing agent in oxidizing $FeCl_2$ to $FeCl_3$.

$$3FeCl_2 + 3HCl + HNO_3 = 3FeCl_3 + NO + 2H_2O$$

In this case one gram molecular weight of $HNO_3$ will effect three units of oxidation (or will undergo three units of reduction), and thus the equivalent weight for this reaction would be one-third the molecular weight. Also, it should be noted that the $FeCl_2$ is being oxidized by only one unit; therefore the equivalent weight of $FeCl_2$ is now identical with the molecular weight and yet in a precipitation reaction it would be one-half the molecular weight.

One of the reagents which shows an unusual range of equivalent weights is $K_2Cr_2O_7$. The following equations will serve to illustrate this situation.

$$(1)\quad K_2Cr_2O_7 + 2KOH = 2K_2CrO_4 + H_2O$$

$$(2)\quad K_2Cr_2O_7 + 2Pb(C_2H_3O_2)_2 + H_2O = 2PbCrO_4 + 2KC_2H_3O_2 + 2HC_2H_3O_2$$

$$(3)\quad K_2Cr_2O_7 + 6FeCl_2 + 14HCl = 2KCl + 2CrCl_3 + 6FeCl_3 + 7H_2O$$

$$(4)\quad K_2Cr_2O_7 + 8HCl + 3H_2S = 2KCl + 2CrCl_3 + 3S + 7H_2O$$

In the first equation the $K_2Cr_2O_7$ is acting as an acid and its equivalent weight is half the molecular weight. In the second reaction, in precipitating $Pb^{++}$ as $PbCrO_4$, the equivalent weight is one-fourth the molecular weight. In the third reaction, as an oxidizing agent for $FeCl_2$, the equivalent weight is one-sixth the molecular weight, but in terms of the decrease in acidity involved it would be one-fourteenth the molecular weight. Finally, in the fourth reaction, as an oxidizing agent its equivalent weight is one-sixth the molecular weight, but in terms of the decrease in acidity it would be one-eighth. It should be clear from these cases that the equivalent weight of a substance can only be calculated with certainty when it is considered in relation to a particular reaction. However, it may be noted that, when one speaks of the normality of an acid or base, the neutralization reaction is always understood unless otherwise stated. Similarly, potassium dichromate is more commonly used as a precipitating agent than as an oxidizing agent; therefore its normality is figured in terms of precipitation of chromates unless another reaction is specifically indicated. Potassium permanganate and ferric chloride are more commonly used as oxidizing agents under conditions whereby the first is reduced to a manganous salt and the second to a ferrous salt; the equivalent weights of these compounds, therefore, normally refer to these reactions.

The problems arising in connection with normality fall into two groups: (*a*) those involving the preparation of such solutions and (*b*) those resulting from their use. In the first division the starting material may be a solid, liquid, or gas of known or unknown purity. The amount needed for a certain volume of solution must be calculated or determined by analysis. In the second group, the amount of solute in a certain sample may be known, whereas the quantity of reagent required to effect complete reaction must be found. Because of the many possible variations, only a few of the examples peculiar to qualitative analysis will be considered.

5. *How many grams of solid* NaOH (85% *pure*) *would be required for* 500 *ml. of* 3 *N solution?*

$$\text{Mol. wt. of NaOH} = 23 + 16 + 1 = 40$$

Since NaOH contains one replaceable hydroxyl per molecule, a normal solution will contain one mole per liter.

$$40 \text{ g.} \times 3 \text{ (normality desired)} \times 0.5 \text{ l (volume needed)}$$
$$= 60 \text{ g. pure NaOH required}$$

Because the NaOH is not pure

$$85\% = 60 \text{ g.}$$

$$100\% = 60 \times 100/85 = 70.6 \text{ g.} \quad \textit{Ans.}$$

What is the molar concentration of the solution? Since the equivalent weight of NaOH is identical with its molecular weight, the solution would be 3 *M*. *Ans.*

6. *Concentrated sulfuric acid, as sold commercially, contains* 5% *water and has a density of* 1.84 *g./ml. Find the normality.*

$$\text{Equivalent weight of } H_2SO_4 = 98/2 = 49$$

$$\text{One liter of the acid weighs } 1.84 \times 1000 = 1840 \text{ g.}$$

$$1840 \times 95\% = 1748 \text{ g. Amount of pure } H_2SO_4 \text{ present}$$

$$1748 \div 49 = 35.6\ N. \quad \textit{Ans.}$$

What is the molar concentration of this solution? Since the equivalent weight is half the molecular weight, this solution would be 35.6/2 or 17.8 *M*. *Ans.*

7. *Find the amount of concentrated* $H_2SO_4$ (*Problem* 6) *required for* 500 *ml. of* 5 *N solution. Express the answer in* (*a*) *milliliters,* (*b*) *grams.*

(*a*) The basic relationship is very helpful here, for the problem becomes

$$x \text{ ml. of } 35.6\ N = 500 \text{ ml. of } 5\ N$$

$$x = 500 \times 5/35.6 = 70.22 \text{ ml.} \quad \textit{Ans.}$$

(*b*) 70.22 × 1.84 g./ml. = 129.20 g. *Ans.*

8. *How many milliliters of* 5 *N* HCl *would be required to precipitate* 75 *mg. of* $Ag^+$?

To solve this problem it is necessary to find the number of milliliters of 5 *N* solution that 75 mg. of $Ag^+$ will form.

$$\text{Equivalent weight of Ag} = 108$$

$$108 \times 5/1000 = 0.54 \text{ g. Ag per ml. of } 5\ N \text{ solution}$$

The amount of Ag is 75 mg. or 0.075 g., hence

$$0.075/0.54 = 0.14 \text{ ml.} \quad \textit{Ans.}$$

(Because 0.14 ml. of 5 *N* $Ag^+ \approx$ 0.14 ml. of 5 *N* HCl.)

9. *How many milliliters of* 5 *N* $HNO_3$ *would be required to dissolve* 100 *mg. of* CuS? (*Assume that the normality refers to neutralization reactions.*)

The equation is

$$3CuS + 8HNO_3 = 3Cu(NO_3)_2 + 3S + 2NO + 4H_2O$$

From the equation it will be noted that 3 molecules of CuS are equivalent to 8 molecules of $HNO_3$; therefore, if $HNO_3$ is the standard (5 $N$ $HNO_3$), the equivalent weight of CuS will be $\frac{3}{8}$ its molecular weight.

$$\tfrac{3}{8} \times 96 = 36$$

1 ml. of 5 $N$ $HNO_3$ is equivalent to 36 × 5 or 180 mg. CuS. 100 mg. CuS would require 100/180 ml. of 5 $N$ $HNO_3$ or 0.56 ml. *Ans.*

Alternative method:

$$5\ N\ HNO_3 = 5 \text{ moles/liter}$$

$$100 \text{ mg. CuS} = \frac{0.100}{96} \text{ moles of CuS}$$

According to the equation, 1 mole of CuS requires $\frac{8}{3}$ mole of $HNO_3$, hence

$$\frac{0.100}{96} \times \frac{8}{3} = 0.0028 \text{ moles } HNO_3 \text{ needed}$$

One milliliter of 5 $N$ $HNO_3$ contains 0.005 mole of the acid; therefore, the number of moles of $HNO_3$ needed divided by 0.005 gives the number of milliliters of 5 $N$ $HNO_3$ required.

$$0.0028 \div 0.005 = 0.56 \text{ ml. } \textit{Ans.}$$

(In actual practice many reactions require a large excess of reagent over the amount theoretically needed. Frequently, the justification for the apparent waste is to be found in the law of mass action.)

**Problems Involving Gases.** If the weight of one liter of a pure gas is determined for standard conditions of temperature and pressure, the molecular weight of the gas divided by the value obtained will give a quotient very close to 22.4.

| | | |
|---|---|---|
| Oxygen, | 32 ÷ 1.42900 | = 22.39 |
| Hydrogen, | 2.016 ÷ 0.0899 | = 22.43 |
| Carbon dioxide, | 44 ÷ 1.9769 | = 22.26 |
| Ammonia, | 17.034 ÷ 0.7621 | = 22.35 |

This has led to the generalization that *one mole of any compound existing as a gas under standard conditions will occupy a volume of about* 22.4 *liters* * which has been named a gram molecular volume.

* This volume is not quite one cubic foot in the English system.

10. *How much* $H_2S$ *will be required to precipitate* 200 *mg. of* $Ag^+$ *as* $Ag_2S$ *assuming* S.T.P. *and a loss of* 25% *of the gas? Express the answer in grams and in milliliters.*

(*a*)
$$\underset{2(108)}{2Ag^+} + \underset{34}{H_2S} \rightarrow Ag_2S$$

$$34 \times 0.2/216 = 0.031 \text{ g. } H_2S$$

$$75\% = 0.031$$

$$0.031 \times 100/75 = 0.041 \text{ g. } H_2S \text{ required.} \quad \textit{Ans.}$$

(*b*)
$$\underset{2(108)}{2Ag^+} + \underset{22{,}400}{H_2S} \rightarrow Ag_2S$$

$$22{,}400 \times 0.2/216 = 20.7 \text{ ml. } H_2S$$

$$75\% = 20.7 \text{ ml.}$$

$$20.7 \times 100/75 = 27.6 \text{ ml. } H_2S \text{ required.} \quad \textit{Ans.}$$

Using the answer obtained in (*a*) the computation reduces to

$$22{,}400 \times 0.041/34 = 27.0 \text{ ml.} \quad \textit{Ans.}$$

(Why the discrepancy of 0.6 ml. in the two answers?)

11. *Calculate the time needed to precipitate* 100 *mg. of* $Cu^{++}$ *as* CuS *if* $H_2S$ *is absorbed by the solution at the rate of* 50 *ml. per minute.*

$$Cu^{++} + H_2S + 2H_2O = CuS + 2H_3O^+$$

$$1 \text{ g. atom of Cu} = 22{,}400 \text{ ml. } H_2S \text{ or } 1 \text{ mg. atom Cu} = 22.4 \text{ ml. } H_2S$$

$$100/63.6 = 1.57 \text{ mg. atoms of } Cu^{++} \text{ in } 100 \text{ mg.}$$

$$1.57 \times 22.4 = 35.2 \text{ ml. of } H_2S \text{ needed}$$

If $H_2S$ is absorbed at the rate of 50 ml. per minute the time needed is

$$35.2/50 = 0.7 \text{ min.} \quad \textit{Ans.}$$

## REVERSIBLE REACTIONS

A reversible reaction is one of a pair of reactions in which the reagents of each reaction are the products of the other. A simple experiment to show the meaning of this definition consists in (*a*) passing $H_2S$ into a solution of $ZnCl_2$ (nearly neutral), and then (*b*) adding a moderate amount of HCl to the resulting system. In the first step a precipitate of ZnS forms, the equation for the reaction being:

(1)
$$Zn^{++} + H_2S + 2H_2O = ZnS + 2H_3O^+$$

In the second step the ZnS dissolves, the equation being:

(2) $$ZnS + 2H_3O^+ = Zn^{++} + H_2S + 2H_2O$$

A comparison of these two equations shows that the reagents of the first reaction are the products of the second, and the reagents of the second are the products of the first. Such a pair of reactions is called a *reversible system*, and each of the reactions, separately, is called a *reversible reaction*. Frequently, the two equations are combined into what appears to be a single equation by writing one of them and then substituting double arrows for the equals sign.

$$Zn^{++} + H_2S + 2H_2O \rightleftarrows ZnS + 2H_3O^+$$

$$ZnS + 2H_3O^+ \rightleftarrows Zn^{++} + H_2S + 2H_2O$$

In this case the double arrows mean that two reactions are being shown, the equation for one of them being read in the usual way from left to right, and the other being read from right to left.

**Chemical Equilibrium.** Many of the reactions which can be demonstrated to be reversible are commonly carried out under such conditions that they run practically to completion. In such situations the ordinary rules of chemical arithmetic apply, so that, knowing how much of one of the materials is present originally, one may calculate how much of the other reagent is needed or how much of a given product will be formed. In other cases, however, the final condition reached is one in which neither reagent of the reversible reaction is reduced to a very low concentration because the reverse reaction is taking place at a sufficiently rapid rate to maintain moderate concentrations of the original materials. In such a system a condition of chemical equilibrium is finally reached with both reactions taking place at the same speed.

A simple experiment to illustrate the incompleteness of some reactions consists in mixing equal volumes of 0.25 $N$ (for pptn.) $BaCl_2$ and $K_2Cr_2O_7$. A bright yellow precipitate of $BaCrO_4$ forms very promptly.

$$2Ba^{++} + Cr_2O_7^{--} + 3H_2O = 2BaCrO_4 + 2H_3O^+$$

After shaking the solution to mix thoroughly and letting it stand a short time to approach equilibrium, the precipitate is filtered out and discarded. The filtrate is now tested for incompleteness of the reaction. (Incidentally, it will be interesting to set aside some of the filtrate for 10–15 minutes and note that a further precipitate of $BaCrO_4$ forms, showing that equilibrium has not been reached and that the formation of the last bit of precipitate is taking place slowly.) The color of the filtrate gives an obvious indication that there is a moderate concentration of $Cr_2O_7^{--}$ present. To show that there is also a moderate amount of $Ba^{++}$ in the solution either of two tests may be used: (*a*) add a few ml. of reagent $(NH_4)_2SO_4$ and obtain a copious precipitate of $BaSO_4$, or (*b*) add a few ml. of reagent $NH_4OH$ which neutralizes the $H_3O^+$ formed in the reaction and yields a fairly heavy precipitate of $BaCrO_4$. Even if the solution is permitted to stand several hours before the original filtration it will be found that the filtrate has a moderate color of $Cr_2O_7^{--}$ and gives a good precipitate of $BaCrO_4$ on neutralizing with $NH_4OH$.

In reactions of this sort where a condition of equilibrium may be set up which is far short of practically complete reaction, the question of main interest to the chemist is: How far will the reaction go when the reagents are brought together in equivalent amounts, and what will be the effect on the completeness of the reaction if excess of one of the reagents is added or one of the products is removed? To the extent to which the reaction takes place the reagents are used up and the products are formed in equivalent amounts, so the rules of simple chemical arithmetic apply. However, if equilibrium may be reached before the reaction has gone very far, it is necessary to have additional information in the form of equilibrium constants before one can calculate how far the reaction has gone. For substances which are slightly ionized these equilibrium constants are called *ionization constants;* for substances which are slightly soluble the constants are called *solubility products.*

**Ionization Constants.** Although most of the common salts, the strong acids, and the strong bases may be regarded as essentially completely ionized in ordinary concentrations of aqueous solutions, there are a moderate number of electrolytes which dissociate to only a small extent. Some of these are important reagents in analytical chemistry in those cases where separations are based on differences of solubility of fairly insoluble compounds.

For these weak electrolytes the process of ionization may be regarded as a reversible reaction between water and the molecular form of the electrolyte with the formation of ions in the solution. Thus acetic acid in dilute aqueous solution may be represented by the system

$$HC_2H_3O_2 + H_2O \rightleftarrows H_3O^+ + C_2H_3O_2^-$$

In such a system a condition of equilibrium will be set up in which the two reactions are both taking place at the same rate. Experimental studies of solutions of acetic acid over a fairly wide range have shown that in all of these solutions, when the temperature is fixed at a given value, the concentrations of the undissociated acid and of the ions will adjust themselves in such a way that the product of the concentrations of the ions, divided by the concentration of the undissociated acid, will have the same value for all the solutions. This numerical value is called the ionization constant of acetic acid. The extent of dissociation of the compound in any particular solution is the fraction of the compound which has been changed to ions in that solution.

The calculations involving ionization constants are of several distinct types: (*a*) to calculate the numerical value for an ionization constant from data showing the extent of dissociation of the compound at a particular concentration, (*b*) to calculate the extent of dissociation of the compound at some desired concentration when the ionization constant is known, and (*c*) to calculate the extent of dissociation of the compound in a specific solution containing a strong electrolyte supplying one of the ions of the original compound. This last case is called the *common ion effect*. Examples of these cases will be explained briefly.

*Case A:* Calculate the ionization constant for acetic acid ($K_{HC_2H_3O_2}$) if the compound is known to be 1.34% ionized in 0.1 *M* solution.

$$K_{HC_2H_3O_2} = \frac{[H_3O^+] \times [C_2H_3O_2^-]}{[HC_2H_3O_2]}$$

In the equation, $K_{HC_2H_3O_2}$ is the symbol for the ionization constant of acetic acid; $[H_3O^+]$, $[C_2H_3O_2^-]$ and $[HC_2H_3O_2]$ are the symbols for the molar concentrations of hydronium ion, acetate ion, and undissociated acetic acid, respectively, and it is assumed that equilibrium has been reached in the 0.1 *M* solution.

If the acetic acid is 1.34% ionized, it is 100 − 1.34% non-ionized. Since the total concentration of the acetic acid is 0.1 *M*, the concentration of the undissociated acid is 100 − 1.34% of 0.1 *M* or 0.0986 *M*. Since each molecule of acetic acid that dissociates supplies one hydronium ion and one acetate ion, the concentrations of each of these ions will be identical with that of the dissociated acetic acid, or 1.34% of 0.1 *M*, which is 0.00134 *M*.

$$[H_3O^+] = 0.00134$$

$$[C_2H_3O_2^-] = 0.00134$$

$$[HC_2H_3O_2] = 0.0986$$

On substituting these values in the original equation and carrying out the indicated operations:

$$\frac{[H_3O^+] \times [C_2H_3O_2^-]}{[HC_2H_3O_2]} = \frac{0.00134 \times 0.00134}{0.0986} = 1.82 \times 10^{-5}$$

$$K_{HC_2H_3O_2} = 1.82 \times 10^{-5} \quad \textit{Ans.}$$

(NOTE: In this form of writing the answer, the exponent −5 indicates that if this were written as a decimal fraction the number 1, immediately preceding the decimal point, would appear in the fifth place beyond the decimal point, i.e., $1.82 \times 10^{-5} = 0.0000182$.)

*Case B:* Calculate the extent of dissociation of acetic acid in 0.5 *M* solution if $K_{HC_2H_3O_2} = 1.8 \times 10^{-5}$.

$$\frac{[H_3O^+] \times [C_2H_3O_2^-]}{[HC_2H_3O_2]} = 1.8 \times 10^{-5}$$

If the total concentration of the acetic acid is 0.5, and $x$ equals the extent of dissociation of the acid in this solution, then $1 - x$ is the fraction of the acetic acid in the non-ionized form.

$$[H_3O^+] = 0.5x$$

$$[C_2H_3O_2^-] = 0.5x$$

$$[HC_2H_3O_2] = 0.5(1 - x)$$

Substitute these values in the expression for $K_{HC_2H_3O_2}$ and solve for $x$.

$$\frac{(0.5x)(0.5x)}{0.5(1 - x)} = 1.8 \times 10^{-5}$$

$$x = 6 \times 10^{-3} \quad \textit{Ans.}$$

This problem might have been stated in another way, such as calculate the concentration of $H_3O^+$ supplied by 0.5 *M* $HC_2H_3O_2$. In this case the solution might take the same form as just used, with $x$ = extent of dissociation of the acetic acid. Or one may start by saying $x$ = concentration of $H_3O^+$. In this latter case the equation would then become

$$\frac{x \times x}{0.5 - x} = 1.8 \times 10^{-5}$$

Solving for $x$ gives the concentration of $H_3O^+$. If the first form is used, it is necessary to remember that $x$ = the extent of dissociation of the acetic acid and $0.5x$ is the concentration of $H_3O^+$. The student occasionally sets the problem up in the first form, solves for $x$, and then calls this the concentration of $H_3O^+$.

*Case C:* Calculate the extent of dissociation of acetic acid in a 0.2 *M* solution containing $NaC_2H_3O_2$ in 0.3 *M* concentration. In this case it is common practice to assume that the sodium acetate is completely ionized into $Na^+$ and $C_2H_3O_2^-$ and thus the concentration of acetate ion supplied by the sodium acetate would be 0.3 *M*. If $x$ = the extent of dissociation of the acetic acid, the concentrations of $H_3O^+$ and $C_2H_3O_2^-$ supplied by this reagent would each be $0.2x$ and the concentration of undissociated $HC_2H_3O_2$ $0.2(1 - x)$.

$$\frac{[H_3O^+] \times [C_2H_3O_2^-]}{[HC_2H_3O_2]} = 1.8 \times 10^{-5}$$

$$[H_3O^+] = 0.2x$$

$$[C_2H_3O_2^-] = 0.3 + 0.2x$$

$$[HC_2H_3O_2] = 0.2(1 - x)$$

$$\frac{(0.2x) \times (0.3 + 0.2x)}{0.2(1 - x)} = 1.8 \times 10^{-5}$$

In this final equation it will be noted that there is only one unknown; therefore, this may be converted to the usual quadratic form and solved for $x$. However, it is frequently possible to set up a much simpler equation which will give very nearly the same value for $x$ but with much less labor of calculation. The principle involved is stated mathematically as follows:

If $x$ is small in comparison with A then A $\pm x$ is approximately equal to A, and A may be used with correspondingly small error in place of A $+ x$ or A $- x$.

Applying this to the system under consideration, it is known that acetic acid is only slightly ionized in ordinary concentrations, whereas sodium acetate is practically completely ionized; therefore the concentration of acetate ion supplied by the dissociation of acetic acid will be small as compared with that furnished by the sodium acetate. Thus, $0.3 + 0.2x$ is approximately equal to 0.3. Similarly, the extent of dissociation of the acetic acid is so small in this solution that $1 - x$ is approximately equal to 1. When these approximations are applied to the original equation, it is simplified to the form:

$$\frac{(0.2x)(0.3)}{0.2} = 1.8 \times 10^{-5}$$

$$0.3x = 1.8 \times 10^{-5} \, *$$

$$x = 6 \times 10^{-5} \quad \textit{Ans.}$$

When approximations are used, as in this particular case, it is always best to check them with the final answer to make sure that no significant error

* This equation may be written $x = \dfrac{K_i}{[salt]}$ where $x$ is the extent of dissociation of the weak electrolyte (acetic acid in this example), $K_i$ is its ionization constant, and [*salt*] is the molar concentration of the strong electrolyte (sodium acetate). Since $[H_3O^+] = x \times [acid]$, substitution and rearrangement give the equation $[H_3O^+] = \dfrac{K_i[acid]}{[salt]}$.

is introduced. In this case, to show that $0.3 + 0.2x$ = approximately 0.3, use the value found for $x$.

$$0.3 + 0.2x = 0.3 + 0.000012 = \text{approx. } 0.3$$

Similarly,

$$1 - x = 1 - 0.00006 = \text{approx. } 1$$

Modifications of these problems are occasionally encountered which involve no new principle but which may call for a careful examination of the data given in order to set up the fundamental equation. Two examples of such modifications will be considered.

*Problem:* At what concentration of acetic acid will the compound be 25% ionized in aqueous solution? $K_{HC_2H_3O_2} = 1.8 \times 10^{-5}$.

In this case, if the compound is 25% ionized, it will be 75% in the non-ionized form. The total concentration will be the sum of the ionized and the non-ionized forms.

$$\text{total concn. of acetic acid} = x$$

$$\text{concn. of } H_3O^+ = 0.25x$$

$$\text{concn. of } C_2H_3O_2^- = 0.25x$$

$$\text{concn. of undissociated } HC_2H_3O_2 = 0.75x$$

If

$$\frac{[H_3O^+] \times [C_2H_3O_2^-]}{[HC_2H_3O_2]} = 1.8 \times 10^{-5}$$

$$\frac{(0.25x)(0.25x)}{0.75x} = 1.8 \times 10^{-5}$$

Simplifying:

$$\frac{0.25x}{3} = 1.8 \times 10^{-5}$$

$$x = 1.8 \times 10^{-5} \times 3 \times 4 = 2.16 \times 10^{-4}$$

In $2.16 \times 10^{-4}$ $M$ acetic acid, the reagent would be 25% ionized. *Ans.*

*Problem:* What concentration of sodium acetate must be present in 0.1 $M$ solution of acetic acid so that the concentration of $H_3O^+$ will be $1 \times 10^{-5}$ $M$? $K_{HC_2H_3O_2} = 1.8 \times 10^{-5}$.

In this case, if $H_3O^+ = 1 \times 10^{-5}$ $M$, then the concentration of $C_2H_3O_2^-$ supplied by the acetic acid will also be $1 \times 10^{-5}$ $M$ and the concentration of undissociated $HC_2H_3O_2$ will be $0.1 - 1 \times 10^{-5}$, which is practically 0.1.

Let $x = [C_2H_3O_2^-]$ from the sodium acetate.

$$\text{Total acetate ion} = x + 1 \times 10^{-5} = \text{approximately } x$$

$$\frac{[H_3O^+] \times [C_2H_3O_2^-]}{[HC_2H_3O_2]} = 1.8 \times 10^{-5}$$

$$\frac{(1 \times 10^{-5})(x)}{0.1} = 1.8 \times 10^{-5}$$

$$1.8 \times 10^{-6} = 1 \times 10^{-5}x$$

$$x = 0.18$$

If a 0.1 *M* solution of acetic acid is also 0.18 *M* with sodium acetate, the concentration of $H_3O^+$ will be $1 \times 10^{-5}$ *M*. *Ans.*

**The Water Constant.** Since water is a weak electrolyte, dissociating very slightly into $H_3O^+$ and $OH^-$, one might expect frequent reference to the ionization constant of water in connection with the discussion of reactions involving neutralization or hydrolysis. However, in dilute aqueous solutions, even though water may be involved as reagent or product in reactions taking place, the actual concentration of undissociated water remains so nearly constant that no serious error is introduced in regarding it as constant. On this basis the product of concentrations of $H_3O^+$ and $OH^-$ will be the same for all dilute aqueous solutions. This product is called the water constant and is referred to by the symbol $K_W$.

$$K_W = [H_3O^+] \times [OH^-] = 1 \times 10^{-14} \quad \text{(at 25°C.)}$$

*Problem:* Calculate the concentration of $H_3O^+$ in pure water at 25°C.

Since there is no other source of $H_3O^+$ or $OH^-$ than the dissociation of the water itself in such a solution, the two concentrations will be equal.

$$[H_3O^+] = [OH^-] = \sqrt{1 \times 10^{-14}} = 1 \times 10^{-7} \quad \textit{Ans.}$$

*Problem:* Calculate the concentration of $H_3O^+$ in 0.1 *M* HCl.

Since HCl is a strong acid it may be regarded as completely ionized; therefore the concentration of $H_3O^+$ supplied by this reagent would be 0.1 *M*. The concentration of $H_3O^+$ supplied by the water would be negligible in comparison with this.

$$[H_3O^+] = 0.1 \quad \textit{Ans.}$$

*Problem:* Calculate the concentration of $H_3O^+$ in 0.1 *M* NaOH.

Since NaOH is a strong base it may be regarded as completely ionized; therefore the concentration of $OH^-$ in this solution would be 0.1 *M*. The concentration of $OH^-$ supplied by the water would be negligible in comparison. But

$$K_W = [H_3O^+] \times [OH^-] = 1 \times 10^{-14}$$

If $[OH^-] = 0.1$,

$$[H_3O^+] = \frac{1 \times 10^{-14}}{0.1} = 1 \times 10^{-13} \quad \textit{Ans.}$$

*Problem:* Calculate the concentration of $H_3O^+$ when a 0.1 *M* solution of $HC_2H_3O_2$ has been treated with an equivalent amount of NaOH (neglect dilution effects). $K_{HC_2H_3O_2} = 1.8 \times 10^{-5}$, $K_W = 1 \times 10^{-14}$.

In this case the acetic acid is only slightly ionized at the start. As NaOH is added the $H_3O^+$ combines with the $OH^-$ thus supplied, causing further dissociation of the $HC_2H_3O_2$. The net reaction may be written:

$$HC_2H_3O_2 + OH^- = H_2O + C_2H_3O_2^-$$

Since the problem stated that the $HC_2H_3O_2$ and NaOH were being brought together in equivalent amounts, the concentrations of $HC_2H_3O_2$ and of $OH^-$ will be essentially equal at all stages in the reaction. Thus, if the reaction stops appreciably short of completion, these two concentrations will still be equal. Also, at equilibrium both the ionization constant of $HC_2H_3O_2$ and the water constant must be satisfied.

$$\frac{[H_3O^+] \times [C_2H_3O_2^-]}{[HC_2H_3O_2]} = 1.8 \times 10^{-5}$$

$$[H_3O^+] \times [OH^-] = 1 \times 10^{-14}$$

If one assumes that the reaction goes nearly to completion $[C_2H_3O_2^-] =$ approx. 0.1. Substituting this value for $[C_2H_3O_2^-]$ and using $[OH^-]$ in place of $[HC_2H_3O_2]$ in the ionization constant of acetic acid,

$$\frac{([H_3O^+])(0.1)}{[OH^-]} = 1.8 \times 10^{-5}$$

Rearrange:

$$[OH^-] = \frac{0.1 \times [H_3O^+]}{1.8 \times 10^{-5}} = \frac{[H_3O^+]}{1.8 \times 10^{-4}}$$

From the water constant:—

$$[OH^-] = \frac{1 \times 10^{-14}}{[H_3O^+]}$$

Equating the two expressions for $[OH^-]$.

$$\frac{[H_3O^+]}{1.8 \times 10^{-4}} = \frac{1 \times 10^{-14}}{[H_3O^+]}$$

$$[H_3O^+]^2 = 1 \times 10^{-14} \times 1.8 \times 10^{-4} = 1.8 \times 10^{-18}$$

$$[H_3O^+] = 1.35 \times 10^{-9} \quad \textit{Ans.}$$

The assumption that $[C_2H_3O_2^-]$ = approx. 0.1 may now be tested as follows: Since $[C_2H_3O_2^-] = 0.1 - [HC_2H_3O_2]$ and $[HC_2H_3O_2] = [OH^-] = \dfrac{1 \times 10^{-14}}{[H_3O^+]} = \dfrac{1 \times 10^{-14}}{1.35 \times 10^{-9}} = 0.75 \times 10^{-5}$, $[C_2H_3O_2^- =]\ 0.1 - 0.75 \times 10^{-5}$. This quantity is obviously very close to 0.1 and therefore the assumption is justified.

*Problem:* Calculate the concentration of $H_3O^+$ in 0.5 *M* sodium acetate solution.

Sodium acetate is regarded as a strong electrolyte, essentially completely ionized into $Na^+$ and $C_2H_3O_2^-$; therefore the concentration of $C_2H_3O_2^-$ should be 0.5 *M*. However, $C_2H_3O_2^-$ is the anion of a moderately weak acid, $HC_2H_3O_2$, and water dissociates to a slight extent into $H_3O^+$ and $OH^-$; therefore some $C_2H_3O_2^-$ will react with the $H_3O^+$ to form undissociated $HC_2H_3O_2$. As this occurs, further dissociation of $H_2O$ takes place and the excess $OH^-$ thus produced accumulates in the solution. The net reaction may be written as follows:

$$C_2H_3O_2^- + H_2O = HC_2H_3O_2 + OH^-$$

If this reaction takes place to any significant extent, the corresponding concentrations of undissociated acetic acid and hydroxyl ion will be equal. Also, at equilibrium, both the ionization constant of $HC_2H_3O_2$ and the water constant must be satisfied.

$$\frac{[H_3O^+] \times [C_2H_3O_2^-]}{[HC_2H_3O_2]} = 1.8 \times 10^{-5}$$

$$[H_3O^+] \times [OH^-] = 1 \times 10^{-14}$$

If one assumes that only a small amount of the $C_2H_3O_2^-$ is used up in the reaction

$$[C_2H_3O_2^-] = \text{approx. } 0.5.$$

Substituting this value in the expression for the ionization constant of $HC_2H_3O_2$, and using $[OH^-]$ in place of $[HC_2H_3O_2]$:

$$\frac{[H_3O^+]0.5}{[OH^-]} = 1.8 \times 10^{-5}$$

Rearrange:

$$[OH^-] = \frac{0.5[H_3O^+]}{1.8 \times 10^{-5}} = \frac{[H_3O^+]}{3.6 \times 10^{-5}}$$

From the water constant:

$$[OH^-] = \frac{1 \times 10^{-14}}{[H_3O^+]}$$

Equating these two values for $[OH^-]$:

$$\frac{[H_3O^+]}{3.6 \times 10^{-5}} = \frac{1 \times 10^{-14}}{[H_3O^+]}$$

$$[H_3O^+]^2 = 1 \times 10^{-14} \times 3.6 \times 10^{-5} = 3.6 \times 10^{-19}$$

$$[H_3O^+] = 6 \times 10^{-10} \quad \textit{Ans.}$$

The assumption that in the final solution $[C_2H_3O_2^-]$ = approx. 0.5 may now be justified by calculating that the approximate concentration of $HC_2H_3O_2$ formed would be $\frac{1 \times 10^{-14}}{6 \times 10^{-10}} = 0.17 \times 10^{-4}$, which would decrease the concentration of $C_2H_3O_2^-$ to only a very minor extent.

**Solubility Products.** The solubility of a compound in water at a given temperature has a definite numerical value which has been determined experimentally for many compounds and recorded in the literature of chemistry. However, these values tell only a small part of the story of actual solubility when other solutes are present in the solution. Aside from those cases in which the other solute enters into chemical reaction with the compound to produce new substances, two divergent effects are commonly recognized, one involving an increase in solubility, the other a decrease. The first of these is called the inter-ionic attraction effect; the other, the common ion effect. Both these effects are explained in terms of the concept that when some of the solute is present in contact with a saturated aqueous solution a condition of dynamic equilibrium is set up in which the solute continues to dissolve, but this is exactly counterbalanced by precipitation from the solution, so that the actual concentration of the solution does not change. The rate of dissolving is proportional to the surface (except in the case of extremely small particles, where an increased solubility is observed), and thus is a constant for unit area at a given temperature. The rate of precipitation from the solution is proportional to the frequency with which the ions come together at the surface of the precipitate. For unit area of the precipitate, this will depend on the concentrations of each of the ions and on their freedom of movement in the solution (mobility). For solutions with relatively low concentrations of ions, each kind of ion has a fairly characteristic freedom of movement. In such a case, to establish a definite rate of precipitation on unit area of surface of the precipitate it is necessary to set up a corresponding definite product of concentrations of the ions of the compound in the solution. Therefore, to match the constant rate of dissolving from unit area of the precipitate it is necessary to have present in the solution a correspondingly constant product of concentrations of the ions of the precipitate. For solutions with low concentrations of ions this product—at a particular temperature—has a definite numerical value characteristic of the compound in question. This constant is called the *solubility product* (also solubility product constant, or ion product constant) for the compound in question.

As the concentrations of various ions in the solution are increased by foreign salts or by compounds supplying a common ion, these charged particles interfere somewhat with the freedom of motion of all ions in the solution and thus require that higher concentrations of the ions of the precipitate must be present in order to maintain a condition of saturation. Thus the numerical value of the solubility product increases somewhat under these conditions. This effect is discussed somewhat more in detail later in this chapter under the heading, Activity of Electrolytes.

**Repression of Solubility by Common Ion Effect.** Since the solubility product is a constant which characterizes saturated solutions of a particular compound, it is evident that the condition of saturation would be disturbed if to such a solution was added a strong electrolyte which supplied one of the ions of the precipitate. With the increased concentration of this ion the precipitate would start to form faster than it was dissolving, thus causing further precipitation and lowering the concentrations of both its ions in solution until a new condition of equilibrium was reached. Since the solubility of the compound is now represented by the lowered concentration of the other ion, it is evident that the solubility has been decreased by the reagent which has supplied one of the ions of the precipitate.

**Calculation of Solubility Product from Solubility.** The solubility product of a compound may be calculated directly from the solubility of the compound in water in those cases where this solubility is sufficient to permit its determination by direct experiment.

*Problem:* Calculate the solubility product of silver chloride if a saturated solution in water contains 1.5 mg. of AgCl per liter.

Since the concentrations are expressed in moles per liter, the first step is to calculate the molar solubility of the AgCl.

$$1.5 \text{ mg.} = 0.0015 \text{ g.} \qquad (\text{mol. wt. of AgCl} = 143.5)$$

$$\text{Molar solubility} = \frac{0.0015}{143.5} = 1.05 \times 10^{-5}$$

i.e., a satd. soln. of AgCl in water at 25°C. = $1.05 \times 10^{-5}$ *M*. If one assumes that the AgCl is completely ionized,

$$[Ag^+] = [Cl^-] = 1.05 \times 10^{-5}$$

On this basis the solubility product of AgCl is

$$(1.05 \times 10^{-5})(1.05 \times 10^{-5}) = 1.1 \times 10^{-10} \quad \textit{Ans.}$$

For compounds dissociating into three or more ions the formula for the solubility product involves raising the concentration of each ion to a power corresponding to its subscript in the formula of the compound, $L_{A_mB_n} = [A]^m[B]^n$.

*Problem:* Calculate the solubility product of $Ag_2CrO_4$ if a saturated solution in water contains 26 mg. of $Ag_2CrO_4$ per liter.

26 mg. = 0.026 g. (mol. wt. $Ag_2CrO_4$ = 332)

$$\text{Molar solubility} = \frac{0.026}{332} = 0.000078$$

If one assumes the $Ag_2CrO_4$ to be completely ionized so that each molecule supplies two silver ions and one chromate ion,

$$[Ag^+] = 2 \times 7.8 \times 10^{-5} = 1.56 \times 10^{-4}$$

$$[CrO_4^{--}] = 7.8 \times 10^{-5}$$

$$[Ag^+]^2 \times [CrO_4^{--}] = (1.56 \times 10^{-4})^2(7.8 \times 10^{-5}) = 2 \times 10^{-12}$$

$$L_{Ag_2CrO_4} = 2 \times 10^{-12} \quad \textit{Ans.}$$

**Calculation of Solubility from Solubility Product.** It should be noted that, although one usually thinks of solubility products as quantities which are calculated from solubility data, there are many compounds whose solubilities are so low that they cannot be determined directly with reasonable accuracy. In such cases it is sometimes possible to obtain experimental measurements of the concentrations of the ions in specially saturated solutions and use these data to calculate the solubility products. From the solubility product thus determined the corresponding solubility of the compound in pure water may be calculated.

As an example of this, consider the data:

(*a*) The potential of a silver electrode in 1.0 *M* $Ag^+$ is −0.8 volt, whereas in 1.0 *M* $I^-$ it is +0.15 volt.

(*b*) A 10-fold change in the concentration of $Ag^+$ corresponds to a change in potential of 0.059 volt. The difference in the two potentials is directly related to the different concentrations of $Ag^+$ in the two solutions.

If $Ag^+$ is $M$ when the potential is $-0.8$ volt, then when $E = +0.15$ volt the concentration of $Ag^+$ is $1 \times 10^{-\frac{0.95}{0.059}} = 1 \times 10^{-16}$ $M$.

$$L_{AgI} = (1 \times 10^{-16})(1.0) = 1 \times 10^{-16}$$

If $L_{AgI} = 1 \times 10^{-16}$, then in a solution saturated with respect to AgI in which the concentrations of $Ag^+$ and $I^-$ are both equal (a solution in pure water), the concentration of each would be the square root of $1 \times 10^{-16}$ or $1 \times 10^{-8}$. Since one $Ag^+$ would be derived from one AgI, the molar solubility of AgI in pure water would be $1 \times 10^{-8}$.

As a general formula for such calculations: if $L_{A_mB_n} = A^m \times B^n$ in a saturated solution, the corresponding molar solubility of $A_mB_n$ in pure water as an inert solvent would be

$$\sqrt[m+n]{\frac{L_{A_mB_n}}{m^m \times n^n}}$$

**Water Is Not Always an Inert Solvent.** Water undergoes measurable dissociation into $H_3O^+$ and $OH^-$ (in pure water at 25°C. $[H_3O^+] = [OH^-] = \sqrt{K_W} = 1 \times 10^{-7}$). In those cases in which the concentrations of $H_3O^+$ or $OH^-$ supplied by water may enter into significant reaction with the saturating compound, the solubility in water may be quite different from that calculated by the application of this formula. This is readily seen in such cases as $Fe(OH)_3$ and CdS.

*Problem:* To calculate the molar solubility of $Fe(OH)_3$ in water if the solubility product is $1.3 \times 10^{-38}$.

If water is assumed to be an inert solvent so that only the ions supplied by the $Fe(OH)_3$ need to be considered, and if the saturated solution in water is so dilute that the $Fe(OH)_3$ may be assumed to be completely ionized into $Fe^{+++}$ and $OH^-$, then the concentration of $OH^-$ would be three times that of $Fe^{+++}$ and the latter would be equal to the molar solubility of the $Fe(OH)_3$. Therefore:

$$[Fe^{+++}] = \text{molar soly. of } Fe(OH)_3$$

$$[OH^-] = 3 \times \text{molar soly. of } Fe(OH)_3$$

$$L_{Fe(OH)_3} = (\text{molar soly.})(3 \times \text{molar soly.})^3$$

$$= (27 \times \text{molar soly.})^4$$

$$\text{Molar soly.} = \sqrt[4]{\frac{1.3 \times 10^{-38}}{27}} = 1.48 \times 10^{-10}$$

However, since the solubility of $Fe(OH)_3$ was calculated to be $1.48 \times 10^{-10}$, it is obvious that the concentration of $OH^-$ supplied by water is many times as great as that from the $Fe(OH)_3$; therefore there should be a considerable repression of solubility by this common ion effect. Thus, assuming that the final concentration of $OH^-$ will not be far from $1 \times 10^{-7}$, one may calculate the corresponding concentration of $Fe^{+++}$ needed to saturate such a solution with $Fe(OH)_3$:

$$[Fe^{+++}] = \frac{1.3 \times 10^{-38}}{(1 \times 10^{-7})^3} = 1.3 \times 10^{-17}$$

Hence the actual solubility of $Fe(OH)_3$ in water would be $1.3 \times 10^{-17}$.

*Problem:* To calculate the molar solubility of CdS in water if $L_{CdS} = 5 \times 10^{-29}$. If one assumes water to be an inert solvent, the molar solubility would be the square root of $5 \times 10^{-29}$ or $7 \times 10^{-15}$. However, if one takes into account the fact that in a neutral solution $[H_3O^+] = [OH^-] = 1 \times 10^{-7}$, it appears that there would be a significant dissolving by hydrolysis according to the equations:

$$CdS + H_2O = Cd^{++} + HS^- + OH^-$$

$$CdS + 2H_2O = Cd^{++} + H_2S + 2OH^-$$

$x$ = approximately $[Cd^{++}]$ (neglecting amount from simple solubility)

$$[Cd^{++}] = [HS^-] + [H_2S]$$

If one assumes the increase in $[OH^-]$ to be small as compared with $1 \times 10^{-7}$, then $[H_3O^+] = [OH^-] = 1 \times 10^{-7}$. From

$$K_{H_2S} = \frac{[H_3O^+][HS^-]}{[H_2S]} = 1 \times 10^{-7}$$

if $[H_3O^+] = 1 \times 10^{-7}$, then

$$\frac{[HS^-]}{[H_2S]} = \frac{1 \times 10^{-7}}{1 \times 10^{-7}} = \frac{1}{1}$$

Under these conditions

$$[HS^-] = [H_2S] = 0.5[Cd^{++}] = 0.5x$$

From $L_{CdS}$,

$$[S^{--}] = \frac{5 \times 10^{-29}}{x}$$

From $K_{HS^-} = 1 \times 10^{-15}$,

$$[S^{--}] = \frac{(1 \times 10^{-15})(0.5x)}{1 \times 10^{-7}}$$

Equating these two values for $[S^{--}]$,

$$\frac{5 \times 10^{-29}}{x} = 5 \times 10^{-9}x$$

$$x = \sqrt{1 \times 10^{-20}} = 1 \times 10^{-10} \quad Ans.$$

In this case the actual solubility in pure water is found to be many times that which is calculated from the solubility product on the assumption that water is an inert solvent.

## ACTIVITY OF ELECTROLYTES

In the calculations involving ionization constants and solubility products, it has been assumed thus far that the presence of foreign salts in the solution would not change the results. Actually the "foreign salt effect" is well recognized and must be given due weight in calculations in which the answer is presumed to have more than "order of magnitude" significance. The detailed treatment of this topic is beyond the scope of a text in qualitative analysis, but a brief introduction may not be out of place.

**Strong Electrolytes vs. Weak Electrolytes.** In the experimental study of solutions of electrolytes, whether by depression of freezing point, elevation of boiling point, electrical conductivity or potentiometric measurement, it was early observed that the calculated value for the molar effect varied with the concentration. In the case of weak electrolytes, this variation showed such regularity that it could be accounted for by the assumption that ionization was taking place and that ionization is a reversible reaction subject to the usual applications of the law of mass action. In the case of strong electrolytes, however, no such regularity was observed. The difference between these two groups of electrolytes is clearly shown by comparing the ionization ratios obtained from conductivity data for acetic acid with that for potassium chloride (see Table I).

TABLE I. IONIZATION RATIOS FOR ACETIC ACID AND POTASSIUM CHLORIDE

| Molar Concn. of Acetic Acid | Apparent Extent of Dissociation $\times 10^2$ | $\frac{[H_3O^+] \times [C_2H_3O_2^-]}{[HC_2H_3O_2]} \times 10^5$ | Molar Concn. of Potassium Chloride | Apparent Extent of Dissociation $\times 10^2$ | $\frac{[K^+] \times [Cl^-]}{[KCl]}$ |
|---|---|---|---|---|---|
| 0.1 | 1.34 | 1.82 | 0.1 | 0.861 | 0.533 |
| 0.08 | 1.50 | 1.83 | 0.05 | 0.885 | 0.341 |
| 0.03 | 2.45 | 1.85 | 0.01 | 0.943 | 0.156 |
| 0.01 | 4.17 | 1.81 | | | |

It is evident that the ionization ratio for acetic acid shows definite constancy over this moderate range of concentrations, thus justifying the use of the term, ionization constant, for this ratio. However, in the case of potassium chloride the ratio varies by a factor of 3.4 for the tenfold change in molarity. Obviously, the data for potassium chloride cannot be accounted for by the simpler assumptions of the theory of ionization. Using potassium chloride as typical of the strong electrolytes, it is easy to see why this group of substances was spoken of as showing "anomalous" behavior.

Another important observation relating to strong electrolytes involves their effect on the solubility of slightly soluble salts. If the strong electrolyte supplies an ion common to the slightly soluble salt, the solubility will be decreased according to the solubility product principle. However, the solubility does not continue to decrease with increase in concentration of the strong electrolyte, but normally reaches a minimum and then rises, even though there is no evidence of complex formation. Further, if the strong electrolyte did not supply a common ion and did not react to produce new substances, one might suppose that there would be no effect on the solubility of the slightly soluble salt. But many careful experiments showed that under these conditions the solubility actually increased. A single example of this may be seen in the data in Table II from an article by Popoff and Neuman.* There is a progressive increase in solubility of silver chloride as the concentration of the potassium nitrate rises, the last figure showing approximately a 12% rise, although the concentration of the strong electrolyte is slightly less than 0.01 $M$. Before an adequate explanation was found for these experimental facts they were commonly spoken of as "foreign salt" effects.

TABLE II. SOLUBILITY OF AgCl IN $KNO_3$ SOLUTIONS

| | | | | | | | |
|---|---|---|---|---|---|---|---|
| Molar Concn. of $KNO_3$ $\times 10^4$ | 0.000 | 0.128 | 2.609 | 5.09 | 10.05 | 49.72 | 99.31 |
| Molar Soly. of AgCl $\times 10^5$ | 1.278 | 1.280 | 1.301 | 1.311 | 1.325 | 1.385 | 1.427 |

**Interionic Attraction Theory.** Considerable progress has been made toward the understanding of these behaviors of strong electrolytes by the development of the interionic attraction theory. In a solution containing an appreciable concentration of a strong electrolyte, it is obvious that the individual ions are not as free to move about as they would be in the absence of these other charged particles. Thus, their activity is less than would be expected from their concentration. On that basis, the methods used to determine the extent of dissociation of strong electrolytes will yield low results.

* Popoff and Neuman, *J. Phys. Chem.* **34,** 1853 (1930).

Since strong electrolytes have always been considered to be largely dissociated in aqueous solution, the above suggestion leads to the point of view that the strong electrolytes may be thought of as completely ionized, with the electrical attractions and repulsions of the ions for each other and hydration effects accounting for the activity being less than anticipated from their concentrations. This belief that the strong electrolytes are completely ionized was strongly reinforced by the x-ray study of crystalline salts which showed that these consist of ions in regular order, with no evidence for the presence of molecules. Thus, the dissolving of the salt in water consists merely in the separation of the ions from each other under the influence of the solvent.

**Ionic Activity Coefficients.** Since the physical properties by which the activities of strong electrolytes are studied show maximum "molar" effects in solutions of extreme dilution it is assumed that under these conditions the ionic activity is practically identical with the ionic concentration. As the concentration increases, the activity rises also, but more slowly than the concentration. For any particular concentration of a given electrolyte at a given temperature there is a definite ratio of activity to concentration. This ratio is a factor by which the concentration of the ions of the electrolyte may be multiplied to calculate the corresponding activity. It is called the ionic activity coefficient. At infinite dilution the ionic activity coefficient of a strong electrolyte is 1; but as the concentration rises to the point where quantitative experimental studies are feasible, it drops to less than 1. As the concentration rises to higher levels, the ionic activity coefficient may drop to a minimum and then rise again, in some cases even exceeding the value of 1.

Since the activity coefficient varies with the concentration of the strong electrolyte it was an obvious step to carry out experimental studies on many electrolytes to see what regularities in behavior might be discovered. At the same time attempts were made to treat the interionic attraction principle mathematically to try and predict relations among strong electrolytes which would check with the experimental facts.

For the lower ranges of concentration a number of regularities were observed. Thus it was noted that the different valence types showed characteristic differences in ionic activity coefficients. The uni-univalent electrolytes (HCl, $KNO_3$, NaCl, etc.) all had practically identical activity coefficients for the same concentrations. The same was true for the bi-univalent or uni-bivalent electrolytes ($BaCl_2$, $Na_2SO_4$, etc.), although as a class these values were lower than those of the uni-univalent group. The ionic activity coefficients of the bi-bivalent salts were still lower, but, as a group, they were very similar. These relationships are easily seen in data taken from Latimer, Oxidation Potentials (1st Ed.), pp. 323–325. See Table III.

TABLE III. IONIC ACTIVITY COEFFICIENTS OF DIFFERENT VALENCE TYPES

| Molar Concn. | Uni-Univalent | | Bi-Univalent or Uni-Bivalent | | Bi-Bivalent | |
|---|---|---|---|---|---|---|
| | $NaNO_3$ | KCl | $Ba(NO_3)_2$ | $Na_2SO_4$ | $CuSO_4$ | $ZnSO_4$ |
| 0.001 | 0.966 | 0.965 | 0.88 | 0.887 | 0.74 | 0.70 |
| 0.002 | 0.953 | 0.952 | 0.84 | 0.847 | .... | 0.61 |
| 0.005 | 0.93 | 0.927 | 0.77 | 0.778 | 0.53 | 0.48 |
| 0.01 | 0.90 | 0.901 | 0.71 | 0.714 | 0.41 | 0.39 |

Further, it was observed that the variation in activity coefficients between the different valence types could be correlated with a quantity called the *ionic strength* of the solution. The ionic strength of a solution is calculated by adding together the products of the concentration and the square of the valence of each of the ions present and dividing this sum by two. Thus, in 0.01 *M* solutions of NaCl, $BaCl_2$, and $CuSO_4$, the corresponding ionic strengths would be:

for 0.01 *M* NaCl $$\frac{(0.01 \times 1) + (0.01 \times 1)}{2} = 0.01$$

for 0.01 *M* $BaCl_2$ $$\frac{(0.01 \times 2^2) + (0.02 \times 1)}{2} = 0.03$$

for 0.01 *M* $CuSO_4$ $$\frac{(0.01 \times 4) + (0.01 \times 4)}{2} = 0.04$$

Mathematically the relation between the ionic activity coefficient and the ionic strength is expressed by the equation, applicable at 25° for very dilute solution,

Log of mean ionic activity coefficient =

0.505 × valence of each ion × square root of the ionic strength

To see how well this equation fits the experimental data it is interesting to calculate the activity coefficients for 0.001 *M* $NaNO_3 \cdot Ba(NO_3)_2$ and $CuSO_4$ and compare with the values in Table III.

*0.001 M $NaNO_3$.* The ionic strength is 0.001 and the ions each have a valence of 1; therefore log activity coefficient $= -0.505\sqrt{.001} = -0.01596$. This may be rewritten as 9.98404 − 10. The corresponding number is 0.964.

*0.001 M $Ba(NO_3)_2$.* The ionic strength is 0.003, and the ions have valences of 2 and 1, respectively.

$$\text{Log activity coefficient} = -0.505 \times 2 \times \sqrt{.003} = -0.05532$$

This may be rewritten as 9.9447 − 10. The corresponding number is 0.880.

*0.001 M $CuSO_4$.* The ionic strength is 0.004 and each ion has a valence of 2.

$$\text{Log activity coefficient} = -0.505 \times 2 \times 2\sqrt{.004} = -0.12774$$

This may be rewritten as 9.87226 − 10. This is the logarithm of 0.746.

It will be observed that these values are very close to those given in Table III.

Finally, in the very dilute solutions it was observed that the activity coefficient of an electrolyte in a solution containing other electrolytes is the same in all solutions of the same ionic strength. This may be seen in Table IV where the activity coefficients of HCl at different concentrations are

TABLE IV. ACTIVITY COEFFICIENT OF HCl IN THE PRESENCE OF OTHER CHLORIDES (25°C) *

| Total Molar Concn. | Pure HCl | 0.1 *M* HCl + LiCl | 0.1 *M* HCl + NaCl | 0.1 *M* HCl + KCl |
|---|---|---|---|---|
| 0.1 | 0.81 | 0.81 | 0.81 | 0.81 |
| 0.2 | 0.78 | 0.78 | 0.78 | 0.78 |
| 0.5 | 0.76 | 0.78 | 0.76 | 0.75 |
| 1.0 | 0.82 | 0.86 | 0.80 | 0.75 |
| 2.0 | 1.02 | 1.09 | 0.94 | 0.84 |

* Data taken from Lewis and Randall, Thermodynamics.

compared with that of 0.1 *M* HCl in the presence of other chlorides. Since the electrolytes in this table are all of the uni-univalent type, the ionic strength in each solution is the same as the total molar concentration.

**Solubility Products and Ionic Strength.** It will be recalled that slightly soluble salts are more soluble in dilute solutions of strong electrolytes than they are in water. This means that the solubility products are not constants when calculated in the usual way as involving the concentrations of the ions. However, it can be assumed that the "activity product" of a slightly soluble salt will be a constant for all saturated aqueous solutions at a given temperature, even though foreign salts may be present. Then the increased solubility in the presence of a foreign salt corresponds to a decreased activity. From this point of view the solubility product of such a salt as AgCl equals the activity product divided by the product of the activity coefficients of $Ag^+$ and $Cl^-$.

When the tables of activity coefficients are consulted, it is found that they are listed under compounds rather than ions. A more careful examination shows that these are "mean molar values." The meaning of this expression is best given mathematically. If a strong electrolyte $A_mB_n$ dissociated into $mA^+$ ions and $nB^-$ ions, the activity, "a," of the salt is equal to $(ma_{A^+}) \times (na_{B^-})$, in which $a_{A^+}$ and $a_{B^-}$ are the activities of the $A^+$ and $B^-$ ions. The "mean activity" of the ions, $a^{\pm}$, is given by the equation, $a^{\pm} = \sqrt[m+n]{a^m{}_{A^+} \times a^n{}_{B^-}}$. Thus for AgCl, $a^{\pm} = \sqrt{a_{Ag^+} \times a_{Cl^-}}$; for $BaCl_2$, $a^{\pm} = \sqrt[3]{a_{Ba^{++}} \times a^2{}_{Cl^-}}$; and for $Fe_2(SO_4)_3$, $a^{\pm} = \sqrt[5]{a^2{}_{Fe^{+++}} \times a^3{}_{SO_4^{--}}}$.

The corresponding "mean molarity" of the ions of the strong electrolyte, $A_mB_n$ at concentration $C$ moles per liter is given by the equation $C^{\pm} = \sqrt[m+n]{(mc)^m \times (nc)^n} = C \sqrt[m+n]{m^m + n^n}$. The mean ionic activity coefficient $(\gamma^{\pm})$ of the electrolyte is then given as $\gamma^{\pm} = \dfrac{a^{\pm}}{c^{\pm}}$. The values found in the tables are these mean activity coefficients. Within the lower concentration ranges the activity coefficient of a given valence type is determined by the ionic strength of the solution. Under these conditions the mean activity coefficients may be used directly as activity coefficients for the individual ions.

Returning now to a consideration of the solubility of AgCl in the presence of such salts as $KNO_3$ or $Ba(NO_3)_2$, it is only necessary to calculate the ionic strength of the solution as compared with that of a saturated solution of AgCl in water and use the corresponding activity coefficients to obtain a value for the increased solubility. The data quoted earlier from Popoff showed the solubility of AgCl in water at 25° is $1.278 \times 10^{-5}$ $M$. This solution would have an ionic strength of $1.278 \times 10^{-5}$. The solubility of AgCl in a solution which is $1.005 \times 10^{-3}$ $M$ with respect to $KNO_3$ was given as $1.325 \times 10^{-5}$ $M$. This solution would have an ionic strength of $1.005 \times 10^{-4} + 1.325 \times 10^{-5}$ or $1.1375 \times 10^{-4}$. The corresponding activity coefficients for a uni-univalent electrolyte in these two solutions may be calculated by using the equation, $\log \gamma^{\pm} = -0.505\sqrt{\mu}$, in which $\mu =$ the ionic strength. The values thus calculated are 0.996 for the saturated solution in water and 0.964 in the presence of the $KNO_3$.

Let $a_{Ag^+}$ and $a_{Cl^-}$ be the respective activities of $Ag^+$ and $Cl^-$ in a saturated solution of AgCl in water with $c^{\pm}$ the mean ionic molarity and $\gamma^{\pm}$ the mean ionic activity coefficient; and let $a'_{Ag^+}$, $a'_{Cl^-}$, $c'^{\pm}$, and $\gamma'^{\pm}$ be the corresponding quantities in a saturated solution of AgCl in the presence of some added electrolyte such as $KNO_3$. The activity product principle assumes that the product of the activities of $Ag^+$ and $Cl^-$ in the two solutions should be the same; that is, $(\gamma^{\pm}c^{\pm})(\gamma^{\pm}c^{\pm}) = (\gamma'^{\pm}c'^{\pm})(\gamma'^{\pm}c'^{\pm})$. Using as $c^{\pm}$ and $c'^{\pm}$ the two solubilities of AgCl and as $\gamma^{\pm}$ and $\gamma'^{\pm}$ the ionic activity coefficients calculated above, the two values for the activity product are $1.62 \times 10^{-10}$ and $1.63 \times 10^{-10}$. These are seen to be essentially identical.

If

$$(\gamma^{\pm}c^{\pm})^2 = (\gamma'^{\pm}c'^{\pm})^2$$

extracting the square root, $\gamma^{\pm}c^{\pm} = \gamma'^{\pm}c'^{\pm}$. From this equation, by rearrangement, one obtains

$$\frac{c^{\pm}}{c'^{\pm}} = \frac{\gamma'^{\pm}}{\gamma^{\pm}}$$

Stated in words, this means that the solubility is inversely proportional to the mean ionic activity coefficients in the two solutions. Thus, from the solubility of AgCl in water one may calculate the solubility in the $KNO_3$ solution by multiplying by the fraction $\frac{0.996}{0.964}$.

$$1.278 \times 10^{-5} \times \frac{0.996}{0.964} = 1.320 \times 10^{-5}$$

On comparing this calculated value with $1.325 \times 10^{-5}$ as determined experimentally, it is clear that a satisfactory explanation for the increased solubility has been found.

Similar studies of the solubility of AgCl in $Ba(NO_3)_2$ solutions showed that, when the concentration of $Ba(NO_3)_2$ was $1.499 \times 10^{-3}$ *M*, the AgCl was $1.372 \times 10^{-5}$ *M*. The ionic strength of this solution would be

| | |
|---|---|
| from the AgCl | $1.372 \times 10^{-5}$ |
| from the $Ba(NO_3)_2$ | $\frac{(4 \times 1.499 \times 10^{-3}) + (2 \times 1.499 \times 10^{-3})}{2}$ |
| | $= 4.497 \times 10^{-3}$ |
| sum of the two | $4.511 \times 10^{-3}$ |

The activity coefficient of AgCl at this ionic strength may be calculated as before and is found to be 0.926. On multiplying the solubility in water by the ratio $\frac{0.996}{0.926}$, the calculated solubility in the $Ba(NO_3)_2$ solution is found to be $1.374 \times 10^{-5}$ *M*. This is essentially identical with the experimental value.

**Ionization Constants and Ionic Strength.** In the same way that the solubility of a slightly soluble salt is increased by the presence of a strong electrolyte (without common ion), it is to be expected that the extent of ionization of a weak electrolyte would be increased under similar conditions. Direct experiments have shown that this is the case. Therefore one may calculate the ionization constant for acetic acid in a 0.02 *M* solution of NaCl by use of activity coefficients if one takes the value of the constant to be $1.754 \times 10^{-5}$ at zero ionic strength. The activity coefficient of a uni-univalent electrolyte at an ionic strength of 0.02 may be calculated as before. The value obtained is 0.848. Assuming that this is in the range in which the activity coefficients of the $H_3O^+$ and $C_2H_3O_2^-$ may be taken as that of the electrolyte

$$K = 1.754 \times 10^{-5} \times \left(\frac{1}{0.848}\right)^2 = 2.44 \times 10^{-5}$$

The value found experimentally is $2.29 \times 10^{-5}$, differing from the calculated value by only slightly more than 2%. However, if the experimentally determined activity coefficient for 0.02 *M* NaCl (0.875) is used, this difference disappears completely.

## ACTIVITY COEFFICIENTS IN MORE CONCENTRATED SOLUTIONS

The simple generalizations which apply in very dilute solutions no longer hold true when more concentrated solutions of strong electrolytes are studied. Even in molar solutions the activity coefficients of such similar salts as NaCl and KCl differ by significant amounts—0.66 and 0.606, respectively—whereas in 2-molar solution the activity coefficient of NaCl is 0.67, while that of KCl has dropped to 0.576. The equations which have been developed to calculate activity coefficients in these more concentrated solutions require additional terms involving both the concentration of the solution and empirical constants which vary from salt to salt. Further, in the case of a mixture of electrolytes it can no longer be assumed that the activity coefficient will be determined by the ionic strength of the solution. In Table IV giving the activity coefficient of 0.1 *M* HCl in the presence of other chlorides, it was shown that the activity coefficients of the HCl in the presence of 0.9 *M* NaCl and of 0.9 *M* KCl were 0.80 and 0.75, respectively. These are in the order suggested by the different activity coefficients of NaCl and KCl at this ionic strength. However, in the case of acetic acid in the presence of these two salts it is found that the ionization constant is slightly higher in molar NaCl than in molar KCl—$3.16 \times 10^{-5}$ as compared with $3.07 \times 10^{-5}$. These are in the reverse order to what would be expected if the activity coefficient of the acetic acid were determined by that of the strong electrolyte.

From this brief discussion it is evident that there is no simple way to apply activity considerations to problems involving solubility products and ionization constants except in very dilute solutions. Therefore these quantities will continue to be used as if they were not affected significantly by the presence of foreign salts. It will be understood, however, that the answers have only approximate value.

# 4

# Introduction to Laboratory Work

## MACRO TECHNIQUE

**Macro Scale.** Until recently in Qualitative Analysis it has been customary to use 15–20 ml. of the solution to be analyzed and to carry out precipitations in volumes ranging up to 50–75 ml. The precipitates are then separated from the mother liquor by filtering and washing. Such analyses use 0.1–0.3 g. of material in order that lesser constituents would yield sufficient precipitate so that it is not lost in the filter.

**Precipitation.** As a general rule the reagent should be added slowly to the hot, reasonably dilute solution, vigorously stirred to promote rapid and thorough mixing. This procedure gives a coarse-grained, easily filtered precipitate. At first only a small amount of reagent should be used. If no precipitate forms, all conditions being right, there is no use continuing the operation. If a precipitate does form and perhaps disappear, add the reagent slowly until reaction is complete. This may be determined by (*a*) letting the precipitate settle, then adding a drop or two of the reagent, (*b*) filtering, then adding a little of the reagent to the filtrate.

When a gelatinous precipitate is expected, it is better to add paper pulp before the separation is started. This will facilitate both filtration and washing, two otherwise tedious operations. (Tablets of ashless filter paper are readily obtained commercially. To prepare the paper pulp, put a piece of the tablet, about one-fourth inch square, in a test tube. Add 10–15 ml. of distilled water, then shake the tube vigorously until the tablet is completely disintegrated. The amount of pulp thus prepared will be sufficient for a precipitate of average size.)

**Addition of a Reagent.** Large quantities of a reagent should never be dumped into a solution being analyzed. Such practice inevitably leads to wasted time and unsatisfactory results. A small amount, i.e., a few drops, should be added first by means of an eye dropper or a glass tube (15 cm. × 5 mm.) fire polished at both ends. Larger quantities, if needed, should be measured in a graduated cylinder. A very handy instrument for both operations is a 5 or 10 ml. graduated pipette.

Frequently, directions for adding reagents are given in what appear to be ambiguous terms, e.g., "add a small amount" or "add an excess." These two directions have, however, a fairly definite meaning, especially when used in connection with reactions in which the interacting substances form first one product, then another. Here a "small amount" indicates sufficient to bring about any first sort of reaction that may take place; an "excess" means more than enough to complete any subsequent reaction.

*Illustration.* If 2 or 3 drops of 5 $N$ $NH_4OH$ are added to 5 ml. of 0.1 $N$ $AgNO_3$, a brown precipitate of $Ag_2O$ will form. Addition of excess $NH_4OH$ causes the precipitate to disappear. Stated in molecular ratios the reactions are:

$$2AgNO_3 + 2NH_4OH(\text{s.a.}) \rightarrow Ag_2O \cdots$$

$$AgNO_3 + 2NH_4OH(\text{xs}) \rightarrow Ag(NH_3)_2{}^{+} \cdots$$

When performing final or confirmatory tests, negative results should always be checked by addition of a drop of solution containing the ion sought to a portion of the finished test sample. If results are still negative, obviously there is something wrong, e.g., wrong reagent, wrong conditions, or some interference.

**Folding and Fitting a Filter Paper.** Carefully fold a filter paper in two so that the opposite edges meet nicely; then press the fold firmly in position (Fig. 2, *a*). Next, fold the doubled paper into a quadrant so that the edges meet nicely, and press the last fold firmly. Then open up one pocket of the folded paper and try fitting into a funnel, pressing smoothly into the funnel and noting whether or not the paper fits accurately. If the funnel is a little off angle, remove the filter paper and modify the folding into quadrants so that one edge overlaps the other a little. Then, according to whether the funnel has too wide or too narrow an angle, open the larger or smaller pocket and test the fit once more. After a proper fit has been made, take out the folded paper again, tear off the outer corner near the edge of the filter, replace in funnel, press well in position, moisten with distilled water, and smooth down onto sides of funnel (Fig. 2, *b*).

**Filling Funnel Stem with Water.** If the funnel is clean and the filter paper well fitted, distilled water poured onto the filter will run through in a solid column displacing the air and filling the stem. Frequently, a trace of grease prevents this. In such a case proceed as follows: With filter paper in position, place finger tightly over the end of the stem and fill funnel with water. Then raise the thick edge of the filter paper (avoid tearing) to permit the water to run into the stem, tilting the stem somewhat if necessary to displace the air. Then carefully force the filter paper into position again so that it fits snugly, and remove finger from end of stem. If the filter paper has been properly fitted to the funnel, the stem will remain full when the water no longer drips from the end. This is very desirable as the slight suction produced increases distinctly the rate of filtering and washing precipitates.

**Washing Precipitates.** Washing a precipitate is the process of displacing the solution in contact with which the precipitate was formed. This is effected by pouring the wash solution over the precipitate in 2–3 ml. portions —directions are usually given for its preparation. The first washing is com-

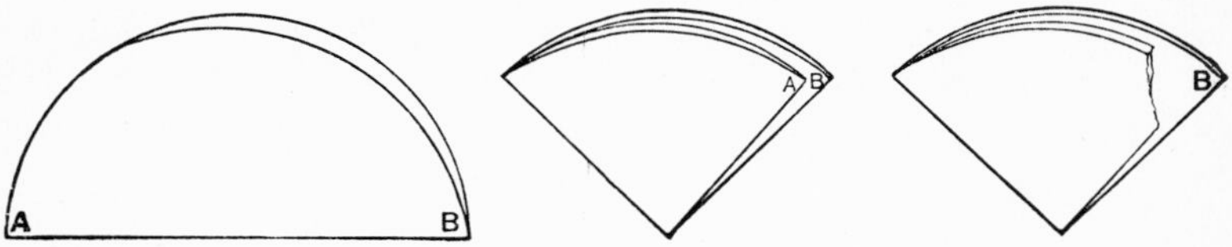


(*a*) Steps in Folding the Filter Paper.

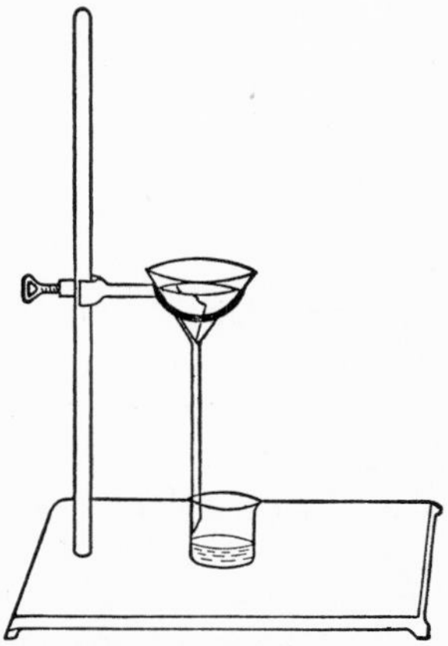

(*b*) **Filter Assembled.**

FIG. 2. Preparation of a Filter.

bined with the main filtrate. Subsequent portions are discarded to avoid undue dilution. If the original operation of precipitation was performed in a sufficiently dilute solution, three or four washings should be ample to displace anything likely to cause trouble later.

**Removing Precipitates from Filter Paper.** Occasionally a precipitate dissolves readily enough in a given reagent so that the reagent may be poured several times through the filter and the filtrate then used for the further operations intended. Usually, however, it is necessary to transfer the precipitate to a beaker or crucible and digest for some time with the given reagent. Three methods of transferring the precipitate are commonly used:

1. Punch a small hole through the tip of the filter paper and use a sharp stream of water from the wash bottle to rinse the precipitate through the stem of the funnel into the dish.

2. Remove filter paper from funnel, open out paper, place edge over dish and rinse precipitate off with wash water.

3. Open filter as in (2) and scrape precipitate off with a spatula. Sometimes, with a small amount of precipitate, it is best to place filter paper and all in the dish for treatment with the given reagent.

## SEMI-MICRO TECHNIQUE

**Semi-Micro Scale.** Within recent years it has become common practice to carry through the operations on a much smaller scale. The reactions involved are sufficiently sensitive so that most of the metals can be identified readily in amounts of a few hundredths of a milligram. Thus, instead of using 15–20 ml. of a solution containing 0.5–10.0 mg. of each metallic constituent per milliliter, it is possible to start with only 0.4–0.5 ml. of such a solution and carry through the usual group separations and confirmatory tests with reasonable accuracy. The usual analytical problems of precipitation, separation of precipitates from the solution, digesting precipitates with reagents, and applying confirmatory tests are all encountered whether working on the macro or the semi-micro scale.

In working on this smaller scale the equipment used is all of a small size. The test tubes are of 3 to 5 ml. capacity; modified medicine droppers are used in adding reagents dropwise; stirring rods are 1 to 2 mm. in diameter; and the delivery tube for gases has a capillary end about 2 inches long with an external diameter of about 1 mm.

One difficulty in carrying out the operations on a small scale lies in the filtering and washing of precipitates. It is awkward to handle small filter papers and the amount of solution absorbed by the paper is such that the filtrate will be diluted considerably by the time an effective washing of precipitate and filter has been accomplished.

**Filtering on a Small Scale.** This difficulty may be overcome by the use of a filter tube in which a thin layer of fine glass wool or absorbent cotton is packed into the tapered tip; then the solution and precipitate are transferred to the tube and the solution forced through the filtering layer by moderate pressure from a rubber bulb. However, it has become general practice to solve the problem by avoiding the filtering process.

**Use of the Centrifuge.** Since filtration is merely a means of separating a solid from most of the solution in which precipitation has taken place, the same result may be obtained by placing the solution and precipitate in a centrifuge tube and running the centrifuge for 1 to 2 minutes at a fairly high speed. When the centrifuge stops and the solution is examined it is usually found that the precipitate is a well packed mass in the tip of the tube and the solution above it is clear. The solution may be drawn off with a special dropper tube with elongated capillary tip and transferred to a clean test tube. In practice the centrifuge tube carrying the solution and precipitate should be counterbalanced by placing in the opposite slot a similar tube containing an equal volume of distilled water.

Most precipitates settle readily enough so that half a minute in the centrifuge is sufficient to pack the precipitate in the tip of the tube. Occasionally, however, the precipitate is so finely divided that this is ineffective. If the precipitate shows reasonable signs of settling out, the centrifuging may be continued for another minute or two. In the case of colloidal suspensions of AgCl, ZnS, MnS, etc., that are sometimes encountered, it is usually necessary to take special steps to handle these precipitates. Thus, AgCl can be coagulated by heating and stirring, but ZnS and MnS respond less readily to this treatment. When filtration is being used these last two can be removed effectively by use of a suspension of filter pulp to provide a thicker mat. For centrifuging, however, it is best to try and obtain slightly coarser particles by keeping the solution hot during the precipitation. Such cases are discussed in the analytical procedures where they are likely to occur.

**Washing Precipitates.** After centrifuging and removal of the clear solution, the remaining volume should be noted and about twice that amount of wash water (usually distilled water) added. Next, mix the precipitate thoroughly with the wash water, whirl in the centrifuge, and remove the clear solution (adding it to the previous solution). This process should be repeated as many times as necessary to carry the separation to the desired degree of completeness (usually 2 washings in qualitative analysis).

**Effectiveness of the Washing Process.** The effectiveness of the washing process is usually discussed mathematically in terms of the volume of solution remaining in contact with the precipitate and the corresponding volume of wash water added. Thus if the volume of wash water is twice that of the remaining mother solution, the latter is diluted to three times its original volume, and after drainage it is assumed that only one-third of the original amount of mother solution is left. After a second washing only one-ninth of the mother solution would be left, and a third washing would leave only one twenty-seventh. In these calculations, however, it is always assumed that the mother liquor mixes freely with the wash solution, which is frequently not true. In the case of a precipitate that is very finely divided or gelatinous and fails to pack well, the operation of washing may be much less effective than the ordinary calculation would lead one to expect. It would appear in these cases that the mother solution is held in some mechanical fashion within the particles of the precipitate and is only slowly displaced by the wash water.

This situation is easily observed in an experiment of the following type. A precipitate of ferric hydroxide, formed in the presence of barium chloride, was washed 5 times and the residue tested for barium by dissolving in dilute hydrochloric acid and treating with ammonium sulfate. The slight precipitate obtained was compared with known amounts of barium freshly precipitated as the sulfate and found to correspond to four or five times as much barium as should have been present if the effectiveness of the washing had followed the mathematical equation.

**The Precipitation Process.** In most cases when the solution is ready to carry out a precipitation all that is necessary is to add 1 or 2 drops of the reagent, stir to mix thoroughly, then let the precipitate settle and add another drop of the reagent to test for completeness of precipitation. If the precipitate is slow in settling one may save time by using the centrifuge to clear the solution before adding the next drop of reagent. However, there are certain cases in which even the dropwise addition of the standard reagent is excessive. Thus, in the precipitation of Group III with $NH_4OH$, the solution must have a fairly high concentration of $NH_4Cl$ and then must be slowly neutralized with $NH_4OH$, avoiding an excess of the latter. Since the solution at this point is acid to start with, reagent $NH_4OH$ may be added dropwise, with stirring after each addition, until a slight permanent precipitate is formed. Then the reagent $NH_4OH$ should be diluted at least tenfold and the diluted reagent added drop by drop, stirring and testing a "micro-drop" after each addition until the solution no longer turns blue litmus red. (The "micro-drop" is obtained by picking up a 1-mm. column of the solution in the capillary of a dropper tube. This may then be touched to the litmus paper.) Another example involving the use of diluted reagents is in adjusting conditions for the precipitation of Group II. Here the solution is first neutralized, then 1 drop of 5 *N* HCl added for each 20 drops of solution. However, it is impossible to obtain satisfactory neutralization of the solution by dropwise use of the 5 *N* reagents. Therefore, after the solution has been carried to the first alkaline reaction by dropwise addition of $NH_4OH$, it is then treated dropwise with HCl that has been diluted at least tenfold, until the first acid reaction is obtained. This may be considered as the neutral solution to which the measured amount of 5 *N* HCl is then added.

**Cleaning Test Tubes, Etc.** The small beakers and crucibles are easily cleaned by use of the ordinary test-tube brush and a little soap powder or other detergent. Sometimes a bit of pumice powder as abrasive will help remove a stubborn stain. In the case of the tapered centrifuge tubes a small tapered brush will take care of the upper part, but a piece of pipe cleaner with a quarter inch doubled back on itself is needed to reach the tip. These tips are quite fragile and easily broken by too vigorous use of a brush. Most precipitates are easily loosened by a few seconds of rotary action with water or a detergent solution present. These tubes are next rinsed 2 or 3 times—first with tap water then with distilled water—wiped on the outside and stood upside down on clean cloth or wipette paper to drain. The dropper tubes are cleaned by connecting with tubing to a slow stream at the water tap and forcing water through for a short time. Any precipitate still adhering may be loosened by use of the pipe cleaner down to the capillary tip. Any precipitate still adhering is best removed by chemical means ($NH_3$ solution for AgCl, HCl + $HNO_3$ for sulfides and hydroxides, $HNO_3$ + $H_2O_2$ for $MnO_2$, etc.). For this the reagent is placed in a centrifuge tube, the dropper tube inserted, and then let stand if necessary.

**Digesting Precipitates with Reagents.** An examination of the rates at which common precipitates react with reagents reveals a considerable range of variation. Some precipitates react very rapidly in the cold, some require half a minute or so, and some must be kept in contact with the reagent for a more extended period of time. Since the reactions usually take place more readily when heat is applied, it is common practice to carry out these slower reactions at elevated temperatures to decrease the time required. When using larger test tubes, beakers, etc., this may be done by holding the container of the solution directly in the flame at the start and then inserting occasionally or clamping a little above the flame after the solution has reached the boiling point. With the smaller equipment used in semi-micro procedure, however, it is important to avoid heating with direct flame because the solution may "bump," with loss of most or all of the solution. To avoid this difficulty it is desirable to keep a covered beaker of water handy, with the temperature near boiling, so that the test tube and its solution may be placed in the beaker and permitted to stand for the necessary time. A 75 or 100 ml. beaker, partly filled with water and placed on a wire gauze a little above a low flame from a micro burner, serves very satisfactorily for this purpose. A more elaborate system involves the use of a small steam or water bath which is kept covered when not in use and which provides small openings into which the test tube will fit without much play. Equipment of this sort is now available from the supply houses.

## CONFIRMATORY TESTS

After a typical process of separation of metals from each other by precipitation of groups and working up the group precipitates, each metal is obtained as a compound insoluble in water or as an ion in solution. If the compound is insoluble in water, the very fact that it has been obtained as a precipitate at the end of a series of separations is usually sufficient evidence that the metal sought is present. If the metal is in solution, it is only necessary to add a reagent that will form a precipitate or a colored solution with the ion in question. If the test is negative, the metal is absent; if positive, the metal is present.

The situation is frequently not so simple as this, however, because the various separations may not have been carried out completely enough to prevent small amounts of interfering metals from being present when the final test is reached. Also it is possible that in the final step a reagent has been added to test for the presence of a metal without actually setting up the conditions necessary to make the test work even if the metal is present. Therefore, it is desirable to employ confirmatory tests to check the positive results and to check the conditions if the results are negative.

The confirmatory tests should be highly selective or characteristic. This means that, even though the separations of other metals have not been complete, these other metals that may be present when the confirmatory test is applied should interfere as little as possible with the identification of the metal in question. In order to accomplish this it is customary to resort to the formation of highly colored substances involving the one metal, whereas the other metals that may be present should show as little color as possible. When color effects are not available, it is necessary to select reagents that form as few precipitates as possible, or that form a precipitate of peculiar and characteristic appearance with the metal in question.

Another important characteristic which a confirmatory test should have is high sensitivity. More or less of the metal may have been lost in the various operations previously carried out, and the amount present originally may have been rather small. It is desirable, therefore, to employ a reagent for the confirmatory test that will give positive results even though the amount of the metal present is very small.

It would be very useful from the point of view of technical examinations of materials if the confirmatory tests for the different metals were all both highly characteristic and highly sensitive. This would relieve one largely of the necessity for carrying out careful separations of the metals from each other. Actually if the tests were completely specific and of high sensitivity, the whole procedure could be changed to one of dividing the original unknown into a sufficient number of separate portions and then testing for each metal on the original material without preliminary separations. Or, while in the mood for wishing, one might even ask that the reagents should not interfere with each other, so that one might start with a portion of the unknown and test this successively for different metals until one is identified, then start with a fresh test portion and continue this process. As yet, however, the reagents commonly available for confirmatory tests usually require that reasonably careful separations be carried out before the final tests are applied. The reason for this lies in the lack of selectivity of many of these reagents so that the actual identification depends both on the accuracy of separation and on the final reaction.

In actual practice, if the formation of a colored substance is involved in the final test, the color can be judged better in daylight against a white background than under artificial light and against a dark background. If the final substance separates as an opaque precipitate, very small amounts are best observed either by placing the solution in a centrifuge tube with cone-shaped tip and packing the precipitate into the narrow tip by centrifugation, or by keeping the precipitate suspended in a tall narrow tube of the nephelometer type—having the upper and lower surfaces of the solution blacked out —while one looks into the tube to observe reflection of light from side illumination by the particles.

**Testing the Confirmatory Tests.** The beginning analyst—and occasionally an experienced chemist—sometimes encounters the situation that a particular metal is actually present in recognizable amounts and yet the confirmatory test for the metal is negative. Either the metal has been lost in earlier operations by which it was supposed to be separated from the other metals or the final test has not been properly carried out. Concerning the first of these two difficulties, there is little that can be done to correct for the errors made earlier in the procedure. In the second case, however, it is sufficient in most cases to add a drop or two of the test solution containing the metal in question. If the test now becomes positive, it is evident that the confirmatory test was properly carried out and the negative result means that the metal was actually absent in the final solution. However, if the test still remains negative, it is necessary to look for sources of error in the final test itself. Sometimes the reagent for the final test is relatively unstable so that it must be checked from time to time to see that it is in usable condition. This situation is encountered with such reagents as stannous chloride, ferrous sulfate, and ammonium sulfide, which are subject to atmospheric oxidation, and with other reagents such as hydrogen peroxide, potassium ferricyanide, ammonium molybdate, and ammonium carbonate, which are subject to complex decomposition, hydrolytic or otherwise. Occasionally special conditions of temperature, acidity, alkalinity, or concentration of reagents must be effectively controlled before a particular reaction will take place satisfactorily. These are all points to be investigated when necessary to convert a false negative test into a correct positive test. When the error in the final test has been discovered, the procedure should be tried again on a fresh portion of the final solution.

**Estimating the Amount of a Metal Present.** Frequently in Qualitative Analysis one is expected not only to identify the various metals or acid radicals but also to indicate the relative amount of each present. These relative amounts may be expressed in various ways, such as (1) molar concentrations in the unknown solution, (2) milligrams of the metal or acid radical per milliliter of the original solution, or (3) use of the terms large, moderate, small, and trace, with some quantitative significance attached to these terms.

The experimental procedure by which one usually judges the relative amount is to note how strongly the final test shows up. If this involves the formation of a precipitate, one may note its approximate volume after it has settled for a moderate length of time. If a colored solution is being produced, its depth of color may be used as a basis for judgment. However, there are a number of difficulties involved in applying such procedures. For example, (1) unless one starts with a definite amount of the original solution there will be no satisfactory basis for stating the significance of the final test; (2) in carrying out a series of operations to separate a metal from several others which may be present, there is usually a moderate loss of this metal by the time the final tests are reached; and (3) if the final test involves the formation of a colored solution, this color may be of such intensity even with small amounts of the metal present as to make it difficult to distinguish between moderate and large amounts. In this last case a dilution technique may be employed, comparing the depth of color with standards after a tenfold, fiftyfold, or one hundredfold dilution.

## SOME SPECIAL PIECES OF EQUIPMENT

Aside from the standard articles which may be purchased from supply houses, a few special items have been devised which have proved very satisfactory. These are illustrated in Fig. 3.

**Dropper Tubes.** The student is shown how to construct his own from 7 mm. soft glass tubing. Heat a 4.5 inch length in a Bunsen (or soft blast lamp) flame with rotation until the central half inch is soft and somewhat thickened. Then remove from the flame and pull slowly to about 6 inches long. After letting cool, scratch the center of the capillary portion with a sharp file and break in two. Fire polish the large ends and use a small whetstone cautiously to round the edges of the capillary ends. A good dropper tube should have a capillary section about $1\frac{1}{2}$ inches long with not too thin walls, and with an inside diameter of 0.5–0.7 mm.

**Rack for Dropper Tubes.** The base is a wooden block about 2 inches wide by 4 inches long, with a slot near one end cut at a slight angle. In the slot is fastened a 4-inch strip of Maisonite prestwood, $\frac{1}{8}$ inch thick and $1\frac{1}{2}$ inches wide, with several slots in the edge $\frac{3}{8}$ inch wide and $\frac{3}{4}$ inch deep.

**Aluminum Hot Plate.** All heating is done on a simple hot plate formed from a $3 \times 14$ inch piece of 16 gauge sheet aluminum. This is bent to form two legs 4 inches long at about 100° angles to the $3 \times 6$ inch flat top. The micro burner is kept under this at one end with the flame adjusted so that a 50 ml. beaker, $\frac{3}{5}$ full of water, will just boil. When the small test tubes are to be heated they are placed in the 50 ml. "water bath," which can be kept anywhere from 60°C. to 100°C. by adjustment of the burner and position on the hot plate. When a solution needs to be actively boiled it is transferred to a porcelain crucible which is placed directly on the hot plate. This would be the case, for example, in dissolving HgS in $HCl + HNO_3$, in reducing the volume of a solution, or in driving off $H_2S$.

**Copper Wire Holder for Crucible.** In removing $NH_4Cl$ after evaporation to dryness the crucible must be heated still more strongly. For this a holder is provided consisting of a small loop of No. 16 copper wire with the legs bent so as to fit onto the hot plate and hold the crucible over one edge. The micro burner may then be placed directly under the crucible.

**Centrifuge Tube Holder.** This is a small wooden block about 1 inch square, with a hole in the center $\frac{3}{8}$ inch in diameter and $\frac{3}{4}$ inch deep. Two

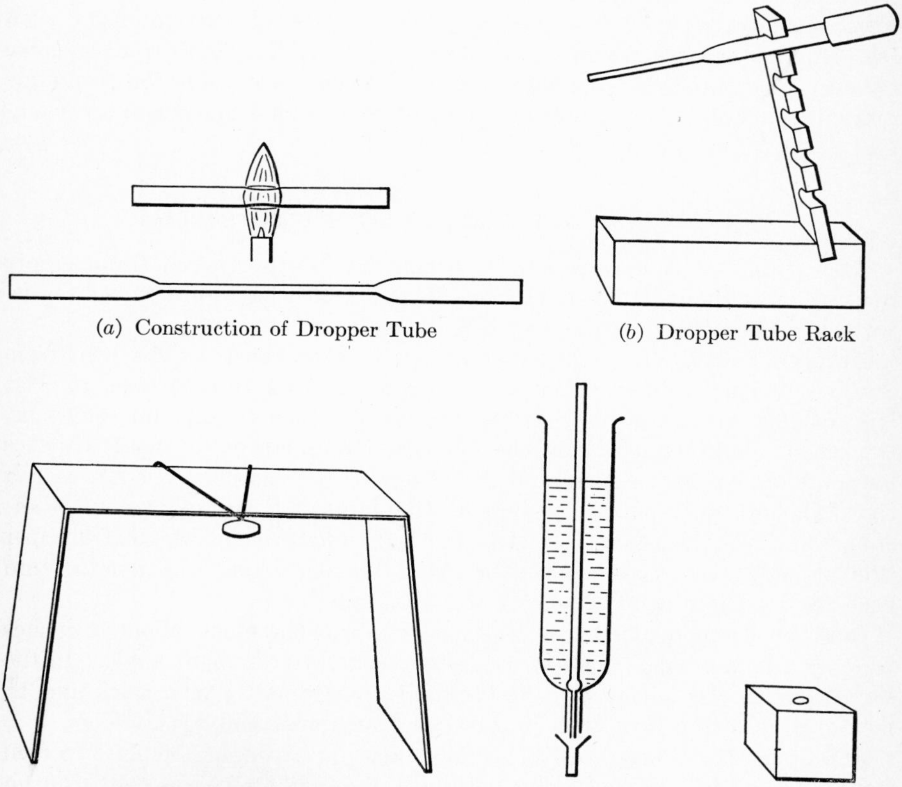

(*a*) Construction of Dropper Tube (*b*) Dropper Tube Rack

(*c*) Al Hot Plate with Cu-wire for Crucible (*d*) $NH_4Cl$ Dispenser (*e*) Centrifuge Tube Holder

FIG. 3. Some Semi-Micro Equipment.

or three of these are convenient to set tubes in while preparing for further tests.

**Ammonium Chloride Dispenser.** For control of the $NH_4^+$ concentration in later groups the $NH_4Cl$ is conveniently measured in small containers graduated to contain 0.2 g. $NH_4Cl$ (the quantity to be added to 1 ml. of solution for the precipitation of the aluminum group). These are made from soft glass tubing with an internal diameter of about 3.5 mm., sealed at one end and flared at the other for ease in filling. To fill the container a special dispenser is used, consisting of a 6-inch calcium chloride tube, fitted with a glass stirring rod which projects about 2 inches from the top, the lower end being provided with a bulge which acts as a stopper at the bottom of the wide portion of the $CaCl_2$ tube, followed by a narrow tip extending to the end of the small section. In use, the dispenser is filled with a fine grained $NH_4Cl$, then the container placed at the lower end and the flow of the $NH_4Cl$ started by moving the glass rod slightly.

**Special Dropper Bulbs for Certain Reagents.** One of the difficulties with semi-micro work is the failure of rubber in contact with a number of reagents, especially conc. HCl, $HNO_3$, and organic liquids. This difficulty has been largely solved by using bulbs made by sealing off short sections of polyethylene tubing. The sealing off is not done easily. The best results have been obtained by clamping the end to be closed between two $\frac{3}{16}$-inch copper rods (glass tends to overheat at the point of the seal and stick to the tubing). The sealing is then done with a very fine flame from a hand torch.

**Test Papers.** In a number of cases it is convenient to use a reagent in the form of a treated paper. This is easily made by using a long strip of filter paper about 1 inch wide. Draw a pencil mark (preferably colored) along one edge of the paper and moisten the other edge with the reagent from a dropper tube. Dry and cut into convenient strips (5–6 to the inch).

## EXPERIMENTAL STUDIES OF THE THEORY OF QUALITATIVE ANALYSIS

I. The separations in qualitative analysis usually involve differential precipitations. In the simplest case, a reagent may form an insoluble compound with one metal whereas the corresponding compound of another metal is readily soluble. This makes it possible to separate the two metals from each other by using an ordinary concentration of the reagent in sufficient excess to precipitate the one metal, then centrifuging and washing the precipitate. The first metal will be in the precipitate; the second will be in the clear solution.

When the compound of the second metal is only slightly soluble the separation is more difficult because, with moderate or large amounts of the second metal present, it will precipitate in part, as excess of the reagent is added to insure complete precipitation of the first metal. In such a case a satisfactory separation may still be obtained by using a fairly dilute solution of the reagent, for the first metal will still precipitate readily, but the second one will not. In particular cases there will be definite limits to the concentrations of reagents that may be used.

When the second compound is in the insoluble range, even though its solubility is still many times as great as that of the first metal, it is no longer feasible to use dilute solutions of strong electrolytes to separate the metals because extreme dilutions would be necessary and this, in turn, would require correspondingly large volumes of the reagent. But if weak electrolytes are available to supply the precipitant ion, and if noninterfering, strong electrolytes may be added as accessory reagents to supply a common ion and thus control more closely the concentration of the precipitant ion introduced, it may still be feasible to carry out separations of the two metals from each other. In such cases the lower the solubility of the second compound the more difficult the separation usually becomes.

In the following short series of experiments some of the common separations of qualitative analysis have been used to illustrate the situations just discussed. The additional points involved in certain of the experiments are noted in connection with the experiments themselves.

In cases where definite concentrations of metal are specified, the student should have available a side-table stock solution containing 10 mg. of the metal per ml. For moderate amounts of the metal a corresponding volume of this solution may be measured out and diluted with water to the desired volume.

Thus, to prepare a solution of $Pb(NO_3)_2$ containing 6 mg. of Pb per ml., take 6 drops of the stock solution, add 4 drops of water and mix thoroughly. To prepare a solution of $AlCl_3$ containing 1 mg. of Al per ml., take 1 drop of the stock solution, add 9 drops of water and mix thoroughly. Note that the dropper tubes used in each case should give essentially the same size drops if the dilution is to be reasonably accurate. Since dropper tubes may vary considerably in this matter it would be best to select two which have been checked or to use the same one for both measurements. Sometimes several solutions are to be set up such that each successive one has half the concentration of the preceding one. In this case, prepare a stock solution having twice the concentration desired in the first tube. For tube No. 1 use 10 drops of this stock solution and 10 drops of water and mix. For tube No. 2 take 10 drops from No. 1 and add 10 drops of water. Continue in this way until the full series is prepared. Be sure that each solution is thoroughly mixed before taking the sample for the next solution.

(a) If one metal forms an insoluble salt while the corresponding salt of the other metal is soluble, the two metals may be separated by treating with a reagent which precipitates the insoluble salt. By filtering, or centrifuging, and washing the precipitate, the separation is completed.

Note that AgCl is insoluble while $CuCl_2$ is soluble. Using stock solutions of $AgNO_3$ and $Cu(NO_3)_2$, place 5 drops of each in a centrifuge tube, add 10 drops of water and 1 drop of 5 *N* $HNO_3$, mix, add 2 drops 5 *N* HCl and mix thoroughly, centrifuge, pipet off the clear solution, add 3 drops of $H_2O$ to the precipitate, mix thoroughly, centrifuge, remove the clear solution and repeat the washing twice more. To test whether the copper has been separated completely, add to the final precipitate 6–8 drops of 5 *N* $NH_3$ reagent to dissolve the AgCl. If the separation is incomplete a blue color of $Cu(NH_3)_4^{++}$ will appear. Note that only a faint color is obtained (due to incomplete washing).

(b) If one of the salts is insoluble and the other slightly soluble, satisfactory separations may be obtained by the use of limited concentrations of the precipitating agent.

Treat 5 drops of stock solutions of $AgNO_3$ and of $Pb(NO_3)_2$ separately with a drop of 5 *N* HCl. Repeat, using 0.1 *N* HCl in place of 5 *N* HCl (0.1 *N* HCl is conveniently prepared by treating 1 drop of 5 *N* HCl with 49 drops of water, or, in 2 stages, 1 drop of 5 *N* HCl + 4 drops of water; then, after mixing, take 1 drop of this solution and add 9 drops of water. Mix thoroughly before use.) Note that only AgCl precipitates with the 0.1 *N* HCl.

(c) When both compounds are relatively insoluble the metals may still be separated if the two compounds show sufficient difference in solubility and a reagent is available slightly enough ionized so that, by common ion effect, the concentration of precipitating ion may be kept very low.

Treat 5 drops of stock solutions of $Al(NO_3)_3$ and of $Mn(NO_3)_2$ separately with 1 drop of 5 *N* $NH_4OH$. Repeat, first adding 0.2 g. $NH_4Cl$ to each of the solutions and shaking, and then adding the $NH_4OH$. Note that only $Al(OH)_3$ precipitates this second time.

To test the effectiveness of this separation treat a mixture of 5 drops each of $Al(NO_3)_3$ and $Mn(NO_3)_2$ with 0.2 g. $NH_4Cl$, warm in the water bath, then add 0.5 *N* $NH_4OH$ (dilute the 5 *N* reagent 1:10) dropwise, mixing thoroughly, until neutral. Centrifuge, pipet off the clear solution, add 5 drops of water to the precipitate, mix, centrifuge, and repeat the washing twice more. To the final precipitate add 4–5 drops of 3 *N* NaOH to dissolve the $Al(OH)_3$. Any Mn left will be precipitated as white $Mn(OH)_2$. Add 1–2 drops of $H_2O_2$ to oxidize Mn to dark brown $MnO_2$ (more readily visible). Note that only a slight precipitate is obtained, showing that most of the Mn has stayed in solution.

(d) Another interesting type of separation occasionally used involves differences in rates of precipitation rather than differences in solubility. This is seen in the following experiment. Place 5 drops of $H_3AsO_3$ solution in one test tube and 5 drops of $H_3AsO_4$ solution in another. Dilute each solution to 1 ml. with water, add 1 drop 5 *N* HCl, warm moderately in the water bath, and then pass $H_2S$ into each solution. Note that $As_2S_3$ starts to precipitate very promptly, but no reaction is observed with the $H_3AsO_4$ solution for some time.

II. Within varying limits excess of reagent may cause more complete precipitation than would be expected from the solubility of the compound in water.

(a) Prepare a saturated solution of $PbCl_2$ by shaking excess of the solid with water for 2–3 minutes. Centrifuge. To 5 drops of the clear solution add 1 drop of 5 *N* HCl. Note the formation of a moderate precipitate of $PbCl_2$.

(b) Set up 5 $Pb(NO_3)_2$ solutions as follows:

1. 10 drops of test solution of $Pb(NO_3)_2$ (10 mg. Pb per ml.)
2. 5 drops of the test solution plus 5 drops of water
3. 3 " " " " " " 7 " " "
4. 2 " " " " " " 8 " " "
5. 1 " " " " " " 9 " " "

To each solution add 1 drop of 5 *N* HCl, mix thoroughly, and let stand a moment for precipitation. To the last two tubes add 2 drops more of the HCl. Is the sensitivity of the precipitation reaction increased appreciably?

(c) In the previous experiment it was shown that there may be a limit to the effectiveness of excess of reagent. In the following experiment it will be shown that large excess of reagent may be less effective than small excess in promoting precipitation.

Prepare a diluted $AgNO_3$ solution as follows: Use 1 drop of test solution (10 mg. $Ag^+$ per ml.), add 9 drops of water and mix thoroughly; then use 2 drops of this solution plus 18 drops of water and mix.

Set up two series of tubes as follows:

Tube No. 1 = 4 drops of the $AgNO_3$ solution plus 6 drops $H_2O$
Tube No. 2 = 3 " " " " " " 7 " "
Tube No. 3 = 2 " " " " " " 8 " "
Tube No. 4 = 1 " " " " " " 9 " "

In the first series add 1 drop of 5 *N* HCl to each tube and mix thoroughly. Note how far the opalescence can be observed. For the second series prepare a very dilute solution of HCl (1 drop 5 *N* HCl + 25 drops $H_2O$, mix, then 2 drops of this solution + 8 drops of $H_2O$). Add 1 drop of the diluted HCl to each of the tubes in the second series and compare the strength of the opalescence in tubes 3 and 4 in the two series.

From the solubility of AgCl in water calculate the relative excess of chloride ion supplied by the two solutions of HCl in the present experiment. Note that when secondary reactions occur between a precipitate and the precipitating agent, there is usually a limit to the excess of reagent which may be used, beyond which the solubility of the precipitate increases perceptibly.

III. Visibility is an important factor sometimes overlooked in considering the delicacy of tests in qualitative analysis.

(*a*) In a precipitation reaction used as a test in qualitative analysis, it is necessary to produce a visible precipitate before the test can be considered positive. If all precipitates formed at the same rate, with particles of the same size and opacity, there would be a fairly simple relation between the solubility of precipitates and the sensitivity of precipitation tests. For example: if $S$ is the solubility of a precipitate in a given volume and $A$ is the amount of precipitate necessary to be visible, then $S + A$ would be the minimum amount that must be produced in the given volume in order to show a positive test. On this basis, if $S_1$ and $S_2$ are the solubilities of two precipitates and $S_1$ is less than $S_2$, then $S_1 + A$ would be less than $S_2 + A$, and it would take less of the first compound than of the second to give a positive test.

Actually, however, individual precipitates show marked differences in visibility. Therefore, in particular cases it sometimes happens that, although the solubility of one precipitate is less than that of another, the amount of the first precipitate required to be visible is much greater than that of the second precipitate. In such a case $S_1$ is less than $S_2$ but $A_1$ is greater than $A_2$. If the difference between $A_1$ and $A_2$ is greater than that between $S_1$ and $S_2$, then $S_1 + A_1$ would be greater than $S_2 + A_2$ and the second precipitation test would be more sensitive than the first, although the first precipitate is less soluble than the second.

Prepare dilute solutions of $AgNO_3$ and of $Al(NO_3)_3$ by diluting the test solutions (10 mg. $Ag^+$ or $Al^{+3}$ per ml.) as follows: 1 drop of the test solution plus 4 drops of $H_2O$, then 2 drops of this diluted solution plus 18 drops of $H_2O$. These solutions should now contain 0.2 mg. of $Ag^+$ or $Al^{+3}$ per ml. Set up a series of three tubes of each using 4, 3, and 2 drops of the diluted solutions and adding 6, 7, and 8 drops of water, respectively. For the precipitation of AgCl, add 1 drop of 5 $N$ HCl to each tube containing $Ag^+$; and for the precipitation of $Al(OH)_3$, add 1 drop of 5 $N$ $NH_4OH$ to each tube containing $Al^{+3}$. Compare the limits of visible precipitation in the two cases. (The solubilities of AgCl and of $Al(OH)_3$ in water are $1 \times 10^{-5}$ and $4 \times 10^{-9}$ moles per liter, respectively.) Try centrifuging the tubes containing $Al(OH)_3$ to see whether the precipitates can be made more visible. Save these tubes for the next experiment.

(*b*) Frequently the development of color will produce visible effects beyond the range in which a simple precipitate can be recognized.

To each of the tubes containing $Al(OH)_3$ in the previous experiment, add 2 drops of 5 $N$ HCl, mix, then add 1 drop of Aluminon reagent and 2 drops of $NH_4OH$. Mix and centrifuge. Note the formation of visible precipitates in all three tubes.

(*c*) One cannot always judge the delicacy of a color test from the depth of color produced in a solution of relatively high concentration.

As a case in point, compare the depth of color of test solutions of $Cr(NO_3)_3$ and $K_2Cr_2O_7$ (containing 10 mg. of Cr per ml.); then dilute each solution to one-tenth its original concentration and note that the color of the chromic solution fades much more rapidly than that of the dichromate solution.

In working with solutions on the semi-micro scale it is sometimes a bit difficult to recognize small amounts of white precipitates when these are not reasonably opaque. Frequently the confirmatory test for a metal can be improved in such a case by picking up the suspension in a dropper tube, then pressing the tip of the capillary firmly against a piece of thick filter paper and slowly squeezing the bulb. The precipitate will be retained as a tiny dot on the filter paper while the solution runs through. This dot may then be treated with a reagent which produces a distinct color. For example, a dot of $Bi(OH)_3$ on treatment with a drop of sodium stannite solution turns black from reduction to metallic Bi. As another example, a slight suspension of CdS becomes much more readily visible if it is concentrated as a yellow dot on the filter paper by this procedure.

## IDENTIFICATION AND SEPARATION OF THE GROUPS

**Group I.** (*a*) To test for the presence of Group I, to 15 drops of the cold, acid solution add 2 drops of 5 *N* HCl, mix, and let stand a moment. A white, flocculent or curdy precipitate shows the presence of the first group.

(*b*) To test for completeness of precipitation of Group I settle the precipitate by whirling in the centrifuge, then add a drop of HCl to the clear solution. If no further precipitate forms, precipitation of the first group is complete.

**Group II.** (*a*) To test for the presence of Group II, make the solution 0.25 *N* with HCl (first neutralize if necessary), then measure the volume by drops, and add 1 drop of 5 *N* HCl for every 19 drops of solution. Warm in the water bath for a moment, and then pass in $H_2S$ for about half a minute. A black, yellow, or red precipitate shows the presence of the second group.

(*b*) To test for completeness of precipitation of Group II, centrifuge the solution, transfer the clear solution to a clean test tube, then pass in $H_2S$ for 20–30 seconds. If no further precipitate is obtained, precipitation of the second group is complete. (Arsenic acid forms a special case that will be discussed in connection with the arsenic division of Group II.)

**Group III.** (*a*) To test for the presence of Group III, the solution must be free of $H_2S$, any Fe or Cr present must be in the form of $Fe^{+3}$ and $Cr^{+3}$, and the solution should contain about 0.2 g. of $NH_4Cl$ for each ml. After removal of Group II the solution should be transferred to a small crucible (No. 000) and boiled for a minute to remove $H_2S$, then 1 drop of *N* $NaNO_2$ added to oxidize any $Fe^{++}$ to $Fe^{+3}$ and the boiling continued for half a minute longer to remove any $N_2O_3$. Add $H_2O$ to give a total volume of 20 drops, transfer to a centrifuge tube, add 0.2 g. $NH_4Cl$, heat in the water bath, then add diluted $NH_4OH$ (0.5 *N*) one drop at a time, mixing thoroughly after each addition until the first alkaline reaction (litmus paper) is obtained. A gelatinous red, green, or white precipitate shows the presence of Group III.

(*b*) To test for completeness of precipitation of Group III, heat the solution for a minute, then centrifuge, and add 1 drop of 0.5 *N* $NH_4OH$ to the clear solution. If no further precipitate is obtained, the third group is completely precipitated.

**Group IV.** (*a*) To test for the presence of Group IV, to the clear solution after the precipitation of Group III add 2–3 drops 5 *N* $NH_4OH$, heat nearly to boiling, and pass in $H_2S$ for 10–15 seconds. A black or nearly white precipitate shows the presence of Group IV.

(*b*) To test for completeness of precipitation of Group IV, centrifuge to settle the precipitate and pass $H_2S$ into the clear solution. If no further precipitate forms, the fourth group is completely precipitated.

**Group V.** (*a*) To test for the presence of Group V, the solution should contain a small amount of $NH_4Cl$ and should be neutral or slightly acid. The clear solution from Group IV is transferred to a crucible, evaporated to dryness, and the residue heated more strongly over the micro burner until all $NH_4Cl$ is volatilized. Cool, add 1 drop HCl and 20 drops $H_2O$, 0.05 g. $NH_4Cl$, and heat a little below boiling. Stir in 4 drops of 5 *N* $NH_4OH$ and 3–4 drops of $(NH_4)_2CO_3$ reagent. Transfer to a centrifuge tube and look for a white precipitate of Group V.

(*b*) To test for completeness of precipitation of Group V, settle the precipitate by centrifuging, then add a drop of $(NH_4)_2CO_3$ reagent to the clear solution. If no further precipitate forms, the fifth group is completely precipitated.

## KNOWN SOLUTIONS

In the laboratory provision should be made for the study of known solutions before unknowns are attempted. These solutions afford opportunity for the student to become acquainted with the separations and tests under such conditions that he may know immediately whether the procedures are working properly. If satisfactory positive tests are not obtained for substances present, or if apparent tests are obtained for substances not present, the student should look for possible sources of trouble. The tests should then be repeated with the errors corrected before working on unknowns.

In the sets of known solutions the metals (or non-metals) are given out in three ranges of concentration: 10 mg. per ml., 2 mg. per ml., and 0.5 mg. per ml. The middle range will be used in most cases, the exceptions being indicated by the letters *l* for large, and *s* for small.

Known solutions: identification of individual groups, no separations.

(1) $Ag^+$ (*s*)
(2) $Hg^{++}$ (*s*)
(3) $Al^{+3}$ (*s*)
(4) $Zn^{++}$ (*s*)
(5) $Ca^{++}$ (*s*)

These solutions contain in 1 liter 1.6 g. of $AgNO_3$, 1.4 g. of $HgCl_2$, 9 g. of $AlCl_3 \cdot 6H_2O$ + 25 ml. of 5 *N* HCl, 4.4 g. of $ZnSO_4 \cdot 7H_2O$, and 3.7 g. of $CaCl_2 \cdot 2H_2O$, respectively.

Take 15 drops of one of the solutions and test for the presence of each group in order according to the directions given on page 75, until the one is reached in which the metal belongs. Negative results should be obtained for earlier groups, but a readily visible precipitate should be obtained in the proper group.

Known solutions: identification of groups, more than one group present requiring separations.

(1) $Ag^+$, $Cd^{++}$
(2) $Cu^{++}$, $Mn^{++}$
(3) $Fe^{+3}$, $Ca^{++}$

These solutions contain per liter (1) 4 g. of $AgNO_3$, 7 g. of $Cd(NO_3)_2 \cdot 4H_2O$ + 5 ml. of 5 *N* $HNO_3$; (2) 7 g. of $CuCl_2 \cdot 2H_2O$, 9 g. of $MnCl_2 \cdot 4H_2O$ + 5 ml. of 5 *N* HCl; (3) 12.1 g. of $FeCl_3 \cdot 6H_2O$, 9.2 g. of $CaCl_2 \cdot 2H_2O$ + 50 ml. of 5 *N* HCl.

Take 15 drops of one of the solutions and test for the presence of each group in order until the first one is reached in which one of the metals belongs. When a precipitate is obtained for a given group, the group reagent is added in small portions until precipitation appears to be complete. The precipitate is then centrifuged and the clear solution tested with a small additional amount of the reagent. When precipitation of one group is complete, the clear solution is tested for the later groups in regular order. Note that in the third solution when $H_2S$ is passed in to test for Group II a cloudy white precipitate of sulfur forms because of the oxidizing action of the $Fe^{+3}$.

# 5

## Group I

## Lead, Silver, Mercury

Group I is precipitated by HCl in a cold, slightly acid solution. The metals included in Group I are Pb, Ag, and Hg. The common ions of these metals are $Pb^{++}$, $Pb(OH)_3^-$, $Ag^+$, $Ag(NH_3)_2^+$, $Hg_2^{++}$, and $Hg^{++}$ (of these last two, only $Hg_2^{++}$ forms an insoluble chloride).

### COMMON COMPOUNDS AND REACTIONS OF IONS OF Pb, Ag, AND Hg (OUS)

**More Common Lead Compounds.** Lead chloride, $PbCl_2$, white; lead nitrate, $Pb(NO_3)_2$, white; leaf sulfate, $PbSO_4$, white; lead acetate, $Pb(C_2H_3O_2)_2 \cdot 3H_2O$, white; lead arsenate, $Pb_3(AsO_4)_2$, white; lead bromide, $PbBr_2$, white; basic lead carbonate, $Pb_3(OH)_2(CO_3)_2$, white; lead chromate, $PbCrO_4$, yellow; lead iodide, $PbI_2$, yellow; lead oxalate, $PbC_2O_4$, white; lead sulfide, PbS, black; lead monoxide, PbO, yellow or red; tri-lead tetroxide (red lead), $Pb_3O_4$, red; lead dioxide, $PbO_2$, chocolate.

**Reactions of Lead Ion.** NaOH or $NH_4OH$ precipitates $Pb(OH)_2$, white, soluble in excess of NaOH, soluble in $HNO_3$. HCl (and soluble, ionized chlorides), when added to a cold, moderately concentrated solution of $Pb(NO_3)_2$, precipitates $PbCl_2$, white, slightly soluble in cold water, moderately soluble in hot water, in $HNO_3$ and in concentrated HCl, soluble in excess NaOH. KBr (and soluble ionized bromides) precipitates $PbBr_2$, white, similar to $PbCl_2$ in properties. KI (and soluble, ionized iodides) precipitates $PbI_2$, yellow, slightly soluble in hot water, in cold $HNO_3$ and in concentrated HCl, soluble in NaOH, in hot $HNO_3$ and in concentrated acetate solutions. $K_2Cr_2O_7$ in neutral or slightly acid solution precipitates $PbCrO_4$, yellow, insoluble in $NH_4C_2H_3O_2$, soluble in NaOH and in moderate excess of $HNO_3$. $H_2SO_4$ (and soluble, ionized sulfates) precipitates $PbSO_4$, white, soluble in NaOH and in concentrated acetate solution, slightly soluble in $HNO_3$ and in HCl. $H_2S$ in acid, neutral or alkaline solution precipitates PbS, black, soluble in $HNO_3$ on heating (oxidation to free sulfur) and in 5 *N* HCl (formation of $H_2S$), insoluble in NaOH or in $NH_4C_2H_3O_2$. The most characteristic reactions are (*a*) the formation of a yellow precipitate, $PbI_2$, in cold, slightly acid solution (absence of acetate), soluble in hot water and crystallizing out in yellow plates as the solution cools, (*b*) the dissolving of $PbSO_4$ in $NH_4C_2H_3O_2$ followed by the formation of a yellow precipitate, $PbCrO_4$ with $K_2Cr_2O_7$.

**More Common Silver Compounds.** Silver chloride, AgCl, white; silver nitrate, $AgNO_3$, white; silver sulfate, $Ag_2SO_4$, white; silver bromide, AgBr, light yellow; silver chromate, $Ag_2CrO_4$, dark red; silver iodide, AgI, light yellow; silver oxalate, $Ag_2C_2O_4$, white; silver sulfide, $Ag_2S$, black; silver oxide, $Ag_2O$, brown.

**Reactions of Silver Ion.** NaOH or $NH_4OH$ precipitates $Ag_2O$, dark brown, soluble in excess of $NH_4OH$ (formation of $Ag(NH_3)_2^+$) soluble in $HNO_3$. HCl (and soluble ionized chlorides) precipitates AgCl, white, insoluble in $HNO_3$, soluble in $NH_4OH$, $Na_2S_2O_3$ ($Ag(S_2O_3)_2^{-3}$) or KCN ($Ag(CN)_2^-$). KBr (and soluble, ionized bromides) precipitates AgBr, light yellow, insoluble in $HNO_3$, slightly soluble in $NH_4OH$, soluble in $Na_2S_2O_3$ or KCN. KI (and soluble ionized iodides) precipitates AgI, light yellow, insoluble in $HNO_3$ or in $NH_4OH$, soluble in $Na_2S_2O_3$ or KCN. $H_2S$ in acid, neutral, or alkaline solution precipitates $Ag_2S$, black, soluble in $HNO_3$ on heating (oxidation to free sulfur), insoluble in $NH_4OH$, $Na_2S_2O_3$ or KCN. The most characteristic reaction is the precipitation of AgI, yellow, on adding KI to a solution of $Ag(NH_3)_2Cl$. $Ag^+$ forms complex ions with many negative ions when the latter are used in excess; e.g., $Ag(CN)_2^-$, $Ag(S_2O_3)_2^{-3}$, $Ag(SO_3)_2^{-3}$, $Ag(CNS)_2^-$, $Ag(NO_2)_2^-$, and $AgI_2^-$.

**More Common Mercurous Compounds.** Mercurous chloride (calomel), $Hg_2Cl_2$, white; mercurous nitrate, $Hg_2(NO_3)_2 \cdot 2H_2O$, white; mercurous sulfate, $Hg_2SO_4$, white; mercurous bromide, $Hg_2Br_2$, white; mercurous iodide, $Hg_2I_2$, green; mercurous oxide, $Hg_2O$, black.

**Reactions of Mercurous Ion.** NaOH precipitates $Hg_2O$, black, soluble in $HNO_3$. $NH_4OH$ precipitates $Hg_2NH_2X$, black, soluble in $HNO_3$. HCl (and soluble, ionized chlorides) precipitates $Hg_2Cl_2$, white, slowly soluble on heating with concentrated $HNO_3$ or aqua regia, more rapidly soluble in a mixture of $HNO_3$ and $Ca(ClO)_2$; turns black on treatment with $NH_4OH$, forming $Hg_2NH_2Cl$, which slowly changes to $HgNH_2Cl + Hg$. KBr (and soluble ionized bromides) precipitates $Hg_2Br_2$, white, similar in general properties to $Hg_2Cl_2$. KI (and soluble, ionized iodides) precipitates $Hg_2I_2$, green, reacting with excess of KI to form Hg and soluble $K_2HgI_4$; slowly soluble on heating in $HNO_3$, aqua regia and in a mixture of $HNO_3$ and $Ca(ClO)_2$. $H_2S$ in acid, neutral, or alkaline solution precipitates $HgS + Hg$, black, soluble in aqua regia and in a mixture of $HNO_3$ and $Ca(ClO)_2$. $SnCl_2$ precipitates $Hg_2Cl_2$, white, and reduces this somewhat slowly to $Hg^\circ$, dark gray. Metallic Cu (clean wire or disks) reduces $Hg_2^{++}$ to $Hg^\circ$, forming a silvery coating on the surface of the Cu. The most characteristic reaction is the formation of the black precipitate with $NH_4OH$.

## PREPARING THE SOLUTION FOR THE PRECIPITATION OF GROUP I

The solution is first tested with litmus paper to learn whether it is acid, neutral, or alkaline. If alkaline it may contain $Pb(OH)_3^-$ or $Ag(NH_3)_2^+$, and, since these ions do not yield precipitates with chloride ion, it is necessary to convert them to $Pb^{++}$ and $Ag^+$. To do this, place in a test tube about 15 drops of the original solution and add 5 $N$ $HNO_3$ 1 drop at a time, stirring or shaking vigorously after each addition, until the solution shows an acid reaction. If a precipitate forms as the solution is neutralized, this usually dissolves readily when 1–2 drops excess of $HNO_3$ are added. (Occasionally, with certain ions of later group metals present, special difficulties are encountered that must be handled separately. See, particularly, $CrO_4^{--}$ in Group III, page 85, and $MnO_4^{--}$ in Group IV, page 85.) After the alkaline solution has been acidified with $HNO_3$ (using sufficient excess to dissolve any precipitate that may form), the solution is cooled thoroughly so that $PbCl_2$ may precipitate effectively.

If the original solution is neutral, the portion taken for analysis should be treated with 1–2 drops of 5 $N$ $HNO_3$ before adding the first group reagent. If the solution appears to be moderately acid it may be used directly for the precipitation of Group I.

## PRECIPITATION AND ANALYSIS OF GROUP I

**Precipitation of Group I.** Add 2 drops of 5 $N$ HCl to the cold, slightly acid solution. Shake or stir vigorously for a moment, centrifuge to settle the precipitate, and then add to the clear solution 1 drop more of HCl. If no more precipitate forms, it may be assumed that precipitation is complete as far as the first group reagent is concerned. If further precipitation occurs in this test, add 1 drop more of 5 $N$ HCl, shake, and repeat the test. When precipitation is finally complete, centrifuge, wash once with 2 drops of 1 $N$ HCl and then 2–3 times with cold water. The precipitate may contain $PbCl_2$, white, $Hg_2Cl_2$, white, and AgCl, white. The clear solution will contain the metals of Groups II, III, etc.

*Explanatory Notes.* (1) When the original solution is alkaline it is acidified with $HNO_3$ rather than HCl, in order to distinguish between the first group chlorides and other precipitates that may form when the solution is neutralized. Further, if the solution were very strongly alkaline, the large amount of acid required might, in the case of HCl, introduce sufficient chloride ion to form complex chlorides of Pb and Ag and thus interfere with effective precipitation of Group I.

(2) When the original solution is neutral, a small amount of $HNO_3$ should be added to assist in the coagulation of AgCl, which otherwise may form a

TABLE V. OUTLINE OF PROCEDURE FOR GROUP I

| $Pb^{++}$ | $Hg_2^{++}$ | $Ag^+$ |
|---|---|---|
| | HCl | |
| $PbCl_2$* | $Hg_2Cl_2$ | AgCl |
| | Hot water | |
| $PbCl_2$ | $Hg_2Cl_2$ | AgCl |
| 1. KI cooling – $PbI_2$ yellow | $NH_4OH$ | |
| 2. $K_2Cr_2O_7$ – $PbCrO_4$ yellow | $Hg_2NH_2Cl$ black | $Ag(NH_3)_2^+$ <br> 1. KI – AgI yellow <br> 2. $HNO_3$ – AgCl white |
| 3. $(NH_4)_2SO_4$ – $PbSO_4$ white | | |

* In these Outlines a straight line under a formula indicates a precipitate; a line with the ends turned up (└──┘) indicates that the substance is in solution.

colloidal suspension difficult to centrifuge. If the Group I precipitate does not settle on adding 2–3 drops of $HNO_3$ and shaking for a short time, it may be necessary to heat to boiling and stir vigorously. In this case, after the precipitate has coagulated, cool the solution thoroughly before centrifuging.

(3) The solution should be cold when Group I is precipitated, to insure the precipitation of $PbCl_2$ when a moderate amount of Pb is present.

(4) In precipitating Group I the solution should be made approximately 0.5 *N* with respect to $Cl^-$. This insures reasonable repression of solubility of $PbCl_2$ and reasonable formation of $BiCl_4^-$, but at the same time avoids excessive increase in solubility of AgCl by formation of the complex ion, $AgCl_3^{--}$.

(5) If no precipitate forms immediately on adding HCl, shake the solution and let stand 1–2 minutes before concluding that Group I is absent. In solutions sufficiently dilute so that only moderate supersaturation is set up, many precipitates are slow to form. This is true in the case of $PbCl_2$.

(6) In precipitating each group it is necessary to test for completeness of precipitation, both to avoid interference in the analysis of later groups, and to avoid missing any metals of the given group, since the more soluble compound is generally the last to precipitate.

(7) In washing the first group precipitate, dilute HCl is used first to prevent precipitation of BiOCl or SbOCl by hydrolysis.

**Separation and Identification of $Ag^+$, $Hg_2^{++}$, and $Pb^{++}$.** Add 8–10 drops of water to the precipitate, stir, and place in the hot water bath for a minute or two, stirring occasionally. $PbCl_2$ dissolves; AgCl and $Hg_2Cl_2$ are left as precipitates. Centrifuge if necessary to settle the precipitate; then use a clean dropper tube to transfer the solution to a spot plate to test for Pb (see next paragraph). To wash the precipitate add 8–10 drops of water, warm, stir, centrifuge, and discard the clear solution. To the precipitate add 4–5 drops of 5 *N* $NH_4OH$, stir, and centrifuge. AgCl dissolves, but the $Hg_2Cl_2$ is changed to a black precipitate, $Hg_2NH_2Cl$. The formation of the black precipitate constitutes a test for mercury. A white precipitate still left may be some AgCl not dissolved or some $Pb(OH)_2$ from action of $NH_4OH$ on the $PbCl_2$ still left after one washing. The clear solution may be divided between two test tubes and tests for Ag applied as follows: (*a*) Add 1 drop of KI solution and look for a creamy white precipitate of AgI; (*b*) add 4–5 drops of 5 *N* $HNO_3$ (sufficient to make the solution acid) and look for a curdy or opalescent white precipitate of AgCl.

**Tests for Pb.** If much Pb is present, a coarse, crystalline, white precipitate of $PbCl_2$ will form as the solution cools on the spot plate. Other, more sensitive tests may be applied as follows: (*a*) Place 2–3 drops of the solution in another depression on the spot plate and add a drop of KI solution. Look for a bright yellow precipitate of $PbI_2$. (*b*) Test a second portion of the solution with a drop of $K_2Cr_2O_7$, looking for a yellow precipitate of $PbCrO_4$. (*c*) Transfer the remainder of the solution to a small test tube and add a drop of 2 *N* $(NH_4)_2SO_4$. A finely divided, white precipitate will be $PbSO_4$.

*Explanatory Notes.* (1) The solubility of $PbCl_2$ at the boiling point is only about three times that at 25°C. whereas the corresponding ratio for silver chloride is nearly fifteen to one. In spite of this a fair separation is obtained due to the very great difference in solubility of the two salts at 25°C. so that a twofold increase in solubility of $PbCl_2$ places it in the moderately soluble class, while a fourteenfold increase in solubility of AgCl still leaves it in the moderately insoluble class. Actually the solubility of $PbCl_2$ in cold water is sufficiently great so that the main effect of heating the water is to increase the rate of dissolving of the $PbCl_2$ rather than the total solubility.

(2) The dissolving of $PbCl_2$ in hot water and the reaction of AgCl with $NH_3$ solution both take place rapidly enough so that only a half minute or so is needed to carry out these separations. In other cases it is frequently necessary to continue the reaction for a longer time to obtain satisfactory results.

(3) If the precipitate is not washed after extracting the $PbCl_2$ with hot water, the $PbCl_2$ still left will form a white precipitate of $Pb(OH)_2$ when the $NH_4OH$ is added. This does not interfere with the confirmatory tests for Ag and Hg, but should not be mistaken for AgCl.

(4) If the test for mercury seems unusually strong in Group I, the black precipitate should be saved to test for Ag in case the regular test for Ag is negative. When the amount of silver is small and that of mercury is large, the silver may be reduced very largely to the metallic form which is insoluble in $NH_4OH$.

$$Hg_2Cl_2 + 2NH_3 = \underline{Hg_2NH_2Cl} + NH_4^+ + Cl^-$$

$$\underline{Hg_2NH_2Cl} = \underline{HgNH_2Cl} + \underline{Hg^\circ}$$

$$\underline{2Hg^\circ} + 2AgCl + 2NH_3 = \underline{2Ag^\circ} + \underline{Hg_2NH_2Cl}$$

In this case the regular test for Ag may fail and the following procedure should be used: Transfer the black precipitate to a small crucible, add 5 drops of 5 *N* $HNO_3$ and 5 drops of a 5% solution of $Ca(ClO)_2$, boil for a minute or two, then add 10 drops of water, centrifuge and wash. The mercury is all converted to soluble $HgCl_2$, whereas the silver is left as AgCl. Dissolve the precipitate in $NH_4OH$ and apply the usual confirmatory tests for silver.

(5) Since $PbCl_2$ is fairly soluble even in cold water one does not obtain the $PbCl_2$ crystals unless the first group precipitate contained considerable lead. Of the other confirmatory tests, $PbSO_4$ precipitates somewhat slowly from dilute solutions, $PbI_2$ precipitates readily if the solution is cold, and $PbCrO_4$ usually precipitates readily, but may precipitate slowly from dilute solution if the solution is appreciably acid because of carelessness in washing the first group precipitate. Slight suspensions of $PbI_2$ or $PbCrO_4$ which may be difficult to recognize as precipitates may be made more visible by transferring to filter paper in the following manner: Pick up the suspension in a dropper tube, then press the tip of the tube rather firmly to a piece of heavy filter paper and slowly squeeze the bulb. The solution will diffuse into the filter, but the precipitate will remain as a fine dot if the procedure is carried out properly.

(6) The precipitation of $PbCrO_4$ rather than $PbCr_2O_7$ on adding $K_2Cr_2O_7$ to the solution of $PbCl_2$ is due to partial hydration of $Cr_2O_7^{--}$ to $HCrO_4^-$ and dissociation of the latter into $H_3O^+$ and $CrO_4^{--}$, and also to the lower solubility of $PbCrO_4$.

$$Cr_2O_7^{--} + H_2O \leftrightarrows 2HCrO_4^-$$

$$H_2O + HCrO_4^- \rightleftarrows H_3O^+ + CrO_4^{--}$$

$$Pb^{++} + CrO_4^{--} \leftrightarrows \underline{PbCrO_4}$$

## REPORTING GROUP I IONS IN AN UNKNOWN SOLUTION

**Lead.** In solution, lead shows only a valence of two, but on account of the amphoteric character of $Pb(OH)_2$ the metal may be found in neutral or acid solution as $Pb^{++}$, and in strongly alkaline solution (NaOH or KOH) as plumbite ion, $Pb(OH)_3^-$. Therefore, if Pb is identified in Group I, note the reaction of the original solution to litmus paper. If neutral or acid, report $Pb^{++}$; if alkaline, report $Pb(OH)_3^-$.

**Silver.** In solution, silver shows only a valence of one. Silver oxide is not amphoteric like $Pb(OH)_2$, but $Ag^+$ combines readily with $NH_3$ to form the complex ion, silver ammonia ion, $Ag(NH_3)_2^+$. There are a number of other soluble complex ions containing silver—$Ag(CN)_2^-$, $Ag(S_2O_3)_2^{-3}$, etc.—but this is the only one being considered in the present course. Since $NH_3$ may be found only in an ammoniacal solution, the following method is used to distinguish between $Ag^+$ and $Ag(NH_3)_2^+$: if the original solution is neutral or acid, silver is present as $Ag^+$; if the solution is alkaline and has an odor of $NH_3$, silver is present as $Ag(NH_3)_2^+$.

**Mercury.** Since only mercurous ion forms an insoluble chloride of mercury, any mercury found in Group I will have a valence of one. Mercurous ion, $Hg_2^{++}$, does not form any common complex ions, although it will be noted that the ion is diatomic. If mercury is identified in Group I, report it as $Hg_2^{++}$ in the original solution.

## GROUP I IN RELATION TO OTHER GROUPS

The general theory of the use of a group reagent assumes that under proper conditions an effective separation is obtained of the metals of the given group from those of later groups. An effective separation implies two things: first, that none of the metals of later groups are left with an earlier group precipitate; and second, that the metals of the given group are precipitated so completely that reasonably small amounts of each can be identified in that group and that there will be no irregularities or interferences in later groups, due to the amount that fails to precipitate in its proper group. It is, of course, a fairly simple matter to determine the best conditions for the separation of two metals from each other by a particular reagent; but when several metals are to be precipitated and a number of others kept in solution, it usually happens that some of the separations are distinctly less satisfactory than others. Thus, the proper excess of reagent to give minimum solubility of one of the precipitates may not be correct to yield minimum solubility in the case of the other precipitates. Further, the special conditions of acidity or alkalinity necessary to prevent the carrying down of certain later group metals in the given group may not be the most effective in other cases. To make this more specific, it should be interesting to note the common irregularities in connection with the separation of Group I from later groups.

If the original solution is alkaline, it must be acidified in order to convert Pb and Ag to the proper ions, $Pb^{++}$ and $Ag^+$, for precipitation as chlorides. In this process of acidifying, as the solution is neutralized various precipitates of later group metals may form which usually dissolve again as the solution is made moderately acid with $HNO_3$. Thus alkaline solutions containing metals whose hydroxides are amphoteric, and some that form complex ammonia ions, yield precipitates of the corresponding hydroxides, which dissolve readily in dilute $HNO_3$. In the case of $CrO_4^{--}$ in the presence of either $Pb(OH)_3^-$ or $Ag(NH_3)_2^+$, when the alkaline solution is neutralized, $PbCrO_4$ or $Ag_2CrO_4$ precipitates and does not dissolve in ordinary excess of $HNO_3$. Further, $MnO_4^{--}$ is stable only in strongly alkaline solution and on acidifying changes into $MnO_4^-$ and $MnO_2$, the latter forming a dark brown precipitate insoluble in $HNO_3$.

$$Pb(OH)_3^- + CrO_4^{--} + 3H_3O^+ = \underline{PbCrO_4} + 6H_2O$$

$$2Ag(NH_3)_2^+ + CrO_4^{--} + 4H_3O^+ = \underline{Ag_2CrO_4} + 4NH_4^+ + 4H_2O$$

$$3MnO_4^{--} + 4H_3O^+ = 2MnO_4^- + \underline{MnO_2} + 6H_2O$$

In these latter cases such precipitates as $PbCrO_4$, $Ag_2CrO_4$, and $MnO_2$ may be centrifuged, washed, treated with 2–3 drops of 5 $N$ HCl and 1 drop of formaldehyde solution, $CH_2O$, and boiled until any yellow precipitate of $PbCrO_4$, red precipitate of $Ag_2CrO_4$, or brown precipitate of $MnO_2$ has disappeared. The solution is then cooled (AgCl and $PbCl_2$ may be present) and combined with the earlier clear solution for precipitation of Group I.

Occasionally, when the original solution is slightly acid, the addition of dilute HCl for the precipitation of Group I may cause the formation of a white precipitate of BiOCl.

$$Bi^{+3} + Cl^- + 3H_2O = BiOCl + 2H_3O^+$$

This precipitate does not interfere seriously in the tests for first group metals, nor is precipitation sufficiently complete to interfere with the regular identification of Bi in Group II, but it is a cause of worry to the student who apparently obtains a first group precipitate but cannot find any of these metals present. The formation of this precipitate can be avoided by having the solution approximately 2 $N$ with $HNO_3$ before HCl is added in Group I, or it may be dissolved by adding an extra 2–3 drops of 5 $N$ HCl.

$$BiOCl + 2H_3O^+ + 3Cl^- = BiCl_4^- + 3H_2O$$

The presence of these larger amounts of $Cl^-$ or $NO_3^-$ causes some interference in the precipitation of certain sulfides in Group II, however, and it is doubtful if much would be gained by these extra precautions.

Following the precipitation of Group I, it is necessary to centrifuge and wash in order to complete the separation of the later group metals from the first group precipitate. Fortunately, the first group chlorides show little tendency to carry down later group metals by occlusion or adsorption (mechanical or colloidal effects whereby precipitates retain materials which are of themselves soluble). If the precipitate is incompletely washed, small amounts of any of the later group metals may still be present and may cause some irregularities in the analysis of Group I.

In considering the completeness with which first group metals are precipitated, it may be stated that $Hg_2Cl_2$ and AgCl are sufficiently insoluble under the conditions recommended for the precipitation of the group so that only negligible amounts of these metals are carried over into later groups. In the case of $PbCl_2$, however, even under the most favorable conditions of temperature, absence of other ions in large amounts, and repression of solubility by common ion effect, the compound is soluble to the extent of about 2 g. per liter. This means that if the amount of lead in solution is small no precipitate of $PbCl_2$ will form, whereas if the amount of lead is large a bulky precipitate of $PbCl_2$ will still leave a moderate amount of lead in solution. Occasionally conditions are encountered under which precipitation may be distinctly less satisfactory than just indicated. Thus, a solution containing high concentration of $Hg^{++}$ and treated with only a drop of 5 $N$ HCl may fail to yield a precipitate even with $Hg_2^{++}$ or $Ag^+$ present, because of the conversion of $Cl^-$ to slightly ionized $HgCl_2$ by excess of the $Hg^{++}$. When more HCl is added, precipitation takes place normally. Again, $Hg_2Cl_2$ and AgCl are appreciably soluble in high concentration of $Cl^-$, so if too much HCl is added precipitation will be less complete than it should, and significant amounts of $Hg_2^{++}$ and $Ag^+$ may escape precipitation in Group I. In the case of $PbCl_2$ minimum solubility is reached in approximately normal HCl, a concentration of $Cl^-$ sufficiently high so that AgCl is appreciably more soluble than in water. Since it is always necessary to look for Pb in Group II as well as in Group I it is general practice to keep the concentration of $Cl^-$ down to 0.5 $N$ or less in precipitating Group I. When a solution contains high concentration of $NO_3^-$ (as in acidifying a strongly alkaline solution with $HNO_3$), $PbCl_2$ precipitates less readily than it does normally; therefore more Pb escapes precipitation in Group I when working with a plumbite solution than when the original solution is neutral or slightly acid.

Failure to precipitate Group I completely may result in the precipitation of these metals as sulfides in Group II. The regular procedure for Group II includes Hg and Pb as normal constituents, the only irregularity that might arise concerning these metals being the failure to recognize $Hg_2^{++}$, since Hg found in Group II is reported as $Hg^{++}$. Any Ag not precipitated in Group I will be found in the second group precipitate, but will be overlooked unless the supplementary procedure is followed that is described in connection with Group II (page 104).

## REACTIONS OF GROUP I METALS IN THE SYSTEMATIC ANALYSIS OF A SOLUTION

### Lead

*If the solution is alkaline*

$$Pb(OH)_3^- + 3H_3O^+ = Pb^{++} + 6H_2O$$

*In Group I*

$$Pb^{++} + 2Cl^- = \underline{PbCl_2}$$
$$\underline{PbCl_2} + \text{hot water} = Pb^{++} + 2Cl^-$$
1. $Pb^{++} + 2I^- \text{ (cold)} = \underline{PbI_2}$
2. $Pb^{++} + HSO_4^- + H_2O = \underline{PbSO_4} + H_3O^+$
3. $2Pb^{++} + Cr_2O_7^{--} + 3H_2O = \underline{2PbCrO_4} + 2H_3O^+$

### Silver

*If the solution is alkaline*

$$Ag(NH_3)_2^+ + 2H_3O^+ = Ag^+ + 2NH_4^+$$

*In Group I*

$$Ag^+ + Cl^- = \underline{AgCl}$$
$$\underline{AgCl} + 2NH_3 = Ag(NH_3)_2^+ + Cl^-$$
1. $Ag(NH_3)_2^+ + Cl^- + 2H_3O^+ = \underline{AgCl} + 2NH_4^+ + 2H_2O$
2. $Ag(NH_3)_2^+ + I^- = \underline{AgI} + 2NH_3$

*In the presence of large amounts of $Hg_2Cl_2$*

$$\underline{2AgCl} + \underline{2Hg} = \underline{2Ag} + \underline{Hg_2Cl_2}$$
$$\underline{2Ag} + HClO + H_3O^+ + Cl^- = \underline{2AgCl} + 2H_2O$$
$$\underline{AgCl} + 2NH_3 = Ag(NH_3)_2^+ + Cl^-$$
$$Ag(NH_3)_2^+ + Cl^- + 2H_3O^+ = \underline{AgCl} + 2NH_4^+ + 2H_2O$$

### Mercury

*In Group I*

Hg₂ NH₂ Cl

$$Hg_2^{++} + 2Cl^- = \underline{Hg_2Cl_2}$$
$$\underline{Hg_2Cl_2} + 2NH_3 = \underline{Hg_2NH_2Cl} + NH_4^+ + Cl^-$$

*In testing the black precipitate for Ag*

$$\underline{Hg_2NH_2Cl} + HClO + 2Cl^- + 3H_3O^+ = 2HgCl_2 + NH_4^+ + 4H_2O$$

## *SUMMARY AND REVIEW*

Preparation of Solution for Precipitation

1. Original soln. acid
2. Original soln. basic

- *A*. Use of $HNO_3$
  - (*a*) Why used?
  - (*b*) How tell when sufficient added?
  - (*c*) Why avoid large excess?
  - (*d*) Difficulty to be expected in Group II analysis

Actual Precipitation

1. Why ppt. from a cold soln.?
2. Addition of reagent
   - *A*. Need for excess
     - (*a*) Insure complete pptn.
     - (*b*) Lower soly. of Group I chlorides
     - (*c*) Prevent pptn. of later group ions (Bi, Sb, etc.)
   - *B*. Need for only slight excess
     - (*a*) Soly. of ppt. in large excess
     - (*b*) Must be neutralized later
   - *C*. Incompleteness of pptn. of Pb
     - (*a*) Effect of temperature
     - (*b*) Effect of excess reagent
3. Filtration
   - Coagulation of ppt.
4. How determine whether pptn. complete?
5. Washing the ppt.
   - *A*. Why wash?
   - *B*. Wash solns. to be used
     - (*a*) Why HCl first?
     - (*b*) Why cold water?
   - *C*. Number of washings necessary

Analysis of the Precipitate

1. Removal and detection of Pb
   - *A*. Technique
   - *B*. $(NH_4)_2SO_4$ test
   - *C*. Iodide test
     - (*a*) Danger of using too much reagent
     - (*b*) Interference of $Hg^{++}$
   - *D*. Dichromate Test
     - (*a*) Amount of reagent
     - (*b*) Source of $CrO_4^{--}$
     - (*c*) Effect of acid and base
   - *E*. Comparative delicacy of tests
2. Separation of AgCl from $Hg_2Cl_2$
   - *A*. $NH_4OH$ Method
     - (*a*) Technique
     - (*b*) Limitations
     - (*c*) Accomplishments
   - *B*. Method when amount AgCl small in comparison with $Hg_2Cl_2$
3. Final tests for Ag
   - *A*. $HNO_3$ test
   - *B*. KI test
     - Interference of Pb(OH)Cl

## LABORATORY EXERCISES

1. Known solutions for laboratory study.
   (*1*) $Ag^+$, $Pb^{++}(l)$, $Hg_2^{++}$
   (*2*) $Ag^+$, $Hg_2^{++}$
   (*3*) $Ag^+(s)$, $Hg_2^{++}(l)$

These solutions contain the following amounts of substances per liter: (*1*) 4 g. $AgNO_3$, 16 g. $Pb(NO_3)_2$, 3.5 g. $Hg_2(NO_3)_2 \cdot 2H_2O$, and 150 ml. of 5 $N$ $HNO_3$; (*2*) 4 g. $AgNO_3$, 3.5 g. $Hg_2(NO_3)_2 \cdot 2H_2O$, and 150 ml. of 5 $N$ $HNO_3$; (*3*) 1.6 g. $AgNO_3$, 14 g. $Hg_2(NO_3)_2 \cdot 2H_2O$, and 150 ml. of 5 $N$ $HNO_3$.

Use 15 drops of the original solution. Carry out the regular scheme of analysis for Group I on each of the first two solutions. In the second solution the tests for lead should be negative.

In the case of the third solution, after obtaining the Group I precipitate and treating with $NH_4OH$ in the regular way, set this ammoniacal solution aside for a moment and work up the black precipitate to test it for silver according to the directions given in note (4), p. 83. After treating the final precipitate with $NH_4OH$, acidify both this solution and the ammoniacal extract of the original precipitate.

2. To 1–2 drops of $AgNO_3$ solution add 2–3 drops excess of reagent $NH_4OH$. Add a drop of $NH_4Cl$ to this solution, then add a drop of KI. Explain the difference in the results obtained.

3. To 1–2 drops of $Pb(NO_3)_2$ solution add excess of reagent NaOH. To this clear solution add $HNO_3$ a drop at a time, with shaking, until the solution becomes neutral. What is the precipitate? Try the effect of more $HNO_3$. Write equations for the two reactions.

4. To 2 drops of $Pb(NO_3)_2$ add 1 drop KI solution, centrifuge and discard the clear solution. Add 10 drops of water to the precipitate, heat in the hot water bath and stir for about a minute. If the precipitate does not dissolve completely, pipet off the clear solution and transfer to a clean test tube. Note the color of the aqueous solution of $PbI_2$. Let the solution cool 2–3 minutes and note the formation of coarse, shiny crystals of $PbI_2$.

5. To 5 drops of $Pb(NO_3)_2$ solution add 2 drops of 5 $N$ HCl. Shake, centrifuge, and add a drop of HCl to test for completeness of precipitation. To this solution add 1–2 drops of KI solution. Explain the result obtained. Discuss the completeness with which lead may be precipitated in Group I.

6. To 2 drops of $AgNO_3$ solution, add a drop of $N$ HCl to precipitate AgCl. Add 10 drops of 5 $N$ $NH_4OH$ to dissolve the precipitate, shake thoroughly, and divide into two equal parts. To one add 5 $N$ $HNO_3$, 1–2 drops at a time until the solution is distinctly acid. To the other add conc. HCl, 1–2 drops at a time until the solution is distinctly acid. Explain the difference in results obtained. Pour the solution that was acidified with HCl into 50 drops of distilled water. Explain the precipitation of AgCl.

## EQUILIBRIUM PROBLEMS IN GROUP I

I. Calculate the concentration of $Cl^-$ introduced for the precipitation of Group I.

Since HCl is a strong electrolyte the concentration of $Cl^-$ will be the same as that of the HCl present. Assume that 2 drops of 5 $N$ reagent are added, that $\frac{1}{4}$ of this is used in the precipitation of Group I, and that the final volume is 20 drops. On this basis the 5 $N$ HCl is being diluted in the ratio 1.5:20.

$$[Cl^-] = 5 \times \frac{1.5}{20} = 0.37$$

II. Calculate the completeness of precipitation of AgCl in Group I if $[Cl^-] = 0.37$ and $L_{AgCl} = 1 \times 10^{-10}$.

If $Ag^+$ is present in the original solution in sufficient concentration to give a precipitate in Group I, and if the excess beyond saturation is thus removed,

$$[Ag^+] \times [Cl^-] = 1 \times 10^{-10}$$

Since $[Cl^-] = 0.37$,

$$[Ag^+] = \frac{1 \times 10^{-10}}{0.37} = 2.7 \times 10^{-10}$$

It is interesting to note that this calculation omits both interionic attraction effects and possible formation of complex ions, such as $AgCl_2^-$ and $AgCl_3^{--}$. Direct experiments show that the minimum solubility of AgCl in the presence of excess $Cl^-$ is about $10^{-7}$ *M* and that, under the conditions used in Group I, the solubility rises above this figure. However, it has also been shown by experiments that the precipitation of AgCl in Group I is reasonably complete unless excessive amounts of HCl are used.

III. Calculate the distribution of Pb between $Pb^{++}$ and $PbCl^+$ in the filtrate from Group I if $[Cl^-] = 0.37$ and $K_{PbCl^+} = 0.08$

$$\frac{[Pb^{++}] \times [Cl^-]}{[PbCl^+]} = 0.08$$

If $[Cl^-] = 0.37$,

$$\frac{[Pb^{++}]}{[PbCl^+]} = \frac{0.08}{0.37}$$

If the lead is assumed to be wholly in these two forms, then the fraction in each form would be:

$$\text{Fraction of Pb as } Pb^{++} = \frac{0.08}{0.08 + 0.37} = \frac{0.08}{0.45} \cong 0.18$$

$$\text{Fraction of Pb as } PbCl^{+} = \frac{0.35}{0.08 + 0.38} = \frac{0.37}{0.45} \cong 0.82$$

IV. Calculate the solubility product of $PbCl_2$ if the solubility of $PbCl_2$ in water at 25°C. is 9.7 g. per liter and $K_{PbCl^+} = 0.08$.

$$\text{Molar solubility of } PbCl_2 = \frac{9.7}{\text{ml. wt. } PbCl_2} = \frac{9.7}{278} = 0.035$$

Let

$$X = [PbCl^+]$$

Then $[Pb^{++}] = 0.035 - X$, and $[Cl^-] = 0.070 - X$.

$$K_{PbCl^+} = \frac{[Pb^{++}] \times [Cl^-]}{[PbCl^+]} = \frac{(.035 - X)(0.070 - X)}{X} = 0.08$$

$$0.00245 - 0.105X + X^2 = 0.08X$$

$$0.00245 - 0.185X + X^2 = 0$$

Solving this quadratic, $X = 0.014 = [PbCl^+]$.

*Note:* In solving this equation by the usual formula, two values for $X$ may be obtained: 0.014 and 0.174. However, since $X = PbCl^+$ and this must be less than the molar solubility of the $PbCl_2$ which is 0.035, only the lower value can be selected as correct.

If the molar solubility of $PbCl_2$ is 0.035 and the Pb is assumed to be present in only the two forms, $Pb^{++}$ and $PbCl^+$,

$$[Pb^{++}] = 0.035 - [PbCl^+] = 0.035 - 0.014 = 0.021$$

$$[Cl^-] = 2 \times 0.035 - [PbCl^+] = 0.070 - 0.014 = 0.056$$

$$L_{PbCl_2} = [Pb^{++}] \times [Cl^-]^2 = 0.021 \times 0.056^2 = 6.6 \times 10^{-5}$$

V. Calculate the number of mg. of Pb left in solution after the precipitation of Group I, assuming (*a*) that the solution is just saturated with $PbCl_2$, (*b*) the volume is 2 ml., and (*c*) the lead is present as $Pb^{++}$ and $PbCl^+$. $Cl^- = 0.37$, $L_{PbCl_2} = 6.6 \times 10^{-5}$, $K_{PbCl^+} = 0.08$.

In the saturated solution,

$$[Pb^{++}] \times [Cl^-]^2 = 6.6 \times 10^{-5}$$

If $[Cl^-] = 0.37$,

$$[Pb^{++}] = \frac{6.6 \times 10^{-5}}{(.37)^2} = 4.8 \times 10^{-4}$$

But

$$\frac{[Pb^{++}] \times [Cl^-]}{[PbCl^+]} = 0.08$$

Therefore,

$$[PbCl^+] = \frac{4.8 \times 10^{-4} \times 0.37}{0.08} = 2.22 \times 10^{-}$$

$$\text{Total } [Pb] = [Pb^{++}] + [PbCl^+] = 4.8 \times 10^{-4} + 2.22 \times 10^{-3} = 2.7 \times 10^{-3}$$

$$\text{mg. of Pb left in solution} = 2.7 \times 10^{-3} \times \text{at. wt. of Pb} \times \text{vol. in ml.}$$

$$2.7 \times 10^{-3} \times 207 \times 2 = 1.1 \text{ mg. of Pb}$$

This is enough Pb to give a distinct precipitate with $H_2S$ in Group II; therefore, the precipitation of Pb in Group I will always be incomplete. Actually the precipitation of $PbCl_2$ takes place somewhat slowly even after it has started, and if the amount of Pb is rather small a moderate degree of supersaturation may persist without any precipitation. Thus, the removal of Pb in Group I is seldom as complete as this figure would indicate.

VI. Calculate the solubility of AgCl in 2 $N$ $NH_3$ solution.

$$L_{AgCl} = 1 \times 10^{-10}, \quad K_{Ag(NH_3)_2^+} = 7 \times 10^{-8}$$

The net reaction involved in dissolving the AgCl is

$$\underline{AgCl} + 2NH_3 = Ag(NH_3)_2^+ + Cl^-$$

In the saturated solution, $[Ag^+] \times [Cl^-] = 1 \times 10^{-10}$, $\frac{[Ag^+] \times [NH_3]^2}{[Ag(NH_3)_2^+]} = 7 \times 10^{-8}$.

From these equations two expressions for $[Ag^+]$ may be obtained and placed equal to each other.

$$[Ag^+] = \frac{1 \times 10^{-10}}{[Cl^-]} = \frac{7 \times 10^{-8}[Ag(NH_3)_2^+]}{[NH_3]^2}$$

In the solution $[Cl^-] = [Ag(NH_3)_2^+] + [Ag^+]$, but $[Ag^+]$ is very small as compared with $[Ag(NH_3)_2^+]$; therefore the $[Cl^-] \cong [Ag(NH_3)_2^+]$. Also, the final $[NH_3]$ will equal the initial $[NH_3] - 2[Ag(NH_3)_2^+]$ since 2 molecules of $NH_3$ are used for every $Ag(NH_3)_2^+$ formed. The original concentration of $NH_3$ was given as 2 $M$; thus the final $NH_3 = 2 - 2[Ag(NH_3)_2^+]$. Substituting these alternate expressions for $[Cl^-]$ and $[NH_3]$ in the equation gives

$$\frac{1 \times 10^{-10}}{[Ag(NH_3)_2^+]} = \frac{7 \times 10^{-8}[Ag(NH_3)_2^+]}{(2 - 2[Ag(NH_3)_2^+])^2}$$

Rearranging:

$$\frac{1 \times 10^{-10}}{7 \times 10^{-8}} = \frac{[Ag(NH_3)_2^+]^2}{(2 - 2[Ag(NH_3)_2^+])^2}$$

Extracting the square root on each side,

$$0.048 = \frac{[Ag(NH_3)_2^+]}{(2 - 2[Ag(NH_3)_2^+])}$$

$$0.076 = 1.076[Ag(NH_3)_2^+]$$

$$[Ag(NH_3)_2^+] = \frac{0.076}{1.076} = 0.07$$

This answer shows that a saturated solution of AgCl in 2 $M$ $NH_3$ solution would be only 0.07 $M$, indicating that a condition of chemical equilibrium is reached with only 7% of the $NH_3$ changed to $Ag(NH_3)_2^+$.

# 6

## Copper Division of Group II

# Mercury, Lead, Bismuth, Copper, Cadmium

The Copper division of Group II is precipitated by $H_2S$ in warm, 0.25 *N* HCl solution. The metals included are Hg, Pb, Bi, Cu, and Cd. The common ions of these metals are $Hg_2^{++}$ (found in Group I), $Hg^{++}$, $Pb^{++}$, $Pb(OH)_3^-$, $Bi^{+++}$, $Cu^{++}$, $Cu(NH_3)_4^{++}$, $Cd^{++}$, and $Cd(NH_3)_4^{++}$.

### COMMON COMPOUNDS AND REACTIONS OF IONS OF Hg (IC), Pb,* Bi, Cu, AND Cd

**More Common Mercuric Compounds.** Mercuric chloride, $HgCl_2$, white; mercuric nitrate, $Hg(NO_3)_2$, white; mercuric sulfate, $HgSO_4$, white; mercuric bromide, $HgBr_2$, white; mercuric iodide, $HgI_2$, red; mercuric sulfide, HgS, black (native HgS, cinnabar, is red); mercuric amino chloride, $HgNH_2Cl$, white; mercuric oxide, HgO, yellow if precipitated cold, red if precipitated hot or formed by decomposition of $Hg(NO_3)_2$.

**Reactions of Mercuric Ion.** NaOH precipitates HgO, yellow, soluble in HCl or $HNO_3$. $NH_4OH$ precipitates $HgNH_2Cl$ (from $HgCl_2$), white, soluble in HCl or $HNO_3$, also soluble in concentrated solutions of ammonium salts, especially $NH_4NO_3$. HCl (and soluble, ionized chlorides) forms $HgCl_2$, slightly ionized but moderately soluble. KBr (and soluble, ionized bromides) forms $HgBr_2$, very slightly ionized but slightly soluble. KI (and soluble, ionized iodides) precipitates $HgI_2$, red, slowly soluble in hot $HNO_3$ and aqua regia through oxidation of $I^-$ to $I_2$ or $HIO_3$, soluble in excess KI as $K_2HgI_4$. $K_2HgI_4$ is not decomposed by NaOH, but in the presence of NaOH reacts with $NH_3$ to form $NH_2Hg_2OI$, a brown precipitate. In acid, neutral or alkaline solution $H_2S$ precipitates HgS, black, insoluble in hot dilute $HNO_3$, soluble in aqua regia (oxidation to free S and formation of slightly ionized $HgCl_4^{--}$), soluble in $Na_2S$-NaOH solution (formation of $HgS_2^{--}$). $SnCl_2$ reduces $Hg^{++}$ readily, with precipitation of $Hg_2Cl_2$, white, which is further reduced to Hg° by excess of reagent. Metallic Cu reduces $Hg^{++}$ to Hg°, forming a silvery coating on the surface of the Cu°. The most characteristic

* See Group I, p. 78.

reaction is the formation of a white precipitate of $Hg_2Cl_2$ with $SnCl_2$ (after insoluble chlorides have been precipitated with HCl).

**More Common Bismuth Compounds.** Bismuth chloride, $BiCl_3$, white; bismuth nitrate, $Bi(NO_3)_3 \cdot 5H_2O$, white; bismuth sulfate, $Bi_2(SO_4)_3$, white; bismuth iodide, $BiI_3$, black; bismuth oxychloride, BiOCl, white; bismuth oxynitrate, $BiONO_3 \cdot 2H_2O$, white; bismuth sulfide, $Bi_2S_3$, black; bismuth trioxide, $Bi_2O_3$, yellowish; sodium bismuthate, $NaBiO_3$, brown.

**Reactions of Bismuth Ion.** NaOH or $NH_4OH$ precipitates $Bi(OH)_3$, white, soluble in HCl or $HNO_3$. HCl (and soluble, ionized chlorides) precipitates from $Bi(NO_3)_3$ solution containing a minimum of free $HNO_3$ BiOCl, white, soluble in excess HCl and in 5 *N* $HNO_3$. KI (and soluble, ionized iodides) precipitates $BiI_3$, black, from a moderate to large concentration of $BiCl_3$, soluble in excess KI, forming $KBiI_4$, brown. (If the amount of free acid is low, KI precipitates BiOI, red, soluble in HCl, only slightly soluble in excess of KI.) $H_2S$ precipitates $Bi_2S_3$, black, soluble in hot 5 *N* $HNO_3$ (oxidation to free S), less readily soluble on boiling with HCl (formation of $H_2S$). In alkaline solution $NaSn(OH)_3$ reduces $Bi(OH)_3$ to $Bi^\circ$, black. The most characteristic reaction is the formation of a yellowish-brown solution, $KBiI_4$, with excess KI in the presence of HCl, the color not being destroyed by $SnCl_2$ (distinction from $I_2$).

**More Common Copper Compounds.** Cupric chloride, $CuCl_2 \cdot 2H_2O$, green; cupric nitrate, $Cu(NO_3)_2 \cdot 3H_2O$, blue; cupric sulfate, $CuSO_4 \cdot 5H_2O$, blue; cuprous iodide, CuI, white; cupric aceto-arsenite (Paris green), $Cu_4(C_2H_3O_2)_2(AsO_3)_2$, green, basic cupric carbonate, azurite, $2CuCO_3 \cdot Cu(OH)_2$, blue, and malachite, $CuCO_3 \cdot Cu(OH)_2$, green; cupric ferrocyanide, $Cu_2Fe(CN)_6$, brown; cupric phosphate, $Cu_3(PO_4)_2$, blue; cupric oxide, CuO, black; and cuprous oxide, $Cu_2O$, red.

**Reactions of Cupric Ion.** NaOH or $NH_4OH$ precipitates $Cu(OH)_2$, blue, soluble in acids and in excess of $NH_4OH$ (forming $Cu(NH_3)_4^{++}$). KI precipitates CuI, white (accompanied by oxidation of $I^-$ to $I_2$ which colors the precipitate brown), soluble in NaCN and in $NH_4OH$ (forming $Cu(CN)_3^{--}$ and $Cu(NH_3)_2^+$), slowly soluble in hot $HNO_3$ and in aqua regia through oxidation of $I^-$ to $I_2$ and $Cu^+$ to $Cu^{++}$. $H_2S$ in acid, neutral or alkaline solution precipitates CuS, black, soluble in hot 5 *N* $HNO_3$ and in NaCN, insoluble in $NH_4OH$. NaCN in neutral solution precipitates CuCN, white, soluble in excess reagent to form the colorless cuprocyanide ion, $Cu(CN)_3^{--}$, which is so slightly ionized that a blue solution of $Cu(NH_3)_4^{++}$ is readily decolorized by NaCN, and if $H_2S$ is passed into the solution containing excess of NaCN no precipitate of copper sulfide forms. $K_4Fe(CN)_6$ precipitates $Cu_2Fe(CN)_6$, brown, insoluble in $NH_4OH$ but converted to a bronze-colored cupric ammonia ferrocyanide, soluble in NaCN. $SnCl_2$ reduces $Cu^{++}$ to $Cu^+$, colorless. Metallic Fe or Zn, in the presence of dilute HCl or $H_2SO_4$, reduces all Cu compounds except the cuprocyanides to $Cu^\circ$. The most characteristic reactions are the formation of a blue solution with excess $NH_4OH$, and the precipitation of $Cu_2Fe(CN)_6$, brown, with $K_4Fe(CN)_6$ in acetic acid solution.

**More Common Cadmium Compounds.** Cadmium chloride $CdCl_2 \cdot 2H_2O$, white; cadmium nitrate, $Cd(NO_3)_2 \cdot 4H_2O$, white; cadmium sulfate, $3CdSO_4 \cdot 8H_2O$, white; cadmium iodide, $CdI_2$, tan; cadmium carbonate, $CdCO_3$, white; cadmium ferrocyanide, $Cd_2Fe(CN)_6$, white; cadmium sulfide, CdS, yellow; cadmium oxide, CdO, brown, and cadmium hydroxide, $Cd(OH)_2$, white.

**Reactions of Cadmium Ion.** NaOH or $NH_4OH$ precipitates $Cd(OH)_2$, white, soluble in acids and in excess of $NH_4OH$ (forming $Cd(NH_3)_4^{++}$). KI does not precipitate $CdI_2$, but when used in excess converts $Cd^{++}$ to $CdI_4^{--}$, which is so slightly ionized that the insoluble cadmium salts dissolve in a concentrated solution of KI. $H_2S$ in slightly acid, neutral, or alkaline solution precipitates CdS, yellow (sometimes green in alkaline solution), soluble in HCl (evolution of $H_2S$) and in $HNO_3$ (oxidation to free S). NaCN in neutral solution precipitates $Cd(CN)_2$, white, soluble in $NH_4OH$ and in excess of NaCN, the latter forming a complex ion, $Cd(CN)_4^{--}$, from which $H_2S$ will still precipitate CdS. $K_4Fe(CN)_6$ precipitates $Cd_2Fe(CN)_6$, white, soluble in $NH_4OH$. There are no common oxidation reduction reactions of $Cd^{++}$, except that some of the more electropositive metals, Zn, etc., will reduce $Cd^{++}$ to $Cd^{\circ}$. The most characteristic reaction is the formation of a yellow or greenish yellow precipitate with $H_2S$ in the presence of $NH_4OH$ and NaCN.

## REACTIONS OF THE COPPER DIVISION METALS IN THE SYSTEMATIC PRECIPITATION OF GROUP I

(1) Alkaline solutions containing $Pb(OH)_3^-$, $Cu(NH_3)_4^{++}$ or $Cd(NH_3)_4^{++}$ may give precipitates of the corresponding hydroxides, soluble in excess of the acid, when nitric acid is added to the solution in preparing for the precipitation of Group I.

(2) $Bi(NO_3)_3$, in a solution containing only a small amount of free $HNO_3$, may give a white precipitate, BiOCl, when a drop of HCl is added to test for the presence of Group I.

(3) In the presence of high concentration of $Hg^{++}$, Group I may fail to precipitate if only a drop of diluted HCl is added, due to the formation of slightly ionized $HgCl_2$.

(4) If large excess of HCl is added in the precipitation of Group I, $Pb^{++}$ and $Cd^{++}$ will be converted to $PbCl_4^{--}$ and $CdCl_4^{--}$ to a sufficient extent to interfere with the precipitation of small amounts of these metals in Group II.

## PREPARING THE SOLUTION FOR THE PRECIPITATION OF THE COPPER DIVISION OF GROUP II

If Group I has been precipitated from the original solution, the filtrate from Group I is adjusted for the precipitation of Group II. If there were no first group metals present, either the solution which has been tested for the presence of Group I or a portion of the original solution may be used. In any case when the solution is ready for precipitation with $H_2S$ it should be approximately 0.25 *N* with HCl to prevent possible precipitation of later group sulfides in Group II. Further, since $H_2S$ is a moderately strong reducing agent, such obvious oxidizing agents as $MnO_4^-$ and $Cr_2O_7^{--}$ should be absent.

In an unknown that may contain later group metals, the clear solution from Group I is examined for $MnO_4^-$ (reddish purple color) and $Cr_2O_7^{--}$ (orange-colored solution which turns green or blue when a small test portion of it is treated with a few drops of $H_2O_2$). If either is present, add 5 drops of 5 *N* HCl, 1–2 drops of formaldehyde or $NaNO_2$ solution and boil for several minutes, letting the solution evaporate almost to dryness. This reduces $MnO_4^-$ and $Cr_2O_7^{--}$.

$$2MnO_4^- + 5CH_2O + 6H_3O^+ = 2Mn^{++} + 5CH_2O_2 + 9H_2O$$

$$Cr_2O_7^{--} + 3CH_2O + 8H_3O^+ = 2Cr^{+3} + 3CH_2O_2 + 12H_2O$$

$$2MnO_4^- + 5HNO_2 + H_3O^+ = 2Mn^{++} + 5NO_3^- + 4H_2O$$

$$Cr_2O_7^{--} + 3HNO_2 + 5H_3O^+ = 2Cr^{+3} + 3NO_3^- + 9H_2O$$

Add 15–20 drops of water and proceed as if neither $MnO_4^-$ nor $Cr_2O_7^{--}$ had been present.

With $MnO_4^-$ and $Cr_2O_7^{--}$ absent, neutralize the excess of acid present by adding $NH_4OH$, 1 drop at a time, with shaking, until the solution is slightly alkaline, then adding 0.5–1.0 *N* HCl, one drop at a time, with shaking, until the first acid reaction is shown. A precipitate remaining at this point may consist of hydroxides of various metals in Groups II, III, and IV. It may dissolve completely in the next step or a granular white precipitate (chiefly BiOCl or $PbCl_2$) may remain after diluting with water. Add to this neutralized solution (with precipitate if present) 2 drops of 5 *N* HCl, dilute with water to 40 drops, and warm the solution to 60°–70°C. (fairly hot, but distinctly below boiling). The solution is now 0.25 *N* with HCl and ready for the precipitation of the copper division of Group II.

If the precipitate formed on neutralization with $NH_4OH$ is unusually heavy and fails to dissolve in the 0.25 *N* HCl, the following procedure is recommended. Transfer the solution to a small crucible, add 6–8 drops of 5 *N* $HNO_3$ and evaporate almost to dryness. This should dissolve the precipitate and remove excess $Cl^-$. Next, add 10–15 drops of water and nearly neutralize by adding 1 *N* $NH_4OH$ dropwise, with stirring, until a slight precipitate, other than the white, flocculent BiOCl, just fails to dissolve. This will neutralize most of the free acid and avoid the heavy precipitate obtained earlier. To this solution add 2 drops of 5 *N* HCl and dilute to 40 drops, heat, and precipitate Group II.

## PRECIPITATION AND ANALYSIS OF THE COPPER DIVISION OF GROUP II

### TABLE VI. OUTLINE OF PROCEDURE FOR COPPER DIVISION

| | | | | |
|---|---|---|---|---|
| | | Solution from Group I. | | |
| $HgCl_4^{--}$ | $PbCl^+$ | $BiCl_4^-$ | $Cu^{++}$ | $CdCl_2$ |
| | | $H_2S$ | | |
| $HgS$ | $PbS$ | $Bi_2S_3$ | $CuS$ | $CdS$ |
| | | $HNO_3$ | | |
| $HgS + S°$ | $Pb^{++}$ | $Bi^{+3}$ | $Cu^{++}$ | $Cd^{++}$ |
| $HCl + HNO_3$ | | $H_2SO_4$ | | |
| $HgCl_4^{--}$ | $PbSO_4$ | $Bi^{+3}$ | $Cu^{++}$ | $Cd^{++}$ |
| 1. $SnCl_2$<br>$\rightarrow Hg_2Cl_2 + Hg°$<br>2. $Cu° \rightarrow Hg°$ | 1. $KI \rightarrow PbI_2$<br>2. $NH_4C_2H_3O_2$<br>$\rightarrow Pb(C_2H_3O_2)_3^-$<br>$K_2Cr_2O_7$<br>$\rightarrow PbCrO_4$ | | $NH_4OH$ | |
| | | $Bi(OH)_3$<br>1. HCl<br>$\rightarrow BiCl_4^-$<br>KI<br>$\rightarrow KBiI_4$<br>2. $NaSn(OH)_3$<br>$\rightarrow Bi°$ | $Cu(NH_3)_4^{++}$ | $Cd(NH_3)_4^{++}$ |
| | | | Divide into two parts.<br>1. Test for Cu<br>$HC_2H_3O_2 \rightarrow Cu^{++}$<br>$K_4Fe(CN)_6 \rightarrow Cu_2Fe(CN)_6$<br>2. Test for Cd<br>If Cu is present:<br>$NaCN \rightarrow Cu(CN)_3^{--}$<br>$+ Cd(CN)_4^{--}$<br>$H_2S \rightarrow CdS$<br>In absence of Cu:<br>$H_2S \rightarrow CdS$ | |

## DESCRIPTION AND EXPLANATION OF STEPS IN PROCEDURE

**Precipitation of the Copper Division of Group II.** To the solution prepared for the precipitation of Group II pass in $H_2S$ at a moderate rate for 0.5–1 minute. Test the solution for the presence of free $H_2S$ by blowing the air out of the test tube above the solution; then draw off a sample of air near the surface of the solution with a dropper tube, place the tip close to a small drop of lead acetate solution absorbed on a piece of filter paper, and squeeze the bulb slowly. If excess $H_2S$ is present the spot should turn dark immediately. If no color develops or if the reaction is rather slow, pass in $H_2S$ again for about half a minute and then repeat the test. Centrifuge, wash the precipitate once with $H_2S$ water containing a few drops of HCl, and then 2–3 times with distilled water.

*Explanatory Notes.* (1) In handling $H_2S$ it should be remembered that this gas is poisonous. Therefore a capillary tube should be used to produce small bubbles which dissolve more readily than large bubbles, and the gas should not escape from the solution at a rate faster than that at which the bubbles can be counted, thus permitting the ventilating flues to carry away the wasted gas as well as decreasing the drain on the $H_2S$ lines.

(2) HgS is the least soluble of the sulfides of the copper division and is thus the first to precipitate. However, it is usually mixed with more or less of a chlorosulfide, $HgCl_2 \cdot HgS$, at the start which dissolves fairly readily in dilute $HNO_3$, thus spoiling the first step in the separation of the copper division metals from each other. If the first treatment with $H_2S$ is carried out for too short a time, this effect may be quite serious, and therefore it is important to test for the presence of excess $H_2S$ before filtering and washing.

(3) On treatment with $H_2S$ the acidity of the solution increases as the less soluble sulfides precipitate. $HgCl_4^{--} + H_2S + 2H_2O = HgS + 4Cl^- + 2H_3O^+$. Since the more soluble sulfides, PbS and CdS, do not precipitate readily if the solution is too acid or the concentration of $Cl^-$ is too high, it is necessary to watch these conditions rather carefully. However, with moderate amounts of Group II metals present the increase in acidity will not be serious if the volume is kept as great as 2 ml.; thus, if a reasonable amount of free $H_2S$ is present in the solution, the precipitation will be fairly complete unless excessive amounts of $Cl^-$ have been permitted to accumulate in the solution.

**Mercury. Separation and Identification.** Add 5 drops of water to the precipitate and transfer to a small crucible. Add 5 drops of 5 *N* $HNO_3$ and heat just to boiling, keeping it at this point for about half a minute. <u>HgS</u> and <u>S</u> should still be left as a precipitate, the other sulfides dissolving. Let the precipitate settle, transfer the clear solution to another crucible, and wash the precipitate about twice with a few drops of distilled water. To the moist precipitate add 6 drops of 5 *N* HCl and 2 drops of 5 *N* $HNO_3$ (or 6 drops of HCl and 4 drops of $Ca(ClO)_2$ solution), and boil for a short time to dissolve the HgS. Centrifuge, if necessary, to settle the precipitate and apply tests for Hg to separate portions of the clear solution as follows: (1) Add 3–4 drops of $SnCl_2$; if $HgCl_2$ is present, a white precipitate of mercurous chloride, $Hg_2Cl_2$, will form, turning dark as it is slowly reduced to metallic mercury. (2) Clean a short length of copper wire with pumice or emery cloth, or by heating a moment in $HNO_3$, place the wire in the solution and let stand for 1–2 minutes. Remove the wire, wipe it off with a clean cloth, and look for a silvery, adherent coating of Hg on the surface of the Cu.

*Explanatory Notes.* (1) A dark spongy residue of free S° may be left from the previous treatment with $HNO_3$. Also, if the $HNO_3$ was too dilute, it may not have attacked $Bi_2S_3$ or CuS effectively, leaving some of these as precipitates.

(2) Occasionally after boiling the Group II sulfides with 2.5 *N* $HNO_3$, the mercury is converted to a light gray flocculent precipitate of $HgCl_2 \cdot HgS$ instead of remaining as a black precipitate of HgS. The gray precipitate will give the regular tests for mercury. The gray precipitate may be due to several causes; incomplete conversion to HgS at the start, failure to wash HCl out of the precipitate at the beginning of Group II, or use of too concentrated $HNO_3$ in the separation of Hg from other metals of the copper division of Group II.

(3) After dissolving HgS in HCl + $HNO_3$, the reagents then act on each other with the formation of $Cl_2$. Since $Cl_2$ is a stronger oxidizing agent than $HgCl_2$, it will be attacked first by any $SnCl_2$ added. Therefore, it is desirable to remove any large excess of $Cl_2$ by boiling, and to add sufficient $SnCl_2$ to produce a test for Hg after the remaining $Cl_2$ has been reduced.

(4) The Cu wire test for Hg is unusually characteristic, but it is a little slow in developing if the concentration of the $HgCl_2$ is low. The test is occasionally missed because it is stopped too quickly. For small amounts of mercury it may be necessary to let the reaction continue for 3–5 minutes to get positive results.

**Lead. Separation and Identification.** Transfer the nitric acid solution (clear solution from HgS) to a crucible, add 2 drops of conc. $H_2SO_4$, evaporate at the hood over an open flame until dense, white, choking fumes of $SO_3$ are first definitely recognized. Let cool, add 20 drops of water, swirl, and rinse into a small beaker. Let stand a moment; then look for a fine white precipitate of $PbSO_4$. If no precipitate forms, lead is absent; if a precipitate is obtained, centrifuge and wash, setting aside the clear solution to be tested later for Bi, Cu, and Cd, and apply confirmatory tests on the precipitate to identify Pb as follows: (1) After washing the precipitate thoroughly, add a drop of KI to the precipitate looking for a bright yellow precipitate of $PbI_2$.

(2) Add 5 drops of 3 $N$ $NH_4C_2H_3O_2$ to dissolve the precipitate, centrifuge if necessary, and to the clear solution add 1–2 drops of $K_2Cr_2O_7$ solution, looking for a bright yellow precipitate of $PbCrO_4$.

*Explanatory Notes.* (1) Since $PbSO_4$ is appreciably soluble in $HNO_3$ and the solution contains a moderate amount of this reagent, it is necessary to remove the $HNO_3$ before $PbSO_4$ will precipitate effectively.

(2) The appearance of fumes of $SO_3$ may be taken to indicate the removal of $HNO_3$ since the $H_2SO_4$ does not decompose readily until a temperature of 160°–180° is reached, whereas $HNO_3$ boils out at 120°–130°. The $SO_3$ fumes are identified by their white appearance and choking effect as contrasted with the sour taste of the $HNO_3$ fumes.

(3) A coarse, granular precipitate, formed in the concentrated $H_2SO_4$ solution after the $HNO_3$ is removed, does not indicate Pb. Both $Bi_2(SO_4)_3$ and $CuSO_4$ (grayish white) are much less soluble in conc. $H_2SO_4$ than in dilute $H_2SO_4$ and may precipitate at this point. These salts dissolve fairly readily in water, however; hence, after diluting the solution with water, let it stand 1–2 minutes for these soluble sulfates to dissolve before looking for the finely divided white precipitate on which to apply a confirmatory test for Pb.

(4) Sufficient $H_2SO_4$ must be used so that after dilution the solution will be 2–3 $N$ with $H_2SO_4$. Since conc. $H_2SO_4$ is 35 $N$, if 2 drops are added and not over 0.5 drop is lost by decomposition and by formation of sulfates of the metals, approximately 1.5 drops are left to establish the acidity of the solution. This amount of acid, after dilution to 20 drops, would make the solution 2.6 $N$ with respect to $H_2SO_4$. This concentration of $H_2SO_4$ is in the range which produces effective repression of solubility of $PbSO_4$ and at the same time prevents hydrolysis of $Bi_2(SO_4)_3$ with precipitation of the white basic salt.

(5) In using the KI test for Pb it is necessary to wash the $PbSO_4$ sufficiently to remove the excess of $SO_4^{--}$ as well as any significant amount of $Bi^{+3}$ and $Cu^{++}$. $PbSO_4$ is less soluble in water than $PbI_2$; therefore the conversion of $PbSO_4$ into $PbI_2$ depends on repression of solubility of $PbI_2$ by common ion effect without appreciable decrease in solubility of $PbSO_4$ by excess of $SO_4^{--}$. With $Bi^{+3}$ or $Cu^{++}$ present, color effects may be obtained due to $BiI_3$ (black), BiOI (red) or $CuI + I_2$ (brown) that interfere with the identification of Pb.

(6) The solubility of $PbSO_4$ in $NH_4C_2H_3O_2$ depends on the formation of a complex ion, $Pb(C_2H_3O_2)_3^-$, whose ionization is kept very low by the high concentration of $C_2H_3O_2^-$ used. If too dilute a solution of $NH_4C_2H_3O_2$ is used, the $PbSO_4$ does not dissolve effectively and the test for Pb may be unsatisfactory. Further, since the concentration of $Pb^{++}$ in the $NH_4C_2H_3O_2$ solution is very low, only the formation of compounds of extremely low solubility, such as $PbCrO_4$, will succeed as an effective test for Pb. The use of

$I^-$ or $SO_4^{--}$ to test for $Pb^{++}$ will fail, although in the latter case sufficient $H_2SO_4$ added to convert the excess of $C_2H_3O_2^-$ to $HC_2H_3O_2$ will bring about precipitation of $PbSO_4$.

**Bismuth. Separation and Identification.** To the filtrate from the precipitated $PbSO_4$ add $NH_4OH$, 2–3 drops at a time, with shaking, until the thoroughly mixed solution has a fairly strong odor of $NH_3$. A white, flocculent precipitate, $Bi(OH)_3$, indicates Bi. Cu and Cd form complex ammonia ions with excess of $NH_4OH$ remaining in solution. Centrifuge, wash, set aside the clear solution to test for Cu and Cd, and examine the precipitate for Bi. Add 5 drops of warm HCl to the precipitate, dissolving the $Bi(OH)_3$, and add 1–2 drops of KI solution to this solution. A straw or tan color may be due to $BiI_4^-$. If no color develops, Bi is absent; if a tan color does appear, add 1 drop of $SnCl_2$ solution to destroy any color due to $I_2$ (reduction to colorless $I^-$). If the color disappears, Bi is absent; if the color persists, Bi is present. Another confirmatory test for Bi is carried out as follows: To 1–2 drops of $SnCl_2$ solution add NaOH in small amounts, with shaking, until the precipitate of $Sn(OH)_2$ largely dissolves in excess of the reagent. Pour the solution over the precipitate of $Bi(OH)_3$. A black stain (reduction of $Bi(OH)_3$ to Bi°) indicates Bi. A third confirmatory test consists in dissolving the $Bi(OH)_3$ in 5 drops of 5 *N* HCl, evaporating to 1 drop and adding to this 15–20 drops of water. A white, flocculent or granular precipitate, BiOCl (formed by hydrolysis of $BiCl_3$), indicates Bi.

*Explanatory Notes.* (1) In precipitating $Bi(OH)_3$ with $NH_4OH$, care must be taken to mix the reagent thoroughly with the solution in order that an upper alkaline layer on a lower acid layer be not mistaken for a solution containing excess of $NH_4OH$. Since 1 drop of concentrated $H_2SO_4$ is equivalent to 7 drops of 5 *N* $NH_4OH$, it is obvious that 12–15 drops or more of $NH_4OH$ may be used in this reaction, while if much more than 2 drops of the concentrated $H_2SO_4$ were used in precipitating $PbSO_4$, the amount of $NH_4OH$ required is correspondingly increased.

(2) If much Cu is present, a slight precipitate of $Bi(OH)_3$ may be masked by a deep blue color of the $Cu(NH_3)_4^{++}$. In case of doubt, centrifuge, wash, and try the confirmatory tests for Bi.

(3) In the KI test for Bi, a little $Cu^{++}$ or $HNO_3$, not completely removed in the earlier procedure, may produce a tan color due to $I_2$, very much like that of $BiI_4^-$. However, the $I_2$ is easily reduced to colorless $I^-$ by a little $SnCl_2$, whereas $BiI_4^-$ is not affected by this reagent.

(4) $NaSn(OH)_3$ will reduce many other metals, Hg, Pb, Cu, etc., to the free state; hence this test for Bi depends to a distinct extent on the accuracy of the earlier separations. The $NaSn(OH)_3$ test for Bi may also be made after the KI test by adding 1–2 drops of $SnCl_2$ and then making strongly alkaline with NaOH. The $BiI_4^-$ is thus reduced forming a black, flocculent precipitate of Bi° in the solution.

(5) In the precipitation of BiOCl it is necessary to remove nearly all the free HCl before diluting the solution with water; otherwise the sensitivity of the test is interfered with seriously.

**Copper and Cadmium. Separation and Identification.** Divide the solution after $Bi(OH)_3$ into two parts, using one for confirmatory tests for Cu and the other to test for Cd.

**Copper.** The deep blue color of $Cu(NH_3)_4^{++}$ is an excellent test for Cu, of moderate delicacy. A slightly more delicate test is carried out as follows: Add acetic acid in slight excess to the ammoniacal solution; then add a few drops of $K_4Fe(CN)_6$. A reddish brown, gelatinous precipitate of $Cu_2Fe(CN)_6$ indicates Cu.

**Cadmium.** In the absence of Cu, pass in $H_2S$ and obtain a yellow or greenish yellow precipitate of CdS if Cd is present. If Cu is present, add 0.5 *N* NaCN solution, 1–2 drops at a time, until the blue color disappears; then add 1–2 drops excess and pass in $H_2S$, looking for the yellow or greenish yellow precipitate of CdS.

Another procedure in testing for Cd when Cu is present: Add 5 *N* $H_2SO_4$, 1 drop at a time, until the solution is moderately acid (1–2 drops excess). Next add about 50 mg. of powdered Fe, let stand 4–5 minutes with frequent shaking, and then centrifuge. Discard the precipitate of Cu and Fe. Nearly neutralize the clear solution with $NH_4OH$ and pass in $H_2S$. A bright yellow precipitate of CdS indicates Cd. A brown to black precipitate indicates incomplete removal of copper or FeS due to too low acidity.

A third procedure in testing for Cd when Cu is present: Acidify the solution with HCl, adding 1 drop excess, then saturate the solution with solid NaCl, and pass in $H_2S$. CuS precipitates, but Cd stays in solution as $CdCl_4^{--}$. Centrifuge, test for completeness of precipitation of CuS, then add slight excess of $NH_4OH$, and pass in $H_2S$. A yellow precipitate of CdS indicates Cd.

A fourth test for cadmium, not involving precipitation of CdS, uses an organic reagent, $\alpha,\alpha'$-dipyridyl, in the presence of $Fe^{++}$ and $I^-$, to form a red, crystalline precipitate of ferrous $\alpha,\alpha'$-dipyridyl cadmium iodide, Fe (dipyridyl)$_3$ $CdI_4$. To 2–3 drops of the ammoniacal solution add a drop of the dipyridyl reagent. This test may be applied in the presence of copper.

*Explanatory Notes.* (1) The only ordinary interference with the blue color of the solution as a test for Cu occurs when Ni is inadvertently carried down in Group II. $Ni(NH_3)_6^{++}$ is also blue, although a different shade from $Cu(NH_3)_4^{++}$.

(2) In the $K_4Fe(CN)_6$ test for Cu the solution must be acid in order to obtain effective precipitation of $Cu_2Fe(CN)_6$. If the amount of Cu is very small, the solution may turn pink without immediate coagulation of the precipitate. If Cd is present, a white precipitate of $Cd_2Fe(CN)_6$ will form, but the color of the Cu precipitate will still be visible.

(3) In the final test for Cd with $H_2S$, a black precipitate is obtained occasionally where the yellow CdS is expected. Through faulty manipulation it is possible for any of the metals of Group I or of the copper division of Group II to slip through to this point. If such a precipitate is obtained, it may be examined for Cd as follows: Centrifuge, wash thoroughly, transfer to a small crucible, pour off any excess of water, then add 5–10 drops of 5 *N* $H_2SO_4$, boil for about 1 minute and centrifuge. CdS dissolves, whereas the other sulfides do not. Discard the precipitate. Nearly neutralize the clear solution with $NH_4OH$ and pass in $H_2S$, looking for the yellow precipitate of CdS.

## REPORTING COPPER DIVISION IONS OF GROUP II IN AN UNKNOWN SOLUTION

**Lead.** As in Group I, lead forms the two common ions—lead ion, $Pb^{++}$, and plumbite ion, $Pb(OH)_3^-$. To distinguish between these, note the action of the original solution on litmus paper. If the solution is neutral or acid, report $Pb^{++}$; if strongly alkaline, report $Pb(OH)_3^-$.

**Mercury.** Since mercurous chloride is fairly insoluble, while mercuric chloride is moderately soluble, any mercury found in the filtrate from Group I will normally be in the mercuric form. Mercury forms several complex ions, such as $HgI_4^{--}$ and $Hg(CN)_4^{--}$, but since only the two types of complex ions—complex ammonia ions and anions of amphoteric acids—are easily recognized, and mercury does not form either of these, it will be given out only in the form of mercuric ion, $Hg^{++}$ or $HgCl_4^{--}$ in HCl solutions. It should be noted that if $Hg_2^{++}$ is present in the original solution, at least a trace of $Hg^{++}$ will be there, due to atmospheric oxidation of the lower valence form. ?

**Bismuth.** As in the case of mercury, complex ions such as $BiCl_4^-$ and $BiI_4^-$ are known, but bismuth does not form a complex ammonia ion, nor is the hydroxide amphoteric; further, in solution, bismuth has only the one valence; therefore, it is given out only in the form of bismuth ion, $Bi^{+3}$ (or $BiCl_4^-$ in HCl solutions).

**Copper.** Copper forms two series of salts, cuprous and cupric, but the former in solution are oxidized fairly readily by atmospheric oxygen and there is no convenient test to identify them in the presence of cupric salts; therefore, only bivalent copper compounds are put in the solution. One exception to this is found in the case of dispensing copper along with stannous ion. $Sn^{++}$ Since the strong reducing agent would reduce any $Cu^{++}$ to $Cu^+$, the copper for such a solution would be present as $Cu^+$. The common ions of copper are cupric ion, $Cu^{++}$, found in slightly or strongly acid solution; and cupric ammonia ion, $Cu(NH_3)_4^{++}$, found in alkaline solution having a strong odor of $NH_3$. Copper forms a number of other less common complex ions with cyanide ion and certain of the organic acid radicals, but these are not included for identification in the present course.

**Cadmium.** The two common ions of cadmium are $Cd^{++}$ and $Cd(NH_3)_4{}^{++}$. Test the original solution with litmus paper. If neutral or acid, report $Cd^{++}$; if alkaline, with odor of $NH_3$, report $Cd(NH_3)_4{}^{++}$. Cadmium forms some other complex ions, such as $CdCl_4{}^{--}$ and $CdI_4{}^{--}$, but these are not included in the present work.

## COPPER DIVISION OF GROUP II IN RELATION TO OTHER GROUPS

The behavior of the copper division metals while precipitating Group I metals has already been mentioned (p. 95). The presence of small amounts of copper division metals in Group I produces no significant irregularity, although $HgCl_2$ in the solution which is being tested for Pb will give a red precipitate, $HgI_2$, with KI, soluble in excess of the reagent.

Attention has also been called to the fact that, when Group I is incompletely precipitated, any of the Group I metals may appear in Group II. Since lead and mercury are already provided for in the scheme for the copper division, the only complication to be feared is the presence of silver in the second group. This metal would precipitate as the sulfide, which is soluble in hot $HNO_3$, and therefore the silver would be found in the clear solution after removing HgS. It may be detected at this point by adding a little HCl, centrifuging, dissolving in $NH_4OH$, and reprecipitating with $HNO_3$. If not removed in this way, it may form a black precipitate of $Ag_2S$ where CdS is expected.

The presence of later group metals may require modification of the usual procedure for preparing the solution for the precipitation of Group II. Thus, $MnO_4{}^-$ and $Cr_2O_7{}^{--}$ must be reduced before treating with $H_2S$ (see p. 120). If the solution contains a large amount of $Fe^{+++}$, this precipitates as $Fe(OH)_3$ when the solution is neutralized with $NH_4OH$. Care must be taken to see that this dissolves fully when the solution is made 0.25 *N* with HCl. If the solution contains a large amount of $Zn^{++}$ and $H_2S$ is passed in for some time, there may be slow precipitation of ZnS even though the solution is 0.25 *N* with HCl.

The presence of small amounts of later group metals in the Group II precipitate may cause some irregularities in the analysis of this precipitate. In the precipitation of $Bi(OH)_3$, the Group III hydroxides, $Al(OH)_3$, $Cr(OH)_3$, and $Fe(OH)_3$ may form. $Fe(OH)_3$ dissolves in HCl and would oxidize some KI to $I_2$, but this would be reduced again by the $SnCl_2$ finally added. Occasionally a small amount of $Fe(OH)_3$ is overlooked in the $Cu(NH_3)_4{}^{++}$ solution and forms $Fe_2S_3$, black, when the solution is tested for Cd. If Ni is carried down in Group II, it is carried through the separations of the copper division, forming a blue nickel ammonia ion, $Ni(NH_3)_6{}^{++}$, along with $Cu(NH_3)_4{}^{++}$ and $Cd(NH_3)_4{}^{++}$. The color is not the same as that of

$Cu(NH_3)_4^{++}$, but might be mistaken for the latter by a careless analyst. Nickel also may be responsible for a black precipitate in the test for Cd with $H_2S$.

Small amounts of Ba or Sr carried down in Group II may show up as sulfates where $PbSO_4$ is expected, but will not interfere with the confirmatory tests for Pb.

Pb and Cd are the metals most frequently carried past Group II, because of too high acidity, excessive amounts of $Cl^-$, or failure to test properly for completeness of precipitation of the group. Pb may precipitate in part as $Pb(OH)_2$, white, in Group III, or it may carry over into Group IV, precipitating there as PbS, black. Cd in the clear solution from Group II precipitates in Group IV.

## REACTIONS OF COPPER DIVISION OF GROUP II METALS IN THE SYSTEMATIC ANALYSIS OF A SOLUTION

**Mercury**

*In precipitating Group I*

$$Hg^{++} + 4Cl^- = HgCl_4^{--}$$

*Adjusting the acidity for precipitation of Group II*

$$HgCl_4^{--} + 2NH_3 = \underline{HgNH_2Cl} + NH_4^+ + 3Cl^-$$
$$\underline{HgNH_2Cl} + 2H_3O^+ + 3Cl^- = HgCl_4^{--} + NH_4^+ + 2H_2O$$

*In Group II*

$$HgCl_4^{--} + H_2S + 2H_2O = \underline{HgS} + 2H_3O^+ + 4Cl^-$$
$$3\underline{HgS} + 12Cl^- + 2NO_3^- + 8H_3O^+ = 3HgCl_4^{--} + \underline{3S} + \overline{2NO} + 12H_2O$$

1. $2HgCl_4^{--} + SnCl_4^{--} = \underline{Hg_2Cl_2} + SnCl_6^{--} + 4Cl^-$

   $\underline{Hg_2Cl_2} + SnCl_4^{--} = \underline{2Hg} + SnCl_6^{--}$

2. $HgCl_4^{--} + Cu = \underline{Hg} + 4Cl^- + Cu^{++}$

**Lead**

*Acidifying an alkaline solution with $HNO_3$*

$$Pb(OH)_3^- + 3H_3O^+ = Pb^{++} + 6H_2O$$

*In precipitating Group I*

$$Pb^{++} + Cl^- = PbCl^+$$

*Adjusting the acidity for precipitation of Group II*

$$PbCl^+ + NH_4OH = \underline{PbOHCl} + NH_4^+$$
$$\underline{PbOHCl} + H_3O^+ = PbCl^+ + 2H_2O$$

*In Group II*

$PbCl^+ + H_2S + 2H_2O = \underline{PbS} + 2H_3O^+ + Cl^-$
$\underline{3PbS} + 2NO_3^- + 8H_3O^+ = 3Pb^{++} + 2NO + \underline{3S} + 12H_2O$
$Pb^{++} + HSO_4^- + H_2O = \underline{PbSO_4} + H_3O^+$
1. $\underline{PbSO_4} + 2I^- = \underline{PbI_2} + SO_4^{--}$
2. $\underline{PbSO_4} + 3C_2H_3O_2^- = Pb(C_2H_3O_2)_3^- + SO_4^{--}$
   $2Pb(C_2H_3O_2)_3^- + Cr_2O_7^{--} + H_2O = \underline{2PbCrO_4} + 2HC_2H_3O_2 + 4C_2H_3O_2^-$

**Bismuth**

*In precipitating Group I*

$Bi^{+++} + 4Cl^- = BiCl_4^-$

*Adjusting the acidity for precipitation of Group II*

$BiCl_4^- + 3NH_4OH = \underline{Bi(OH)_3} + 3NH_4^+ + 4Cl^-$
$\underline{Bi(OH)_3} + H_3O^+ + Cl^- = \underline{BiOCl} + 3H_2O$
$\underline{BiOCl} + 2H_3O^+ + 3Cl^- = BiCl_4^- + 3H_2O$

*In Group II*

$\underline{2BiOCl} + 3H_2S = \underline{Bi_2S_3} + 2H_3O^+ + 2Cl^-$
$2BiCl_4^- + 3H_2S + 6H_2O = \underline{Bi_2S_3} + 6H_3O^+ + 8Cl^-$
$\underline{Bi_2S_3} + 2NO_3^- + 8H_3O^+ = 2Bi^{+++} + \underline{3S} + 2NO + 12H_2O$
$Bi^{+++} + 3NH_4OH = \underline{Bi(OH)_3} + 3NH_4^+$
1. $\underline{Bi(OH)_3} + 3H_3O^+ + 4Cl^- = BiCl_4^- + 6H_2O$
   a. $BiCl_4^- + 4I^- = BiI_4^- + 4Cl^-$
   b. $BiCl_4^- + 3H_2O = \underline{BiOCl} + 3Cl^- + 2H_3O^+$
2. $\underline{2Bi(OH)_3} + 3Sn(OH)_3^- = \underline{2Bi} + 3Sn(OH)_5^-$

**Copper**

*Acidifying an alkaline solution with $HNO_3$*

$Cu(NH_3)_4^{++} + 4H_3O^+ = Cu^{++} + 4NH_4^+ + 4H_2O$

*Adjusting the acidity for precipitation of Group II*

$Cu^{++} + 2NH_4OH = \underline{Cu(OH)_2} + 2NH_4^+$
$\underline{Cu(OH)_2} + 2H_3O^+ = Cu^{++} + 4H_2O$

*In Group II*

$Cu^{++} + H_2S + 2H_2O = \underline{CuS} + 2H_3O^+$
$\underline{3CuS} + 2NO_3^- + 8H_3O^+ = 3Cu^{++} + 2NO + \underline{3S} + 12H_2O$
$Cu^{++} + 4NH_3 = Cu(NH_3)_4^{++}$
$Cu(NH_3)_4^{++} + 4HC_2H_3O_2 = Cu^{++} + 4NH_4^+ + 4C_2H_3O_2^-$
$2Cu^{++} + Fe(CN)_6^{-4} = \underline{Cu_2Fe(CN)_6}$

*Preventing the interference of Cu in test for Cd*

1. $2Cu(NH_3)_4^{++} + 8CN^- = 2Cu(CN)_3^{--} + (CN)_2 + 8NH_3$
   $2Cu(NH_3)_4^{++} + 7CN^- + H_2O = 2Cu(CN)_3^{--} + CNO^- + 6NH_3 + 2NH_4^+$
2. $Cu(NH_3)_4^{++} + 4H_3O^+ = Cu^{++} + 4NH_4^+ + 4H_2O$
   $Cu^{++} + \overline{Fe} = \underline{Cu} + Fe^{++}$
3. $Cu(NH_3)_4^{++} + 4H_3O^+ = Cu^{++} + 4NH_4^+ + 4H_2O$
   $Cu^{++} + Cl^-$ (satd. NaCl) $= CuCl^+$
   $CuCl^+ + H_2S + 2H_2O = \underline{CuS} + 2H_3O^+ + Cl^-$

## Cadmium

*Acidifying an alkaline solution with $HNO_3$*

$Cd(NH_3)_4^{++} + 4H_3O^+ = Cd^{++} + 4NH_3 + 4H_2O$

*In precipitating Group I*

$Cd^{++} + 2Cl^- = CdCl_2$

*Adjusting the acidity for precipitation of Group II*

$CdCl_2 + 2NH_4OH = \underline{Cd(OH)_2} + 2NH_4^+ + 2Cl^-$
$\underline{Cd(OH)_2} + 2Cl^- + 2H_3O^+ = CdCl_2 + 4H_2O$

*In Group II*

$CdCl_2 + H_2S + H_2O = \underline{CdS} + 2H_3O^+ + 2Cl^-$
$\underline{3CdS} + 2NO_3^- + 8H_3O^+ = 3Cd^{++} + \underline{3S} + 8H_2O$
$Cd^{++} + 4NH_3 = Cd(NH_3)_4^{++}$

*In test for Cu*

$Cd(NH_3)_4^{++} + 4HC_2H_3O_2 = Cd^{++} + 4NH_4^+ + 4C_2H_3O_2^-$
$2Cd^{++} + Fe(CN)_6^{-4} = \underline{Cd_2Fe(CN)_6}$

*Final tests for Cd*

(Cu absent)
$Cd(NH_3)_4^{++} + H_2S = \underline{CdS} + 2NH_4^+ + 2NH_3$
(Cu present)

1. $Cd(NH_3)_4^{++} + 4CN^- = Cd(CN)_4^{--} + 4NH_3$
   $Cd(CN)_4^{--} + H_2S + 2NH_3 = \underline{CdS} + 4CN^- + 2NH_4^+$
2. $Cd(NH_3)_4^{++} + 4H_3O^+ = Cd^{++} + 4NH_4^+ + 4H_2O$
   $Cd^{++} + Fe =$ no reaction
   $Cd^{++} + H_2S + 2H_2O = \underline{CdS} + 2H_3O^+$
3. $Cd(NH_3)_4^{++} + 4H_3O^+ = Cd^{++} + 4NH_3 + 4H_2O$
   $Cd^{++} + 4Cl^-$ (satd. NaCl) $= CdCl_4^{--}$
   $CdCl_4^{--} + H_2S =$ no reaction
   $CdCl_4^{--} + H_2S + 2NH_3 = \underline{CdS} + 2NH_4^+ + 4Cl^-$

## *SUMMARY AND REVIEW*

### *Group II, Cu-Division*

Precipitation of the Group

1. Adjustment of acidity
   *A*. How adjusted?
   (Neutralize, then add 2 drops of 5 *N* HCl and dilute to 40 drops.) Procedure in case a ppt. remains?
   *B*. Why adjusted?
   (*a*) Soln. less than 0.25 *N*
   (*b*) Soln. greater than 0.25 *N*
2. Actual pptn.
   *A*. Flask
   *B*. Heat to boiling point
   (*a*) Increase speed of reaction
   (*b*) Resulting ppt. flocculent and easily filtered
   *C*. Introduction of $H_2S$
   (*a*) Colors of Group II sulfides
   (*b*) Danger of incomplete conversion of Hg to HgS
   *D*. Filtration
   *E*. Testing filtrate for completeness of pptn. (Dilute with equal volume of water, heat and pass in $H_2S$ again.)
   (*a*) Why dilute?
   (*b*) How test second filtrate?
3. Washing ppt.
   *A*. Why use $H_2S$ water first?
   *B*. Why use $NH_4NO_3$?
   *C*. Why use *hot* $NH_4NO_3$ soln.?
   *D*. Why necessary to remove $Cl^-$?

Analysis of the Precipitate

1. Dissolving ppt.
   *A*. Why use 2–2.5 *N* $HNO_3$?
   *B*. Why avoid long boiling?
   *C*. Nature of residue
   *D*. Nature of dissolving process ($S^{--} + HNO_3 \rightarrow S + NO + H_2O$)
   *E*. Why HgS does not dissolve?
2. Testing residue for Hg
   *A*. Boiling with aqua regia
   Nature of reaction $Cl_2 + S^{--} \rightarrow Cl^- + S$, $Hg^{++} + 4Cl^- = HgCl_4^{--}$
   *B*. Removal of excess $Cl_2$
   *C*. Testing with (*a*) $SnCl_2$ (*b*) Cu
3. Treatment of filtrate
   *A*. Removal and detection of Pb
   (*a*) Evaporation to fumes of $SO_3$. Why?
   (*b*) Dissolving $PbSO_4$ in $NH_4C_2H_3O_2$
   (1) Nature of reaction
   Why $HC_2H_3O_2$ not effective?
   (*c*) Testing for Pb
   (1) Why KI test fails in acetate solution?
   (2) Interference of Bi with $K_2Cr_2O_7$ test

*B*. Removal and detection of Bi
  (*a*) Nature and visibility of ppt.
  (*b*) Testing for Bi
    (1) KI test and interference of Fe or Cu
    (2) $NaSn(OH)_3$ test
  (*c*) Loss of Bi particularly when removing Pb
*C*. Detection of Cu
  (*a*) Reliability of ammonia test
  (*b*) Ferrocyanide test
*D*. Detection of Cd
  (*a*) Cu absent
  (*b*) Cu present
    (1) Action of NaCN
    (2) Action of Fe
    (3) Action of NaCl
  (*c*) Procedure if a black ppt. obtained
    (1) Possible causes
    (2) Method for sepn. and detection of Cd

## LABORATORY EXERCISES

1. Known solutions containing Group I and lead and mercury of Group II.

(*1*) $Ag^+$, $Pb^{++}(l)$, $Hg^{++}$
(*2*) $Hg_2^{++}$, $Pb^{++}(s)$, $Hg^{++}$
(*3*) $Pb(OH)_3^-(l)$

These solutions contain the following amounts of substance per liter of solution: (*1*) 4 g. $AgNO_3$, 16 g. $Pb(NO_3)_2$, 4 g. $Hg(NO_3)_2$, and 50 ml. of 5 *N* $HNO_3$; (*2*) 3.5 g. $Hg_2(NO_3)_2 \cdot 2H_2O$, 1.6 g. $Pb(NO_3)_2$, 4 g. $Hg(NO_3)_2$, and 150 ml. of 5 *N* $HNO_3$; (*3*) 16 g. $Pb(NO_3)_2$ and 100 g. NaOH.

Use 15 drops of each solution. Precipitate Group I, centrifuge, and wash. Analyze the precipitate for Group I and use the clear solution to precipitate Group II, testing any precipitate obtained for lead and mercury.

*Solution 1*. Lead should be found in both groups, mercury only in Group II.

*Solution 2*. Mercury should be found in both groups, lead only in Group II.

*Solution 3*. (*a*) Make the solution slightly acid with $HNO_3$; then cool thoroughly before adding HCl to precipitate Group I. A white precipitate of $Pb(OH)_2$ forms as the $HNO_3$ is added, dissolving readily in excess of the acid.

(*b*) Due to other ions present in this solution precipitation of lead in Group I will be less complete than in the first of these known solutions. This leaves more lead to precipitate in Group II so the test there should be fairly strong.

2. Known solutions containing Group I and the copper division of Group II.

(*1*) $Bi^{+3}$, $Cd^{++}$
(*2*) $Ag^+$, $Hg^{++}(s)$, $Bi^{+3}(s)$, $Cu^{++}$
(*3*) $Ag(NH_3)_2^+$, $Cu(NH_3)_4^{++}$, $Cd(NH_3)_4^{++}$

These solutions contain the following amounts of substance per liter of solution: (*1*) 6 g. $Bi(NO_3)_3 \cdot 5H_2O$, 7 g. $Cd(NO_3)_2 \cdot 4H_2O$, and 100 ml. of 5 *N* $HNO_3$; (*2*) 4 g. $AgNO_3$, 1.6 g. $Hg(NO_3)_2$, 2.3 g. $Bi(NO_3)_3 \cdot 5H_2O$, 10 g. $Cu(NO_3)_2 \cdot 3H_2O$, and 100 ml. of 5 *N* $HNO_3$; (*3*) 4 g. $AgNO_3$, 10 g. $Cu(NO_3)_2 \cdot 3H_2O$, 7 g. $Cd(NO_3)_2 \cdot 4H_2O$, 80 g. $NH_4NO_3$, and 200 ml. of 5 *N* $NH_4OH$.

Use 15 drops of each solution. Test for the presence of Group I. If present, precipitate with excess HCl, centrifuge, examine the precipitate for Group I metals and use the clear solution to precipitate Group II and test for the metals of the copper division of Group II.

*Solution 1.* (*a*) The addition of a drop of HCl (as in testing for the presence of Group I) may give a white precipitate of BiOCl. Upon adding 2 drops or more of the 5 *N* HCl, this precipitate will dissolve.

(*b*) When the solution is made 0.25 *N* with HCl for the precipitation of Group II, a white precipitate of BiOCl may still persist. It is not necessary to dissolve this precipitate before passing in $H_2S$.

(*c*) When dissolving the sulfides in $HNO_3$, the black residue of S° may be mistaken for HgS. Centrifuge and try the confirmatory test for Hg on this residue.

(*d*) After evaporating to fumes of $SO_3$ in the procedure for separation from Pb, a coarse granular residue of $Bi_2(SO_4)_3$ may form. This dissolves readily when the cooled solution is treated with water and thus should not be mistaken for $PbSO_4$.

*Solution 2.* (*a*) Be sure to obtain a satisfactory test for Hg in Group II.

(*b*) When $NH_4OH$ is added to separate Bi from Cu, the precipitate of $Bi(OH)_3$ may be somewhat masked by the deep blue of the $Cu(NH_3)_4^{++}$ in solution. Centrifuge, wash, and apply the test for Bi to the residue.

(*c*) In trying the final test for Cd a slight yellow color may develop (due to action of $H_2S$ on $(CN)_2$ in the solution) but no precipitate should form. A black precipitate indicates unsatisfactory earlier separations.

*Solution 3.* (*a*) If this solution is treated carefully with $HNO_3$ a precipitate will form near the neutral point, dissolving readily when excess of $HNO_3$ is added.

(*b*) In Group II, after adding excess of $NH_4OH$ in the regular separations, divide the solution into three or four parts and try several of the alternative methods of identifying Cd when Cu is present.

3. Prepare a precipitate of $PbSO_4$. Centrifuge, wash, and treat with 10 drops of 3 *N* $NH_4C_2H_3O_2$. Divide the solution into 2 parts, adding a drop of KI solution to one portion and $K_2Cr_2O_7$ solution to the other. Explain any difference in results observed.

4. Prepare a precipitate of CuS. Centrifuge, wash, and transfer to a small crucible. Add 10–15 drops of 2.5 *N* $HNO_3$, heat to boiling and hold a piece of filter paper moistened with lead acetate solution in the fumes. Why is no black stain of PbS obtained on the test paper?

5. Effect of $Hg(NO_3)_2$ on the precipitation of $PbCl_2$. In one test tube place 2 drops of $Pb(NO_3)_2$ solution and 5 drops of $Hg(NO_3)_2$ solution; in another, place 2 drops of $Pb(NO_3)_2$ solution and 5 drops of water. Add a drop of HCl to each, noting the difference in readiness of precipitation of $PbCl_2$. Next add excess of HCl in both cases, let the precipitate settle, and judge whether there is a significant difference in the amount of precipitate in the two cases. Explain the results obtained.

6. Behavior of Ag in Group II. (Sometimes Ag is carried past Group I in small amounts.) To 1 drop of $AgNO_3$ solution add 3–5 drops of $H_2O$ and 1 drop of reagent $HNO_3$. Warm and pass in $H_2S$. Centrifuge, wash, dissolve in 2.5 *N* $HNO_3$, and carry the resulting solution through the processes of evaporating with $H_2SO_4$, diluting with water, making ammoniacal, and treating with $H_2S$. Note that the Ag might be precipitated with HCl after the sulfides are dissolved in $HNO_3$.

7. To 5 drops of $Cu(NO_3)_2$ solution add 1 *N* $NH_4OH$, 1 drop at a time, with shaking, until a clear, deep blue solution is obtained. Note the precipitation of $Cu(OH)_2$ as an intermediate reaction. To the ammoniacal solution add 1 *N* $HNO_3$, 1 drop at a time, with shaking, until a clear, light blue solution is obtained. Note the precipitation of $Cu(OH)_2$ as an intermediate reaction. Explain.

## EQUILIBRIUM PROBLEMS IN GROUP II

I. Calculate the concentration of $S^{--}$ for the precipitation of Group II. $K_{H_2S} = 1 \times 10^{-7}$; $K_{HS^-} = 1 \times 10^{-15}$. Assume that the solution is 0.25 *M* with HCl and 0.1 *M* with $H_2S$.

Since $H_2S$ and $HS^-$ are very weak electrolytes, the amount of $H_3O^+$ supplied by them will be negligible as compared with that from the HCl; therefore $[H_3O^+] = 0.25$.

$$\frac{[H_3O^+] \times [HS^-]}{[H_2S]} = \frac{0.25[HS^-]}{0.1} = 1 \times 10^{-7}$$

$$[HS^-] = \frac{1 \times 10^{-7} \times 0.1}{0.25} = 4 \times 10^{-8}$$

$$\frac{[H_3O^+] \times [S^{--}]}{[HS^-]} = \frac{0.25[S^{--}]}{4 \times 10^{-8}} = 1 \times 10^{-15}$$

$$[S^{--}] = \frac{1 \times 10^{-15} \times 4 \times 10^{-8}}{0.25} = 1.6 \times 10^{-22}$$

It may be noted that, instead of solving this problem in two steps, the constants for $H_2S$ and $HS^-$ may be multiplied together to form a combined constant which eliminates $[HS^-]$.

$$\frac{[H_3O^+] \times [HS^-]}{[H_2S]} \times \frac{[H_3O^+] \times [S^{--}]}{[HS^-]} = \frac{[H_3O^+]^2 \times [S^{--}]}{[H_2S]} = 1 \times 10^{-7} \times 1 \times 10^{-15}$$

$$= 1 \times 10^{-22}$$

Then using this constant to solve the problem

$$\frac{[H_3O^+]^2 \times [S^{--}]}{[H_2S]} = \frac{(0.25)^2[S^{--}]}{0.1} = 1 \times 10^{-2}$$

$$[S^{--}] = \frac{1 \times 10^{-22} \times 0.1}{(0.25)^2} = 1.6 \times 10^{-22}$$

The combined constant is convenient to use when dealing with acid solutions in which the concentrations of $HS^-$ and $S^{--}$ are very small as compared with that of $H_2S$, but in alkaline solutions, where much of the $H_2S$ would be changed to $HS^-$ it is simpler to use the constants for $H_2S$ and $HS^-$ separately.

II. Calculate the concentration of $Cd^{++}$ that would remain in solution in the precipitation of Group II.

$$[S^{--}] = 1.6 \times 10^{-22}, \quad L_{CdS} = 5 \times 10^{-29}$$

$$[Cd^{++}] \times [S^{--}] = 5 \times 10^{-29}$$

$$[Cd^{++}] = \frac{5 \times 10^{-29}}{[S^{--}]} = \frac{5 \times 10^{-29}}{1.6 \times 10^{-22}} = 3 \times 10^{-7}$$

III. Calculate the distribution of Cd among the several forms, $Cd^{++}$, $CdCl^+$, and $CdCl_2$ at the beginning of Group II, assuming $K_{CdCl^+} = 0.04$ and $K_{CdCl_2} = 0.0061$, if $Cl^- = 0.5$.

$$\frac{[Cd^{++}] \times [Cl^-]}{[CdCl^+]} = 0.04 \qquad \frac{[Cd^{++}] \times [Cl^-]^2}{[CdCl_2]} = 0.0061$$

$$\frac{[Cd^{++}]}{[CdCl^+]} = \frac{0.04}{0.5} = \frac{0.08}{1} \qquad \frac{[Cd^{++}]}{[CdCl_2]} = \frac{0.0061}{(0.5)^2} = \frac{0.0244}{1}$$

This yields two proportions

$$[Cd^{++}]:[CdCl^+]::0.08:1$$

$$[Cd^{++}]:[CdCl_2]::0.0244:1$$

In order to combine these into a single proportion the numbers in the second proportion may each be multiplied by the fraction $\frac{0.08}{0.0244}$ so that $Cd^{++}$ will be represented by the same number in both.

$$[Cd^{++}]:[CdCl_2]::0.0244 \times \frac{0.08}{0.0244} : \frac{0.08}{0.0244}$$

$$[Cd^{++}]:[CdCl_2]::0.08:3.28$$

The combined proportion then becomes

$$[Cd^{++}]:[CdCl^+]:[CdCl_2]::0.08:1:3.28$$

From this it may be shown that less than 2% of the combined forms will be present as $Cd^{++}$.

IV. Calculate the total concentration of Bi that might be present in the filtrate from Group I if

$$[H_3O^+] = 0.5, \quad [Cl^-] = 0.37, \quad L_{Bi(OH)_2Cl} = 2.5 \times 10^{-31},$$

$$K_{BiCl_4^-} = 0.01, \quad \text{and} \quad K_W = 1 \times 10^{-14}$$

In the saturated solution $[Bi^{+++}] \times [OH^-]^2 \times [Cl^-] = 2.5 \times 10^{-31}$

$$[OH^-] = \frac{1 \times 10^{-14}}{[H_3O^+]} = \frac{1 \times 10^{-14}}{0.5} = 2 \times 10^{-14}$$

$$[Bi^{+++}] = \frac{2.5 \times 10^{-31}}{(2 \times 10^{-14})^2 \times 0.37} = 1.7 \times 10^{-3}$$

But

$$\frac{[Bi^{+++}] \times [Cl^-]^4}{[BiCl_4^-]} = 0.01$$

$$[BiCl_4^-] = \frac{1.7 \times 10^{-3} \times (0.5)^4}{0.01} = 1.06 \times 10^{-2}$$

$$\text{Total concn. of Bi} = [Bi^{+++}] + [BiCl_4^-] = 1.7 \times 10^{-3} + 1.06 \times 10^{-2}$$

$$= 1.23 \times 10^{-2}\ M$$

This value is small enough so that the separation of bismuth from Group I is a border-line case. If the amount of Bi present is rather large or if the amount of HCl added is too small to convert most of the Bi to $BiCl_4$, a precipitate of BiOCl will be obtained in Group I. This is easily demonstrated by an experiment.

*Expt.* To 5 drops of a test solution of $Bi(NO_3)_3$ add 15 drops of water and 1 drop of 5 *N* HCl. Shake to mix thoroughly and let stand a moment. Note that a distinct precipitate of BiOCl is formed. Next add 1 drop more of 5 *N* HCl, shake and let stand. The BiOCl slowly dissolves in the excess HCl. If the experiment is repeated using 2 drops of the HCl at the start, no precipitate will form.

V. Calculate the solubilities of CuS and of HgS in *M* $H_3O^+$, assuming no loss of $H_2S$ from the solution.

$$L_{CuS} = 1.2 \times 10^{-42}, \quad L_{HgS} = 1 \times 10^{-53}, \quad K_{1,2H_2S} = 1 \times 10^{-22}$$

The net reactions would be

$$\underline{CuS} + 2H_3O^+ = Cu^{++} + H_2S + 2H_2O$$

$$\underline{HgS} + 2H_3O^+ = Hg^{++} + H_2S + 2H_2O$$

In each case the concentration of $H_2S$ = $[Cu^{++}]$ or $[Hg^{++}]$. For CuS

$$[Cu^{++}] \times [S^{--}] = 1.2 \times 10^{-42}$$

$$\frac{[H_3O^+]^2 \times [S^{--}]}{[H_2S]} = 1 \times 10^{-22}$$

From these equations two expressions for $[S^{--}]$ may be obtained and placed equal to each other.

$$[S^{--}] = \frac{1.2 \times 10^{-42}}{[Cu^{++}]} = \frac{1 \times 10^{-22}[H_2S]}{(1)^2}$$

Since $[H_2S] = [Cu^{++}]$, the latter may be used in place of $[H_2S]$. Or substituting and rearranging:

$$\frac{1.2 \times 10^{-42}}{1 \times 10^{-22}} = [Cu^{++}]^2 = 1.2 \times 10^{-20}$$

$$[Cu^{++}] = 1.1 \times 10^{-10}$$

For HgS the final equation becomes

$$\frac{1 \times 10^{-53}}{1 \times 10^{-22}} = [Hg^{++}]^2$$

$$[Hg^{++}] = 3.2 \times 10^{-16}$$

These concentrations are so low that CuS and HgS do not dissolve readily in $H_3O^+$ even on heating, thus allowing any $H_2S$ to escape from the solution. When an oxidizing agent such as $NO_3^-$ is also present in the hot solution, the $H_2S$ is effectively removed by oxidation in the case of CuS, but not in the case of HgS.

VI. Calculate the solubility of HgS in 1 *M* $H_3O^+$ + 1 *M* $Cl^-$, assuming no loss of $H_2S$ from the solution.

$$L_{HgS} = 1 \times 10^{-53}, \quad K_{1,2H_2S} = 1 \times 10^{-22}, \quad K_{HgCl_4^{--}} = 6 \times 10^{-17}$$

Equilibria in the saturated solution

$$(1) \qquad [Hg^{++}] \times [S^{--}] = 1 \times 10^{-53}$$

$$(2) \qquad \frac{[H_3O^+]^2 \times [S^{--}]}{[H_2S]} = 1 \times 10^{-22}$$

$$(3) \qquad \frac{[Hg^{++}] \times [Cl^-]^4}{[HgCl_4^{--}]} = 6 \times 10^{-17}$$

The net reaction for the dissolving process is

$$\underline{HgS} + 2H_3O^+ + 4Cl^- = HgCl_4^{--} + H_2S + 2H_2O$$

If the dissolving takes place to a relatively small extent,

$$[H_3O^+] = 1, \quad [Cl^-] = 1, \quad [HgCl_4^{--}] = [H_2S]$$

From equation (3),

$$[Hg^{++}] = \frac{6 \times 10^{-17}[HgCl_4^{--}]}{(1)^4}$$

Substituting this in equation (1),

$$6 \times 10^{-17}[HgCl_4^{--}] \times [S^{--}] = 1 \times 10^{-53}$$

From this equation,

$$[S^{--}] = \frac{1 \times 10^{-53}}{6 \times 10^{-17}[HgCl_4^{--}]}$$

Substituting $[HgCl_4^{--}]$ for $[H_2S]$ in equation (2),

$$\frac{[H_3O^+]^2 \times [S^{--}]}{[HgCl_4^{--}]} = 1 \times 10^{-22}$$

From this equation,

$$[S^{--}] = \frac{1 \times 10^{-22}[HgCl_4^{--}]}{(1)^2}$$

The two expressions for $[S^{--}]$ are equal.

$$\frac{1 \times 10^{-53}}{6 \times 10^{-17}[HgCl_4^{--}]} = 1 \times 10^{-22}[HgCl_4^{--}]$$

$$[HgCl_4^{--}]^2 = \frac{1 \times 10^{-53}}{6 \times 10^{-17} \times 1 \times 10^{-22}} = 16.7 \times 10^{-16}$$

$$[HgCl_4^{--}] = 4 \times 10^{-8}$$

If this value is compared with the answers in problem V, it is seen that, with 1 *M* $Cl^-$ present, the solubility of HgS in 1 *M* $H_3O^+$ is even greater than that of CuS; therefore the concentration of $H_2S$ thus produced is now sufficient to permit ready oxidation by hot $NO_3^-$.

VII. Show by calculation whether or not a precipitate of $Cu_2S$ would form on passing $H_2S$ into an ammoniacal solution of $Na_2Cu(CN)_3$ under the following conditions.

$$[Cu(CN)_3^{--}] = 0.05, \quad [CN^-] = 0.01, \quad [H_3O^+] = 1 \times 10^{-8}, \quad [HS^-] = 0.1$$

$$L_{Cu_2S} = 2.5 \times 10^{-53}, \quad K_{Cu(CN)_3^{--}} = 5 \times 10^{-28}, \quad K_{HS^-} = 1 \times 10^{-15}$$

*1st step:* Calculate the $[Cu^+]$ supplied.
From $K_{Cu(CN)_3^{--}}$,

$$\frac{[Cu^+] \times [CN^-]^3}{[Cu(CN)_3^{--}]} = 5 \times 10^{-28}$$

Inserting 0.01 for $[CN^-]$ and 0.05 for $[Cu(CN)_3^{--}]$ and rearranging

$$[Cu^+] = \frac{5 \times 10^{-28} \times 0.05}{(0.01)^3} = 2.5 \times 10^{-23}$$

*2nd step:* Calculate the $[Cu^+]$ needed to saturate the solution with $Cu_2S$.
From $K_{HS^-}$,

$$\frac{[H_3O^+] \times [S^{--}]}{[HS^-]} = 1 \times 10^{-15}$$

Inserting $1 \times 10^{-8}$ for $H_3O^+$ and 0.1 for $HS^-$,

$$[S^{--}] = \frac{1 \times 10^{-15} \times 0.1}{1 \times 10^{-8}} = 1 \times 10^{-8}$$

From $L_{Cu_2S}$, for saturation,

$$[Cu^+]^2 \times [S^{--}] = 2.5 \times 10^{-53}$$

If $[S^{--}] = 1 \times 10^{-8}$,

$$[Cu^+]^2 = \frac{2.5 \times 10^{-53}}{1 \times 10^{-8}} = 2.5 \times 10^{-45}$$

$$[Cu^+] = 5 \times 10^{-23}$$

*3rd step:* Compare the two concentrations of $Cu^+$.

$[Cu^+]$ as supplied $= 2.5 \times 10^{-23}$, whereas that required for saturation with $Cu_2S$ is $5 \times 10^{-23}$; therefore no precipitate should form.

VIII. Calculate the total concentration of Cd needed to saturate the solution with CdS when $H_2S$ is passed into an ammoniacal solution containing $Na_2Cd(CN)_4$ and NaCN if the final conditions set up are:

$$[NH_3] = 2, \quad [CN^-] = 0.01, \quad [OH^-] = 1 \times 10^{-5}, \quad \text{and} \quad [HS^-] = 0.1$$

$$L_{CdS} = 5 \times 10^{-29}, \quad K_{Cd(CN)_4^{--}} = 1.4 \times 10^{-17}, \quad K_{Cd(NH_3)_4^{++}} = 1 \times 10^{-7},$$

$$K_W = 1 \times 10^{-14}, \quad K_{HS^-} = 1 \times 10^{-15}$$

*1st step:* Calculate $[S^{--}]$, if $[OH^-] = 1 \times 10^{-15}$, $K_W = 1 \times 10^{-14}$, $K_{HS^-} = 1 \times 10^{-15}$ and $[HS^-] = 0.1$.

$$[H_3O^+] = \frac{1 \times 10^{-14}}{[OH^-]} = \frac{1 \times 10^{-14}}{1 \times 10^{-5}} = 1 \times 10^{-9}$$

$$\frac{[H_3O^+] \times [S^{--}]}{[HS^-]} = 1 \times 10^{-15}, \quad \frac{1 \times 10^{-9} \times [S^{--}]}{0.1} = 1 \times 10^{-15}$$

$$[S^{--}] = \frac{1 \times 10^{-15} \times 0.1}{1 \times 10^{-9}} = 1 \times 10^{-7}$$

*2nd step:* Calculate $[Cd^{++}]$ for saturation.

$$[Cd^{++}] \times [S^{--}] = 5 \times 10^{-29}, \quad [Cd^{++}] = \frac{5 \times 10^{-29}}{1 \times 10^{-7}} = 5 \times 10^{-22}$$

*3rd step:* Calculate $[Cd(CN)_4^{--}]$ if $[Cd^{++}] = 5 \times 10^{-22}$ and $[CN^-] = 0.01$.

$$\frac{[Cd^{++}] \times [CN^-]^4}{[Cd(CN)_4^{--}]} = 1.4 \times 10^{-1}.$$

$$Cd(CN)_4^{--}] = \frac{5 \times 10^{-22} \times (0.01)^4}{1.4 \times 10^{-17}} = 3.6 \times 10^{-13}$$

*4th step:* Calculate $[Cd(NH_3)_4^{++}]$ if $[Cd^{++}] = 5 \times 10^{-22}$ and $[NH_3] = 2$.

$$\frac{[Cd^{++}] \times [NH_3]^4}{[Cd(NH_3)_4^{++}]} = 1 \times 10^{-7}$$

$$[Cd(NH_3)_4^{++}] = \frac{5 \times 10^{-22} \times (2)^4}{1 \times 10^{-7}} = 0.8 \times 10^{-2}$$

$$\text{Total } [Cd] = [Cd^{++}] + [Cd(CN)_4^{--}] + [Cd(NH_3)_4^{++}]$$

$$= 3.6 \times 10^{-13} + 0.8 \times 10^{-13} = 4.4 \times 10^{-13} \text{ (neglecting } Cd^{++}\text{)}$$

# 7

## Group III

# Iron, Chromium, Aluminum

Group III is precipitated by the use of $NH_4OH$ in the presence of high concentration of $NH_4Cl$. The metals included in Group III are Fe, Cr, and Al. The common ions of these metals are $Fe^{++}$, $Fe^{+3}$, $Cr^{+3}$, $CrO_4^{--}$, $Cr_2O_7^{--}$ (Cr also forms $Cr(OH)_4^{-}$, but the solution is unstable, slowly precipitating through secondary reaction), $Al^{+3}$ and $Al(OH)_4^{-}$.

## COMMON COMPOUNDS AND REACTIONS OF IONS OF Fe, Cr AND Al

**More Common Ferrous Compounds.** Ferrous chloride, $FeCl_2 \cdot 4H_2O$, white; ferrous sulfate (copperas, green vitriol), $FeSO_4 \cdot 7H_2O$, pale green; ferrous ammonium sulfate (Mohr's salt), $FeSO_4 \cdot (NH_4)_2SO_4 \cdot 6H_2O$, pale green; ferrous sulfide, FeS, black; ferrous oxalate, $FeC_2O_4 \cdot 2H_2O$, yellow; potassium ferrous oxalate, $K_2Fe(C_2O_4)_2 \cdot 2H_2O$, yellow; ferrous ferricyanide (Turnbull's blue), $Fe_3[Fe(CN)_6]_2$, dark blue; ferroso-ferric oxide (magnetic iron oxide, magnetite), $Fe_3O_4$, black.

**Reactions of Ferrous Ion.** NaOH and $NH_4OH$ precipitate $Fe(OH)_2$, white, which turns black through oxidation to hydrated $Fe_3O_4$ as oxygen is absorbed from the air; readily soluble in common strong acids; precipitation by $NH_4OH$ is incomplete in the presence of much $NH_4Cl$. $H_2S$ in alkaline solution ($Na_2S$ or $(NH_4)_2S$) precipitates FeS, black, soluble in common strong acids. $Fe^{++}$ is readily oxidized to $Fe^{+++}$ by $Cl_2$, $K_2Cr_2O_7$, $KMnO_4$, etc., the oxidation is incomplete with $I_2$ and other mild oxidizing agents. The most characteristic reaction of $Fe^{++}$ is the formation of a dark blue precipitate, $Fe_3[Fe(CN)_6]_2$, with $K_3Fe(CN)_6$.

**More Common Ferric Compounds.** Ferric chloride, $FeCl_3 \cdot 6H_2O$, yellow; ferric nitrate, $Fe(NO_3)_3 \cdot 6H_2O$, white; ferric sulfate, $Fe_2(SO_4)_3 \cdot 9H_2O$, pale yellow; ferric ammonium sulfate (ammonium iron alum), $Fe_2(SO_4)_3 \cdot (NH_4)_2SO_4 \cdot 24H_2O$, white; ferric potassium sulfate (potassium iron alum), $Fe_2(SO_4)_3 \cdot K_2SO_4 \cdot 24H_2O$, white; ferric oxalate, $Fe_2(C_2O_4)_3$, green; potassium ferric oxalate, $K_2Fe_2(C_2O_4)_4 \cdot 5H_2O$, olive brown; ferric oxide (hematite), $Fe_2O_3$, red; ferroso ferric oxide (magnetite), $Fe_3O_4$, black; ferric ferrocyanide (Prussian blue), $Fe_4[Fe(CN)_6]_3$.

**Reactions of Ferric Ion.** NaOH or $NH_4OH$ precipitates $Fe(OH)_3$, red brown, readily soluble in common strong acids when freshly precipitated, but becoming somewhat inert on long standing. $Na_2S$ or $(NH_4)_2S$ forms $Fe_2S_3$, black, soluble in common strong acids. $Fe^{+3}$ is reduced to $Fe^{++}$ by moderately strong reducing agents such as $SnCl_2$, $H_2S$, Zn, etc., the reduction being incomplete when HI and other mild reducing agents are used. The most characteristic reactions of $Fe^{+3}$ are (1) the formation of a red soluble compound, $Fe(CNS)_3$, with KCNS and (2) the formation of a dark blue precipitate, $Fe_4[Fe(CN)_6]_3$, with $K_4Fe(CN)_6$.

**More Common Chromic Compounds.** Chromic chloride, $CrCl_3 \cdot 6H_2O$, blue-violet; chromic nitrate, $Cr(NO_3)_3 \cdot 9H_2O$, blue-violet; chromic sulfate, $Cr_2(SO_4)_3 \cdot 18H_2O$, violet; potassium chromic sulfate (chrome alum), $Cr_2(SO_4)_3 \cdot K_2SO_4 \cdot 24H_2O$, dark red; ammonium chromic sulfate (chrome ammonium alum), $Cr_2(SO_4)_3 \cdot (NH_4)_2SO_4 \cdot 24H_2O$, dark red, chromic oxide, $Cr_2O_3$, green; chromic chromate, $Cr_2(CrO_4)_3$, red-brown.

**Reactions of Chromic Ion.** NaOH precipitates $Cr(OH)_3$, green, readily soluble in the common strong acids, soluble in excess of NaOH to form $Cr(OH)_4^-$, from which a less soluble chromic hydroxide slowly precipitates on standing, more rapidly on boiling. $NH_4OH$ precipitates $Cr(OH)_3$, green, somewhat soluble in excess of $NH_4OH$ when precipitated in a cold solution, forming complex chromic ammonia ion, $Cr(NH_3)_6^{+3}$, lavender to red. $Na_2S$ or $(NH_4)_2S$ precipitates $Cr(OH)_3$. $Cr^{+++}$ is oxidized to $Cr_2O_7^{--}$ in the presence of strong, nonreducing acids ($HNO_3$, $H_2SO_4$, etc.) by very strong oxidizing agents, $KMnO_4$, $KIO_4$, $K_2S_2O_8 + AgNO_3$, etc. In the presence of NaOH, $Cr(OH)_4^-$ or $Cr(OH)_3$ is readily oxidized to $CrO_4^{--}$ by $H_2O_2$ $Cl_2$, $Br_2$, $I_2$, etc. The most characteristic reaction of $Cr^{+3}$ is the formation of a chromate or dichromate on oxidation.

**More Common Chromates and Dichromates.** Sodium chromate, $Na_2CrO_4 \cdot 10H_2O$, yellow; potassium chromate, $K_2CrO_4 \cdot 2H_2O$, yellow; ammonium chromate, $(NH_4)_2CrO_4$, yellow; silver chromate, $Ag_2CrO_4$, dark red; lead chromate, $PbCrO_4$, yellow; zinc chromate, $ZnCrO_4$, yellow; barium chromate, $BaCrO_4$, yellow; strontium chromate, $SrCrO_4$, yellow; calcium chromate, $CaCrO_4$, yellow; chromic chromate, $Cr_2(CrO_4)_3$, red-brown; potassium dichromate, $K_2Cr_2O_7$, orange; sodium dichromate, $Na_2Cr_2O_7 \cdot 2H_2O$, red; ammonium dichromate, $(NH_4)_2Cr_2O_7$, orange; chromic anhydride, $CrO_3$, red.

**Reactions of Chromate Ion.** Acids convert $CrO_4^{--}$, yellow, to $Cr_2O_7^{--}$, orange. $BaCl_2$ precipitates $BaCrO_4$, yellow, soluble in HCl or $HNO_3$; $Pb(C_2H_3O_2)_2$ precipitates $PbCrO_4$, yellow, moderately soluble in $HNO_3$; $AgNO_3$ precipitates $Ag_2CrO_4$, dark red, moderately soluble in $HNO_3$ (large excess of $HNO_3$ may convert $PbCrO_4$ and $Ag_2CrO_4$ to the slightly soluble $PbCr_2O_7$ and $Ag_2Cr_2O_7$, similar in color to the chromates), soluble in $NH_4OH$, readily converted by $Cl^-$ to AgCl, white. Strong reducing agents, $H_2S$, $Fe^{++}$, $SnO_2^{--}$, etc., will reduce $CrO_4^{--}$ to $Cr(OH)_3$ or $Cr(OH)_4^-$ in neutral or alkaline solutions. The most characteristic reactions of $CrO_4^{--}$ are (1) the conversion to $Cr_2O_7^{--}$, orange, on acidifying, (2) the formation of a yellow precipitate, $PbCrO_4$, with $Pb(C_2H_3O_2)_2$, and (3) the formation of a yellow precipitate, $BaCrO_4$, with $BaCl_2$.

**Reactions of Dichromate Ion.** NaOH, $NH_4OH$, etc., convert $Cr_2O_7^{--}$, orange, to $CrO_4^{--}$, yellow. In slightly acid solution $BaCl_2$, $Pb(C_2H_3O_2)_2$ and $AgNO_3$ precipitate $BaCrO_4$, yellow, $PbCrO_4$, yellow, and $Ag_2CrO_4$, dark red, respectively. In strong $HNO_3$ solutions, $Pb^{++}$ and $Ag^+$ may precipitate $PbCr_2O_7$, yellow, and $Ag_2Cr_2O_7$, dark red, respectively. $H_2O_2$ in the presence of $HNO_3$ or $H_2SO_4$, reacts in the cold to form chromium peroxide, $CrO_5$, blue, unstable, breaking down readily to give $Cr^{+3}$, pale blue-violet. $Cr_2O_7^{--}$ is readily reduced to $Cr^{+3}$ by most reducing agents, HI, $Fe^{++}$, $H_2SO_3$, $H_2S$, $CH_2O$, $NO_2^-$, etc., the milder reducing agents requiring the presence of strong acids and heat. The most characteristic reactions are (1) the formation of a blue solution, $CrO_5$, with $H_2O_2$, and (2) the formation of a yellow precipitate, $PbCrO_4$, with $Pb(C_2H_3O_2)_2$.

**More Common Aluminum Compounds.** Aluminum chloride, anhydrous, $AlCl_3$, white, hydrated, $AlCl_3 \cdot 6H_2O$, white; aluminum nitrate, $Al(NO_3)_3 \cdot 9H_2O$, white; aluminum sulfate, $Al_2(SO_4)_3 \cdot 18H_2O$, white; aluminum potassium sulfate (alum), $Al_2(SO_4)_3 \cdot K_2SO_4 \cdot 24H_2O$, white; aluminum ammonium sulfate (ammonium alum), $Al_2(SO_4)_2 \cdot (NH_4)_2SO_4 \cdot 24H_2O$, white; aluminum sodium sulfate (sodium alum), $Al_2(SO_4)_3 \cdot Na_2SO_4 \cdot 24H_2O$, aluminum oxide, $Al_2O_3$, white.

**Reactions of Aluminum Ion.** NaOH precipitates $Al(OH)_3$, white, readily soluble in strong acids, soluble in excess of NaOH to form $Al(OH)_4^-$, from which excess of $NH_4Cl$ reprecipitates $Al(OH)_3$. $NH_4OH$ precipitates $Al(OH)_3$, white, slightly soluble in large excess of $NH_4OH$, less soluble in the presence of high concentration of $NH_4Cl$. $Na_2S$, $(NH_4)_2S$, $Na_2CO_3$, etc., precipitate $Al(OH)_3$ instead of $Al_2S_3$ or $Al_2(CO_3)_3$. $Al^{+3}$ does not undergo any common oxidation or reduction reactions. The most characteristic reaction of $Al^{+3}$ is the formation of a red precipitate (lake), when $Al(OH)_3$ is precipitated from an acid solution in the presence of a dilute solution of ammonium aurin tricarboxylate.

## PREPARING AN ORIGINAL SOLUTION FOR PRECIPITATION OF GROUP III

In order that precipitation may be complete Fe must be in the form of ferric ion, $Fe^{+3}$ ($Fe^{++}$ does not precipitate completely under the conditions used for the precipitation of Group III), Cr must be in the form of $Cr^{+3}$ ($CrO_4^{--}$ and $Cr_2O_7^{--}$ do not precipitate with $NH_4OH$), and Al must be in the form of $Al^{+3}$.

(1) If the solution is acid, test for $Fe^{++}$. Dilute 1 drop of the solution to 10 drops with water. Add a drop of HCl and a drop of $K_3Fe(CN)_6$. A blue precipitate ($Fe_3[Fe(CN)_6]_2$) indicates $Fe^{++}$. If the test is positive, add to

15 drops of the solution 5 drops of 5 *N* HCl and 1–2 drops of 5 *N* $NHO_3$ and boil 1 minute. Test again for $Fe^{++}$. If the test is still positive, continue the boiling and testing until it becomes negative. This completely oxidizes the Fe to $Fe^{+3}$.

An alternative method for oxidizing $Fe^{++}$ makes use of a molar solution of $NaNO_2$ in place of $HNO_3$. In this case add 5 drops of 5 *N* HCl, heat nearly to boiling, and add the $NaNO_2$ 1 drop at a time, with stirring, until the reaction appears to be complete, as judged by the disappearance of the brown color of $FeNO^{++}$ which may at first be formed. The solution is then boiled 1 minute to remove the excess $HNO_2$. This reagent oxidizes the $Fe^{++}$ more rapidly and at lower acidity than does $HNO_3$.

(2) If $Fe^{++}$ is absent, test for $CrO_4^{--}$ or $Cr_2O_7^{--}$. Test 1 drop of the solution with litmus. If neutral or alkaline acidify with 5 *N* $HNO_3$, adding 1 drop excess ($CrO_4^{--}$ changes to $Cr_2O_7^{--}$). If slightly acid add 1 drop of 5 *N* $H_2SO_4$. Cool and add 1 drop of $H_2O_2$. A blue color ($CrO_5$) indicates $CrO_4^{--}$ or $Cr_2O_7^{--}$. If the test is positive, to 15 drops of the solution add 5 drops excess of HCl and 1 drop of formaldehyde. Boil 2–3 minutes and test again for $Cr_2O_7^{--}$. If the test is still positive, continue the boiling and testing until it becomes negative. This converts any $CrO_4^{--}$ or $Cr_2O_7^{--}$ to $Cr^{+3}$.

The alternative method for reducing $CrO_4^{--}$ or $Cr_2O_7^{--}$ consists in acidifying with 5 *N* HCl, adding about 5 drops excess, heating nearly to boiling, and then adding 1 *M* $NaNO_2$ solution 1 drop at a time, and stirring, until the change in color suggests the complete reduction of the $Cr_2O_7^{--}$. This reagent reduces the $Cr_2O_7^{--}$ more rapidly and at lower acidity than does $CH_2O$. After the reduction is complete, the solution should be boiled for 1–2 minutes to remove the excess $HNO_2$.

(3) If the solution is alkaline and $CrO_4^{--}$ is absent, acidify with HCl. This converts any $Al(OH)_4^-$ to $Al^{+3}$ (and $Cr(OH)_4^-$ to $Cr^{+3}$).

## REACTIONS OF GROUP III METALS IN THE SYSTEMATIC PRECIPITATION OF GROUPS I AND II

(1) $Al(OH)_4^-$ (and $Cr(OH)_4^-$) gives a precipitate of the hydroxide, soluble in excess of the acid, when nitric acid is added to the original, alkaline solution.

(2) $CrO_4^{--}$ with $Ag(NH_3)_2^+$ or $Pb(OH)_3^-$ gives a precipitate, $Ag_2CrO_4$ or $PbCrO_4$, when the alkaline solution is acidified. If there is much of this precipitate, it does not dissolve readily in excess of the $HNO_3$. In such a case after using several drops excess of $HNO_3$ add HCl as for the precipitation of Group I. The $Ag_2CrO_4$ changes at once to AgCl, which is less soluble than $Ag_2CrO_4$, and by alternate heating and cooling, the $PbCrO_4$ can be converted to $PbCl_2$ and $H_2CrO_4$. Or, if desired, formaldehyde may be

added along with the HCl and, by boiling, the $CrO_4^{--}$ is reduced to $Cr^{+3}$, thus dissolving the $PbCrO_4$. Sodium nitrite may be used as the reducing agent in place of formaldehyde, in which case the solution does not need to be evaporated nearly to dryness but should be boiled for 1–2 minutes to remove any free $HNO_2$.

(3) If the solution after Group I contains $Cr_2O_7^{--}$, this should be reduced before attempting to precipitate Group II with $H_2S$. If this is not done, the $Cr_2O_7^{--}$ would be reduced by the $H_2S$ and the acidity of the solution lowered as shown by the equation:

$$Cr_2O_7^{--} + 8H_3O^+ + 3H_2S = 2Cr^{+3} + 3S + 15H_2O$$

Since sulfides and basic salts of third and fourth group metals will precipitate in Group II unless the acidity is kept reasonably high, it is evident that the $Cr_2O_7^{--}$ must be reduced before adjusting the acidity of the solution for precipitation of Group II. Otherwise later group metals may be carried down in Group II.

(4) When the solution is neutralized with $NH_4OH$ as a first step in adjusting the acidity before precipitating Group II, the third group metals will precipitate as hydroxides. Then when a measured amount of HCl is added, part of this acid will be used in dissolving these hydroxides—($Al(OH)_3 + 3H_3O^+ = Al^{+3} + 6H_2O$)—and thus the final concentration of HCl will be less than calculated from the volume of the solution and the quantity of HCl added. If the precipitate does not dissolve in the amount of acid used, add more HCl, 1 drop at a time, and warm until the third group hydroxides have dissolved. Since it requires a slight excess of acid to do this, one may assume that the acidity is properly adjusted when just enough acid has been added to redissolve the third group hydroxides. (Note that a white, granular precipitate of BiOCl may be left even after the third group hydroxides are dissolved. This does not need to be dissolved since it is converted by $H_2S$ to $Bi_2S_3$.)

(5) The difficulty noted in (4) can be avoided largely by working with a larger volume of solution for the precipitation of Group II. The amount of HCl used by the hydroxide depends upon the amount of hydroxide (5 mg. of Fe as $Fe(OH)_3$ are equivalent to 0.5 drop of 5 $N$ HCl), but the amount of HCl needed to make a neutral solution 0.25 $N$ with HCl depends on the volume of the solution (1 drop of 5 $N$ HCl to 19 drops of neutral solution, 2 drops of 5 $N$ HCl to 38 drops of neutral solution, etc.). Thus the amount of HCl reacting with the third group hydroxides will become a minor fraction of the quantity of HCl added if the volume of the solution is sufficiently large. For moderate amounts of third group metals this will be true if the volume of the solution is increased to 50–100 drops.

(6) The clear solution after Group II contains $H_2S$ which must be removed before precipitating Group III; otherwise sulfides of Group IV may precipi-

tate along with the third group hydroxides. The $H_2S$ is removed by boiling until the fumes no longer produce a black stain on a piece of filter paper moistened with lead acetate solution.

(7) Any iron present in the solution after Group II will be there as $Fe^{++}$, since $H_2S$ will reduce $Fe^{+3}$ to $Fe^{++}$ ($2Fe^{+3} + H_2S + 2H_2O = 2Fe^{++} + S + 2H_3O^+$). Therefore, after removal of $H_2S$ by boiling, test a small portion of the solution for $Fe^{++}$. If present, oxidize to $Fe^{+3}$ with $HNO_3$ or $NaNO_2$. (Add 1 drop of 5 *N* $HNO_3$ and boil until the test for $Fe^{++}$ becomes negative.) If $NaNO_2$ is used, add the 1 *M* reagent 1 drop at a time to the hot solution until the reaction appears to be complete, then boil out the oxides of nitrogen and repeat the test for $Fe^{++}$.

(8) It is not safe to try to combine the operations of boiling out $H_2S$ and oxidizing $Fe^{++}$ into a single operation, because under these conditions there may be appreciable oxidation of the $H_2S$ to $H_2SO_4$ with precipitation of $BaSO_4$ and $SrSO_4$ if $Ba^{++}$ and $Sr^{++}$ are present in the solution.

## PRECIPITATION AND ANALYSIS OF GROUP III

**Precipitation of Group III.** Add 0.2 g. of solid $NH_4Cl$ for each 1 ml. volume. Let stand in hot water bath (near boiling) for a minute, then add $NH_4OH$ cautiously, 1 drop at a time, with vigorous mixing, until slight precipitate persists. Then use 1 *N* $NH_4OH$ (reagent $NH_4OH$ diluted fivefold) a drop at a time, mixing and testing after each drop until a "micro-drop" no longer turns blue litmus paper red. Let stand 1–2 minutes longer in the hot water bath; then centrifuge. Transfer the clear solution to a clean test tube for later groups. Wash the precipitate 2–3 times with 2% $NH_4NO_3$ solution containing a drop of 1 *N* $NH_4OH$. The precipitate may contain $Fe(OH)_3$, red-brown, $Cr(OH)_3$, green, and $Al(OH)_3$, white.

*Explanatory Notes.* (1) Unless high concentration of $NH_4Cl$ is used, and $NH_4OH$ added in only slight excess, considerable amounts of fourth group metals will precipitate in Group III.

(2) The solution should be hot rather than cold when the $NH_4OH$ is added; otherwise a fairly stable chromic ammonia complex salt of lavender color may form, from which $Cr(OH)_3$ is slow to precipitate even on boiling. If the solution is hot when $NH_4OH$ is added, $Cr(OH)_3$ precipitates promptly.

(3) The third group hydroxides, when freshly precipitated, are slow to settle and wash because of their gelatinous character. By boiling and letting stand a short time they become distinctly more flocculent, permitting the centrifuging and washing to be carried out more rapidly.

(4) Very small amounts of third group metals may be overlooked because of the gelatinous, nonsettling character of the hydroxides. If no precipitate is immediately apparent, boil the solution and let stand a few minutes before judging the complete absence of Group III.

TABLE VII. OUTLINE OF PROCEDURE FOR GROUP III

| | | |
|---|---|---|
| $FeCl^{++}$ | $Al^{+3}$ | $Cr^{+3}$ |
| | $NH_4Cl + NH_4OH$ | |
| $Fe(OH)_3$ | $Al(OH)_3$ | $Cr(OH)_3$ |
| | $NaOH + H_2O_2$ | |
| $Fe(OH)_3$ | $Al(OH)_4^-$ | $CrO_4^{--}$ |
| $H_2SO_4 \rightarrow Fe^{+3}$ | $NH_4Cl$ | |
| 1. $KCNS \rightarrow FeCNS^{++}$<br>red<br>2. $K_4Fe(CN)_6 \rightarrow Fe_4[Fe(CN)_6]_3$<br>dark blue | $Al(OH)_3$<br>$HCl \rightarrow Al^{+3}$<br>$NH_4C_2H_3O_2$<br>+ Aluminon reagent<br>$+ NH_4OH \rightarrow Al(OH)_3$<br>red lake | $CrO_4^{--}$<br>1. $HNO_3 \rightarrow Cr_2O_7^{--}$<br>$H_2O_2 \rightarrow CrO_5$<br>blue<br>2. $HC_2H_3O_2 \rightarrow Cr_2O_7^{--}$<br>$Pb(C_2H_3O_2)_2 \rightarrow PbCrO_4$<br>yellow |

**Iron, Aluminum and Chromium. Separation and Detection.** Transfer the precipitate to a small crucible, add 5–10 drops of 3 *N* NaOH and 3–5 drops of $H_2O_2$, heat to boiling, and keep at the boiling point 1–2 minutes. (Prolonged boiling should be avoided to prevent serious attack on the container.) $Al(OH)_3$ and $Cr(OH)_3$ dissolve; $Fe(OH)_3$ is left as a precipitate. Cool, centrifuge and wash. Set the clear solution aside to test for Al and Cr. Examine the precipitate for Fe as follows: Dissolve in 3–5 drops of 5 *N* $H_2SO_4$. To part of the solution add a drop of $K_4Fe(CN)_6$. A dark blue precipitate, $Fe_4[Fe(CN)_6]_3$, indicates Fe. To the rest of the solution add 1–2 drops of KCNS. A deep-red solution, $FeCNS^{++}$, indicates Fe.

To the clear solution after $Fe(OH)_3$, add 0.2 g. of solid $NH_4Cl$,* stir, let stand a minute in the hot water bath, centrifuge and wash. Set the clear solution aside to test for Cr. Examine the precipitate for Al as follows: Add 1 drop of 5 *N* HCl and 4 drops of water to the precipitate; then add 5 drops of 3 *N* $NH_4C_2H_3O_2$, 2–3 drops of "aluminon-reagent" (0.1% solution of ammonium aurin tricarboxylate), and 2–3 drops of 5 *N* $NH_4OH$. A red precipitate, $Al(OH)_3$-lake, indicates Al.

To test the solution after $Al(OH)_3$ for Cr, first boil the solution until the odor of ammonia disappears. Then cool the solution. To one portion add

* This amount is equivalent to 1.2 ml. of 3 *N* NaOH.

2–3 drops of $HC_2H_3O_2$ and 1 drop of $Pb(C_2H_3O_2)_2$ solution. A bright yellow precipitate, $PbCrO_4$, indicates Cr. To a second portion of the solution add 1-2 drops of 5 *N* $HNO_3$, cool, and add 1 drop of $H_2O_2$. A blue color, $CrO_5$, indicates chromium.

*Explanatory Notes.* (1) $Al(OH)_3$ in dissolving in NaOH reacts as a weak acid, combining with the $OH^-$ to form a complex ion:

$$Al(OH)_3 + OH^- = Al(OH)_4^-$$

(2) $Cr(OH)_3$ does not dissolve effectively in NaOH alone, but it is readily oxidized by the $H_2O_2$ in the alkaline solution.

$$2Cr(OH)_3 + OH^- + 3HO_2^- = 2CrO_4^{--} + 5H_2O$$

(3) If a large amount of Cr is present, or if the $H_2O_2$ is of lower concentration than usual, the Cr may be oxidized only in part to $CrO_4^{--}$. In this case a reddish brown gelatinous precipitate may form, $Cr_2(CrO_4)_3$, similar in appearance to $Fe(OH)_3$. The oxidation may be completed by using more $H_2O_2$.

(4) When the test for Fe is faint, the Fe is probably an impurity in other materials present.

(5) The precipitation of $Al(OH)_3$ by the action of $NH_4Cl$ on the solution of $Al(OH)_4^-$ depends upon lowering the concentration of $OH^-$ from the NaOH, through the formation of the weak base, $NH_3$, and consequent increase in the concentration of $H_3O^+$. The net reaction is

$$Al(OH)_4^- + NH_4^+ = Al(OH)_3 + NH_3 + H_2O$$

(6) In adding $NH_4Cl$ to precipitate $Al(OH)_3$ it is necessary to use more than an amount equivalent to the NaOH added at the beginning of the separations in Group III. One may be certain that at least an equivalent amount has been added by boiling the solution until the free $NH_3$ is removed and then testing the solution with litmus paper. The solution will be neutral if enough $NH_4Cl$ was added. If the solution is still alkaline, test the vapors once more for $NH_3$, and if this is absent add 0.2 g. more of $NH_4Cl$ and look for $Al(OH)_3$ again. A slight precipitate is frequently obtained by the action of $NH_4Cl$, even when Al is absent. This may be $Pb(OH)_2$ or basic $PbCO_3$ from incomplete precipitation of Pb in Group II, or $H_2SiO_3$ from $Na_2SiO_3$ in the NaOH.

(7) In the confirmatory test for Al the light red precipitate frequently obtained when the organic reagent is added to the acid solution should not be mistaken for the actual test. If Al is absent, this precipitate will dissolve and yield a light tan-colored solution when excess of $NH_4OH$ is added; but, if Al is present, the organic reagent will be adsorbed by the $Al(OH)_3$, yielding a bright red precipitate when the solution is made alkaline.

(8) The purpose of boiling the solution until the odor of ammonia disappears is twofold. First, if insufficient $NH_4Cl$ was used to precipitate the Al, the solution will still react alkaline (see note 6), and one may add more $NH_4Cl$ to precipitate any Al present. Second, it is necessary to decompose the excess of $H_2O_2$ added, otherwise some $CrO_4^{--}$ may be reduced to $Cr^{+3}$ as the solution is acidified and the test for smaller amounts of Cr will fail.

$$2CrO_4^{--} + 7H_2O_2 + 10H_3O^+ = 2Cr^{+3} + 5O_2 + 22H_2O$$

The decomposition of $H_2O_2$ by boiling is somewhat slow even in alkaline solution, but the time required to remove $NH_3$ from the solution is sufficient to prevent any serious interference with the test for Cr.

(9) In the test for $Cr_2O_7^{--}$ with $Pb(C_2H_3O_2)_2$, a white precipitate, $Pb_3(OH)_2(CO_3)_2$, is occasionally obtained. By centrifuging and washing, any $PbCrO_4$ present may be recognized by the yellow tinge which is readily visible against white paper. In the laboratory one often finds a solution to which the student has added much $NH_4Cl$ in the preceding step. This very high concentration of $Cl^-$ interferes with the precipitation of $PbCrO_4$.

(10) $CrO_5$ is an unstable compound and therefore the blue color obtained in the $H_2O_2$ test for Cr disappears rather quickly. Under favorable conditions the color lasts half a minute or longer and the test is both delicate and characteristic. Under unfavorable conditions the color may disappear in less than one second and the test becomes unsatisfactory. The particular precautions to be observed are (1) avoid large excess of $HNO_3$, (2) have the solution cold, (3) add only a small amount of $H_2O_2$.

## REPORTING GROUP III IONS IN AN UNKNOWN SOLUTION

**Iron.** Valence tests may be tried on the original solution to recognize $Fe^{++}$ and $Fe^{+3}$. If the original solution is alkaline, no simple ions of iron may be present. If the solution contains strong oxidizing agents, $MnO_4^-$, $Cr_2O_7^{--}$, etc., any Fe will be entirely in the form of $Fe^{+3}$. If the solution contains strong reducing agents, $SnCl_2$, $H_2S$, etc., any Fe will be entirely in the form of $Fe^{++}$.

**Test for $Fe^{++}$.** To 1 drop of the original solution add 1 drop of HCl, dilute to 10 drops and add a drop of $K_3Fe(CN)_6$. A blue precipitate, $Fe_3[Fe(CN)_6]_2$, indicates $Fe^{++}$. The chief interference with this test lies in the fact that many other metals give colored precipitates with $K_3Fe(CN)_6$. If too much reagent is added, these other precipitates may conceal the ferrous precipitate. Fortunately, the ferrous compound is sufficiently insoluble so that it is one of the first to precipitate; therefore, with the above procedure, fair results may be obtained.

**Test for $Fe^{+3}$.** To 1 drop of the original solution add 1 drop of HCl, dilute to 10 drops and add (*a*) a drop of $K_4Fe(CN)_6$, or (*b*) 1 drop of KCNS. A dark blue precipitate, $Fe_4[Fe(CN)_6]_3$, or a blood-red solution, $FeCNS^{++}$, indicates $Fe^{+3}$. In the $K_4Fe(CN)_6$ test for $Fe^{+3}$ the same difficulty is encountered as in the test for $Fe^{++}$: many metals form insoluble ferrocyanides that may mask the ferric precipitate. An additional difficulty is occasionally encountered when strong oxidizing agents are present. These reagents may oxidize the ferrocyanide to ferricyanide so that no blue precipitate forms even though $Fe^{+3}$ is present. If excess of $K_4Fe(CN)_6$ is added, the test will then be positive unless concealed by ferrocyanides and ferricyanides of other metals. The KCNS test for $Fe^{+3}$ is subject to less interference. With strong oxidizing agents a light red color occasionally develops as a result of oxidation of the KCNS (forming $H(CNS)_3$). Further, in the presence of $Hg^{++}$ the test may fail because of the formation of nonionized $Hg(CNS)_2$. In this case the addition of more KCNS will finally produce a satisfactory test. Because of the marked delicacy of the KCNS test for $Fe^{+3}$, it is necessary to remember that a light red or pink color indicates only the small amount of Fe which may be only a normal impurity in other salts.

**Chromium.** There are four common ions of chromium: $Cr^{+3}$, blue-violet; $Cr(OH)_4^-$, green; $CrO_4^{--}$, yellow; and $Cr_2O_7^{--}$, orange. Of these there is only one that can be identified by simple chemical test in the presence of other colored materials. $Cr_2O_7^{--}$ may be recognized by the vanishing blue test ($H_2O_2$, used in a cold, slightly acid solution, forms $CrO_5$, blue). However, $CrO_4^{--}$ may be converted to $Cr_2O_7^{--}$ by merely acidifying the solution so that this same test may be used for either $CrO_4^{--}$ or $Cr_2O_7^{--}$.

**Test for Hexavalent Cr ($CrO_4^{--}$ and $Cr_2O_7^{--}$).** To 1 drop of the cold, slightly acid solution (if alkaline acidify with 5 *N* $HNO_3$), add 3–5 drops of $H_2O$, 1 drop excess $HNO_3$ and 1 drop of $H_2O_2$. A blue color, $CrO_5$, indicates hexavalent Cr. Test the original solution with litmus paper. If vanishing blue test was positive and the solution is alkaline, report $CrO_4^{--}$; if acid, report $Cr_2O_7^{--}$.

**Test for Trivalent Cr ($Cr^{+3}$ and $Cr(OH)_4^-$).** If the vanishing blue test for hexavalent Cr was negative but Cr was found in Group III, the solution contains trivalent Cr. Test the original solution with litmus paper. If reaction is acid, report $Cr^{+3}$; if alkaline, report $Cr(OH)_4^-$. In the absence of hexavalent Cr it is also possible to identify trivalent Cr in the original solution by treating with excess of NaOH, adding $H_2O_2$ and boiling. This will convert Cr to $CrO_4^{--}$ which may then be identified as follows: Centrifuge if necessary, decompose excess $H_2O_2$, cool, acidify with $HNO_3$ and apply the vanishing blue test. If the test was negative originally but now becomes positive, trivalent Cr is present in the original solution.*

* *Note to teacher.* There is no simple way of separating the two valence states of Cr for individual identification; therefore unless special procedures are given it is best to put only one form of Cr in any one solution.

**Aluminum.** The two common ions of Al are $Al^{+3}$ and $Al(OH)_4^-$. $Al(OH)_3$ is relatively insoluble, precipitating from a solution containing $Al^{+3}$ by the addition of $OH^-$ and from one containing $Al(OH)_4^-$ by the addition of $H_3O^+$.

$$Al^{+3} + 3OH^- = Al(OH)_3$$

$$Al(OH)_4^- + H_3O^+ = Al(OH)_3 + H_2O$$

To prevent such precipitation requires the presence of an appreciable concentration of $H_3O^+$ along with $Al^{+3}$ (to keep the concentration of $OH^-$ very low), and an appreciable concentration of $OH^-$ along with $Al(OH)_4^-$ (to keep the concentration of $H_3O^+$ very low). Therefore a solution containing $Al^{+3}$ will react acid and one containing $Al(OH)_4^-$ will react alkaline. To distinguish between the two, test the original solution with litmus paper. If Al is present (found in Group III) and the solution is acid, report $Al^{+3}$; if alkaline, report $Al(OH)_4^-$.

## GROUP III IN RELATION TO OTHER GROUPS

Attention has already been directed to the reactions of third group metals in the adjustment of conditions for, and actual precipitation of, Groups I and II (see pp. 85 and 104).

Incomplete washing of the precipitates for Groups I and II may leave small amounts of third group metals with these precipitates. The chief interference thus produced is found in Group II. The third group hydroxides may precipitate where $Bi(OH)_3$ is expected in the separation of Bi from Cu and Cd. $Fe(OH)_3$ interferes somewhat with the $NaSn(OH)_3$ test for Bi, being reduced to black ferro-ferric hydroxide by this reagent. It interferes less with the KI test for Bi, producing color due to free iodine which is readily removed by $SnCl_2$.

$$Fe(OH)_3 + 3H_3O^+ + Cl^- = FeCl^{++} + 6H_2O$$

$$2FeCl^{++} + 2I^- = 2Fe^{++} + I_2 + 2Cl^-$$

$$I_2 + SnCl_4^{--} + 2Cl^- = 2I^- + SnCl_6^{--}$$

Failure to precipitate earlier group metals completely with their proper group reagents will permit such metals to precipitate in certain of the later groups. Of the earlier group metals, lead and cadmium are the chief ones to escape effective precipitation in Group II. Of these Pb may precipitate in part in Group III, forming an opaque white precipitate of PbOHCl which stays with the Al in the third group separations.

$$PbCl^+ + NH_4OH = \underline{PbOHCl} + NH_4^+$$

$$\underline{PbOHCl} + 2OH^- = Pb(OH)_3^- + Cl^-$$

$$Pb(OH)_3^- + NH_4^+ = \underline{Pb(OH)_2} + NH_4OH$$

This precipitate of $Pb(OH)_2$ where $Al(OH)_3$ is expected does not interfere with the confirmatory test for Al.

Aside from the inclusion of small amounts of later group metals in Group III, because of incomplete washing of the third group precipitate, the chief ways in which later group metals may appear in Group III are as follows: (1) The hydroxides of Zn, Co, and Ni are sufficiently insoluble so that they may form and be co-precipitated with the third group hydroxides unless considerable care is taken to use high concentration of $NH_4Cl$ and keep the concentration of $NH_4OH$ very low in precipitating Group III. Normally, small amounts of these metals are found in Group III; under unfavorable conditions they may precipitate largely in Group III.

(2) In alkaline solution $Mn^{++}$ undergoes oxidation fairly readily and precipitates as $Mn(OH)_3$, brown. The filtrate from Group III occasionally develops a brown scum of $Mn(OH)_3$ on standing due to atmospheric oxidation.

$$4Mn^{++} + 8NH_4OH + O_2 + 2H_2O = 4Mn(OH)_3 + 8NH_4^+$$

This reaction takes place slowly enough in a faintly alkaline solution so that little Mn precipitates in Group III. Occasionally, however, in oxidizing $Fe^{++}$ to $Fe^{+3}$ with $HNO_3$ in the filtrate from Group II some $Cl_2$ is formed in the solution. This would oxidize the $Mn^{++}$ readily when $NH_4OH$ is added, causing more pronounced precipitation of $Mn(OH)_3$ in Group III.

(3) The ordinary reagent $NH_4OH$ contains small amounts of $(NH_4)_2CO_3$ as a result of absorption of $CO_2$ from the air. Since $(NH_4)_2CO_3$ is the reagent used to precipitate Ba, Sr, and Ca as carbonates in Group V, it might be expected that small amounts of these metals would precipitate and be lost in Group III. Actually, however, this takes place only to a negligible extent because of the fact that the high concentration of $NH_4Cl$ and low concentration of $NH_4OH$ keeps the solution practically neutral in the precipitation of Group III.

(4) If certain acids, particularly $H_3PO_4$ and $H_2C_2O_4$, are present in the original solution they will be neutralized by the $NH_4OH$ added in precipitating Group III, thus introducing $PO_4^{-3}$ and $C_2O_4^{--}$ into the solution in sufficient amounts to cause the precipitation of oxalates and phosphates of several later group metals in Group III. In such cases the completeness of precipitation depends largely on the amount of phosphoric or oxalic acid present. If one is analyzing unknowns in which this situation may arise, it becomes necessary to examine the filtrate from Group II for $H_3PO_4$ and $H_2C_2O_4$ and remove these if present before continuing with the precipitation of Group III (see p. 229).

In the analysis of the third group precipitate, after treatment with NaOH + $H_2O_2$, the later group metals will be distributed as follows: Zn will be in solution as $Zn(OH)_3^-$, along with $Al(OH)_4^-$ and $CrO_4^{--}$; the rest will be precipitated along with the $Fe(OH)_3$. Co forms $Co(OH)_3$, black; Ni, $Ni(OH)_2$, green, partly oxidized to $NiO_2$, black; Mn forms $Mn(OH)_3$, brown; Ba, Sr, Ca, and Mg will be precipitated chiefly as carbonates, white. On adding $NH_4Cl$ to the solution to precipitate $Al(OH)_3$, most of the Zn precipitates at the same time. However, it does not interfere with the tests for either Al or Cr. On dissolving the precipitate of $Fe(OH)_3$ in dilute $H_2SO_4$ the other precipitates may dissolve in part. They do not interfere seriously with the test for Fe. The fourth group metals may be dissolved more effectively if a little $H_2O_2$ is used along with the $H_2SO_4$. Portions of this solution may then be used, if desired, to try individual tests for Co, Ni, and Mn according to the confirmatory procedures given in Group IV.

Incomplete precipitation of Group III may result in the precipitation of these metals in Group IV. The chief ways in which third group metals may escape removal in Group III are:

(1) Failure to oxidize all $Fe^{++}$ in preparing the solution for the precipitation of Group III. $Fe(OH)_2$ is much more soluble than $Fe(OH)_3$ and precipitates incompletely under the conditions recommended for the third group precipitation.

(2) Failure to recognize the formation of a third group precipitate when the amount of third group metal is small. The precipitate may not flocculate immediately; hence, unless the solution is permitted to stand for a few minutes small amounts of third group metals may be overlooked.

(3) If Group III is precipitated from a cool solution and excess of $NH_4OH$ added (contrary to the specific instructions given above), Cr may be found in the filtrate as a lavender-colored complex chromic ammonia salt. The color resembles the pink of $Co(NH_3)_6^{++}$ more than any other ions of later group metals, and occasionally the student wastes time repeating the tests for Co as a result of this irregularity.

These third group metals are separated in Group IV: Fe as FeS or $Fe_2S_3$, Cr and Al as hydroxides. These dissolve in part on treatment with cold dilute HCl in the fourth group separations; Fe interferes slightly with the test for Co, also precipitates as $Fe(OH)_3$ where $MnO_2$ is expected; Cr and Al interfere slightly in the test for Zn.

## REACTIONS OF GROUP III METALS IN THE SYSTEMATIC ANALYSIS OF A SOLUTION

### Iron

*In the precipitation of Group I*

$$Fe^{+++} + Cl^- = FeCl^{++}$$

*Adjusting the acidity for the precipitation of Group II*

$$Fe^{++} + 2NH_4OH = \underline{Fe(OH)_2} + 2NH_4^+$$
$$FeCl^{++} + 3NH_4OH = \underline{Fe(OH)_3} + 3NH_4^+ + Cl^-$$
$$2FeCl^{++} + Fe^{++} + 8NH_4OH = \underline{Fe_3(OH)_8} + 8NH_4^+ + 2Cl^-$$
$$\underline{Fe(OH)_2} + 2H_3O^+ = Fe^{++} + 4H_2O$$
$$\underline{Fe(OH)_3} + 3H_3O^+ + Cl^- = FeCl^{++} + 6H_2O$$
$$\underline{Fe_3(OH)_8} + 8H_3O^+ + 2Cl^- = Fe^{++} + 2FeCl^{++} + 16H_2O$$

*In the precipitation of Group II*

$$2FeCl^{++} + H_2S + 2H_2O = 2Fe^{++} + 2Cl^- + \underline{S} + 2H_3O^+$$

*In the solution after Group II*

$$3Fe^{++} + 2Fe(CN)_6^{-3} = \underline{Fe_3[Fe(CN)_6]_2}$$
$$Fe^{++} + HNO_2 + Cl^- + H_3O^+ = FeCl^{++} + NO + 2H_2O$$

*In Group III*

$$FeCl^{++} + 3NH_4OH = \underline{Fe(OH)_3} + 3NH_4^+ + Cl^-$$
$$\underline{Fe(OH)_3} + 3H_3O^+ = Fe^{+++} + 6H_2O$$

1. $Fe^{+++} + CNS^- = Fe(CNS)^{++}$
2. $4Fe^{+++} + 3Fe(CN)_6^{-4} = \underline{Fe_4[Fe(CN)_6]_3}$

**Chromium**

*Acidifying an alkaline solution with $HNO_3$*

$$2CrO_4^{--} + 2H_3O^+ = Cr_2O_7^{--} + 3H_2O$$
$$Cr(OH)_4^- + 4H_3O^+ = Cr^{+++} + 8H_2O$$

*In the filtrate from Group I*

$$Cr_2O_7^{--} + 4H_2O_2 + 2H_3O^+ = \underbrace{2CrO_5}_{\text{blue}} + 7H_2O$$
$$Cr_2O_7^{--} + 5H_3O^+ + 3HNO_2 = 2Cr^{+++} + 3NO_3^- + 9H_2O$$

*Adjusting the acidity for the precipitation of Group II*

$$Cr^{+++} + 3NH_4OH = \underline{Cr(OH)_3} + 3NH_4^+$$
$$\underline{Cr(OH)_3} + 3H_3O^+ = Cr^{+++} + 6H_2O$$

*In Group III*

$$Cr^{+++} + 3NH_4OH = \underline{Cr(OH)_3} + 3NH_4^+$$
$$\underline{2Cr(OH)_3} + 3H_2O_2 + 4OH^- = 2CrO_4^{--} + 8H_2O$$

1. $2CrO_4^{--} + 2H_3O^+ = Cr_2O_7^{--} + 3H_2O$
   $Cr_2O_7^{--} + 4H_2O_2 + 2H_3O^+ = 2CrO_5 + 7H_2O$
2. $2CrO_4^{--} + 2HC_2H_3O_2 = Cr_2O_7^{--} + 2C_2H_3O_2^-$
   $Cr_2O_7^{--} + 2Pb(C_2H_3O_2)_2 + H_2O = \underline{2PbCrO_4} + 2HC_2H_3O_2 + 2C_2H_3O_2^-$

**Aluminum**

*Acidifying an alkaline solution with $HNO_3$*

$$Al(OH)_4^- + 4H_3O^+ = Al^{+++} + 8H_2O$$

*Adjusting the acidity for precipitation of Group II*

$$Al^{+++} + 3NH_4OH = \underline{Al(OH)_3} + 3NH_4^+$$
$$\underline{Al(OH)_3} + 3H_3O^+ = Al^{+++} + 6H_2O$$

*In Group III*

$$Al^{+++} + 3NH_4OH = \underline{Al(OH)_3} + 3NH_4^+$$
$$\underline{Al(OH)_3} + OH^- = Al(OH)_4^-$$
$$Al(OH)_4^- + NH_4^+ = \underline{Al(OH)_3} + NH_3 + H_2O$$
$$\underline{Al(OH)_3} + 3H_3O^+ = Al^{+++} + 6H_2O$$
$$Al^{+++} + \text{Aluminon} + 3NH_4OH = \underline{Al(OH)_3 + \text{Aluminon}} + 3NH_4^+$$

## SUMMARY AND REVIEW

Assuming that all earlier steps have been properly consummated, the Group II filtrate will be acid and contain (*a*) $Cl^-$, $S^{--}$; (*b*) $Fe^{++}$, $Al^{+3}$, $Cr^{+3}$; (*c*) later group ions. In order to avoid various difficulties the following steps are therefore necessary:

Preparation for Precipitation

1. Removal of $H_2S$
   *A*. How removed?
   Boil until lead acetate test is negative
   *B*. Why avoid delay?
   $H_2S$ + oxidation $\rightarrow$ $SO_4^{--}$ endangering pptn. of Ba and Sr
   *C*. Why removed?
   (1) $H_2S + HNO_3 \rightarrow$ S and $SO_4^{--}$
   (2) $H_2S + NH_4OH \rightarrow (NH_4)_2S$, the Group IV reagent
2. Oxidation of $Fe^{++}$
   (Regardless of the form of Fe in the original solution, it is in the ferrous state in the Group II filtrate. Why?)
   *A*. Test for $Fe^{++}$
   *B*. How oxidized?
   $Fe^{++} + HNO_3$ + boiling $\rightarrow Fe^{+3}$
   or: $Fe^{++} + HCl + NaNO_2 \rightarrow Fe^{+3}$
   *C*. How tell when oxidation complete?
   $K_3Fe(CN)_6$ test
   *D*. Why oxidized?
   $Fe^{++}$ incompletely pptd. in Group III
3. Addition of $NH_4Cl$
   *A*. To repress ionization of $NH_4OH$
   (1) Prevent pptn. of Mn and Mg
   (2) Insure complete pptn. of Al and Cr
   *B*. Aid in formation of Group IV complex ions
   *C*. Prevent Group III ppt. from becoming colloidal

4. Addition of paper pulp
   *A*. How prepared?
   *B*. Why used?
5. Heat to boiling
   *A*. Removal of air
   (Mn in alkaline soln. readily oxidized by oxygen of the dissolved air)
   *B*. Ppt. will be in better form
   *C*. Prevent formation of Cr complex

Actual Precipitation

1. Addition of $NH_4OH$
   *A*. Technique
   *B*. How tell when sufficient added?
   *C*. Why only a slight excess?
2. Keep hot 1 or 2 minutes
   *A*. Helps coagulate the gelatinous precipitate
   *B*. Why avoid excessive boiling?
3. Filtration
   *A*. Testing filtrate for completeness of pptn.
4. Washing the precipitate
   *A*. Why wash?
   *B*. Why use hot water?
   *C*. Number of washings necessary?

Analysis of the Precipitate

1. Dissolving ppt.
   *A*. Action of NaOH
      (1) Impurities in NaOH
      (2) Why avoid glass container?
   *B*. Action of $H_2O_2$
      (1) Danger of incomplete oxidation
         (*a*) $Cr_2(CrO_4)_3$ resembles $Fe(OH)_3$
         (*b*) $NaCr(OH)_3$ interferes with test for Al
      (2) Removal of excess peroxide
   *C*. Filtration
      (1) Difficulty if NaOH too concentrated
      (2) Washing residue
2. Testing residue for Fe
   (A brown residue is not proof that Fe is present. Why?) See 1, *B*, (1), (*a*) above.
   *A*. Dissolving residue
   *B*. $K_4Fe(CN)_6$ test
   *C*. KCNS test
3. Treatment of filtrate
   *A*. Pptn. and detection of Al
      (1) Specific action of $NH_4Cl$
      (2) Aluminon test
   *B*. Detection of Cr
      (1) $Pb(C_2H_3O_2)_2$ test
      (2) Vanishing blue test

## *LABORATORY EXERCISES*

1. Known solutions containing Groups I and II with $Fe^{+3}$, $Cr^{+3}$, and $Al^{+3}$.

(*1*) $Hg_2^{++}$, $Hg^{++}$, $Fe^{+3}$, $Cr^{+3}$, $Al^{+3}$
(*2*) $Pb^{++}(l)$, $Cr^{+3}$
(*3*) $Ag^+$, $Fe^{+3}(s)$

These solutions contain the following amounts of substance per liter of solution: (*1*) 3.5 g. $Hg_2(NO_3)_2 \cdot 2H_2O$, 4 g. $Hg(NO_3)_2$, 18 g. $Fe(NO_3)_3 \cdot 9H_2O$, 19 g. $Cr(NO_3)_3 \cdot 9H_2O$ 34 g. $Al(NO_3)_3 \cdot 9H_2O$, and 150 ml. of 5 *N* $HNO_3$; (*2*) 16 g. $Pb(NO_3)_2$, 19 g. $Cr(NO_3)_3 \cdot 9H_2O$, and 50 ml. of 5 *N* $HNO_3$; (*3*) 4 g. $AgNO_3$, 7 g. $Fe(NO_3)_3 \cdot 9H_2O$, and 50 ml. of 5 *N* $HNO_3$.

Use 15 drops of the original solution, precipitating Group I with HCl, using the clear solution after Group I for Group II, and the solution after Group II for Group III. Be sure to test for completeness of precipitation of each group.

SPECIAL NOTES. *Solution 1.* (*a*) Occasionally a basic chromic nitrate is found that converts $Hg_2Cl_2$ and AgCl into very fine suspensions when excess $Cl^-$ is added. These precipitates do not settle readily on centrifuging. In such a case a special procedure may be used in precipitating Group I. Add 1 *N* HCl a drop at a time, shaking after each addition, until the first appearance of a colloidal precipitate is obtained. Next add more of the original solution, 1 drop at a time, shaking after each addition, until the precipitate coagulates again. Now dilute 1 drop of the 5 *N* HCl to 100 drops and add this a drop at a time, with shaking, until the precipitate barely starts to become colloidal. Centrifuge and wash.

This procedure may precipitate Bi as BiOCl and will fail to precipitate $PbCl_2$ even though there is a large amount of $Pb^{++}$ in the solution. To take care of these two cases digest the first group precipitate with 2 drops of 5 *N* HCl, centrifuge, and add the solution to the original filtrate from Group I. The BiOCl will be extracted from the first group precipitate and $PbCl_2$ will now precipitate. If such a precipitate forms, centrifuge, wash, and combine it with the earlier precipitate for first group analysis.

(*b*) When making the solution 0.25 *N* with HCl at the beginning of Group II, the gelatinous precipitate of third group hydroxides may not redissolve readily. In such a case add more HCl, a drop at a time, warm and stir the solution. Continue until the third group hydroxides dissolve. Note the difference in the appearance of these hydroxides from the granular precipitate of BiOCl encountered earlier.

(*c*) If trouble is encountered in centrifuging the second group sulfides (colloidal effect similar to Group I), a very effective procedure consists in adding 5–6 drops of 5 *N* HCl, evaporating practically to dryness to remove the $HNO_3$ and repeating this operation. To the final residue add 2 drops of 5 *N* HCl, dilute with 10–15 drops of $H_2O$, and warm to complete solution. Dilute to 40 drops and precipitate with $H_2S$.

*Solution 2.* (*a*) Be sure to obtain a satisfactory test for Pb in Group II.

(*b*) In Group III apply tests for Fe and Al, usually obtaining faint tests due to the presence of these metals as impurities in chromic salts.

*Solution 3.* (*a*) In precipitating Group II with $H_2S$ the $Fe^{+3}$ is reduced, oxidizing some of the $H_2S$ to S°. This may be coagulated by boiling.

(*b*) Apply tests for Cr and Al in Group III, obtaining satisfactory blank tests.

(*c*) Note that the test for Fe in this solution, which contains only a small amount of Fe, is distinctly greater than that obtained in the second solution where the Fe is present as an impurity in the chromic salt.

2. Known solutions containing Groups I–III (including $Fe^{++}$, $CrO_4^{--}$, $Cr_2O_7^{--}$ and $Al(OH)_4^-$).

(*1*) $Bi^{+3}(s)$, $Fe^{++}$, $Fe^{+3}$, $Al^{+3}$
(*2*) $Ag^+(s)$, $Pb^{++}(s)$, $Fe^{+3}$, $Cr_2O_7^{--}$
(*3*) $Pb(OH)_3^-(l)$, $Al(OH)_4^-(s)$, $CrO_4^{--}(s)$

These solutions contain the following amounts of substance per liter of solution: (*1*) 1.5 g. $BiCl_3$, 18 g. $Fe(NH_4)_2(SO_4)_2 \cdot 6H_2O$, 12 g. $FeCl_3 \cdot 6H_2O$, 23 g. $AlCl_3 \cdot 6H_2O$, and 300 ml. of 5 *N* HCl; (*2*) 1.6 g. $AgNO_3$, 1.6 g. $Pb(NO_3)_2$, 18 g. $Fe(NO_3)_3 \cdot 9H_2O$, 7 g. $K_2Cr_2O_7$, and 500 ml. of 5 *N* $HNO_3$; (*3*) 14 g. $Pb(NO_3)_2$, 13 g. $Al(NO_3)_3 \cdot 9H_2O$, 1.5 g. $K_2Cr_2O_7$ and 125 g. NaOH.

Use 15 drops of the original solution for systematic analysis of Groups I–III. Use small separate portions of the original solution to apply any additional tests to distinguish between the different ions of each metal.

Special Notes. *Solution 1.* (*a*) Tests to distinguish between $Fe^{++}$ and $Fe^{+3}$ are made on the original solution.

(*b*) Identify Bi after the separations in Group II.

*Solution 2.* (*a*) This solution is strongly acid to prevent the precipitation of $Ag_2CrO_4$ and $PbCrO_4$.

(*b*) Reduce $Cr_2O_7^{--}$ in the filtrate from Group I, evaporate to 2–3 drops, dilute to 15–20 drops, then adjust the acidity for the precipitation of Group II.

(*c*) Obtain a test for Pb in Group II.

(*d*) Try the test for Al in Group III. A white precipitate where $Al(OH)_3$ is expected may be $Pb(OH)_2$.

(*e*) After precipitating Group III with $NH_4OH$ test the clear solution with $H_2S$. If earlier group precipitations were satisfactory no precipitate will be obtained. A black precipitate may be PbS, due to incomplete precipitation of Group II, or FeS, due to incomplete oxidation of $Fe^{++}$ at the beginning of Group III.

(*f*) Identify Cr in Group III and $Cr_2O_7^{--}$ in the original solution.

*Solution 3.* (*a*) This solution is strongly alkaline to prevent the precipitation of $PbCrO_4$. Add $HNO_3$ until barely acid. Note the precipitation of $PbCrO_4$ as well as $Pb(OH)_2$. Treat with excess of the acid and note that the chromate does not dissolve as readily as the hydroxide. With large amounts of $PbCrO_4$ it may be desirable to reduce the chromate with HCl and $CH_2O$, then cool thoroughly and remove the first group precipitate. Evaporate the clear solution to a small volume to remove excess of HCl and $CH_2O$ before adjusting the acidity for the precipitation of Group II.

(*b*) The high concentration of $NO_3^-$ introduced in acidifying the solution may interfere somewhat with the precipitation of Group II (this effect is less marked than for a corresponding amount of $Cl^-$). In an extreme case it may be necessary to precipitate from neutral or alkaline solution with $H_2S$, centrifuge, wash, dissolve the precipitate in $HCl + HNO_3$, evaporate to 2–3 drops to remove excess of acids, then dilute and adjust the acidity for the precipitation of Group II. The precipitate now obtained is tested in the usual way for Group II, the clear solution being analyzed for Groups III and IV.

## EQUILIBRIUM PROBLEMS IN GROUP III

I. Calculate the concentration of $OH^-$ introduced for the precipitation of Group III. Assume that the total volume is 2 ml. and that this contains 0.4 g. of $NH_4Cl$ and 0.05 ml. of *N* $NH_4OH$.

$$K_{NH_4OH} = 1.8 \times 10^{-5}$$

$$NH_4{}^{+}] \text{ from the } NH_4Cl = \frac{0.4 \times 1000}{(\text{vol. in ml.})(\text{mol. wt. } NH_4Cl)} = \frac{400}{2 \times 53.5} = 3.7$$

$$[NH_4OH] \text{ (excess added)} = \frac{0.05}{2} = 0.025$$

$$\frac{[NH_4{}^{+}] \times [OH^{-}]}{[NH_4OH]} = 1.8 \times 10^{-5}$$

Total $[NH_4{}^{+}] = 3.7$ since that supplied by the $NH_4OH$ will be very small.

$$OH^{-}] = 1.8 \times 10^{-5} \times \frac{0.025}{3.7} = 1.2 \times 10^{-7} \quad \textit{Ans.}$$

II. Calculate the concentration of $Cr^{+++}$ which might remain in solution after the precipitation of Group III.

$$[OH^{-}] = 1.2 \times 10^{-7}, \quad L_{Cr(OH)_3} = 3 \times 10^{-29}$$

for saturated solution $[Cr^{+++}] \times [OH^{-}]^3 = 3 \times 10^{-29}$

$$[Cr^{+++}] = \frac{3 \times 10^{-29}}{[OH^{-}]^3} = \frac{3 \times 10^{-29}}{(1.2 \times 10^{7})^3} = 1.7 \times 10^{-8} \quad \textit{Ans.}$$

III. Calculate the distribution of Fe among the forms $Fe^{+++}$, $FeCl^{++}$, and $FeCl_2$ in the filtrate from Group I if $Cl^{-} = 0.37\ M$.

$$K_{FeCl^{++}} = 0.03, \quad K_{FeCl_2{}^{+}} = 0.222$$

From $K_{FeCl^{++}}$,

$$\frac{[Fe^{+++}] \times [Cl^{-}]}{[FeCl^{--}]} = 0.03, \quad \frac{[Fe^{+++}]}{[FeCl^{++}]} = \frac{0.03}{0.37} = \frac{0.081}{1}$$

$$[Fe^{+++}]:[FeCl^{++}]::0.081:1$$

From $K_{FeCl_2{}^{+}}$,

$$\frac{[Fe^{+++}] \times [Cl^{-}]^2}{[FeCl_2{}^{+}]} = 0.222, \quad \frac{[Fe^{+++}]}{[FeCl_2{}^{+}]} = \frac{0.222}{(0.37)^2} = \frac{1.62}{1}$$

$$[Fe^{+++}]:[FeCl_2{}^{+}]::1.62:1$$

Multiply the numbers in the last ratio by $\frac{0.081}{1.62}$ to convert the number representing $Fe^{+++}$ to the same as that in the first ratio.

$$[Fe^{+++}]:[FeCl_2{}^{+}]::1.62 \times \frac{0.081}{1.62} : \frac{0.081}{1.62} = 0.081:0.05$$

Combining the two proportions into one:

$$[Fe^{+++}]:[FeCl^{++}]:[FeCl_2{}^{+}]::0.081:1:0.05$$

From this it is seen that nearly 90% of the ferric iron in the solution after Group I will be present as $FeCl^{++}$.

IV. Calculate the concentration of $H_3O^+$ formed by hydrolysis of $Al^{+++}$ in 0.05 *M* solution of $Al(NO_3)_3$.

$$K_{AlOH^{++}} = 7 \times 10^{-10}, \quad K_W = 1 \times 10^{-14}$$

Equation for the net reaction:

$$Al^{+++} + 2H_2O = AlOH^{++} + H_3O^+$$

If hydrolysis takes place to only a moderate extent

$$[Al^{+++}] \cong 0.05, \quad [AlOH^{++}] = [H_3O^+] \quad \text{and} \quad [OH^-] = \frac{1 \times 10^{-14}}{[H_3O^+]}$$

From $K_{AlOH^{++}}$,

$$\frac{[Al^{+++}] \times [OH^-]}{[AlOH^{++}]} = 7 \times 10^{-10}$$

Substituting 0.05 for $[Al^{+++}]$, $[H_3O^+]$ for $[AlOH^{++}]$, and $\frac{1 \times 10^{-14}}{[H_3O^+]}$ for $[OH^-]$,

$$\frac{0.05 \times \frac{1 \times 10^{-14}}{[H_3O^+]}}{[H_3O^+]} = 7 \times 10^{-10}$$

Rearranging,

$$[H_3O^+]^2 = \frac{0.05 \times 1 \times 10^{-14}}{7 \times 10^{-10}} = 0.71 \times 10^{-}$$

$$[H_3O^+] = 8.5 \times 10^{-4}$$

By using this as equal to the concentration of $AlOH^{++}$ formed, one may calculate the concentration of $Al^{+++}$ still left as $0.05 - 8.5 \times 10^{-4} = 0.049$. The error involved in using 0.05 for $Al^{+++}$ is approximately 2%, which is negligible in problems of this type.

# 8

## Group IV

# Zinc, Manganese, Cobalt, Nickel

Group IV is precipitated by $H_2S$ in an ammoniacal solution containing a fairly large amount of $NH_4Cl$. The metals are zinc, manganese, cobalt, and nickel. Their common ions are zinc ion, $Zn^{++}$; zincate ion, $Zn(OH)_3^-$; zinc ammonia ion, $Zn(NH_3)_4^{++}$; manganous ion, $Mn^{++}$; manganate ion, $MnO_4^{--}$; permanganate ion, $MnO_4^-$; cobalt ion, $Co^{++}$; cobaltous ammonia ion, $Co(NH_3)_6^{++}$; nickel ion, $Ni^{++}$; nickelous ammonia ion, $Ni(NH_3)_6^{++}$.

## COMMON COMPOUNDS AND REACTIONS OF IONS OF Zn, Mn, Co AND Ni

**More Common Compounds of Zinc.** Zinc chloride, $ZnCl_2$, white; zinc nitrate, $Zn(NO_3)_2$, white; zinc sulfate, $ZnSO_4 \cdot 7H_2O$, white; zinc carbonate, $ZnCO_3$, white; zinc chromate, $ZnCrO_4$, yellow; zinc ferrocyanide, $Zn_2Fe(CN)_6 \cdot 3H_2O$, white; zinc oxalate, $ZnC_2O_4 \cdot H_2O$, white; zinc phosphate, $Zn_3(PO_4)_2$, white; zinc sulfide, ZnS, white; zinc oxide, ZnO, white.

**Reactions of Zinc Ion.** NaOH or $NH_4OH$ precipitates $Zn(OH)_2$, white, soluble in excess NaOH (forming $Zn(OH)_3^-$), and in excess $NH_4OH$ (forming $Zn(NH_3)_4^{++}$), soluble in $HC_2H_3O_2$, HCl, or $HNO_3$. $H_2S$ in faintly acid, neutral, or alkaline solution precipitates ZnS, white, insoluble in $HC_2H_3O_2$, $NH_4OH$, or NaOH; soluble in HCl or $HNO_3$. $K_4Fe(CN)_6$ precipitates $Zn_2Fe(CN)_6$, white, insoluble in $HC_2H_3O_2$ or dilute HCl; soluble in NaOH. With high concentration of $Cl^-$, $Br^-$, or $I^-$, $Zn^{++}$ is converted to an appreciable extent to a complex ion of the type $ZnCl_4^{--}$, although in the ordinary dilute solution the zinc will be present chiefly in the form of the simple ion. There are no common oxidation reduction reactions involving $Zn^{++}$. Metallic Zn is a strong reducing agent in the presence of dilute $H_2SO_4$, reducing many of the more electropositive metals to the free state, including the displacement of Ag even from the insoluble halides. Most characteristic reaction: precipitation of ZnS, white, with $H_2S$ in either NaOH or $HC_2H_3O_2$ solution.

**More Common Compounds of Manganese.** Manganous chloride, $MnCl_2 \cdot 4H_2O$, deliquescent, pink; manganous nitrate, $Mn(NO_3)_2 \cdot 6H_2O$, deliquescent, pink; manganous sulfate, $MnSO_4 \cdot 2H_2O$, pink; manganous ammonium phosphate, $MnNH_4PO_4 \cdot 4H_2O$, white; manganous carbonate, $MnCO_3$, pink; manganous sulfide, MnS, two forms, pink (usual), and green; manganous hydroxide, $Mn(OH)_2$, white; manganese dioxide, $MnO_2$, dark brown; potassium permanganate, $KMnO_4$, purple; potassium manganate, $K_2MnO_4$, green.

**Reactions of Manganous Ion.** NaOH or $NH_4OH$ precipitates $Mn(OH)_2$, white, insoluble in excess reagent, soluble in HCl or $HNO_3$, also soluble in $NH_4Cl$ or $NH_4NO_3$ solution. $H_2S$ in alkaline solution precipitates MnS, pink, soluble in $HC_2H_3O_2$ and stronger acids. $Mn(OH)_2$ is not amphoteric nor does $Mn^{++}$ form a complex ammonia ion, although there are complex cyanides and fluorides of manganese. In acid solution $Mn^{++}$ can be oxidized to $MnO_4^-$ by such powerful oxidizing agents as $Pb_3O_4$, $K_2S_2O_8 + AgNO_3$, $KIO_4$, and $NaBiO_3$. In the presence of $NH_4OH$ or NaOH $Mn^{++}$ (or $Mn(OH)_2$) is oxidized very readily by $H_2O_2$, $Br_2$, or even by absorption of oxygen from the air, forming a brown precipitate of $Mn(OH)_3$ or hydrated $MnO_2$. Stronger oxidizing agents such as $Cl_2$ and $Ca(ClO)_2$, especially in the presence of a copper salt as catalyst (which also makes $Br_2$ effective), oxidize $Mn^{++}$ to $MnO_4^{--}$ and $MnO_4^-$. Most characteristic reaction: formation of $MnO_4^-$, purple, by oxidation in $HNO_3$ or $H_2SO_4$ solution by $KIO_4$ or other powerful oxidizing agents.

**More Common Permanganates.** Potassium permanganate, $KMnO_4$, purple, is the the chief salt technically available, although several other permanganates, such as $NaMnO_4$, $Zn(MnO_4)_2$, and $AgMnO_4$, are made.

**Reactions of Permanganate Ion.** All the various permanganates are soluble so there are no simple precipitation reactions. Permanganate ion is a strong oxidizing agent, especially in the presence of $HNO_3$ or $H_2SO_4$, oxidizing the ordinary reducing agents such as $Fe^{++}$, $Sn^{++}$, and $H_2SO_3$ very readily, and even such mild reducing agents as $H_2O_2$, $Cl^-$, and $Cr^{+3}$, forming $O_2$, $Cl_2$, and $Cr_2O_7^{--}$ when the solution is heated. Iodine with excess $KMnO_4$ forms $HIO_3$. In alkaline solution $KMnO_4$ is reduced first to dark green $MnO_4^{--}$, but if excess of reducing agent is used further reduction takes place readily with formation of dark brown, hydrated $MnO_2$. With $H_2S$ in alkaline solution the $MnO_2$ is slowly reduced to MnS, usually yielding the green modification. $NH_4OH$ slowly reduces $MnO_4^-$ in the cold with precipitation of $MnO_2$ and escape of $N_2$.

**More Common Manganates.** Potassium manganate, $K_2MnO_4$, dark green, may be obtained by fusing $MnO_2$ with $K_2CO_3$ with access of air or other effective oxidizing agent such as $KNO_3$ or $KClO_3$. It is thus prepared as an intermediate in the older method of manufacturing $KMnO_4$. With $KMnO_4$ available, a simpler method of preparing a manganate solution involves fusing $KMnO_4$ with KOH in a silver dish, or boiling a concentrated solution of $KMnO_4$ and KOH in a porcelain crucible.

**Reactions of Manganate Ion.** Nonreducing acids such as $HNO_3$ and $H_2SO_4$ (even $H_2CO_3$) convert $MnO_4^{--}$ to a mixture of $MnO_4^-$, purple, and $MnO_2$, brown. $Cl_2$ oxidizes $MnO_4^{--}$ to $MnO_4^-$. Reducing agents, even $NH_4OH$, reduce $MnO_4^{--}$ with precipitation of hydrated $MnO_2$.

**More Common Compounds of Cobalt.** Cobalt chloride, $CoCl_2 \cdot 6H_2O$, red; cobalt nitrate, $Co(NO_3)_2 \cdot 6H_2O$, red; cobalt sulfate, $CoSO_4 \cdot 7H_2O$, red; cobalt bromide, $CoBr_2 \cdot 6H_2O$, red, deliquescent; cobalt carbonate, $CoCO_3$, red; cobalt oxalate, $CoC_2O_4$, pink; cobalt phosphate, $Co_3(PO_4)_2$, pink; cobalt sulfide, CoS, black; cobalt hydroxide, $Co(OH)_2$, pink; cobalt oxide, CoO, brown; cobaltic oxide, $Co_2O_3$, brown.

**Reactions of Cobalt Ion.** NaOH precipitates $Co(OH)_2$, pink, soluble in acids, slightly soluble in $NH_4OH$ (formation of $Co(NH_3)_6^{++}$). $NH_4OH$ precipitates a basic salt, CoOHCl, green, changing with more $NH_4OH$ to $Co(OH)_2$, pink, and finally dissolving in excess $NH_4OH$. $H_2S$ in neutral or alkaline solution precipitates CoS, black, slowly soluble in HCl, readily soluble on heating in $HNO_3$ or aqua regia. In the presence of NaOH, NaCN dissolves $Co(OH)_2$, forming $Na_4Co(CN)_6$, which, with excess $Br_2$, is oxidized to $Na_3Co(CN)_6$ (separation from Ni, which precipitates as black, hydrated $NiO_2$). In $NH_4OH$ solution $Co(NH_3)_6^{++}$ is oxidized fairly readily by $H_2O_2$, $K_2S_2O_8$, etc., even by oxygen from the air, forming very stable, deep red, cobaltic ammonia ion, $Co(NH_3)_6^{+3}$. This ion is so stable that it can be acidified with HCl without decomposition, even precipitating as a slightly soluble $Co(NH_3)_5Cl_3 \cdot H_2O$, from strong HCl solution. The decomposition of this complex ion is best accomplished by boiling with NaOH, which drives off $NH_3$, precipitating $Co(OH)_3$, black. $NH_4CNS$ in concentrated solution forms a complex salt, $(NH_4)_2Co(CNS)_4$, blue in solution, and more soluble in amyl alcohol than in water. $H_2O_2$ in a neutral, buffered solution (prepared by shaking with excess of solid $NaHCO_3$) forms a dark green, slightly soluble compound, $Na_3Co(HCO_3)_6$. Concentrated HCl converts the pink solution of $CoCl_2$ to a sky blue, probably through the formation of a chlorocobaltite ion, $CoCl_4^{--}$. Careful evaporation of a solution of $CoCl_2$ yields a pink residue of the hydrated crystals, $CoCl_2 \cdot 6H_2O$. On heating this residue, blue, anhydrous $CoCl_2$ is formed. Most characteristic reaction: formation of $Co(CNS)_4^{--}$, blue, with concentrated $NH_4CNS$ solution, soluble in amyl alcohol, not decolorized by $SnCl_2$.

**More Common Compounds of Nickel.** Nickel chloride, $NiCl_2 \cdot 6H_2O$, green; nickel nitrate, $Ni(NO_3)_2 \cdot 6H_2O$, green; nickel sulfate, $NiSO_4 \cdot 6H_2O$; nickel bromide, $NiBr_2 \cdot 3H_2O$, green, deliquescent; nickel carbonate, $NiCO_3$, green; nickel dimethyl dioxime, $Ni(C_4H_7N_2O_2)_2$, scarlet; nickel oxalate, $NiC_2O_4$, light green; nickel phosphate, $Ni_3(PO_4)_2 \cdot 7H_2O$, green; nickel sulfide, NiS, black; nickelous hydroxide, $Ni(OH)_2$, green; nickelic hydroxide (hydrated nickel dioxide), $NiO_2 \cdot xH_2O$, black; nickel oxide, NiO, green.

**Reactions of Nickel Ion.** NaOH or $NH_4OH$ precipitates $Ni(OH)_2$, green, soluble in acids, in concentrated $NH_4Cl$ (or the ammonium salts), in NaCN (forming $Ni(CN)_4^{--}$), and in excess $NH_4OH$ (forming $Ni(NH_3)_6^{++}$, blue). $H_2S$ in neutral or alkaline solution precipitates NiS, black, slowly soluble in HCl, readily soluble on heating in $HNO_3$ or aqua regia. In the presence of NaOH, NaCN dissolves $Ni(OH)_2$, forming $Na_2Ni(CN)_4$, which undergoes oxidation with excess $Br_2$, precipitating as $NiO_2 \cdot xH_2O$, black (distinction from Co which forms a soluble cobalticyanide, $Co(CN)_6^{-3}$). In $NH_4OH$ solution $Ni(NH_3)_6^{++}$ is not readily oxidized, although if excess NaOH is added $K_2S_2O_8$ will precipitate $NiO_2 \cdot xH_2O$, black, even in the cold. In slightly ammoniacal, neutral or acetic acid solution, dimethyl dioxime forms a scarlet red, bulky, crystalline precipitate, $Ni(C_4H_7N_2O_2)_2$, often used for the quantitative estimation of nickel. Large amounts of cobalt interfere with the delicacy of the test and require special treatment. Most characteristic reaction: formation of the scarlet precipitate, $Ni(C_4H_7N_2O_2)_2$, with dimethyl dioxime in slightly ammoniacal solution.

## REACTIONS OF GROUP IV METALS IN THE SYSTEMATIC ANALYSIS OF EARLIER GROUPS

**At the Beginning of Group I.** Alkaline solutions containing $Zn(OH)_3^-$, $Zn(NH_3)_4^{++}$, $Co(NH_3)_6^{++}$ or $Ni(NH_3)_6^{++}$ may give precipitates of the hydroxides, soluble in excess of the acid, when nitric acid is added in preparing the solution for the precipitation of Group I. $MnO_4^-$ is unaffected at this point, but $MnO_4^{--}$ changes to a mixture of $MnO_4^-$ and hydrated manganese dioxide, $MnO_2 \cdot xH_2O$, this latter forming a brown precipitate insoluble in excess $HNO_3$. In this case the precipitate may be separated, dissolved in $HCl + CH_2O$ (reduced to $MnCl_2$), and the solution added to the solution after Group I.

**At the Beginning of Group II.** The clear solution after Group I should be examined for $MnO_4^-$, reddish purple. If present, this must be reduced with HCl and $CH_2O$ or $NaNO_2$ in the same way as in the case of $Cr_2O_7^{--}$, to avoid interference with effective control of the acidity of the solution while precipitating with $H_2S$. (Interfering reaction: $2MnO_4^- + 6H_3O^+ + 5H_2S = 2Mn^{++} + 5S + 14H_2O$.) Occasionally a red solution, originally ammoniacal, is mistaken for a permanganate, and on heating with HCl forms a dark red crystalline precipitate. This precipitate is due to $Co(NH_3)_6^{++}$, oxidized in $NH_4OH$ solution by atmospheric oxygen, or other reagents in the solution, to the stable cobaltic ammonia ion, $Co(NH_3)_6^{+++}$, which precipitates as a slightly soluble chloride, $Co(NH_3)_5Cl_3 \cdot H_2O$, when the solution is heated with HCl. Such a precipitate may be separated, boiled with NaOH (which converts the Co to $Co(OH)_3$, black), dissolved in $HCl + H_2O_2$ and the regular confirmatory tests tried as in Group IV, using the $NH_4CNS$-amyl alcohol reaction or the $NaHCO_3 + H_2O_2$ test. On neutralizing with $NH_4OH$ preparatory to making 0.25 $N$ with HCl, the fourth group metals may precipitate as hydroxides, dissolving again as the HCl is added. Occasionally when Mn is present, it is oxidized to $MnO_2$ if $NH_4OH$ is added and fails to redissolve in the dilute HCl. In such a case a drop of $H_2O_2$ will aid in dissolving the precipitate (reduces $MnO_2$ to $MnCl_2$). In the precipitation of Group II, ZnS may occasionally form if the acidity of the solution is somewhat low and $H_2S$ is passed in for a longer period than usual. Further, if $CH_2O$ is used in the reduction of $Cr_2O_7^{--}$ or $MnO_4^-$ and the excess is not removed by evaporation nearly to dryness, white, flocculent organic sulfur compounds may be obtained, when treating with $H_2S$, that may carry appreciable amounts of fourth group metals into the second group precipitate even though the solution is of proper acidity. In the analysis of the copper division of Group II the fourth group metals are found chiefly with Cu and Cd. The blue $Ni(NH_3)_6^{++}$ is occasionally encountered where $Cu(NH_3)_4^{++}$ is expected, although the difference in shade is sufficient to warn the alert analyst unless he is suffering some defect in color vision. If the final test for Cd is made in ammoniacal solution, a black precipitate of CoS or NiS, or a white precipitate of ZnS may be obtained.

In the precipitation of Group III it is necessary to maintain a high concentration of $NH_4^+$ and to add the reagent in $NH_4OH$ cautiously so as to avoid the introduction of more than 1 drop excess. Under these conditions only a small amount of the fourth group metals precipitates in Group III, $Zn(OH)_2$ being carried down to a greater extent than the others and $Mn(OH)_2$ to the least extent. It might be expected that with larger excess of $NH_4OH$, $Co^{++}$, $Ni^{++}$, and $Zn^{++}$ would be converted to complex ammonia ions, thus improving the separation. Actually, the separation is very much worse if too much $NH_4OH$ is added. In the case of $Mn^{++}$ oxidizing conditions are sometimes set up, particularly through using excessive amounts of $HNO_3$ in oxidizing $Fe^{++}$ to $Fe^{+3}$, such that in the alkaline solution $Mn(OH)_3$ or even $MnO_2$ is formed. These compounds are of the same order of solubility as $Fe(OH)_3$ and therefore precipitate readily. In the analysis of the third group precipitate any $Zn(OH)_2$ divides itself between the $Fe(OH)_3$ precipitate and NaOH solution. In either case it does not interfere with any of the regular tests and its presence is not recognized unless special tests are applied. Of these latter, the simplest is to use the solution after precipitation of $Al(OH)_3$ with excess $NH_4Cl$ ($Zn(OH)_3^-$ precipitates in part as $Zn(OH)_2$ with the $Al(OH)_3$, but some stays in solution as $Zn(NH_3)_4^{++}$ along with any $CrO_4^{--}$): Acidify with $HC_2H_3O_2$, precipitate any $CrO_4^{--}$ or $Cr_2O_7^{--}$ with excess $BaCl_2$, centrifuge, and test the clear solution with $H_2S$, looking for a white precipitate of ZnS. Mn, Co, and Ni all stay as precipitates ($MnO_2 \cdot xH_2O$, $Co(OH)_3$, $Ni(OH)_2$) after treatment with $NaOH + H_2O_2$, and therefore will be removed along with $Fe(OH)_3$. The combined precipitate may be dissolved in dilute $H_2SO_4$ with the aid of a little $H_2O_2$ as reducing agent for $MnO_2$ and $Co(OH)_3$. This solution may then be divided into several portions and individual tests applied for $Fe^{+3}$, $Co^{++}$, $Ni^{++}$ and $Mn^{++}$, following the regular procedures for their confirmatory tests at the end of the usual separations.

## PREPARING THE SOLUTION FOR THE PRECIPITATION OF GROUP IV

If earlier groups have been present, the filtrate from Group III is already adjusted for the precipitation of Group IV. If no earlier groups are present, the only preliminary precautions necessary are to look for $MnO_4^-$, reddish purple, and $MnO_4^{--}$, dark green in strongly alkaline solution. If either is present, acidify with HCl, adding about 5 drops excess, then reduce to $Mn^{++}$ with formaldehyde or sodium nitrite in the regular way. This solution is then treated with 0.2 g. of $NH_4Cl$, diluted to 25 drops and made alkaline with $NH_4OH$. To this solution, or to the solution after Group III, add 5 drops of 5 *N* $NH_4OH$ and proceed with the precipitation of Group IV.

## PRECIPITATION AND ANALYSIS OF GROUP IV

**Precipitation of Group IV and Separation of Co and Ni from Zn and Mn.** Heat the test tube in the hot water bath for 1–2 minutes, then pass in $H_2S$ for about 10–15 seconds, and centrifuge. Test the solution with a little more $H_2S$ to make sure precipitation is complete. If not, treat with $H_2S$ 10–15 seconds longer and repeat the test. Centrifuge, set the clear solution aside to test for later groups, and wash the precipitate 2–3 times with distilled water. Add to the precipitate 20 drops of $H_2O$, let stand 5–10 minutes, then 5 drops of 5 *N* HCl, and stir for about 1 minute to mix thoroughly. Centrifuge and wash, setting the precipitate aside to test for Co and Ni and examining the clear solution for Mn and Zn (after removal of $H_2S$).

$$MnS + H_3O^+ = Mn^{++} + H_2S + 2H_2O$$

$$ZnS + 2H_3O^+ = Zn^{++} + H_2S + 2H_2O$$

*Explanatory Notes.* (1) Moderate excess of $NH_4OH$ is necessary in order to obtain ready precipitation of MnS.

(2) $H_2S$ dissolves more readily in the ammoniacal solution in Group IV than it does in the acid solution in Group II. Therefore, less is wasted and it takes correspondingly less time to reach an equivalent concentration of $H_2S$ in solution in Group IV. Further, in Group II it was important to pass in $H_2S$ for a fair length of time to avoid the presence of a chloro-sulfide of mercury, $HgCl_2 \cdot HgS$, in Group II. In Group IV, however, if $H_2S$ is passed in for a little while after the sulfides are precipitated, NiS may be changed from its usual flocculent character to a colloidal suspension that fails to settle readily on centrifuging. If this effect is observed, transfer the cloudy so-

lution (above the precipitation) to a small crucible, neutralize with $HC_2H_3O_2$, and boil for half a minute. This coagulates the NiS so that it may be centrifuged, washed, and combined with the regular fourth group precipitate or examined directly for Ni.

TABLE VIII. OUTLINE OF PROCEDURE FOR GROUP IV

| $Co(NH_3)_6^{++}$ | $Ni(NH_3)_6^{++}$ | $Zn(NH_3)_4^{++}$ | $Mn^{++}$ |
|---|---|---|---|
| $H_2S$ | | | |
| CoS | NiS | ZnS | MnS |
| HCl | | | |
| CoS | NiS | $Zn^{++}$ | $Mn^{++}$ |
| $HCl + HNO_3$ | | Boil out $H_2S$, then add $NaOH + Br_2$ | |
| $Co^{++}$ | $Ni^{++}$ | $Zn(OH)_3^{-}$ | $MnO_2$ |
| Divide into two parts.<br>Test one for Co and the other for Ni. | | $NH_4OH$ + boil | $HNO_3 + H_2O_2$ |
| *A*. Co<br>1. $NH_4CNS \rightarrow (NH_4)_2Co(CNS)_4$<br>blue<br>solution in amyl alcohol<br>2. $NaHCO_3 + H_2O_2$<br>$\rightarrow Co(HCO_3)_6^{-3}$<br>green | | 1. $H_2S \rightarrow ZnS$<br>white<br>2. $HC_2H_3O_2$<br>$\rightarrow Zn^{++}$<br>$K_4Fe(CN)_6$<br>$\rightarrow Zn_2Fe(CN)_6$<br>white | $Mn^{++}$<br>1. $HNO_3 + Pb_3O_4$<br>$\rightarrow MnO_4^{-}$<br>purple<br>2. $AgNO_3 + K_2S_2O_8$<br>$\rightarrow MnO_4^{-}$<br>purple<br>3. $HNO_3 + KIO_4$<br>$\rightarrow MnO_4^{-}$<br>purple |
| *B*. Ni<br>$NH_4Cl + NH_4OH + C_4H_8N_2O_2$<br>$\rightarrow Ni(C_4H_7N_2O_2)_2$<br>red | | | |

(3) MnS and ZnS usually precipitate in very finely divided form which is difficult either to filter or to settle fully with the centrifuge. When filtration is used the directions call for adding filter paper pulp to the solution and stirring before attempting to filter if the group precipitate is light colored (absence of significant amounts of CoS or NiS). The filter paper pulp forms a matte on the filter which fills in with the MnS and ZnS, retaining the precipitates effectively. When CoS or NiS is present it is usually a flocculent

precipitate, easily retained by the filter paper, and effective in retaining any MnS or ZnS.

To assist in settling the MnS and ZnS by centrifuging, the solution should be hot when treated with $H_2S$ for precipitation of the group. Even then it may be necessary to extend the time of centrifuging to 2–3 minutes.

(4) The separation of Mn and Zn from Co and Ni by the action of cold dilute HCl on the sulfides depends primarily on a difference in the rate of dissolving of the two sets of sulfides. MnS and ZnS dissolve rapidly, whereas CoS and NiS dissolve slowly. By letting the sulfides stand a little while before treating with HCl, the sulfides of Co and Ni react rather more slowly and the separation is improved to that extent. However, it should be noted that small amounts of $CoCl_2$ and $NiCl_2$ are regularly present in the solution which is supposed to contain only $ZnCl_2$ and $MnCl_2$. In the analysis of this solution the $Co^{++}$ and $Ni^{++}$ do not interfere seriously with the tests for Mn and Zn, although they may cause some slight irregularities.

**Separation of Zn from Mn and Identification of Zinc.** Boil the dilute HCl solution containing $MnCl_2$ and $ZnCl_2$ for 1 minute to remove $H_2S$, noting the odor or testing the vapors with lead acetate paper from time to time to make sure that all the $H_2S$ is gone. Then add NaOH until strongly alkaline, 5–10 drops excess, and test the vapors of the solution for $NH_3$ with a strip of moist red litmus paper held just above the surface of the solution. If the litmus paper turns blue within half a minute, boil the solution 1 minute to remove the $NH_3$ and repeat the test. When the test becomes negative, add 5 drops of $Br_2$ water and stir thoroughly. This precipitates Mn as $MnO_2$, brown; but Zn stays in solution as $Zn(OH)_3^-$. Centrifuge and wash, setting the precipitate aside to test for Mn. To the solution add 1–2 drops of $NH_4OH$ and again heat to boiling. This removes any $BrO^-$ ($2NH_3 + 3BrO^- = N_2 + 3Br^- + 3H_2O$). Then pass in $H_2S$ for 15–20 seconds and look for a white precipitate of ZnS.

*Explanatory Notes.* (1) If $H_2S$ is not removed, the sulfides of Mn and Zn will reprecipitate when NaOH is added, and the $Br_2$ may not be present in sufficient amount to oxidize MnS and ZnS to the proper forms for an effective separation of Mn from Zn.

(2) If the solution contains $NH_4OH$ when the bromine water is added, the latter may be reduced by the $NH_3$ without oxidizing the Mn, Co, or Ni. Under these conditions no separation of Zn from the other metals is obtained.

(3) If Co is present and too little $Br_2$ is added, it may be found in solution with Zn as a cobaltite, $Co(OH)_3^-$, which is blue in color. Co in this form is easily separated from Zn by adding more bromine water which precipitates the Co as black $Co(OH)_3$. On centrifuging, the clear solution may then be tested for Zn in the regular way.

(4) It is necessary to reduce any $BrO^-$ before testing for Zn with $H_2S$ to prevent oxidation of $H_2S$ to S°. The latter might precipitate or impart a yellow color to the alkaline solution, being mistaken for ZnS.

(5) As an alternative procedure the final alkaline solution may be acidified with $HC_2H_3O_2$, then tested for Zn by adding either $K_4Fe(CN)_6$ or $H_2S$, obtaining white $Zn_2Fe(CN)_6$ or ZnS, respectively.

**Dissolving $MnO_2$ and Identification of Mn.** Add a mixture of 5 drops of 5 *N* $HNO_3$ and 1 drop of $H_2O_2$ to the precipitate of $MnO_2$. The $MnO_2$ dissolves according to the following reaction:

$$MnO_2 + H_3O^+ + H_2O_2 = Mn^{++} + O_2 + 4H_2O$$

If the amount of precipitate was fairly large, use 1 drop portions of the solution and try several of the reactions for oxidizing $Mn^{++}$ to $MnO_4^-$. If the amount of precipitate was small, use a larger fraction of the solution and try only one or two of the following tests.

(*a*) *Red Lead Method.* Add 5 drops of 5 *N* $HNO_3$ and about 50 mg. $Pb_3O_4$ and heat to boiling. Let the solution stand a moment until the excess $PbO_2$ settles; then look for the purple color of $MnO_4^-$ in the clear, upper layer of the solution.

(*b*) *Periodate Method.* Add 5 drops of 5 *N* $HNO_3$ and about 50 mg. of $KIO_4$. Heat to boiling and keep at the boiling point for 2–3 minutes if the purple color does not develop in a shorter time. $Mn^{++}$ is oxidized to $MnO_4^-$, purple.

(*c*) *Persulfate Method.* Add 5 drops of 5 *N* $HNO_3$, dilute to 15–20 drops, and add $AgNO_3$ a drop at a time until any chloride is precipitated as AgCl; then add 1 drop excess of $AgNO_3$ and 0.1 g. of $K_2S_2O_8$, and heat to boiling. $Mn^{++}$ is oxidized to $MnO_4^-$, purple.

(*d*) *Bismuthate Method.* Add 5 drops of 5 *N* $HNO_3$, dilute to 15–20 drops, boil 1 minute, then cool thoroughly and add about 50 mg. of $NaBiO_3$. $Mn^{++}$ is oxidized to $MnO_4^-$, purple, the excess $NaBiO_3$ settling out as a brownish black precipitate.

(*e*) *Hypochlorite Method.* Add 5 drops of 5% $Ca(ClO)_2$ solution, 1–2 drops of $CuSO_4$, and 5 drops excess of NaOH. Heat to boiling, then let stand until the brown CuO settles. A purple color of $MnO_4^-$ indicates Mn.

*Explanatory Notes.* (1) $H_2O_2$ is a very effective reducing agent for $MnO_2$ in acid solution. Any $Co(OH)_3$ and $NiO_2 \cdot xH_2O$ that may be present with the $MnO_2$ may dissolve at the same time with formation of $Co(NO_3)_2$ and $Ni(NO_3)_2$. However, the $Co(OH)_3$ and $NiO_2 \cdot xH_2O$ dissolve less readily than $MnO_2$; so if any difficulty is encountered at this point in getting complete solution, the precipitate may be discarded and the clear solution used to test for Mn.

(2) The final test for Mn involves oxidation to $MnO_4^-$ which in ordinary concentration imparts a rich purple to the solution, but in very dilute solution is light red with the purple tinge practically absent. Since Co is frequently present from incomplete separation by action of dilute HCl on the sulfides, the analyst occasionally mistakes the light red of $Co^{++}$ for a very dilute solution of $MnO_4^-$. If desired, the Mn may be separated from any

Co (or Ni) by reprecipitating as $MnO_2$ in an ammoniacal solution. The directions are as follows: To the $HNO_3$ solution add 5–10 drops of $NH_4Cl$ solution and about 5 drops excess of 5 *N* $NH_4OH$, then add 0.1 g. of $K_2S_2O_8$, boil for a moment, centrifuge, and wash. Co and Ni stay in solution as complex ammonia salts while the $MnO_2$ precipitates. The $MnO_2$ may then be dissolved in $HNO_3 + H_2O_2$ and the regular tests for Mn applied.

(3) If the earlier separations have been carried out effectively, the student usually encounters more difficulty in handling large amounts of Mn than moderate or small amounts. Since the purple color of $MnO_4^-$ is readily visible with less than 0.1 mg. of Mn present, it is desirable to try the test first with small amounts of the final solution. In this way failures due to precipitation of $MnO_2$ (partly caused by too little oxidizing agent for the amount of Mn) may be avoided. If the test fails on this sample, a larger portion may then be used to insure the identification of minor amounts of Mn.

(4) In the red lead test it is necessary to use excess of $Pb_3O_4$ to oxidize $Mn^{++}$ beyond the stage of $MnO_2$ and to use sufficient $HNO_3$ so that the solution will be moderately acid even after the reaction between $Pb_3O_4$ and $HNO_3$ ($Pb_3O_4 + 4H_3O^+ = 2Pb^{++} + PbO_2 + 6H_2O$).

(5) In the $NaBiO_3$ method the solution is boiled for a short time to remove any $HNO_2$ ($2HNO_2 = H_2O + NO + NO_2$) commonly present in $HNO_3$. $NaBiO_3$ is the only one of the oxidizing agents strong enough to convert moderate amounts of $Mn^{++}$ to $MnO_4^-$ readily in a cold solution.

(6) $KIO_4$ is a little slower than the others, but is less likely to cause precipitation of $MnO_2$ than some of the others.

(7) The persulfate method is the least satisfactory for more than small amounts of Mn. With larger amounts of Mn there will be precipitation of $MnO_2$ and frequently none of the Mn is oxidized beyond this stage.

(8) One of the most common difficulties with the test for Mn lies in using excessive amounts of $H_2O_2$ when dissolving $MnO_2$ in $HNO_3 + H_2O_2$. This extra $H_2O_2$ uses up the oxidizing agent added to oxidize the $Mn^{++}$ to $MnO_4^-$ and thus the test fails even though Mn is present. This condition may be recognized in the laboratory by the unusual amount of effervescence as the $H_2O_2$ is oxidized to $O_2$. In such a case, continue adding the oxidizing agent in small amounts until the effervescence stops and then continue with the test in the regular way.

**Identification of Co and Ni.** Transfer to a small crucible the residue insoluble in dilute HCl. Add 2–3 drops of 5 *N* $HNO_3$ and 5–10 drops of 5*N* HCl, heat to boiling and continue the reaction until the CoS and NiS have dissolved (except for a residue of free sulfur).

$$3CoS + 8H_3O^+ + 2NO_3^- = 3Co^{++} + 2NO + 3S + 12H_2O$$

$$3NiS + 8H_3O^+ + 2NO_3^- = 3Ni^{++} + 2NO + 3S + 12H_2O$$

Evaporate very nearly to dryness, heating carefully at the last to avoid formation of insoluble basic salts. Redissolve in 10 drops of water, remove any residue of S°, and use separate portions of the solution to test for Co and Ni.

**Test for Co.** To 1–2 drops of this solution add 1–2 drops of amyl alcohol, then add 3–4 drops of a 50% solution of $NH_4CNS$ (or add 0.1 g. of $NH_4CNS$ crystals). Shake thoroughly and let stand a moment for the amyl alcohol to form a layer again. If the alcohol layer is blue, cobalt is present.

$$Co^{++} + 2NH_4^+ + 4CNS^- = (NH_4)_2Co(CNS)_4$$

If the alcohol layer is red or green in color (some $FeCNS^{++}$ present), add a drop of $SnCl_2$ to reduce any $Fe^{+3}$ to $Fe^{++}$, shake, and look for the blue color in the alcohol layer.

**Test for Ni.** To 1–2 drops of the solution add 2–3 drops of $NH_4Cl$ solution, make slightly alkaline with $NH_4OH$, and add 2–3 drops of the reagent dimethyl dioxime (a dilute solution in alcohol). A bright red precipitate indicates the presence of Ni.

$$Ni^{++} + 2NH_3 + 2C_4H_8N_2O_2 = \underline{Ni(C_4H_7N_2O_2)_2} + 2NH_4^+$$

If the test for Ni is uncertain or negative, but the earlier test for Co was strong, the test for Ni should be tried again as follows: To 4–5 drops of the solution to be tested add 15–20 drops of water and then add 3 *N* NaOH a drop at a time with thorough mixing until a slight precipitate persists. Add 1 *N* HCl dropwise until this precipitate barely dissolves. Now add 1 drop of 5 *N* $NH_4OH$ and mix thoroughly. This precipitates much of the Co as a green basic salt, leaving most of the Ni in solution.

$$Co^{++} + NH_4OH + Cl^- = \underline{CoOHCl} + NH_4^+$$

Centrifuge, add 2 drops of dimethyl dioxime solution to the clear solution, and look for the formation of a scarlet precipitate.

*Explanatory Notes.* (1) After evaporating the nitrohydrochloric acid solution containing any $CoCl_2$ and $NiCl_2$, a test for Co may be applied as follows: Tilt the crucible at a moderate angle and heat the bottom, near its upper edge, for a few seconds. If Co is present, a blue color will develop because of the conversion of the pink, crystallized $CoCl_2 \cdot 6H_2O$ to blue, anhydrous $CoCl_2$.

$$CoCl_2 \cdot 6H_2O = CoCl_2 + 6H_2O$$

After the crucible has cooled again and water is added, the $CoCl_2$ dissolves to form a pink solution.

(2) In the confirmatory test for Co with $NH_4CNS$, it is necessary to keep the concentration of the reagent very high in order to obtain effective conversion of the $Co^{++}$ to $Co(CNS)_4^{--}$. For this reason it is recommended

that only a small amount of solution be taken for the test so that the amount of reagent needed may be kept small. If the concentration of the reagent is too low, the test is practically worthless, but when properly carried out it is both delicate and characteristic.

(3) If more than a very small amount of $Fe^{+3}$ is present when the $NH_4CNS$ test is applied, the red $FeCNS^{++}$ will mask the blue of the cobalt compound completely, but with small amounts of $Fe^{+3}$ (normal impurities in salts) the color may be shifted only to a green. In this case a drop of $SnCl_2$ will destroy the color of the $FeCNS^{++}$ so that the blue may be readily seen. It is not advisable to reduce larger amounts of $Fe^{+3}$ in this way because of the dilution effect when more $SnCl_2$ is added.

(4) An alternative test for Co, which uses only ordinary reagents, may be carried out as follows: To 2–3 drops of the test solution add 0.1 g. of solid $NaHCO_3$, more than sufficient to saturate the solution. Then add 1 drop of $H_2O_2$, shake, and centrifuge. If Co is present, the solution will be green. In this test the $NaHCO_3$ sets up a neutral, buffered solution in which the $H_2O_2$ will oxidize Co to a green compound, $Na_3Co(HCO_3)_6$, slightly soluble.

$$2Co^{++} + 14HCO_3^{-} + H_2O_2 = 2Co(HCO_3)_6^{-3} + 2CO_3^{--} + 2H_2O$$

(5) If much $Co^{++}$ is present, it interferes with the test for $Ni^{++}$ by combining with the dimethyl dioxime to form a soluble complex compound which prevents the precipitation of $Ni(C_4H_7N_2O_2)_2$ when the solution contains only a small amount of $Ni^{++}$. Thus, ordinary cobalt salts usually contain 0.5–1% of Ni, yet may fail to give a test for Ni in routine tests. In the alternative procedure suggested for this case, it is necessary to avoid the use of $NH_4Cl$ (or the presence of significant amounts of free acid that would react with the $NH_4OH$); otherwise the precipitation of CoOHCl may be so incomplete that the test for $Ni^{++}$ is still unsatisfactory.

## REPORTING GROUP IV IONS IN AN UNKNOWN SOLUTION

**Cobalt.** In solution cobalt shows only a valence of two for the simple ion, although oxidation in alkaline solution may produce complex ions in which the valence is three. Since there is no simple test to identify the higher valence, only the lower valence is commonly given out for study. $Co(OH)_2$ is not significantly amphoteric, but $Co^{++}$ does combine with $NH_3$ to form $Co(NH_3)_6^{++}$. If the original solution is acid, report $Co^{++}$; if it is alkaline and has an odor of $NH_3$, report $Co(NH_3)_6^{++}$.

**Nickel.** In solution nickel shows only the valence of two. The hydroxide is not amphoteric, but $Ni^{++}$ will combine with excess of $NH_3$ to form the complex ion $Ni(NH_3)_6^{++}$. If the original solution is acid, report $Ni^{++}$; if it is alkaline and has the odor of $NH_3$, report $Ni(NH_3)_6^{++}$.

**Zinc.** In solution zinc shows only the valence of two. The hydroxide is amphoteric forming alkaline solutions which contain zincate ion, $Zn(OH)_3^-$. Also $Zn^{++}$ combines readily with excess of $NH_3$ to form a complex ammonia ion, $Zn(NH_3)_4^{++}$. To distinguish between these note the reaction of the solution to litmus; and, if the solution is alkaline, test for the presence of $NH_3$ by odor or by holding moist red litmus paper in the fumes above the solution (out of contact with the solution). If the solution is acid, report $Zn^{++}$; if alkaline with negative test for $NH_3$, report $Zn(OH)_3^-$; if alkaline with positive test for $NH_3$, report $Zn(NH_3)_4^{++}$.

**Manganese.** In solution manganese shows three common valences: two, six, and seven, the first a positive ion, $Mn^{++}$, the other two negative ions, $MnO_4^{--}$ and $MnO_4^-$. The most characteristic distinguishing feature is the difference in color of these ions: $Mn^{++}$ is colorless in dilute solution, faint pink in concentrated solution; $MnO_4^{--}$, manganate ion, is dark green in color and is found only in a solution strongly alkaline with NaOH or KOH; $MnO_4^-$, permanganate ion, is purple in color, shading off to a light red in very dilute solution, and may be found in acid, neutral, or alkaline solution.

## GROUP IV METALS IN RELATION TO OTHER GROUPS

The behavior of the fourth group metals in the precipitation of earlier groups has already been discussed in this chapter (page 140).

Metals of Groups II and III, incompletely precipitated in their regular place, may precipitate in Group IV. The chief instances of this are $Cd^{++}$, $Pb^{++}$, $Fe^{++}$, and $Fe^{+3}$. Occasionally small amounts of $Cd^{++}$ and $Pb^{++}$ escape precipitation in Group II because of excessive acidity or the presence of high concentration of $Cl^-$. In Group IV the slight alkalinity increases the concentration of $S^{--}$ supplied to such an extent that CdS and PbS would form readily. In the case of Fe, incomplete oxidation of $Fe^{++}$ before adding $NH_4OH$ will permit some Fe to be found in the filtrate from Group III. Also when there is only a very small amount of third group metal present the hydroxide may not flocculate into visible particles and thus may be overlooked unless the solution stands for a short time before continuing with Group IV. Fe in the solution after Group III forms FeS or $Fe_2S_3$, black, in Group IV. In the analysis of the fourth group precipitate the sulfides of Fe dissolve in the 1 $N$ HCl; CdS and PbS partially dissolve. In the separation of Mn from Zn a white precipitate of $Cd(OH)_2$ occasionally appears, this being the chief way in which one becomes aware that there is anything wrong with earlier group separations. In the cases of Fe and Pb, whose sulfides are black, there is little interference with the usual confirmatory tests for $Co^{++}$ and $Ni^{++}$, which are commonly present when the precipitate in Group IV is black. The small amount of $Fe(OH)_3$ will not obscure the scarlet precipitate of $Ni(C_4H_7N_2O_2)_2$ obtained with ordinary amounts of $Ni^{++}$; and the red $FeCNS^{++}$ obtained in the $NH_4CNS$ test for $Co^{++}$ is easily reduced to colorless $Fe^{++}$ by a little $SnCl_2$.

There are no serious irregularities in Group IV due to the presence of later group metals. With high concentration of $NH_4Cl$ present in the solution after Group III, the moderate amount of $NH_4OH$ then added does not introduce a sufficiently high concentration of $OH^-$ to cause the precipitation of any of the later group metals in Group IV. With higher concentrations of $OH^-$ the main losses of later group metals will be as follows: Carbonates of Ca, Sr, and Ba may precipitate as a result of $CO_3^{--}$ in the $NH_4OH$ ($CO_2$ absorbed from the air); $Mg(OH)_2$ may precipitate in part if the concentration of $Mg^{++}$ is not too low; CaS may precipitate in part when $H_2S$ is passed in if the concentration of $Ca^{++}$ is fairly high. These are all white precipitates that might be mistaken for ZnS if no confirmatory tests were tried, but there are no interferences with the regular tests for fourth group metals.

Under ordinary conditions the fourth group metals are all precipitated satisfactorily as the sulfides, but ZnS and MnS are difficult to centrifuge and occasionally are not fully separated from Groups V and VI. In this case the Zn is lost, but the Mn will form a white granular precipitate of $MnNH_4PO_4$ when the test for Mg is being applied. Since this is similar in appearance to $MgNH_4PO_4$, it interferes with this test. The presence of Mn at this point may be recognized by centrifuging, washing, dissolving the precipitate in $HNO_3$ and then using $KIO_4$ or one of the other strong oxidizing agents to convert $Mn^{++}$ to $MnO_4^-$. If this test is positive, the test for $Mg^{++}$ is doubtful unless the precipitate was fairly bulky and the amount of $Mn^{++}$ indicated is small.

## REACTIONS OF GROUP IV METALS IN THE SYSTEMATIC ANALYSIS OF A SOLUTION

### Zinc

*Acidifying an alkaline solution with $HNO_3$*

$$Zn(OH)_3^- + 3H_3O^+ = Zn^{++} + 6H_2O$$
$$Zn(NH_3)_4^{++} + 4H_3O^+ = Zn^{++} + 4NH_4^+ + 4H_2O$$

*Adjusting the acidity for the precipitation of Group II*

$$Zn^{++} + 2NH_4OH = \underline{Zn(OH)_2} + 2NH_4^+$$
$$\underline{Zn(OH)_2} + 2H_3O^+ = Zn^{++} + 4H_2O$$

*Adding excess $NH_3$ solution before precipitating Group IV*

$$Zn^{++} + 4NH_3 = Zn(NH_3)_4^{++}$$

*In Group IV*

$$Zn(NH_3)_4^{++} + HS^- = \underline{ZnS} + NH_4^+ + 3NH_3$$

$$\underline{ZnS} + 2H_3O^+ = Zn^{++} + H_2S + 2H_2O$$
$$Zn^{++} + 3OH^- = Zn(OH)_3^-$$
$$1.\ Zn(OH)_3^- + HS^- = \underline{ZnS} + H_2O + 2OH^-$$
$$2.\ Zn(OH)_3^- + 3HC_2H_3O_2 = Zn^{++} + 3H_2O + 3C_2H_3O_2^-$$
$$(a)\ Zn^{++} + H_2S + 2C_2H_3O_2^- = \underline{ZnS} + 2HC_2H_3O_2$$
$$(b)\ 2Zn^{++} + Fe(CN)_6^{-4} = \underline{Zn_2Fe(CN)_6}$$

**Manganese**

*Acidifying in alkaline solution with $HNO_3$*

$$3MnO_4^{--} + 4H_3O^+ = 2MnO_4^- + \underline{MnO_2} + 6H_2O$$

*Reducing with $HCl + CH_2O$ or $NaNO_2$*

$$2MnO_4^- + 6H_3O^+ + 5CH_2O = 2Mn^{++} + 5CH_2O_2 + 9H_2O$$
$$\text{or } 2MnO_4^- + 5HNO_2 + H_3O^+ = 2Mn^{++} + 5NO_3^- + 4H_2O$$
$$\underline{MnO_2} + 2H_3O^+ + CH_2O = Mn^{++} + CH_2O_2 + 3H_2O$$
$$\text{or } \underline{MnO_2} + HNO_2 + H_3O^+ = Mn^{++} + NO_3^- + 2H_2O$$

*Adjusting the acidity for the precipitation of Group II*

$$Mn^{++} + 2NH_4OH = \underline{Mn(OH)_2} + 2NH_4^+$$
$$\underline{Mn(OH)_2} + 2H_3O^+ = Mn^{++} + 4H_2O$$

*In Group IV*

$$Mn^{++} + NH_3 + HS^- = \underline{MnS} + NH_4^+$$
$$\underline{MnS} + 2H_3O^+ = Mn^{++} + H_2S + 2H_2O$$
$$Mn^{++} + ClO^- + 2OH^- = \underline{MnO_2} + Cl^- + H_2O$$
$$\underline{MnO_2} + 2H_3O^+ + H_2O_2 = Mn^{++} + O_2 + 3H_2O$$
$$1.\ 2Mn^{++} + 5IO_4^- + 9H_2O = 2MnO_4^- + 5IO_3^- + 6H_3O^+$$
$$2.\ 2Mn^{++} + 5Pb_3O_4 + 24H_3O^+ = 2MnO_4^- + 15Pb^{++} + 36H_2O$$
$$3.\ 2Mn^{++} + \underline{5K_2S_2O_8} + 14H_2O\ (+\ Ag^+) = 2MnO_4^- + 10K^+ + 10HSO_4^- + 6H_3O^+$$
$$4.\ 2Mn^{++} + \underline{5NaBiO_3} + 14H_3O^+ = 2MnO_4^- + 5Na^+ + 5Bi^{+3} + 21H_2O$$
$$5.\ 2Mn^{++} + 5ClO^- + 6OH^-\ (+\ Cu^{++}) = 2MnO_4^- + 5Cl^- + 3H_2O$$

**Cobalt**

*Slow oxidation of an ammoniacal solution*

$$4Co(NH_3)_6^{++} + O_2 + 4NH_4^+ = 4Co(NH_3)_6^{+3} + 4NH_3 + 2H_2O$$

*Acidifying an alkaline solution with $HNO_3$*

$$Co(NH_3)_6^{++} + 6H_3O^+ = Co^{++} + 6NH_4^+ + 6H_2O$$

*Heating with excess HCl in the reduction of $Cr_2O_7^{--}$*

$$Co(NH_3)_6^{+3} + 3Cl^- + H_3O^+ = \underline{Co(NH_3)_5Cl_3} + NH_4^+ + H_2O$$

*Adjusting the acidity for the precipitation of Group II*

$$Co^{++} + NH_4OH + Cl^- = \underline{CoOHCl} + NH_4^+$$
$$\underline{CoOHCl} + H_3O^+ = Co^{++} + Cl^- + 2H_2O$$

*Adding excess $NH_3$ before precipitating Group IV*

$$Co^{++} + 6NH_3 = Co(NH_3)_6^{++}$$

*In Group IV*

$$Co(NH_3)_6^{++} + HS^- = \underline{CoS} + NH_4^+ + 5NH_3$$
$$\underline{3CoS} + 2NO_3^- + 8H_3O^+ = 3Co^{++} + \underline{3S} + 2NO + 12H_2O$$
$$1.\ Co^{++} + 4CNS^- = \underbrace{Co(CNS)_4^{--}}_{\text{blue}}$$
$$2.\ 2Co^{++} + 14HCO_3^- + H_2O_2 = \underbrace{2Co(HCO_3)_6^{-3}}_{\text{green}} + 2CO_3^{--} + 2H_2O$$

*In the procedures for Mn*

$$2Co^{++} + ClO^- + 4OH^- + H_2O = \underline{2Co(OH)_3} + Cl^-$$
$$\underline{4Co(OH)_3} + 2H_2O_2 + 8H_3O^+ = 4Co^{++} + 20H_2O + 2O_2$$

*Separation from Mn*

$$Co^{++} + 6NH_3 = Co(NH_3)_6^{++}$$
$$2Co(NH_3)_6^{++} + \underline{K_2S_2O_8} = 2Co(NH_3)_6^{+3} + 2SO_4^{--} + 2K^+$$

**Nickel**

*Acidifying an alkaline solution with $HNO_3$*

$$Ni(NH_3)_6^{++} + 6H_3O^+ = Ni^{++} + 6NH_4^+ + 6H_2O$$

*Adjusting the acidity for the precipitation of Group II*

$$Ni^{++} + 2NH_4OH = \underline{Ni(OH)_2} + 2NH_4^+$$
$$\underline{Ni(OH)_2} + 2H_3O^+ = Ni^{++} + 4H_2O$$

*Adding excess $NH_3$ before precipitating Group IV*

$$Ni^{++} + 6NH_3 = Ni(NH_3)_6^{++}$$

*In Group IV*

$$Ni(NH_3)_6^{++} + HS^- = \underline{NiS} + NH_4^+ + 5NH_3$$
$$\underline{3NiS} + 2NO_3^- + 8H_3O^+ = 3Ni^{++} + 2NO + 3S + 12H_2O$$
$$Ni^{++} + 2NH_3 + 2C_4H_8N_2O_2 = \underline{Ni(C_4H_7N_2O_2)_2} + 2NH_4^+$$

## SUMMARY AND REVIEW

Preliminary Operations

1. Reduction of permanganate
   When? How? Why?
2. Losses in Group II
   (*A*) Mn due to pptn. of MnOOH when adjusting acidity
   (*B*) Zn due to pptn. of ZnS
3. Incomplete removal of $H_2S$ before pptn. of Group III
4. Incomplete oxidation of $Fe^{++}$ before pptn. of Group III

5. (*A*) Pptn. of MnOOH in Group III
   Detection in Group III
   (*B*) Pptn. of Zn, Co and Ni in Group III
   (*C*) (Combined method for Groups III and IV)

Preparation of Group III Filtrate for Precipitation of Group IV

(*A*) Condition of Group III filtrate
(*B*) Addition of $NH_4OH$

Actual Precipitation

1. (*A*) Why avoid large excess of $H_2S$?
   Effect on (*a*) Zn, (*b*) Ni, (*c*) Mn
   (*B*) Why not use $(NH_4)_2S_2$?
   Effect on (*a*) Zn, (*b*) Ni, (*c*) Mn
   (*C*) Use of $S^{--}$ to ppt. Group II as compared with Group IV
2. Ppt. light colored
   (*A*) Conclusions justified
   (*B*) Difficulty in filtration
   Remedies
3. Ppt. black
   (*A*) Conclusions justified
4. Filtration
   (*A*) Why wait 5–10 minutes before adding HCl to the precipitate?
   (*B*) Testing for complete pptn.
   (*C*) Color of filtrate
5. Washing the precipitate
   (*A*) Why wash?
   (*B*) Number of washings necessary

Analysis of the Precipitates

1. Solution in 1 *N* HCl
   (*A*) Precautions
   (*B*) Incompleteness of the operation
   (*C*) Insolubility of NiS and CoS in dilute acid
2. Treatment of the filtrate
   (*A*) Removal of $H_2S$
   (*B*) Action of (*a*) NaOH, (*b*) $Br_2$
   (*C*) Removal of $MnO_2$
   (1) Why a brown ppt. is not proof of presence of Mn?
   (2) Washing the ppt.
   (3) Dissolving the ppt.
   (4) Testing for Mn
   (*a*) Red lead test
   (*b*) Persulfate test
   (*c*) Hypochlorite test
   (*d*) Periodate test
   (*e*) Bismuthate test
   (*D*) Testing for Zn
   (1) Why acidify and boil?
   (2) The $H_2S$ test
   (3) The $K_4Fe(CN)_6$ test

3. Treatment of Residue
   (*A*) Washing residue
   (*B*) Dissolving residue
   (*C*) Test for Co
   (*D*) Test for Ni

Valence Tests for Mn

Such tests make use of the fact that $Mn^{++}$ is colorless to pale pink while $MnO_4^-$ is a deep purple. The change in color from one form to the other is generally easily discernible.

1. $Mn^{++}$ + oxidation gives $MnO_4^-$
2. $MnO_4^-$ + reduction gives $Mn^{++}$

(It is assumed in both cases that intermediate stages are avoided.)

## LABORATORY EXERCISES

1. Known solutions containing metals of Group I, copper division of Group II, Group III, and Mn and Zn of Group IV.

(*1*) $Ag^+$, $Fe^{+3}(l)$, $Mn^{++}$, $Zn^{++}$
(*2*) $Cd^{++}$, $Cr_2O_7^{--}$, $MnO_4^-$
(*3*) $Al(OH)_4^-$, $MnO_4^{--}$, $Zn(OH)_3^-$
(*4*) $Cu(NH_3)_4^{++}$, $CrO_4^{--}$, $Zn(NH_3)_4^{++}$

These solutions contain the following amounts of substance per liter of solution: (*1*) 4 g. $AgNO_3$, 70 g. $Fe(NO_3)_3 \cdot 9H_2O$, 13 g. $Mn(NO_3)_2 \cdot 6H_2O$ (or 17 g. of 50% $Mn(NO_3)_2$ solution), 7.5 g. $Zn(NO_3)_2$, and 100 ml. of 5 *N* $HNO_3$; (*2*) 7.5 g. $Cd(NO_3)_2 \cdot 4H_2O$, 7 g. $K_2Cr_2O_7$, 7 g. $KMnO_4$, and 50 ml. of 5 *N* $HNO_3$; (*3*) 23 g. $AlCl_3 \cdot 6H_2O$, 7 g. $KMnO_4$ reduced to $K_2MnO_4$, 5 g. $ZnCl_2$, and 100 g. NaOH; (*4*) 10 g. $Cu(NO_3)_2 \cdot 3H_2O$, 7 g. $K_2Cr_2O_7$, 7 g. $Zn(NO_3)_2$, 160 g. $NH_4NO_3$, and 200 ml. of 5 *N* $NH_4OH$.

(For the preparation of the third solution: place the NaOH in a liter crucible, add the $KMnO_4$ and 100 ml. of water, cover with a watch glass and boil carefully until decomposition to $MnO_4^{--}$ is complete. Cool slightly, pour into 500 ml. of water using this solution to dissolve the residue in the crucible. Dissolve the $AlCl_3$ and $ZnCl_2$ in 300–400 ml. of water and pour this slowly, with stirring, into the $MnO_4^{--}$ solution. Dilute to 1 liter.)

Use 15 drops of the original solution and test for Groups I–IV in regular order. Study the chemical methods as well as color differences in distinguishing between the different ions of Mn and Zn.

*Solution 1.* (*a*) Note the difficulty in adjusting the acidity at the beginning of Group II.

(*b*) On testing the solution with $H_2S$ for Group II a pale yellow precipitate of sulfur is obtained.

(*c*) Be sure that $Fe^{++}$ is all oxidized before precipitating Group III.

(*d*) In Group IV MnS and ZnS are nearly white. If a black precipitate is obtained it is probably FeS, due to incomplete oxidation and precipitation of Fe in Group III.

(*e*) ZnS and MnS usually settle out rather slowly on centrifuging. This can be improved by precipitation from a hot solution.

*Solution 2.* (*a*) Try the valence test for $Cr_2O_7^{--}$ on the original solution. Note that the purple color of $MnO_4^-$ disappears as excess of $H_2O_2$ is added (reduction to $Mn^{++}$), permitting the blue chromium peroxide to be seen without interference.

(*b*) Reduce $Cr_2O_7^{--}$ and $MnO_4^-$ with HCl and $CH_2O$ before adjusting the acidity to precipitate Group II.

*Solution 3.* (*a*) On acidifying with $HNO_3$ note the change of color from dark green ($MnO_4^{--}$) to purple ($MnO_4^-$) and the formation of a brown flocculent precipitate of $MnO_2$. In such a case the solution and precipitate may be treated directly with HCl + $CH_2O$, evaporated to 2–3 drops, diluted, and prepared for precipitation of Group II.

(*b*) In Group III treat the precipitate of $Al(OH)_3$ with NaOH + $H_2O_2$. A brown precipitate of $MnO_2$ indicates Mn carried down in Group III. Centrifuge, transfer the clear solution to a small crucible, and boil 1–2 minutes to decompose any excess $H_2O_2$. Pass in $H_2S$ for 5–10 seconds. A white precipitate of ZnS indicates Zn carried down in Group III. (If $H_2S$ is passed in long enough, a precipitate of $Al(OH)_3$ will be obtained.) Compare the amounts of Mn and Zn lost in Group III with the amounts found in Group IV.

*Solution 4.* Note the color of the solution, due to $Cu(NH_3)_4^{++}$ (blue) and $CrO_4^{--}$ (yellow). The color changes somewhat as the solution is acidified. Try the vanishing blue test for $Cr^{VI}$ on the cold acidified solution.

2. Known solutions containing metals of Groups I–IV.

(*1*) $Pb^{++}(l)$, $Co^{++}$, $Ni^{++}$, $Zn^{++}$
(*2*) $Bi^{+3}$, $Al^{+3}$, $Co^{++}$, $Mn^{++}(s)$
(*3*) $Cd(NH_3)_4^{++}$, $CrO_4^{--}(s)$, $Ni(NH_3)_6^{++}$

These solutions contain the following amounts of substance per liter: (*1*) 16 g. $Pb(NO_3)_2$, 12.5 g. $Co(NO_3)_2 \cdot 6H_2O$, 12.5 g. $Ni(NO_3)_2 \cdot 6H_2O$, 7 g. $Zn(NO_3)_2$, and 25 ml. of 5 *N* $HNO_3$; (*2*) 6 g. $Bi(NO_3)_3 \cdot 5H_2O$, 38 g. $Al(NO_3)_3 \cdot 9H_2O$, 12.5 g. $Co(NO_3)_2 \cdot 6H_2O$, 5 g. $Mn(NO_3)_2 \cdot 6H_2O$ (or 6 g. of 50% $Mn(NO_3)_2$ solution), and 100 ml. of 5 *N* $HNO_3$; (*3*) 7 g. $Cd(NO_3)_2 \cdot 4H_2O$, 2.8 g. $K_2Cr_2O_7$, 12.5 g. $Ni(NO_3)_2 \cdot 6H_2O$, 160 g. $NH_4NO_3$, and 200 ml. of 5 *N* $NH_4OH$.

Use 15 drops of the original solution for systematic analysis, testing for the presence of each group in regular order whether present or not, and completing the analysis of Group IV.

*Solution 1.* (*a*) In Group II note that the hydroxides of Co, Ni, and Zn precipitate when the solution is neutralized with $NH_4OH$, but redissolve when it is made 0.25 *N* with HCl.

(*b*) Obtain a test for Pb in Group II. After the $PbSO_4$ has been separated make the solution alkaline with $NH_4OH$ and pass in $H_2S$ to see if any of the fourth group metals were incompletely separated from Group II.

(*c*) In Group III, after adding $NH_4Cl$ and $NH_4OH$ for the precipitation of the group, centrifuge and note the slight stain of $Fe(OH)_3$ at the tip of the tube due to impurity in the other salts.

(*d*) In Group IV, note that CoS and NiS are readily centrifuged. (In case of excessive treatment with $H_2S$ the NiS may remain as a black colloidal suspension. If this occurs, neutralize with $HC_2H_3O_2$, boil to coagulate the NiS, centrifuge, wash, and combine this residue with the regular fourth group precipitate.)

(*e*) In analyzing the fourth group precipitate, a small black precipitate of $Co(OH)_3$ or $NiO_2 \cdot xH_2O$ may be obtained where $MnO_2$ would appear. Try the confirmatory test for Mn.

*Solution 2.* (*a*) A white precipitate of BiOCl may appear when testing for the presence of Group I. This dissolves fairly readily in excess of HCl. The same precipitate may be left after the solution has been made 0.25 *N* with HCl at the beginning of Group II. In this latter case treat the solution and precipitate with $H_2S$.

(*b*) In Group III note the color of the $Al(OH)_3$ after centrifuging and washing. This is due to a small amount of Co adsorbed by the $Al(OH)_3$. On treating with NaOH and $H_2O_2$ the $Al(OH)_3$ dissolves leaving a small black precipitate of $Co(OH)_3$.

(*c*) Obtain a satisfactory test for Mn in Group IV.

*Solution 3*. (*a*) The color of the solution is due to a combination of $CrO_4^{--}$, yellow, and $Ni(NH_3)_6^{++}$, blue.

(*b*) Negative tests for Groups I and II should be obtained.

(*c*) In Group III, after oxidizing the $Cr(OH)_3$ with NaOH and $H_2O_2$, a green to black precipitate ($Ni(OH)_2 \rightarrow NiO_2 \cdot xH_2O$) is usually obtained, the Ni being carried down by the $Cr(OH)_3$ in the group precipitation. Most of the Ni should be in the solution after Group III, however, and will be identified in Group IV.

3. Effect of $NH_4Cl$ in the separation of Group III from Group IV. To 10 drops of $AlCl_3$ solution add 2 drops of $CoCl_2$ solution, dilute to 20 drops, mix thoroughly and put half in each of two test tubes. To one add 2–3 drops of 5 *N* $NH_4Cl$ solution, heat to boiling, add 1 *N* $NH_4OH$, 1 drop at a time, with shaking, until the first faint alkaline reaction is obtained. Centrifuge, wash, and examine the precipitate of $Al(OH)_3$ for Co. To the second tube add 0.2 g. of solid $NH_4Cl$, heat to boiling, and precipitate $Al(OH)_3$ as before. Examine the precipitate for Co. Compare the results obtained.

4. Effect of excess $NH_4OH$ in the separation of Group III from Group IV. To 10 drops of $AlCl_3$ solution add 2 drops of $CoCl_2$ solution, and dilute to 20 drops. Add 0.2 g. of solid $NH_4Cl$, warm to dissolve, mix thoroughly, and put half in each of two test tubes. Precipitate $Al(OH)_3$ in the first tube by adding 1 *N* $NH_4OH$, 1 drop at a time, until a barely alkaline reaction is obtained. In the second tube add 2–3 drops excess of 5 *N* $NH_4OH$. Centrifuge, wash and examine the two precipitates for Co. Compare the results obtained.

5. Ions of Co, Ni, and Zn. Try the action of NaOH and of $NH_4OH$, in small amounts and in excess, on $CoCl_2$, $NiCl_2$, and $ZnCl_2$. Tabulate the results.

6. Ions of Mn. Compare the colors of $KMnO_4$, $Na_2MnO_4$, and $Mn(NO_3)_2$ solutions. Test individual portions of $KMnO_4$, $Na_2MnO_4$, and $Mn(NO_3)_2$ with 2–3 drops of each of the following reagents: (*a*) $HNO_3$, (*b*) NaOH, (*c*) $NH_4OH$. Warm moderately to hasten the reaction of $NH_4OH$ with $KMnO_4$ and with $Na_2MnO_4$. Tabulate the results. What are the conditions of stability for $Mn^{++}$, $MnO_4^-$, $MnO_4^{--}$?

7. Conversion of one ion of manganese to another.

(*a*) To 1 drop of $KMnO_4$ solution add 3–5 drops of HCl and 1 drop of $CH_2O$. Heat nearly to boiling. Note the reduction to $Mn^{++}$. What other reducing agents might be used? (*b*) To a drop of $Mn(NO_3)_2$ solution add 5 drops of reagent $HNO_3$ and 50 mg. of $KIO_4$. Boil for a minute or two and account for the color change that takes place. (*c*) To 1 drop of $KMnO_4$ solution add 2–3 drops of reagent NaOH, then add diluted KI solution (1 drop from side shelf diluted to 50 drops), 1 drop at a time, with shaking, until the permanganate color just disappears. To what is the new color due? Assuming that the KI is oxidized to $KIO_3$, write the equation for this reaction.

(*d*) To 1 drop of $Na_2MnO_4$ solution, or to the solution obtained in (*c*), add 5–8 drops of 5% NaClO solution (Chlorox, Roman Cleanser or Oxol as purchased at a grocery store). Heat nearly to boiling and note the change in color. Write the equation for this reaction.

8. Separation of NiS from ZnS by dilute HCl. (*a*) Mix 5 drops each of $NiCl_2$ and $ZnCl_2$, add 2–3 drops of $NH_4Cl$ solution and 3–5 drops of reagent $NH_4OH$. Precipitate with $H_2S$, centrifuge and wash. To the precipitate add 20 drops of water and 5 drops of 5 *N* HCl, stir for 1 minute and then centrifuge. Transfer the clear solution to a small crucible and boil to remove $H_2S$. Add 3–5 drops excess NaOH and look for a

green flocculent precipitate of $Ni(OH)_2$ due to slight dissolving of NiS in the dilute HCl. (*b*) Repeat the experiment except that the sulfides are permitted to stand covered with water for 10–15 minutes before treating with HCl. Compare the amount of $Ni(OH)_2$ now obtained with that found in (*a*).

9. Test for Ni in a cobalt salt. (*a*) Use 4–5 drops of $CoCl_2$ solution, add 5 drops of $NH_4Cl$ solution and slight excess of $NH_4OH$. Then add 2 drops of dimethyl dioxime reagent, centrifuge if necessary and look for the usual scarlet precipitate of $Ni(C_4H_7N_2O_2)_2$.

(*b*) To 4–5 drops of $CoCl_2$ solution add 15–20 drops of $H_2O$, then add 1 drop of 5 *N* $NH_4OH$ and mix thoroughly, obtaining a green precipitate of CoOHCl. Centrifuge, transfer the clear solution to a clean test tube, and add 2 drops of dimethyl dioxime reagent to test for Ni. Compare the results in (*a*) and (*b*). (If the solution contains enough free acid neutralized by $NH_4OH$ so the ammonium salts interfere with the precipitation of Co(OH)Cl the second procedure becomes the same as that in (*a*). How might the precipitate of CoS and NiS be treated to obtain a solution free from excess acid?)

## *EQUILIBRIUM PROBLEMS IN GROUP IV*

I. Calculate the concentration of $S^{--}$ introduced for the precipitation of Group IV.

*Conditions.* The solution from Group III is treated with 0.2 ml. of 5 *N* $NH_4OH$ and $H_2S$ passed in for short periods until a positive test for excess $H_2S$ is obtained. The volume has increased from 2 ml. to approximately 2.5 ml.; therefore, the concentration of $NH_4^+$ has been reduced from 3.7 to 3 *M*. The concentration of $NH_4OH$ in the solution is $5 \times \frac{0.2}{2.5} = 0.4\ M$. If 2 ml. excess of $H_2S$ are absorbed by the solution, its concentration, if it remained as free $H_2S$, would be

$$H_2S = \frac{2 \times 1000}{22{,}400 \times 2.5} = 0.04\ M$$

The problem may now be restated in more specific form. Calculate the concentration of $S^{--}$ obtained by absorbing 0.04 mole per liter of $H_2S$ in a solution in which $NH_4^+$ is 3 *M* and $NH_4OH$ is 0.4 *M*.

$$K_{H_2S} = 1 \times 10^{-7}, \quad K_{HS^-} = 1 \times 10^{-15}, \quad K_W = 1 \times 10^{-14}, \quad K_{NH_4OH} = 1.8 \times 10^{-5}$$

In this case the problem is more complex than merely applying the ionization constants of $H_2S$ and $HS^-$ to find the concentration of $S^{--}$ in a 0.04 *M* solution of $H_2S$ in water. This solution contains a small amount of $OH^-$ from dissociation of $NH_4OH$, and $H_3O^+$ as obtained from the dissociation of the $H_2S$ will react with this $OH^-$ with formation of $H_2O$. This in turn will bring about some further dissociation of both $H_2S$ and $NH_4OH$. The extent to which $H_3O^+$ will be supplied will be controlled by the ionization constants of $H_2S$ and $HS^-$, the concentration of $OH^-$ will depend on the ionization constant of $NH_4OH$, and the extent of reaction between $H_3O^+$ and $OH^-$ will be controlled by the water constant. Therefore, all these constants are required to calculate the final conditions that will be reached.

Probably the simplest method of attack on this problem is:

1. Write the net reactions for the neutralization of $H_2S$ and $HS^-$ by the $NH_4OH$.
2. Make a tentative assumption as to the extent to which these reactions will take place.

3. Calculate the concentration of $OH^-$ that would be present in the final solution on the basis of the starting conditions and the tentative assumption of (2).
4. Obtain the corresponding concentration of $H_3O^+$ by application of the water constant, substitute this value in the constants for $H_2S$ and $HS^-$, and derive the ratios for $\frac{[HS^-]}{[H_2S]}$ and $\frac{[S^{--}]}{[HS^-]}$.
5. Use these ratios to test the validity of the tentative assumption.
6. If necessary, correct the tentative assumption in the light of these ratios and repeat the calculation.
7. Finally, apply the final ratios to calculate the concentration of $S^{--}$.

These steps will now be shown in detail for this problem.

1. Net reactions:

$$H_2S + NH_4OH = HS^- + NH_4^+ + H_2O \tag{a}$$

$$HS^- + NH_4OH = S^{--} + NH_4^+ + H_2O \tag{b}$$

2. Tentative assumption:

Any one of three assumptions might be used as a basis for starting the actual calculation. The two extremes would be (*a*) to assume that neither reaction takes place to any great extent, and (*b*) to assume that both reactions go practically to completion. A third assumption would be intermediate between these and might take the middle ground (*c*) to assume that the first reaction goes nearly to completion, but the second takes place to only a minor extent. Incidentally, it should be noted that these two reactions are so related that the first will always take place to a greater extent than the second. On that basis there is some justification for starting this problem with this third assumption—namely, that the first reaction is practically complete, but the second takes place to only a minor extent.

3. Calculation of $[OH^-]$ based on the starting conditions and the third tentative assumption:

$$[NH_4^+] \text{ in the original soln.} = 3.0$$

$$[NH_4OH] \text{ in original soln.} = 0.4$$

$$\text{Increase in } NH_4^+ \text{ due to 1st reaction} = 0.04$$

$$\text{Decrease in } NH_4OH \text{ due to 1st reaction} = 0.04$$

Final tentative concentrations: $[NH_4^+] = 3.04$, $[NH_4OH] = 0.36$.

Using these values for $[NH_4^+]$ and $[NH_4OH]$ in $K_{NH_4OH}$,

$$\frac{3.04[OH^-]}{0.36} = 1.8 \times 10^{-5} \qquad [OH^-] = 2.1 \times 10^{-6}$$

4. Calculation of $[H_3O^+]$ and the corresponding ratios $\frac{[HS^-]}{[H_2S]}$ and $\frac{[S^{--}]}{[HS^-]}$:

$$[H_3O^+][OH^-] = 1 \times 10^{-14}$$

if

$$[OH^-] = 2.1 \times 10^{-6}$$

$$[H_3O^+] = \frac{1 \times 10^{-14}}{2.1 \times 10^{-6}} = 4.8 \times 10^{-9}$$

$$\frac{[H_3O^+][HS^-]}{[H_2S]} = 1 \times 10^{-7} \qquad \frac{[HS^-]}{[H_2S]} = \frac{1 \times 10^{-7}}{4.8 \times 10^{-9}} = \frac{21}{1}$$

$$\frac{[H_3O^+][S^{--}]}{[HS^-]} = 1 \times 10^{-15} \qquad \frac{[S^{--}]}{[HS^-]} = \frac{1 \times 10^{-15}}{4.8 \times 10^{-9}} = 2.1 \times 10^{-7}$$

5. Testing the validity of the tentative assumption:

$$\frac{[HS^-]}{[H_2S]} = \frac{21}{1}$$

If this ratio was established by the first reaction, the extent of the neutralization of the $H_2S$ by the $NH_4OH$ would be $\frac{21}{22}$, leaving only $\frac{1}{22}$ of the original $H_2S$ as such. This is reasonably close to the first half of the assumption made.

$$\frac{[S^{--}]}{[HS^-]} = \frac{2.1 \times 10^{-7}}{1}$$

If this ratio was established by the neutralization of the $HS^-$ by the $NH_4OH$, the extent of the reaction would be only 2.1 parts in 10,000,000, leaving practically all the $HS^-$ as such. This is identical with the second half of the assumption made.

6. If necessary, correct the tentative assumption, etc.

Since the tentative assumption has been justified no correction is necessary.

7. Calculation of $[S^{--}]$:

If the first reaction is practically complete, $[HS^-] = 0.04\ M$.

If the second reaction takes place to the extent of 2.1 parts in 10,000,000, the concentration of $[S^{--}] = 0.04 \times 2.1 \times 10^{-7} = 8.4 \times 10^{-9}$. *Ans.*

II. Manganous sulfide is the most soluble of the Group IV sulfides, having a solubility product of $7 \times 10^{-16}$.

*Problem:* Calculate the number of mg. of $Mn^{++}$ in the filtrate from Group IV, assuming that the total volume is 2.5 ml., that the concentration of $S^{--}$ is $8.4 \times 10^{-9}$, and that the solution is just saturated with MnS.

I

$$L_{MnS} = 7 \times 10^{-16} \qquad \text{(At. wt. Mn = 55)}$$

$$[S^{--}] = 8.4 \times 10^{-9}$$

$$[Mn^{++}] = \frac{7 \times 10^{-16}}{8.4 \times 10^{-9}} = 8.3 \times 10^{-8}$$

$$\text{Wt. } Mn^{++} = (8.3 \times 10^{-8})(55)(2.5)$$

$$= 1.1 \times 10^{-5} \text{ mg. } Mn^{++} \text{ in 2.5 ml.} \quad \textit{Ans.}$$

On this basis the precipitation of Group IV as sulfides should be unusually complete. This is in accord with actual experience; therefore, when a fourth group metal is found in the filtrate from Group IV, either too little $H_2S$ was passed in or the sulfide was not properly removed by centrifuging. In connection with this last point, it should be remembered that, since too much $H_2S$ may cause certain of the sulfides to become colloidal, particularly NiS, care should be taken to stop the current of $H_2S$ as soon as precipitation is complete.

III. Calculate the maximum concentration of $Zn^{++}$ that might be present after the precipitation of Group II with $H_2S$.

Of the later group metals, although NiS and CoS on standing change over to less soluble modifications whose solubility products are practically identical with that of CdS, only ZnS precipitates with appreciable readiness from slightly acid solutions. In attempting to apply solubility product considerations to the problem of finding the extent to which ZnS might precipitate in Group II a very real difficulty is encountered in trying to select a proper value for the solubility product of ZnS. Thus, Latimer * gives the value $4.5 \times 10^{-24}$ with the statement "this figure is probably as reliable as any of the direct experimental values." On the other hand, Swift † gives experiments to show that the precipitation of $Zn^{++}$ as ZnS (starting with 257 mg. of Zn in 250 ml. of a solution containing $NaHSO_4$ and $H_2SO_4$) will be complete "to less than 0.25 mg. at a hydrogen ion concentration of 0.025 *M*." From these data and the ionization constants of $H_2S$ and $HS^-$, and assuming that the $H_2S$ is 0.1 *M*, one may calculate a value $L_{ZnS} = 2.4 \times 10^{-25}$.

*Problem:* Calculate the amount of $Zn^{++}$ present in the filtrate from Group II if the total volume is 2 ml., $[S^{--}]$ is $1.6 \times 10^{-22}$, and the solution is assumed to be just saturated with ZnS. (*a*) Use $L_{ZnS} = 4.5 \times 10^{-24}$. (*b*) Use $L_{ZnS} = 2.4 \times 10^{-25}$.

(*a*) $$[Zn^{++}] = \frac{4.5 \times 10^{-24}}{1.6 \times 10^{-22}} = 3 \times 10^{-2} \qquad \text{(At. wt. Zn = 65)}$$

Wt. Zn in 2 ml. = (0.03)(65)(2) = 3.9 mg. $Zn^{++}$ *Ans.*

(*b*) $$[Zn^{++}] = \frac{2.4 \times 10^{-25}}{1.6 \times 10^{-22}} = 1.5 \times 10^{-}$$

Wt. Zn. in 2 ml. = (0.0015)(65)(2) = 0.2 mg. $Zn^{++}$ *Ans.*

On the basis of the value for $L_{ZnS}$ given by Latimer the zinc should carry past Group II quite effectively, but in terms of the figure given by Swift one might expect the zinc to precipitate to a considerable extent in Group II. However, Swift points out ‡ that with high concentration of chloride ion present the ZnS starts to precipitate more slowly and actually precipitates less completely. Since precipitation experiments normally lead to high values rather than low ones, it would appear that the value given by Swift is probably nearer the truth than the one by Latimer. On this basis the separation of Group II from zinc depends on the slowness of precipitation of ZnS from solutions which are only moderately supersaturated as well as on the actual solubility of ZnS under the conditions used. It is interesting, further, to note that after certain sulfides have been precipitated in Group II the ZnS starts to precipitate on their surfaces, although none forms in their absence even on long standing. Therefore, the accuracy of the separation is improved by fairly prompt filtering.

IV. Zinc hydroxide is the least soluble of the later group hydroxides, the value for the solubility product favored by Latimer being $4.5 \times 10^{-17}$.

*Problem:* Calculate the number of mg. of $Zn^{++}$ in the filtrate from Group III if the volume is 2 ml., the concentration of $OH^-$ is $1.2 \times 10^{-7}$, and the solution is assumed to be just saturated with $Zn(OH)_2$.

* *Oxidation Potentials*, Prentice-Hall, 1938, p. 157.
† *A System of Chemical Analysis*, Prentice-Hall, 1939, p. 324.
‡ *Op. cit.*, p. 325.

If $[OH^-]$ is $1.2 \times 10^{-7}$

$$[Zn^{++}] = \frac{4.5 \times 10^{-17}}{(1.2 \times 10^{-7})^2} = 2.8 \times 10^{-3} \qquad \text{(At. wt. Zn = 65}$$

$$(2.8 \times 10^{-3})(65)(2) = 0.59 \text{ mg. } Zn^{++} \quad \textit{Ans.}$$

In this case it is evident that if equilibrium conditions were reached and the simple calculations were applicable, much of the zinc should precipitate in Group III. As factors operating to improve this situation one may mention inter-ionic attraction effects and some conversion of $Zn^{++}$ to $Zn(NH_3)_4^{++}$ and $ZnCl_4^{--}$ by the small amount of $NH_4OH$ and high concentration of $Cl^-$ present. On the other hand, direct experimental studies of the separation of Group III metals from Group IV show that, although it is a simple matter to set up conditions such that the Group IV metals will not precipitate by themselves, these same conditions will not prevent a considerable carrying down of Group IV metals by a Group III precipitate. In this carrying down of later group metals probably several factors are at work, such as, supersaturation effects overcome by a precipitate formed in the solution, adsorption on the surface of the gelatinous hydroxides of Group III, and formation of aluminates, chromites, and zincates as insoluble compounds. The extent to which such effects interfere with the separation of Group III from Group IV has commonly led to the abandonment of this procedure by many chemists. However, it should be noted that a fair separation can be obtained by careful attention to three details of procedure—namely, (*a*) keep the solution hot during the precipitation, (*b*) have a high concentration of $NH_4Cl$ present, and (*c*) use only a very slight excess of $NH_4OH$. Because of the simplicity of presenting this procedure to beginning students, it has been retained in this text although its shortcomings are well known.

V. Calculate the solubility of ZnS in 1 *M* $H_3O^+$.

$$L_{ZnS} = 2.4 \times 10^{-25}, \quad K_{1,2H_2S} = 1 \times 10^{-22}$$

The equation for the net reaction would be

$$\underline{ZnS} + 2H_3O^+ = Zn^{++} + H_2S + 2H_2O$$

Let $X = [Zn^{++}] = [H_2S]$, $[H_3O^+] = 1 - 2X$

from $L_{ZnS}$,

$$[S^{--}] = \frac{2.4 \times 10^{-25}}{X}$$

from $K_{1,2H_2S}$,

$$[S^{--}] = \frac{1 \times 10^{-22}X}{(1 - 2X)^2}$$

Combining these two expressions for $S^{--}$,

$$\frac{2.4 \times 10^{-25}}{X} = \frac{1 \times 10^{-22}X}{(1 - 2X)^2}$$

Rearranging

$$\frac{X^2}{(1 - 2X)^2} = \frac{2.4 \times 10^{-25}}{1 \times 10^{22}} = 2.4 \times 10^{-3}$$

Extracting the square root:

$$\frac{X}{1 - 2X} = 0.05$$

$$1.1X = 0.05, \quad X = 0.045 = \text{molar soly. of ZnS.} \quad \textit{Ans.}$$

# 9

## Group V

# Barium, Strontium, Calcium

Group V is precipitated by $(NH_4)_2CO_3$ in an ammoniacal solution containing a small amount of $NH_4Cl$. The metals are barium, strontium, and calcium. Their common ions are barium ion, $Ba^{++}$; strontium ion, $Sr^{++}$; and calcium ion, $Ca^{++}$.

## COMMON COMPOUNDS AND REACTIONS OF IONS OF Ba, Sr, AND Ca

**More Common Compounds of Barium.** Barium chloride, $BaCl_2 \cdot 2H_2O$, white; barium nitrate, $Ba(NO_3)_2$, white; barium sulfate, $BaSO_4$, white; barium carbonate, $BaCO_3$, white; barium chromate, $BaCrO_4$, yellow; barium oxalate, $BaC_2O_4$, white; barium perchlorate, $Ba(ClO_4)_2$, white (very hygroscopic); barium phosphate, $Ba_3(PO_4)_2$, white; barium hydroxide, $Ba(OH)_2 \cdot 8H_2O$, white; barium oxide, BaO, white.

**Reactions of Barium Ion.** NaOH precipitates $Ba(OH)_2$, white, from not too dilute solutions, slightly soluble in water, readily soluble in $HC_2H_3O_2$, HCl, or $HNO_3$, soluble in $NH_4Cl$ solution. $NH_4OH$ shows no reaction with $Ba^{++}$ except for a slight precipitate of $BaCO_3$ due to $CO_2$ absorbed by the alkaline solution. HCl, HBr, HI, and $H_2S$ show no reaction with $Ba^{++}$. $H_2SO_4$ precipitates $BaSO_4$, white, insoluble in dilute HCl, largely transposed to $BaCO_3$ by boiling with concentrated $Na_2CO_3$ solution or by fusing with $Na_2CO_3$. $(NH_4)_2CO_3$ precipitates $BaCO_3$, white, soluble in HCl, $HNO_3$ or $HC_2H_3O_2$, slightly soluble in moderately concentrated $NH_4Cl$. $K_2CrO_4$ or $K_2Cr_2O_7$ precipitates $BaCrO_4$, yellow, insoluble in $HC_2H_3O_2$, soluble in HCl or $HNO_3$. $(NH_4)_2C_2O_4$ precipitates $BaC_2O_4$, white, insoluble in $HC_2H_3O_2$, soluble in HCl or $HNO_3$. $(NH_4)_2HPO_4$ forms $BaHPO_4$ ($Ba_3(PO_4)_2$ if $NH_4OH$ is present), white, soluble in HCl, moderately soluble in $HC_2H_3O_2$. There are no common complex ions containing $Ba^{++}$, nor does $Ba^{++}$ undergo any common oxidation or reduction reaction. Most characteristic reaction: precipitation of $BaCrO_4$, yellow, with $K_2Cr_2O_7$ in a solution containing $NH_4C_2H_3O_2$

$+ HC_2H_3O_2$. (Note that this is not sufficiently characteristic to be used on the original solution in the possible presence of $Ag^+$, $Pb^{++}$, etc.)

**More Common Compounds of Strontium.** Strontium chloride, $SrCl_2 \cdot 6H_2O$, white (efflorescent); strontium nitrate, $Sr(NO_3)_2$, white; strontium sulfate, $SrSO_4$, white; strontium carbonate, $SrCO_3$, white; strontium chromate, $SrCrO_4$, yellow; strontium oxalate, $SrC_2O_4$, white; strontium hydroxide, $Sr(OH)_2 \cdot 8H_2O$, white; strontium oxide, SrO, white.

**Reactions of Strontium Ion.** NaOH precipitates $Sr(OH)_2$, white, from not too dilute solutions, slightly soluble in water, readily soluble in HCl, $HNO_3$, or $HC_2H_3O_2$, soluble in $NH_4Cl$ solution. $NH_4OH$, free from $(NH_4)_2CO_3$, shows no reaction with $Sr^{++}$. HCl, KI, and $H_2S$ do not affect $Sr^{++}$. $H_2SO_4$ precipitates $SrSO_4$, white, insoluble in dilute HCl, slightly soluble in 5 *N* HCl, transposed to $SrCO_3$ by boiling with concentrated $Na_2CO_3$ solution. $(NH_4)_2CO_3$ precipitates $SrCO_3$, white, soluble in HCl or $HC_2H_3O_2$, slightly soluble in concentrated $NH_4Cl$ solution. $K_2CrO_4$, if fairly concentrated, precipitates $SrCrO_4$, yellow, soluble in HCl or $HC_2H_3O_2$. $(NH_4)_2C_2O_4$ precipitates $SrC_2O_4$, white, soluble in HCl, insoluble in $HC_2H_3O_2$. $(NH_4)_2HPO_4$ precipitates $SrHPO_4$ ($Sr_3(PO_4)_2$ if $NH_4OH$ is present), white, soluble in HCl, moderately soluble in $HC_2H_3O_2$. Most characteristic reaction: precipitation of $SrSO_4$, white, with dilute $(NH_4)_2SO_4$ or with saturated $CaSO_4$ solution, the precipitate forming slowly in the cold but readily as the solution is heated to the boiling point. (Note that $Sr^{++}$ must be separated from other metals whose sulfates are of similar or lower solubility before this test can be used. Note also that high concentration of $Ca^{++}$ interferes seriously with the delicacy of this test.)

**More Common Calcium Compounds.** Calcium chloride, $CaCl_2 \cdot 6H_2O$, white (deliquescent); calcium nitrate, $Ca(NO_3)_2 \cdot 4H_2O$, white; calcium sulfate (gypsum), $CaSO_4 \cdot 2H_2O$, white; calcium arsenate, $Ca_3(AsO_4)_2$, white; calcium carbonate, $CaCO_3$, white; calcium chromate, $CaCrO_4$, yellow; potassium calcium ferrocyanide, $K_2CaFe(CN)_6$, white; calcium oxalate, $Ca_2C_2O_4$, white; calcium phosphate, $Ca_3(PO_4)_2$, white; calcium sulfide, CaS, white; calcium hydroxide, $Ca(OH)_2$, white; calcium oxide, CaO, white.

**Reactions of Calcium Ion.** NaOH precipitates $Ca(OH)_2$, white, from not too dilute solutions, slightly soluble in water, readily soluble in HCl, $HNO_3$, or $HC_2H_3O_2$, soluble in $NH_4Cl$ solution. $NH_4OH$, free from $(NH_4)_2CO_3$, shows no reaction with $Ca^{++}$. HCl and KI do not affect $Ca^{++}$. $H_2S$ in a strongly alkaline solution precipitates CaS, white, from not too dilute a solution of $Ca^{++}$. $H_2SO_4$ precipitates $CaSO_4$, white, from not too dilute solutions, slightly soluble in water, more readily soluble in HCl, easily transposed by $Na_2CO_3$ or $(NH_4)_2CO_3$ into $CaCO_3$. $(NH_4)_2CO_3$ precipitates $CaCO_3$, white, soluble in HCl or $HC_2H_3O_2$, slightly soluble in concentrated $NH_4Cl$ solution. $(NH_4)_2C_2O_4$ precipitates $CaC_2O_4$, white, soluble in HCl, insoluble in $HC_2H_3O_2$. $(NH_4)_2HPO_4$ precipitates $CaHPO_4$ ($Ca_3(PO_4)_2$ if $NH_4OH$ is present), white, soluble in HCl, moderately soluble in $HC_2H_3O_2$. $K_4Fe(CN)_6$ in a neutral or slightly alkaline solution containing a high concentration of $NH_4Cl$, precipitates $KNH_4CaFe(CN)_6$ (composition somewhat variable), white, precipitating slowly in the cold, more readily from a warm solution on stirring. The most characteristic reaction is the precipitation of $CaC_2O_4$, white, with $(NH_4)_2C_2O_4$, after previous separation of earlier groups and precipitation of $BaSO_4$ and $SrSO_4$ with excess $(NH_4)_2SO_4$.

## REACTIONS OF GROUP V METALS IN THE SYSTEMATIC PRECIPITATION OF EARLIER GROUPS

The Group V metals show none of the common precipitation reactions when acidifying an alkaline solution with $HNO_3$, when neutralizing the filtrate from Group I with $NH_4OH$, or when adding excess of $NH_4OH$ in the precipitation of either Group III or Group IV. Small amounts of $Ba^{++}$ and $Sr^{++}$ may be lost as sulfates in Groups II and IV from atmospheric oxidation of the moist sulfides precipitated in these groups. In boiling the solution after Group II to remove $H_2S$, oxidizing conditions may be encountered such that an appreciable precipitate of $BaSO_4$ or $SrSO_4$ may be formed. This precipitate should be centrifuged, washed, boiled for several minutes with 15–20 drops of 3 *N* $Na_2CO_3$ solution and recentrifuged. The resulting $BaCO_3$ and $SrCO_3$ may then be dissolved in $HC_2H_3O_2$ and carried through the regular fifth group procedure to identify Ba and Sr. In Groups III and IV the reagent $NH_4OH$ contains small amounts of $(NH_4)_2CO_3$, which might be expected to cause losses of fifth group metals in these groups. However, the large amount of $NH_4Cl$ and the very slight excess of $NH_4OH$ recommended in the precipitation of Group III effectively prevent any loss in that group, and even in Group IV, with the larger amount of $NH_4OH$ added, the losses are rather small if the concentration of $NH_4Cl$ is 2.5–3 *N*.

## PREPARING THE ORIGINAL SOLUTION FOR THE PRECIPITATION OF GROUP V

In case none of the metals of Groups I–IV are present it is a very simple matter to prepare the solution for the precipitation of Group V. To 15 drops of the original solution add 3–5 drops of 5 *N* $NH_4Cl$ or 50–100 mg. of the salt and 3–5 drops of 5 *N* $NH_4OH$. The solution is now ready for treatment with $(NH_4)_2CO_3$.

## PREPARING THE SOLUTION FROM GROUP IV FOR THE PRECIPITATION OF GROUP V

The high concentration of $NH_4Cl$ used in Group III interferes seriously with the effective precipitation of Group V metals as carbonates. This is due in part to the hydrolysis of $CO_3^{--}$ to $HCO_3^-$, and in part to the fact that the carbonates of Ba, Sr, and Ca are distinctly more soluble than the usual group precipitates. It is necessary, therefore, in preparing the solution for the precipitation of Group V, to readjust the concentration of $NH_4^+$, keeping this sufficiently high to prevent the precipitation of $Mg(OH)_2$ or $MgCO_3$ in Group V, and at the same time sufficiently low to permit satisfactory precipitation of $BaCO_3$ (most soluble of the three carbonates of Group V). To do this the best procedure is to remove the $NH_4Cl$ by evaporating to dryness and heating the residue until fumes of $NH_4Cl$ are no longer given off, then dissolving the residue and adjusting the concentrations of $NH_4Cl$ and $NH_4OH$. The directions are as follows: acidify the filtrate from Group IV with HCl, transfer to a small crucible and heat carefully over a low open flame until the dense white fumes of $NH_4Cl$ no longer appear. Let cool, add 15–20 drops of water and 1 drop of 5 *N* HCl. Stir to dissolve the salts. A slight residue of silica may be discarded. To the clear solution add 50–100 mg. $NH_4Cl$ and 3–5 drops excess of 5 *N* $NH_4OH$. The solution is now ready for the precipitation of Group V.

TABLE IX. OUTLINE OF PROCEDURE FOR GROUP V

| | | | | |
|---|---|---|---|---|
| $Ba^{++}$ | $Sr^{++}$ | | | $Ca^{++}$ |
| | | $(NH_4)_2CO_3$ | | |
| $BaCO_3$ | $SrCO_3$ | | | $CaCO_3$ |
| | | $HC_2H_3O_2$ | | |
| $Ba^{++}$ | $Sr^{++}$ | | | $Ca^{++}$ |
| | | $K_2Cr_2O_7$ | | |
| $BaCrO_4$ | $Sr^{++}$ | | | $Ca^{++}$ |
| HCl | Divide into two parts | | | |
| $Ba^{++}$ | 0.1 *N* $(NH_4)_2SO_4$ | 2 *N* $(NH_4)_2SO_4$ | | |
| 0.1 *N* $(NH_4)_2SO_4$ | $SrSO_4$ | $SrSO_4$ | $CaSO_4$ | $Ca^{++}$ |
| $BaSO_4$ | flame test | discard | | $(NH_4)_2C_2O_4$ |
| flame test | | | | $CaC_2O_4$ |
| | | | | flame test |

## PRECIPITATION AND ANALYSIS OF GROUP V

**Precipitation of Group V.** After adjusting the concentrations of $NH_4Cl$ and $NH_4OH$ as described above, heat the solution nearly to boiling and add $(NH_4)_2CO_3$, 1–2 drops at a time, until precipitation appears to be complete. Centrifuge and test the clear solution with a little more $(NH_4)_2CO_3$ for completeness of precipitation. Barium, strontium, and calcium form white precipitates of the carbonates. Wash the precipitate 2–3 times with distilled water. Set the solution aside to analyze for $Mg^{++}$, $K^+$, and $Na^+$. Before starting the analysis of the Group V precipitate, add 1–2 drops each of $(NH_4)_2SO_4$ and of $(NH_4)_2C_2O_4$ to the filtrate, heat nearly to boiling, and let stand while the fifth group precipitate is being analyzed. If a slight precipitate forms because of incomplete removal of fifth group metals as carbonates, this precipitate should be removed before the test for $Mg^{++}$ is applied.

*Explanatory Notes.* (1) The solution should be warm when Group V is precipitated, since the carbonates are thus obtained in a more granular form, easily centrifuged and washed. However, the solution should not be boiled, since this decomposes the reagent and may result in some redissolving of the carbonates.

$$(NH_4)_2CO_3 = 2NH_3 + H_2O + CO_2$$

$$BaCO_3 + 2NH_4^+ = Ba^{++} + 2NH_3 + H_2O + CO_2$$

(2) Even under favorable conditions it is necessary to keep the concentration of $CO_3^{--}$ low to prevent the precipitation of some $MgCO_3$ in Group V; therefore it is not surprising if a small amount of the fifth group metals may escape precipitation as carbonates but produce visible precipitates with $(NH_4)_2SO_4$ and $(NH_4)_2C_2O_4$, which are only slightly hydrolyzed. If the amount of precipitate obtained with these reagents is sufficient to indicate serious incompleteness of precipitation of the carbonates, this precipitate may be examined for fifth group metals as follows: Centrifuge, wash, transfer to a small crucible, add 15 drops of 3 *N* $Na_2CO_3$ solution, heat to the boiling point and keep hot for several minutes with frequent stirring. This converts the sulfates and oxalates to carbonates, which are still left as a white precipitate. Centrifuge, wash, and apply the regular procedure for Ba, Sr, and Ca on this precipitate.

**Dissolving the Group V Precipitate and Testing for Barium.** Add 4–5 drops of 5 *N* $HC_2H_3O_2$ to the precipitate and stir to dissolve.

To the clear solution add 2–3 drops of 3 *N* $NH_4C_2H_3O_2$ and 1 drop of 0.5 *N* $K_2Cr_2O_7$. A bright yellow precipitate of $BaCrO_4$ may form. In this case add more $K_2Cr_2O_7$, 1 drop at a time, with shaking, until the orange color of the solution indicates a distinct excess of $K_2Cr_2O_7$. Let stand 2–3 minutes, for more complete precipitation of $BaCrO_4$, then centrifuge and wash. Set the solution aside to test for Sr and Ca. Dissolve the precipitate in 5 drops of 5 *N* HCl. Heat the HCl solution nearly to boiling and add 0.1 *N* $(NH_4)_2SO_4$ reagent dropwise, with shaking, until 4–5 drops have been added, and look for a white precipitate of $BaSO_4$. Centrifuge, wash thoroughly with distilled water, moisten with 2 drops of 5 *N* HCl and apply the flame test with a clean platinum wire. An apple green color indicates $Ba^{++}$.

*Explanatory Notes.* (1) $BaCrO_4$ precipitates a little slowly from a straight $HC_2H_3O_2$ solution. By adding a little $NH_4C_2H_3O_2$ to decrease the concentration of $H_3O^+$, precipitation takes place more readily. However, it is necessary to maintain a slight acidity to prevent possible precipitation of $SrCrO_4$.

(2) When $BaSO_4$ is precipitated rapidly, it forms a very finely divided precipitate which settles slowly. By precipitating slowly from a hot solution a coarser precipitate is obtained.

(3) In applying the flame test on $BaSO_4$, 1–2 drops of 5 *N* HCl are dropped on the precipitate. Next dip the platinum wire into some reagent HCl in a test tube, hold the wire in the outer edge of the Bunsen flame and heat until any volatile residues are removed, then dip again into HCl and place in the flame once more. When the wire has thus been fully cleaned of residues from earlier use, stir the wire about in contact with the precipitate, then hold in the flame again, and look for the green color characteristic of Ba.

**Precipitation and Identification of Strontium and Calcium.** Divide the solution after removing $BaCrO_4$ into two parts, using the first to test for Sr and Ca, and the second to test for Sr if Ca is present and no test for Sr is obtained in the first portion.

To the first portion add 5 drops of 0.1 *N* $(NH_4)_2SO_4$, heat to boiling, stir with a glass rod, and let stand 5–10 minutes. A finely divided white precipitate indicates Sr. Centrifuge, setting the clear solution aside to test for Ca. Wash the precipitate 3–4 times, moisten with HCl, and apply the flame test, using the manipulation described in the note under barium. A crimson-colored flame indicates Sr.

If a precipitate of $SrSO_4$ was obtained, add to the filtrate 5–10 drops of 2 *N* $(NH_4)_2SO_4$, heat again to boiling, stir, and let stand a few minutes. If no precipitate was obtained earlier with 0.1 *N* $(NH_4)_2SO_4$, add 5–10 drops of 2 *N* $(NH_4)_2SO_4$ to the solution, heat, and let stand several minutes. Centrifuge, discard the precipitate, heat the solution to boiling, add reagent $(NH_4)_2C_2O_4$ dropwise, with stirring or shaking, until 4–5 drops have been added, and look for the formation of a finely divided, white precipitate of $CaC_2O_4$. If a precipitate forms, centrifuge, wash, moisten with HCl, and apply the flame test. A brick-red flame indicates Ca.

If no test for Sr was obtained in the first procedure and the precipitate obtained with 2 *N* $(NH_4)_2SO_4$ was fairly heavy, treat the second portion of the solution (reserved above) with $NH_4OH$ and $(NH_4)_2CO_3$ to reprecipitate

Sr and Ca as carbonates. Centrifuge, wash, dissolve in dilute HCl, neutralize with $NH_4OH$, add 0.2 g. of solid $NH_4Cl$ and warm to dissolve, then add 4–5 drops of 2 *N* $K_4Fe(CN)_6$, heat nearly to boiling, and stir if necessary to start the precipitation of white $CaKNH_4Fe(CN)_6$. After several minutes centrifuge, test the clear solution with a little more $K_4Fe(CN)_6$ for complete removal of $Ca^{++}$, discard the precipitate, and finally add 1–2 drops of $(NH_4)_2C_2O_4$ to precipitate any $Sr^{++}$ as white $SrC_2O_4$. If a precipitate is obtained, centrifuge, wash, moisten with a few drops of HCl, and apply the flame test for Sr.

*Explanatory Notes.* (1) The first method of testing for strontium depends upon the fact that $SrSO_4$ is distinctly less soluble than $CaSO_4$ and will precipitate with a more dilute solution of $SO_4^{--}$ than that required to precipitate $CaSO_4$. By using a limited amount of 0.1 *N* $(NH_4)_2SO_4$ only $SrSO_4$ will precipitate and this can be separated and identified by the flame test.

(2) It is important to apply the flame test on any suspected $SrSO_4$, since incomplete precipitation of $Ba^{++}$ as $BaCrO_4$ will permit the formation of $BaSO_4$ where $SrSO_4$ is expected. The flame test will distinguish $SrSO_4$ from $BaSO_4$.

(3) It is necessary to remove $Sr^{++}$ before testing for $Ca^{++}$ with $(NH_4)_2C_2O_4$, since $SrC_2O_4$ also precipitates readily and it would be impossible to recognize Ca in the presence of Sr by the flame test. By using excess of a more concentrated $(NH_4)_2SO_4$ solution, strontium may be precipitated so completely as to eliminate this difficulty. It is necessary to wait several minutes after heating the solution since $SrSO_4$ precipitates somewhat slowly.

(4) If the solution contains a moderate or high concentration of $Ca^{++}$, part of this will precipitate as $CaSO_4$ along with the $SrSO_4$ and be discarded. However, $CaSO_4$ is sufficiently soluble so that ample remains in solution to permit a satisfactory confirmatory test for $Ca^{++}$.

(5) The first test for Sr may fail, even though there is a small amount of $Sr^{++}$ in the solution, if there is much $Ca^{++}$ present, since $Ca^{++}$ interferes seriously with the precipitation of $SrSO_4$ with limited amounts of $SO_4^{--}$. If the first treatment using 0.1 *N* $(NH_4)_2SO_4$ failed to give a precipitate, but a fairly heavy precipitate was obtained with 2 *N* $(NH_4)_2SO_4$, this indicates that there may be sufficient $Ca^{++}$ present to require an alternative method of testing for $Sr^{++}$. In this alternative procedure the $Ca^{++}$ is removed as $CaKNH_4Fe(CN)_6$, leaving $Sr^{++}$ in solution. In a neutral solution containing a high concentration of $NH_4Cl$, $K_4Fe(CN)_6$ precipitates the calcium quite fully, although precipitation takes place slowly; it is necessary therefore to wait a little while before centrifuging and discarding the precipitate. This method is not suited to test for $Ca^{++}$ since the reagent undergoes some decomposition and may form a precipitate even when $Ca^{++}$ is absent.

(6) After removal of $Ca^{++}$ as $CaKNH_4Fe(CN)_6$, the $Sr^{++}$ is precipitated with $(NH_4)_2C_2O_4$ rather than $(NH_4)_2SO_4$ because $SrC_2O_4$ precipitates much

more readily than $SrSO_4$ and is more readily soluble in HCl, giving a better flame test.

## REPORTING GROUP V IONS IN AN UNKNOWN SOLUTION

Since barium, strontium, and calcium are found in solution only with valence of two, since these metals form no common complex ions, and since the hydroxides are not amphoteric, these metals are reported as $Ba^{++}$, $Sr^{++}$ or $Ca^{++}$ in any aqueous solution in which they are identified.

## GROUP V IN RELATION TO OTHER GROUPS

The reactions of barium, strontium, and calcium in the usual processes of precipitating earlier groups have already been discussed (see p. 164). The small amounts of fifth group metals thus lost do not interfere with the regular tests for the metals of the earlier groups, nor are they sufficient to interfere with the regular qualitative identification of these metals in Group V if reasonable attention is paid to the proper details of precipitating the earlier groups. In the presence of certain acid radicals, particularly $C_2O_4^{--}$ and $PO_4^{-3}$, fifth group metals will be carried down in Group III when the solution is neutralized. In solutions that may present this problem it is necessary to carry out an extra procedure for removal of $C_2O_4^{--}$ and $PO_4^{-3}$ before precipitating Group III. The details of this procedure are given elsewhere (see p. 229). For the present it may be assumed that this complication will be avoided intentionally until otherwise stated.

None of the earlier group metals which escape precipitation in their regular groups will appear in Group V, with the possible exception of Mn, whose hydroxide might precipitate in Group V if one were unusually careless in testing for complete precipitation of Group IV. Actually, however, the small amounts of Mn occasionally missed in Group IV fail to precipitate in Group V, but do interfere in the phosphate test for Mg.

Small amounts of fifth group metals may escape precipitation as carbonates because of the fairly low concentration of $CO_3^{--}$ introduced by the group reagent and to the relatively large values for the solubility products of these carbonates. Unless they are removed by precipitation with $(NH_4)_2C_2O_4$ and $(NH_4)_2SO_4$, they will form white precipitates in the phosphate test for Mg.

## REACTIONS OF GROUP V METALS IN THE SYSTEMATIC ANALYSIS OF A SOLUTION

### Barium

*Precipitation as sulfate from oxidation of moist sulfides in Groups II and IV*

$$Ba^{++} + CuS + 2O_2 = \underline{BaSO_4} + Cu^{++}$$

*Precipitation as sulfate when boiling filtrate from Group II*

$$3Ba^{++} + 3H_2S + 8NO_3^- + 2H_3O^+ = \underline{3BaSO_4} + 8NO + 6H_2O$$

*Precipitation as carbonate in Group IV*

$$Ba^{++} + 2NH_3 + CO_2 + H_2O = \underline{BaCO_3} + 2NH_4^+$$

*In Group V*

$$Ba^{++} + HCO_3^- + NH_3 = \underline{BaCO_3} + NH_4^+$$
$$\underline{BaCO_3} + 2HC_2H_3O_2 = Ba^{++} + 2C_2H_3O_2^- + H_2O + CO_2$$
$$2Ba^{++} + Cr_2O_7^{--} + 2C_2H_3O_2^- + H_2O = \underline{2BaCrO_4} + 2HC_2H_3O_2$$
$$\underline{2BaCrO_4} + 2H_3O^+ = 2Ba^{++} + Cr_2O_7^{--} + 3H_2O$$
$$Ba^{++} + HSO_4^- + H_2O = \underline{BaSO_4} + H_3O^+$$

*Interference in test for Sr if incompletely precipitated as $BaCrO_4$*

$$Ba^{++} + SO_4^{--} = \underline{BaSO_4}$$

*Interference in test for Mg if incompletely precipitated in Group V*

$$3Ba^{++} + 2HPO_4^{--} + 2NH_3 = \underline{Ba_3(PO_4)_2} + 2NH_4^+$$

### Strontium

*Reactions by which strontium may be lost in Groups II–IV similar to those for barium*

*In Group V*

$$Sr^{++} + HCO_3^- + NH_3 = \underline{SrCO_3} + NH_4^+$$
$$\underline{SrCO_3} + 2HC_2H_3O_2 = Sr^{++} + 2C_2H_3O_2^- + H_2O + CO_2$$

1. $Sr^{++} + SO_4^{--} = \underline{SrSO_4}$
2. $Sr^{++} + HCO_3^- + NH_3 = \underline{SrCO_3} + NH_4^+$

   $\underline{SrCO_3} + 2H_3O^+ = Sr^{++} + CO_2 + 3H_2O$

   $Sr^{++} + C_2O_4^{--} = \underline{SrC_2O_4}$

   $\underline{SrC_2O_4} + 2H_3O^+ = Sr^{++} + H_2C_2O_4 + 2H_2O$

   $Sr^{++} + 2Cl^- + \text{heat} = SrCl_2\uparrow$

*Interference in test for Ca if incompletely precipitated as $SrSO_4$*

$$Sr^{++} + C_2O_4^{--} = \underline{SrC_2O_4}$$

*Interference in test for Mg if incompletely precipitated in Group V*

$$3Sr^{++} + 2HPO_4^- + 2NH_3 = \underline{Sr_3(PO_4)_2} + 2NH_4^+$$

**Calcium**

*Precipitation as carbonate in Group IV*

$$Ca^{++} + 2NH_3 + CO_2 + H_2O = \underline{CaCO_3} + 2NH_4^+$$

*In Group V*

$$Ca^{++} + HCO_3^- + NH_3 = \underline{CaCO_3} + NH_4^+$$
$$\underline{CaCO_3} + 2HC_2H_3O_2 = Ca^{++} + 2C_2H_3O_2^- + H_2O + CO_2$$
$$Ca^{++} + C_2O_4^{--} = \underline{CaC_2O_4}$$
$$\underline{CaC_2O_4} + 2H_3O^+ = Ca^{++} + H_2C_2O_4$$
$$Ca^{++} + 2Cl^- + heat = CaCl_2\uparrow$$

*Partial precipitation of Ca when removing Sr*

$$Ca^{++} + SO_4^{--} = \underline{CaSO_4}$$

*Removal of Ca before alternative test for Sr*

$$Ca^{++} + HCO_3^- + NH_3 = \underline{CaCO_3} + NH_4^+$$
$$\underline{CaCO_3} + 2H_3O^+ = Ca^{++} + 3H_2O + CO_2$$
$$Ca^{++} + Fe(CN)_6^{-4} + NH_4^+ + K^+ = \underline{CaKNH_4Fe(CN)_6}$$

*Interference in test for Mg if incompletely precipitated in Group V*

$$3Ca^{++} + 2HPO_4^{--} + 2NH_3 = \underline{Ca_3(PO_4)_2} + 2NH_4^+$$

## SUMMARY AND REVIEW

Loss of Group V Ions in Earlier Groups

1. In Group II due to oxidation of $H_2S$ to $SO_4^{--}$
2. In Group III due to $CO_3^{--}$ in the $NH_4OH$
3. In Group IV due to oxidation of $H_2S$ to $SO_4^{--}$ and absorption of $CO_2$

Precipitation of the Group

1. Removal of $NH_4^+$ salts from the fourth group filtrate
   *A*. How removed?
      Evapn. and baking after acidifying with HCl
   *B*. Why remove the large excess of $NH_4^+$ salts?
      (*a*) Mass action effect resulting in incomplete pptn. of Group V
      (*b*) Increased hydrolysis of reagent
   *C*. Dissolving ppt. in HCl
2. Actual pptn.
   *A*. Why have soln. ammoniacal?
      (*a*) If acid the Group V reagent is decomposed
      (*b*) If NaOH added it will ppt. $Mg(OH)_2$
      (*c*) Slight amount $NH_4^+$ present represses ionization of $NH_4OH$ thus preventing pptn. of $Mg(OH)_2$
      (*d*) $NH_4OH$ decreases hydrolysis of $(NH_4)_2CO_3$
   *B*. Heat to boiling before adding Group V reagent
   *C*. Technique of pptn.
   *D*. Boiling during pptn. results in decomposition of reagent

3. Filtration and washing of ppt.
   *A*. Why wash?
   *B*. Why use dilute $NH_4OH$?
   *C*. Number of washings necessary
4. Testing filtrate for complete pptn.
   *A*. For $Ba^{++}$ add $(NH_4)_2SO_4$
   *B*. For $Sr^{++}$ and $Ca^{++}$ add $(NH_4)_2C_2O_4$
5. Testing filtrate for Mg
   *A*. Removal of Group V metals
   *B*. Pptn. with $(NH_4)_2HPO_4$
      (*a*) Conditions necessary
      (*b*) Stirring to start crystallization

Analysis of the Precipitate

1. Dissolving ppt.
   *A*. Use of acetic acid
   *B*. Why avoid an excess
2. Testing small portion for $Ba^{++}$
   (If absent $NH_4C_2H_3O_2$ and $K_2Cr_2O_7$ should not be added, especially the latter, since it interferes with subsequent steps owing to its color and the low solubility of $SrCrO_4$)
3. Removal of $Ba^{++}$ if present
   *A*. Addition of $NH_4C_2H_3O_2$ to repress ionization of $HC_2H_3O_2$
   *B*. Source of $CrO_4^{--}$ ion effecting the reaction $Ba^{++} + CrO_4^{--} \rightarrow BaCrO_4$
   *C*. Filtration and washing ppt.
   *D*. Dissolving and testing ppt. for $Ba^{++}$
      (*a*) $(NH_4)_2SO_4$
      (*b*) Flame test
         (1) Why HCl soln. used
         (2) Technique of test
         (3) Interferences
4. Sepn. of Sr and Ca from excess $CrO_4^{--}$
5. Detection of Sr
   *A*. Pptn. with 0.1 *N* $(NH_4)_2SO_4$
   *B*. Flame test
      (*a*) Why HCl soln. used?
      (*b*) Technique
      (*c*) Interferences
      (*d*) Why the formation of a ppt. with $(NH_4)_2SO_4$ is not sufficient proof of the presence of Sr?
   *C*. Detection of small amounts of Sr in the presence of Ca
6. Detection of Ca
   *A*. Removal of Sr (and Ba) with $(NH_4)_2SO_4$
   *B*. Pptn. of $Ca^{++}$ as $CaC_2O_4$
   *C*. Flame test
      Used only as a confirmatory test

## *LABORATORY EXERCISES*

1. Known solutions containing metals of Groups I–V.

(*1*) $Cu^{++}$, $Fe^{+3}$, $Ni^{++}$, $Ba^{++}$, $Sr^{++}$
(*2*) $Sr^{++}(s)$, $Ca^{++}$

These solutions contain the following amounts of substance per liter of solution: (*1*) 10 g. $Cu(NO_3)_2 \cdot 3H_2O$, 12 g. $Fe(NO_3)_3 \cdot 9H_2O$, 12.5 g. $Ni(NO_3)_2 \cdot 6H_2O$, 4.5 g. $BaCl_2 \cdot 2H_2O$, 7.5 g. $SrCl_2 \cdot 6H_2O$, and 50 ml. of 5 *N* HCl; (*2*) 3 g. $SrCl_2 \cdot 6H_2O$ and 9 g. $CaCl_2 \cdot 2H_2O$.

Use 15 drops of the original solution to test for the presence of Groups I–V. Analyze the fifth group precipitate for Ba, Sr, and Ca.

*Solution 1.* (*a*) In attempting to boil out $H_2S$ in the solution from Group II, a white, finely divided precipitate of $BaSO_4$ may form. If it is of significant amount it may be centrifuged, washed, and tested for Ba by moistening with HCl and applying the flame test.

(*b*) After precipitating Group IV with $H_2S$, the clear solution may be warmed and treated with 1–2 drops of $(NH_4)_2CO_3$ solution to test for the presence of any large amount of Group V. After this the solution and precipitate should be transferred to a small crucible and treated for removal of ammonium salts in order that Group V may be precipitated more effectively.

(*c*) In analyzing Group V, after removal of Ba as $BaCrO_4$, a satisfactory precipitate of $SrSO_4$ should be obtained with either $CaSO_4$ solution or 0.1 *N* $(NH_4)_2SO_4$ solution.

*Solution 2.* This solution may be adjusted directly for the precipitation of Group V without testing for previous groups. In analyzing the precipitate try precipitating $SrSO_4$ with 5 drops of 0.1 *N* $(NH_4)_2SO_4$. Note that the calcium interferes seriously. Try the alternative procedure for Sr, involving removal of Ca with $K_4Fe(CN)_6$ in a concentrated $NH_4Cl$ solution, followed by precipitation of Sr as $SrC_2O_4$.

2. (*a*) Try the flame tests for Ba, Sr, and Ca on portions of the test solutions on the side shelves. (These solutions contain 10 mg. of metal per ml.)

(*b*) Prepare more dilute solutions of $BaCl_2$, $SrCl_2$, and $CaCl_2$, containing 1 mg. of metal per ml. Try the flame tests on these solutions. Then precipitate the metals as $BaSO_4$, $SrSO_4$, and $CaC_2O_4$, respectively, centrifuge, wash thoroughly, moisten with HCl and try the flame tests again. Note that the tests are more pronounced and that the colors are no longer interfered with by the small amount of sodium commonly present in solutions kept in glass containers.

3. Place 5 drops of $BaCl_2$ solution (10 mg. of $Ba^{++}$ per ml.) in each of two test tubes. To one tube add 2–3 drops of $NH_4C_2H_3O_2$ solution, to the other 2–3 drops of water, then add $K_2Cr_2O_7$ to both solutions, 1–2 drops at a time, until precipitation of $BaCrO_4$ seems to be stopped and the solution is orange in color from excess of the reagent. Shake, let stand a minute or two. Note differences in appearance and amounts of the two precipitates. Centrifuge and add slight excess of $NH_4OH$ to the clear solution and note differences in amounts of precipitate obtained. Explain the effect of the $NH_4C_2H_3O_2$.

To a third portion of the $BaCl_2$ add excess $(NH_4)_2CO_3$, centrifuge, and wash. Dissolve the $BaCO_3$ in 3–4 drops of acetic acid, add to the solution excess of $K_2Cr_2O_7$, shake, let stand a moment, and centrifuge. To the clear solution add $NH_4OH$ until alkaline. Compare the completeness of precipitation of $BaCrO_4$ from a $Ba(C_2H_3O_2)_2 + HC_2H_3O_2$ solution with that obtained from a $BaCl_2 + NH_4C_2H_3O_2$ solution.

## *EQUILIBRIUM PROBLEMS IN GROUP V*

I. Calculate the concentration of $CO_3^{--}$ supplied for the precipitation of Group V.

For the precipitation of Group V the clear solution from Group IV is evaporated to dryness and the residue heated to remove the $NH_4Cl$. Finally, after dissolving the residue in water, 0.05 g. of $NH_4Cl$, 0.2 ml. of 5 *N* $NH_4OH$, and 0.2 ml. of 2 *M* $(NH_4)_2CO_3$ are added to the warm solution to precipitate the carbonates of barium, strontium, and calcium. In this case the problem of calculating the concentration of $CO_3^{--}$ supplied for the precipitation of Group V involves the question: To what extent does the $CO_3^{--}$ undergo hydrolysis in the presence of $NH_4^+$ and $NH_4OH$? The $(NH_4)_2CO_3$, like $NH_4Cl$, is a strong electrolyte, essentially completely ionized into $NH_4^+$ and $CO_3^{--}$. But $CO_3^{--}$ combines fairly readily with $H_3O^+$ (supplied by dissociation of water), and the $NH_4^+$ present in the solution prevents any significant accumulation of $OH^-$ to interfere with that reaction. Similarly, although to a much smaller extent, $HCO_3^-$ may combine with $H_3O^+$ to form $H_2CO_3$ and the $NH_4^+$ again prevents any corresponding accumulation of $OH^-$.

*Problem:* Calculate the concentration of $CO_3^{--}$ supplied for the precipitation of Group V if the total volume is 1.5 ml., containing 0.05 g. *N* $H_4Cl$, 0.2 ml. 5 *N* $NH_4OH$, and 0.2 ml. 2 *M* $(NH_4)_2CO_3$. $K_{NH_4OH} = 1.8 \times 10^{-5}$, $K_W = 1 \times 10^{-14}$, $K_{HCO_3^-} = 6 \times 10^{-11}$, $K_{H_2CO_3} = 3 \times 10^{-7}$.

The solution of this problem involves steps very similar to those for Group IV.

(1) Net reactions:

(*a*) $$CO_3^{--} + NH_4^+ = HCO_3^- + NH_3$$

(*b*) $$HCO_3^- + NH_4^+ = H_2CO_3 + NH_3$$

(2) Tentative assumption: the first reaction goes practically to completion, but the second takes place to only a very minor extent.

(3) Calculation of $OH^-$ based on the starting conditions and the tentative assumption:

$$[NH_4^+] \text{ from } NH_4Cl = \frac{0.05 \times 1000}{1.5 \times 53.5} = 0.62$$

$$[NH_4^+] \text{ from } (NH_4)_2CO_3 = 2 \times 2 \times \frac{0.2}{1.5} = 0.54$$

$$[NH_3] + [NH_4OH] \text{ as added} = 5 \times \frac{0.2}{1.5} = 0.67$$

$$[CO_3^{--}] \text{ if there were no hydrolysis} = 2 \times \frac{0.2}{1.5} = 0.27\ M$$

But, according to the tentative assumption that the first reaction goes practically to completion, the concentrations of $NH_4^+$ and of $NH_3 + NH_4OH$ must be changed by an amount equivalent to the $HCO_3^-$ formed.

$$[NH_4^+] = 0.62 + 0.54 - 0.27 = 0.89$$

$$[NH_3] + [NH_4OH] = 0.67 + 0.27 = 0.94$$

Using these data in $K_{NH_4OH}$,

$$\frac{0.89[OH^-]}{0.94} = 1.8 \times 10^{-}$$

$$[OH^-] = 1.9 \times 10^{-5}$$

(4) Calculations of $[H_3O^+]$ and the ratios $\frac{[CO_3^{--}]}{[HCO_3^-]}$ and $\frac{[HCO_3^-]}{[H_2CO_3]}$:

If $[OH^-] = 1.9 \times 10^{-5}$,

$$[H_3O^+] = \frac{1 \times 10^{-14}}{1.9 \times 10^{-5}} = 5.3 \times 10^{-10}$$

From $K_{HCO_3^-}$

$$\frac{[CO_3^{--}]}{[HCO_3^-]} = \frac{6 \times 10^{-11}}{5.3 \times 10^{-10}} = 0.115$$

From $K_{H_2CO}$

$$\frac{[HCO_3^-]}{[H_2CO_3]} = \frac{3 \times 10^{-7}}{5.3 \times 10^{-10}} = \frac{566}{1}$$

(5) Testing the validity of the tentative assumption:

If the ratio $CO_3^{--}/HCO_3^- = 0.115/1$ was established by the hydrolysis of $CO_3^{--}$ in accordance with the first reaction, the extent of this hydrolysis would be 1/1.115 or only 89%, leaving 11% of the original $CO_3^{--}$ as such. This is not quite as close to the tentative assumption as would be desirable.

If the ratio $[HCO_3^-]/[H_2CO_3] = 566/1$ was established by the hydrolysis of $HCO_3^-$ in accordance with the second reaction, the extent of this hydrolysis would be only 1 part in 567, which is quite in keeping with the second part of the tentative assumption.

(6) Correction of the tentative assumption:

In view of the results of the first calculation, assume that the first reaction takes place to the extent of 89%. On this basis the decrease in concentration of $NH_4^+$ and the increase in concentration of $NH_4OH$ by this reaction will be only $0.89 \times 0.27$ or 0.24.

$$[NH_4^+] = 0.62 + 0.54 - 0.24 = 0.92$$

$$[NH_3] + [NH_4OH] = 0.67 + 0.24 = 0.91$$

$$[OH^-] = 1.8 \times 10^{-5} \times 0.91/0.92 = 1.8 \times 10^{-5}$$

$$[H_3O^+] = \frac{1 \times 10^{-14}}{1.8 \times 10^{-5}} = 5.6 \times 10^{-10}$$

Substituting this value in the ionization constant for $HCO_3^-$:

$$\frac{[CO_3^{--}]}{[HCO_3^-]} = \frac{6 \times 10^{-11}}{5.6 \times 10^{-10}} = \frac{0.107}{1}$$

This gives a new value for the extent of the reaction of 1/1.107 or 90%, which is so close to that obtained from the earlier calculation that it may be accepted as the final value.

(7) Calculation of $[CO_3^{--}]$:

If 90% of the carbonate radical has been hydrolyzed to form $HCO_3^-$, 10% will be left as $CO_3^{--}$.

$$[CO_3^{--}] = 0.27 \times 0.1 = 0.027 = \text{approx. } 0.03. \quad \textit{Ans.}$$

II. Calculate the amount of $Ba^{++}$ in the clear solution after Group V if the total volume is 1.5 ml., $[CO_3^{--}]$ is 0.03, and the solution is assumed to be just saturated with $BaCO_3$.

The most soluble carbonate of Group V is $BaCO_3$ (practically identical with $CaCO_3$, but the higher atomic weight of Ba makes this a more critical case to consider).

$$L_{BaCO_3} = 1 \times 10^{-8}$$

$$[Ba^{++}] = \frac{1 \times 10^{-8}}{0.03} = 3.3 \times 10^{-7} \qquad \text{(At. wt. Ba = 137)}$$

$$\text{Wt. } Ba^{++} = (3.3 \times 10^{-7})(137)(1.5)$$

$$= 6.9 \times 10^{-5} \text{ mg. in 1.5 ml.} \quad \textit{Ans.}$$

This would indicate a satisfactory precipitation of Group V, but it should be noted that the concentrations of ions in this solution are sufficiently high to increase the solubility of the carbonate somewhat above this figure. Still more important, the precipitation of Group V carbonates takes place rather slowly from more dilute solutions containing a considerable concentration of other ions; therefore, small amounts of Group V metals are occasionally overlooked from failure to allow a reasonable time before assuming that Group V is absent.

III. Calculate the possible loss of $Sr^{++}$ by precipitation as $SrCO_3$ in Group IV if the excess $NH_4OH$ is 1% changed to $(NH_4)_2CO_3$ by absorption of $CO_2$ from the air. The final conditions in Group IV were as follows: volume = 2.5 ml., free $NH_4OH$ = 0.36, and $H_3O^+ = 4.8 \times 10^{-9}$. $L_{SrCO_3} = 6 \times 10^{-9}$, $K_{HCO_3^-} = 6 \times 10^{-11}$.

If 1% of the $NH_4OH$ is changed to $(NH_4)_2CO_3$,

$$\text{molar concn. of } (NH_4)_2CO_3 = 0.36 \times 0.01 \times 0.5 = 0.0018$$

Extent of hydrolysis of $CO_3^{--}$ if $H_3O^+ = 4.8 \times 10^{-9}$

$$\frac{[CO_3^{--}]}{[HCO_3^-]} = \frac{6 \times 10^{-11}}{4.8 \times 10^{-9}} = \frac{0.012}{1}$$

The fraction left as $CO_3^{--}$ would be $\frac{0.012}{1.012}$ or approx. 0.012.

$$[CO_3^{--}] = 0.0018 \times 0.012 = 2.3 \times 10^{-5}$$

In saturated solution of $SrCO_3$,

$$[Sr^{++}] \times [CO_3^{--}] = 6 \times 10^{-9}$$

If $[CO_3^{--}] = 2.2 \times 10^{-5}$,

$$[Sr^{++}] = \frac{6 \times 10^{-9}}{2.2 \times 10^{-5}} = 2.7 \times 10^{-4}$$

Wt. Sr in 2.5 ml.,

$$2.7 \times 10^{-4} \times 87.6 \times 2.5 = 0.059 \text{ mg.}$$

On this basis one might expect that strontium would precipitate quite fully in Group IV as the carbonate. However, it should be noted that the total amount of carbonate radical as $[CO_3^{--}] + [HCO_3^-]$ is only about 0.0018 mole per liter, and that if this were all used in the precipitation of $SrCO_3$ it would only be equivalent to some 0.39 mg. of $Sr^{++}$. Further, the high concentrations of ions in the solution raises somewhat the solubility product of $SrCO_3$ and decreases the rate of formation of the precipitate. Therefore, although small amounts of strontium may be lost in Group IV by precipitation as the carbonate, there will normally be sufficient left in solution to identify in Group V.

Since this point has been raised in connection with Group IV, it may be worthwhile to call attention to the slightly similar conditions in Group III. In this case, also, the solution is made slightly alkaline and contains a small amount of free $NH_4OH$. However, the concentration of $H_3O^+$ is so much higher and that of $NH_4OH$ so much lower than in Group IV that the concentration of $CO_3^{--}$ would be too low to cause any precipitation of $SrCO_3$. Thus, approximate calculations show that at least 7 mg. of $Sr^{++}$ would need to be present for saturation and that not more than 0.05 mg. could precipitate in Group III under the conditions given.

# 10

## Group VI

# Magnesium, Sodium, Potassium, Ammonium Radical

Group VI consists of those metals that are not precipitated by previous group reagents. There is no group reagent for the precipitation of this group. The metals included are Mg, Na, K, and $NH_4^+$. None of these form more than a single common ion, the formulas being $Mg^{++}$, $Na^+$, $K^+$, and $NH_4^+$.

### COMMON COMPOUNDS AND REACTIONS OF THE IONS OF Mg, Na, K, AND $NH_4^+$

**More Common Magnesium Compounds.** Magnesium chloride, $MgCl_2 \cdot 6H_2O$, white, deliquescent; magnesium nitrate, $Mg(NO_3)_2 \cdot 6H_2O$, white, deliquescent; magnesium sulfate (Epsom salt), $MgSO_4 \cdot 7H_2O$, white; magnesium ammonium arsenate, $MgNH_4AsO_4$, white; magnesium ammonium chloride, $MgCl_2 \cdot 2NH_4Cl \cdot 6H_2O$, white, deliquescent; magnesium ammonium phosphate, $MgNH_4PO_4$, white; magnesium carbonate (magnesite), $MgCO_3$, white; magnesium hydroxide, $Mg(OH)_2$, white; magnesium oxide, MgO, white; magnesium perchlorate, $Mg(ClO_4)_2 \cdot 6H_2O$, white; magnesium phosphate, $Mg_3(PO_4)_2$, white; magnesium potassium chloride (carnallite), $MgCl_2 \cdot KCl \cdot 6H_2O$, white; magnesium potassium sulfate, $MgSO_4 \cdot K_2SO_4 \cdot 6H_2O$, white.

**Reactions of Magnesium Ion.** NaOH or $NH_4OH$ precipitates $Mg(OH)_2$, white, soluble in HCl, $HC_2H_3O_2$, or $NH_4Cl$. The common acids do not affect $Mg^{++}$. $H_2S$ does not react with $Mg^{++}$ even in alkaline solution. There are no common complex ions of Mg, although a number of double salts may be formed by crystallization under the proper conditions. $MgCl_2$ reacts with MgO to form an insoluble basic salt, $Mg_2OCl_2$, white, used extensively as a cement. In ammoniacal solution ammonium phosphate and ammonium arsenate precipitate the corresponding double salts, $MgNH_4PO_4$, and $MgNH_4AsO_4$. There are no common oxidation-reduction reactions of $Mg^{++}$, although under very strong reducing conditions or by electrolysis of fused $MgCl_2$, $Mg^{++}$ may be reduced to metallic Mg. Mg° is a very strong reducing agent in dilute acid solution. The most characteristic reaction is the formation of a light blue, adsorption complex when $Mg(OH)_2$ is precipitated from acid solution with NaOH in the presence of a small amount of paranitrobenzene-azo-resorcinol.

**More Common Sodium Compounds.** Sodium chloride, NaCl, white; sodium nitrate (Chili saltpeter), $NaNO_3$, white; sodium sulfate, $Na_2SO_4$, white; sodium acetate, $NaC_2H_3O_2$, white; sodium ammonium phosphate (micro-cosmic salt), $NaNH_4HPO_4 \cdot 4H_2O$; sodium arsenate, $Na_2HAsO_4 \cdot 7H_2O$, white; sodium bismuthate, $NaBiO_3$, brown; sodium bromide, NaBr, white; sodium tetraborate (borax), $Na_2B_4O_7 \cdot 5H_2O$, white; sodium bromide, NaBr, white; sodium carbonate (anhydrous), $Na_2CO_3$, white; sodium carbonate decahydrate (washing soda), $Na_2CO_3 \cdot 10H_2O$, white; sodium bicarbonate (baking soda), $NaHCO_3$, white; sodium chromate, $Na_2CrO_4$, yellow; sodium dichromate, $Na_2Cr_2O_7 \cdot 2H_2O$, red; sodium hydroxide, NaOH, white, deliquescent; sodium iodide, NaI, white; sodium oxalate, $Na_2C_2O_4$, white; sodium acid oxalate, $NaHC_2O_4 \cdot H_2O$, white; sodium manganate, $Na_2MnO_4$, green; sodium permanganate, $NaMnO_4 \cdot 3H_2O$, purple; sodium peroxide, $Na_2O_2$, white; mono-sodium phosphate, $NaH_2PO_4 \cdot 2H_2O$, white; di-sodium phosphate, $Na_2HPO_4 \cdot 12H_2O$, white; tri-sodium phosphate, $Na_3PO_4 \cdot 12H_2O$, white; sodium silicate, $Na_2SiO_3$, white; sodium acid sulfite, $NaHSO_3$, white; sodium sulfite, $Na_2SO_3 \cdot 7H_2O$, white; sodium acid sulfate, $NaHSO_4$, white; sodium thiosulfate, $Na_2S_2O_3 \cdot 5H_2O$.

**Reactions of Sodium Ion.** Sodium ion is unusually inert, undergoing very few precipitation reactions, forming a fair number of double salts, and undergoing reduction only by electrolysis of NaOH under favorable conditions. With alcohol present to reduce the solubility, NaCl may be precipitated fairly completely by saturating the solution with HCl (gas). Potassium acid antimonate precipitates $NaSb(OH)_6$, white, from a neutral or slightly alkaline solution. Uranyl acetate, in a concentrated solution of magnesium acetate, forms a greenish yellow crystalline precipitate of a triple acetate of Na, Mg and U, $NaMg(UO_2)_3(C_2H_3O_2)_9$. (Zinc acetate may be substituted for the magnesium acetate.) The most characteristic reactions of Na are (1) the formation of a yellow flame when NaCl is volatilized in a Bunsen flame, and (2) the precipitation of $NaMg(UO_2)_3(C_2H_3O_2)_9$, greenish-yellow, with a mixture of $Mg(C_2H_3O_2)_2$ and $UO_2(C_2H_3O_2)_2$.

**More Common Potassium Compounds.** Potassium chloride, KCl, white; potassium nitrate (niter, saltpeter), $KNO_3$, white; potassium sulfate, $K_2SO_4$, white; potassium antimonyl tartrate (tartar emetic), $KSbOC_4H_4O_6 \cdot \frac{1}{2}H_2O$, white; potassium arsenate, $K_2HAsO_4 \cdot H_2O$, white; potassium arsenite (meta-), $KAsO_2$, white; potassium bromate, $KBrO_3$, white; potassium bromide, KBr, white; potassium carbonate, $K_2CO_3$, white; potassium carbonate trihydrate, $2K_2CO_3 \cdot 3H_2O$, white; potassium acid carbonate (bicarbonate), $KHCO_3$, white; potassium chlorate, $KClO_3$, white; potassium chloride, KCl, white; potassium chloroplatinate, $K_2PtCl_6$, yellow; potassium chromate, $K_2CrO_4$, yellow; potassium cobaltinitrite, $K_3Co(NO_2)_6 \cdot 1\frac{1}{2}H_2O$, yellow; potassium cobaltosulfate, $K_2Co(SO_4)_2 \cdot 6H_2O$, red; potassium cyanide, KCN, white; potassium dichromate, $K_2Cr_2O_7$, red; potassium ferricyanide, $K_3Fe(CN)_6$, red; potassium ferrocyanide, $K_4Fe(CN)_6$, yellow; potassium hydroxide, KOH, white, deliquescent; potassium iodate, $KIO_3$, white; potassium iodide, KI, white; potassium manganate, $K_2MnO_4$, green; potassium nickel sulfate, $K_2Ni(SO_4)_2 \cdot 6H_2O$, green; potassium nitrite, $KNO_2$, white; potassium oxalate, $K_2C_2O_4 \cdot H_2O$, white; potassium binoxalate, $KHC_2O_4 \cdot \frac{1}{2}H_2O$, white; potassium tetraoxalate, $KH_3(C_2O_4)_2 \cdot 2H_2O$, white; potassium perchlorate, $KClO_4$, white; potassium periodate, $KIO_4$, white; potassium permanganate, $KMnO_4$, purple; potassium persulfate, $K_2S_2O_8$, white; mono-potassium phosphate, $KH_2PO_4$, white; dipotassium phosphate, $K_2HPO_4$, white; tri-potassium phosphate, $K_3PO_4$, white; potassium sulfite, $K_2SO_3 \cdot 2H_2O$, white; potassium acid sulfite, $KHSO_3$, white; potassium thiocyanate, KCNS, white.

**Reactions of Potassium Ion.** Like sodium ion, potassium ion is unusually inert, undergoing a few precipitation reactions, forming a considerable number of double salts, and undergoing reduction only by electrolysis of KOH solution under favorable conditions. The common precipitation reactions are: precipitation with $Na_3Co(NO_2)_6$, forming $K_2NaCo(NO_2)_6$, yellow; with $H_2PtCl_6$, forming $K_2PtCl_6$, yellow; with $HClO_4$, forming $KClO_4$, and with $H_2C_4H_4O_6$, forming $KHC_4H_4O_6$, white. In the cases of $K_2PtCl_6$ and $KClO_4$, alcohol should be present to decrease the solubility of the precipitate. The most characteristic reactions of potassium are: (1) the formation of a violet color when KCl is volatilized in a Bunsen flame, the color being visible when viewed through a cobalt glass, and (2) the precipitation of $KClO_4$, white, when $HClO_4$ is added to a KCl solution (after removal of heavy metals and ammonium salts), the solution then evaporated to fumes, cooled, and treated with absolute alcohol.

**More Common Ammonium Compounds.** Ammonium chloride (sal ammoniac), $NH_4Cl$, white; ammonium nitrate, $NH_4NO_3$, white; ammonium sulfate, $(NH_4)_2SO_4$, white; ammonium acetate, $NH_4C_2H_3O_2$, white, hygroscopic; ammonium arsenate, $(NH_4)_2HAsO_4$, white; ammonium arsenite, $NH_4AsO_2$, white; ammonium bromide, $NH_4Br$, white; ammonium carbonate-carbamate, $NH_4HCO_3 \cdot NH_4NH_2CO_2$, white; ammonium chloroplatinate, $(NH_4)_2PtCl_6$, yellow; ammonium chlorostannate, $(NH_4)_2SnCl_6$, pink; ammonium chromate, $(NH_4)_2CrO_4$, yellow; ammonium dichromate, $(NH_4)_2Cr_2O_7$, red; ammonium hydroxide (known in solution only), $NH_4OH$, colorless; ammonium magnesium arsenate, $MgNH_4AsO_4 \cdot 6H_2O$, white; ammonium magnesium phosphate, $MgNH_4PO_4 \cdot 6H_2O$, white; ammonium molybdate, $(NH_4)_2MoO_4$, white; ammonium hepta-molybdate (commercial ammonium molybdate), $(NH_4)_6Mo_7O_{24} \cdot 4H_2O$, white; ammonium oxalate, $(NH_4)_2C_2O_4 \cdot H_2O$, white; ammonium perchlorate, $NH_4ClO_4$, white; ammonium persulfate, $(NH_4)_2S_2O_8$, white; mono-ammonium phosphate, $NH_4H_2PO_4$, white; di-ammonium phosphate, $(NH_4)_2HPO_4$, white; ammonium molybdi-arsenate, $(NH_4)_3As(Mo_3O_{10})_4 \cdot 3H_2O$, yellow; ammonium molybdi-phosphate, $(NH_4)_3P(Mo_3O_{10})_4 \cdot 3H_2O$, yellow; ammonium sulfide, $(NH_4)_2S$, white; ammonium sulfite, $(NH_4)_2SO_3 \cdot H_2O$, white; ammonium acid sulfite, $NH_4HSO_3$, white; ammonium thiocyanate, $NH_4CNS$, white.

**Reactions of Ammonium Ion.** Ammonium ion forms slightly soluble compounds, $(NH_4)_3Co(NO_2)_6$ and $(NH_4)_2PtCl_6$, similar to potassium. The other common precipitation reactions involve the formation of (1) double salts, $MgNH_4PO_4$, white (formed in the estimation of Mg, As, or P); (2) the ammonium salts of molybdi-arsenic acid and molybdi-phosphoric acid, $(NH_4)_3As(Mo_3O_{10})_4 \cdot 3H_2O$, and $(NH_4)_3P(Mo_3O_{10})_4 \cdot 3H_2O$, both yellow (formed in the identification and estimation of As and P); (3) amino compounds of mercury, $NH_2HgCl$, white; and $NH_2IHg_2O$, brown (used in the identification and estimation of small amounts of $NH_3$). $NH_4OH$, formed by the action of $NaOH$ on $NH_4^+$, is unstable, being largely decomposed in aqueous solution into $H_2O$ and $NH_3$, a gas of characteristic odor, very soluble in water. Electrolysis of $NH_4Cl$ solution using a mercury cathode produces an unstable ammonium amalgam. Strong oxidizing agents oxidize $NH_4^+$ to $N_2$ or even to $HNO_3$; $HCl + HNO_3$ forming $N_2$ and $N_2O$ in hot fairly concentrated solution, and $Cl_2$, $KMnO_4$, etc., forming $N_2$ in the presence of $NaOH$. $NH_3$ enters into the formation of complex ions, $Ag(NH_3)_2^+$, $Cu(NH_3)_4^{++}$, etc., with a number of the common metals. $NH_4^+$ forms a number of soluble double salts with salts of heavy metals. The most characteristic reaction is the formation of the gas $NH_3$ when $NH_4^+$ is treated with $NaOH$ and the solution heated. The $NH_3$ may be identified by odor, by absorption with moist red litmus paper whose color is thus changed to blue, or by passing into Nessler's reagent (a strong alkaline solution of $K_2HgI_4$), which forms a brown, gelatinous precipitate, $NH_2IHg_2O$.

## REACTIONS OF GROUP VI METALS IN THE SYSTEMATIC ANALYSIS OF EARLIER GROUPS

The only cases where any sixth group metal reacts in the procedures for earlier groups are the partial precipitation of $Mg(OH)_2$, when the solution is neutralized with $NH_4OH$ at the beginning of Group II and the carrying down of some $MgCO_3$ in Group V, particularly when $Ca^{++}$ is present. If the solution is strongly acid (or contains much $NH_4^+$), no precipitate of $Mg(OH)_2$ will form because of repression of ionization of the $NH_4OH$ by $NH_4^+$ accumulating as the solution is neutralized.

## ANALYSIS OF GROUP VI

Since there is no group reagent for these ions, individual tests are applied separately for $Mg^{++}$, $Na^+$, $K^+$, and $NH_4^+$.

**Identification of Magnesium.** To the solution after Group V add 1–2 drops each of $(NH_4)_2SO_4$ and $(NH_4)_2C_2O_4$ solution, heat to boiling and let stand several minutes. If a very small precipitate forms, this may be removed and discarded, using the solution to test for $Mg^{++}$. If the precipitate is moderate in amount, it should be washed and set aside to test for any fifth group metal that may have escaped precipitation with $(NH_4)_2CO_3$. To the clear solution add 1 drop of $(NH_4)_2HPO_4$, cool and, if no precipitate forms immediately, stir to start crystallization. A white, crystalline precipitate, $MgNH_4PO_4$, forms if $Mg^{++}$ is present.

*Explanatory Notes.* (1) In using the phosphate test for $Mg^{++}$ it is necessary to remove such small amounts of fifth group metals as may have failed to precipitate with $(NH_4)_2CO_3$, since these metals form insoluble phosphates that might be mistaken for the $MgNH_4PO_4$. $(NH_4)_2SO_4$ and $(NH_4)_2C_2O_4$ together precipitate Ba, Sr, and Ca more effectively than does $(NH_4)_2CO_3$ and so may be used to avoid this error. (2) If the precipitate with $(NH_4)_2SO_4$ and $(NH_4)_2C_2O_4$ is sufficient to warrant applying tests for fifth group metals, the simplest procedure consists in transferring the precipitate to a small crucible, adding 15–20 drops of 3 *N* $Na_2CO_3$, covering with a watch glass and digesting near the boiling point for 5–10 minutes. This transposes the insoluble sulfates and oxalates to carbonates. Centrifuge, wash, dissolve the precipitate in acetic acid, and analyze this solution by the regular fifth group procedure.

(3) An alternative test for $Mg^{++}$ consists in precipitating $Mg(OH)_2$ in the presence of a little paranitrobenzene-azo-resorcinol, forming a blue adsorption complex. This may be applied to the precipitate of $MgNH_4PO_4$ by dissolving the precipitate in HCl, adding a drop of the reagent, and then treating with excess of NaOH. The ammonium and phosphate ions interfere somewhat with the test, but by washing the precipitate carefully and adding 4–5 drops excess of NaOH these interferences become very slight. For moderate amounts of $Mg^{++}$, since Group V metals do not interfere with this test, it is possible to apply this test on the solution obtained after removal of excess ammonium salts from the solution after Group IV. Dilute 1–2 drops of this solution to 5–10 drops with water, add 1 drop of 5 *N* HCl and 1 drop of the 0.001% solution of the dye in *N* NaOH, shake thoroughly and add 5–10 drops of 3 *N* NaOH. In the absence of $Mg^{++}$ a reddish purple color appears as a result of the dye itself, and if Group V metals are present white precipitates of hydroxides or carbonates may form. If $Mg^{++}$ is present, a blue color develops and, as the solution stands a short time, a blue precipitate coagulates and settles. For very small amounts of $Mg^{++}$ a little of the dye may be diluted with 5–10 times its volume of water and 1 drop of this diluted solution used, thus decreasing the depth of color in the solution due to excess of the dye added.

**Identification of Sodium.** If the original solution is alkaline, acidify with HCl, dip into the solution a freshly cleaned platinum wire and then insert the wire into the edge of a Bunsen flame. If a moderate amount of $Na^+$ is present a bright yellow color will appear. Sr and Ca interfere with the recognition of small amounts of Na. In such a case the clear solution from Group V should be tested. If $NaNO_2$ was used earlier in the reduction of dichromate or permanganate, a fresh portion of the original solution may be treated with $NH_4Cl$, $NH_4OH$, and $H_2S$ to precipitate Groups I–IV, the filtrate then treated with $(NH_4)_2CO_3$ to remove Group V, and the final solution used to test for $Na^+$.

An alternative procedure consists in testing a portion of the solution obtained after removing ammonium salts from the solution after Group IV. To 2–3 drops of this solution add 5 drops of magnesium uranyl acetate solution.

Stir if necessary to start crystallization. A fine, greenish yellow, crystalline precipitate $NaMg(UO_2)_3(C_2H_3O_2)_9$ forms promptly if even a small amount of $Na^+$ is present.

*Explanatory Note.* Sodium is commonly present in small amounts as an impurity in most salts. Even if the latter have been carefully purified, it is difficult to keep them free from sodium since NaCl is present in the dust of the air, and aqueous solutions pick up some sodium from the glass containers. It is desirable, therefore, to set up a known solution to represent the amount of sodium that may be present as an impurity and try the tests on this as an aid in judging whether or not sodium is present as an intentional constituent of an unknown. Prepare two NaCl solutions, one containing 0.2 mg. $Na^+$ per ml., the other 0.5 mg. of $Na^+$ per ml. Try the flame test several times on each of these, cleaning the platinum wire between tests. Note that there is a recognizable difference in the brightness and duration of the yellow color in the two cases. Next, to 5 drops of each of the solutions add 5 drops of the magnesium uranyl acetate reagent, stir to start crystallization, and note the difference in readiness of precipitation and amount of precipitate formed. Assuming that the more dilute of the solutions being tested represents the maximum amount of $Na^+$ commonly present as an impurity, the student should not report $Na^+$ unless the unknown shows a stronger test than this solution gives.

**Identification of Potassium.** Try the flame test with a clean platinum wire on the clear solution after Group V. A lavender color, lasting for only a very short time, indicates $K^+$. If a yellow sodium flame is obtained, repeat the test, observing the flame through a cobalt glass. With the yellow rays filtered out the potassium flame shows reddish violet.

*Explanatory Notes.* (1) Since the potassium flame disappears quickly, it is necessary to watch the flame as the platinum wire is inserted. If the cobalt glass is being used, hold the dipped wire in front of the flame, then look through the glass and move the wire back into the flame.

(2) Occasionally a cobalt glass may not give a satisfactory blank test with a moderately concentrated NaCl solution, the color of the flame looking like potassium but persisting for a longer time. It is also possible to find glasses that are so opaque that the delicacy of the test for $K^+$ is decreased appreciably. For these reasons the student should try preliminary tests on known solutions, one containing 10 mg. of $Na^+$ (in the form of NaCl) per ml., a second containing 10 mg. of $Na^+$ and 2 mg. of $K^+$ per ml. (the salts as chlorides), and a third containing 5 mg. of $K^+$ (as KCl) per ml. The third shows what the potassium flame looks like, and if the cobalt glass is satisfactory there should be no serious difficulty in obtaining a blank test in number one and recognizing the $K^+$ in number two.

(3) Other substances besides glass colored by cobalt oxide may be used to absorb the sodium light in this test for $K^+$. Thus a thin, flat bottle containing a concentrated solution of chrome alum ($KCr(SO_4)_2 \cdot 12H_2O$) serves as a

satisfactory filter. A satisfactory glass is also made by thoroughly fixing and washing an unexposed lantern slide and staining the film with a 1% solution of crystal violet. After drying, the film may be protected by a cover glass and mounted in a wooden frame.

(4) The precipitation tests for $K^+$ usually require removal of $NH_4^+$ first. This may be done by evaporating a portion of the filtrate from Group V to dryness and heating moderately (slightly below red heat) until no more fumes of $NH_4Cl$ appear. Cool, dissolve in a little water, and add 2–3 drops of $Na_3Co(NO_2)_6$ solution. A bright yellow precipitate, $K_2NaCo(NO_2)_6$ forms if $K^+$ is present. The reagent is somewhat unstable and should be tested with a known solution occasionally.

**Identification of Ammonium Ion.** Place 5 drops of NaOH reagent and 5 drops of the unknown solution in a centrifuge tube, mix, and warm slightly. Insert a plug of absorbent cotton close to the surface of the solution, and rest a piece of moist red litmus paper on the cotton plug. If $NH_4^+$ is present the litmus paper will turn blue within 15–20 seconds. The odor of $NH_3$ may also be used to identify this gas.

*Explanatory Notes.* (1) The test for $NH_4^+$ depends upon the fact that $NH_4OH$ is a weak, unstable base and that the $NH_3$ formed, although very soluble in water, volatilizes readily from the solution at higher temperatures.

(2) It is possible to distinguish between a small amount of $NH_4^+$ and a moderate or large amount by trying the test first without heating. If the odor is uncertain and the litmus turns color slowly, only a small amount of $NH_4^+$ is present.

(3) In heating the solution to obtain a more abundant evolution of $NH_3$, care should be taken to avoid boiling when the test is made with litmus paper; otherwise the spray from the solution will turn the litmus blue even though $NH_3$ is absent.

(4) A more delicate test for $NH_3$ consists in fitting a test tube with a 1-hole stopper and delivery tube, boiling the solution, and passing the evolved gases into a second test tube containing 3–5 drops of Nessler's reagent (a strongly alkaline solution of $K_2HgI_4$). A reddish brown precipitate, $NH_2IHg_2O$, indicates $NH_3$. In using this test it is commonly desirable to try a blank test on distilled water and NaOH solution. Because of the frequent use of $NH_4OH$ as a reagent in the laboratory, most solutions will give a slight test for $NH_4^+$. However, in such cases the reagent shows only a tan to brown color, whereas with ordinary amounts of $NH_4^+$ present a marked precipitate is obtained.

## REPORTING GROUP VI IONS IN AN UNKNOWN SOLUTION

Since all these ions are of the simple positive type regardless of whether the solution is acid, neutral, or alkaline, the sixth group metals are reported as

$Mg^{++}$, $Na^{+}$, $K^{+}$, and $NH_4^{+}$ whenever any of these are identified in unknown solutions.

## GROUP VI METALS IN RELATION TO OTHER GROUPS

The behavior of sixth group metals in the precipitation of earlier groups has already been discussed in this chapter.

Of the earlier group metals that may escape precipitation in the regular scheme and thus be present when the test for Mg is applied, Mn, Ba, Sr, and Ca are the chief offenders. All these form white precipitates with $(NH_4)_2$-$HPO_4$ in the presence of $NH_4OH$, and thus will interfere with this test for $Mg^{++}$. By using the supplementary procedure of centrifuging, washing, dissolving in HCl, adding a drop of paranitrobenzene-azo-resorcinol reagent, and then treating with excess NaOH, a definite confirmatory test for $Mg^{++}$ can be obtained whether these other metals are present or not.

## REACTIONS OF GROUP VI METALS IN THE SYSTEMATIC ANALYSIS OF A SOLUTION

**Magnesium**

*Adjusting the acidity for the precipitation of Group II*

$$Mg^{++} + NH_4OH + Cl^- = \underline{MgOHCl} + NH_4^+$$
$$\underline{MgOHCl} + H_3O^+ = Mg^{++} + 2H_2O + Cl^-$$

*Partial precipitation as carbonate in Group V*

$$Mg^{++} + HCO_3^- + NH_3 = \underline{MgCO_3} + NH_4^+$$

*In Group VI*

$$Mg^{++} + HPO_4^{--} + NH_3 = \underline{MgNH_4PO_4}$$
$$\underline{MgNH_4PO_4} + 3H_3O^+ = Mg^{++} + NH_4^+ + H_3PO_4 + 3H_2O$$
$$Mg^{++} + \text{organic-reagent} + 2OH^- = \underline{Mg(OH)_2 + \text{reagent}}$$

**Sodium**

*In Group VI, direct tests*

1. $Na^+ + Sb(OH)_6^- = \underline{NaSb(OH)_6}$
2. $Na^+ + Mg^{++} + 3UO_2^{++} + 9C_2H_3O_2^- = \underline{NaMg(UO_2)_3(C_2H_3O_2)_9}$

**Potassium**

*In Group VI, direct tests*

1. $2K^+ + Co(NO_2)_6^{-3} + Na^+ = \underline{K_2NaCo(NO_2)_6}$
2. $K^+ + ClO_4^- = \underline{KClO_4}$ (soly. lowered in alcohol)
3. $2K^+ + H_2PtCl_6 + 2H_2O = \underline{K_2PtCl_6} + 2H_3O^+$

**Ammonium**

*Direct test on original solution*

$NH_4^+ + OH^- = NH_3\uparrow + H_2O$
1. $NH_3 + H_2O = NH_4^+ + OH^-$ (litmus paper test)
2. $NH_3 + 2HgI_4^{--} + 3OH^- = \underline{NH_2IHg_2O} + 7I^- + 2H_2O$

## *LABORATORY EXERCISES*

1. Known solutions containing metals of Groups I–VI.

(*1*) $Al^{+3}$, $Mn^{++}$, $Ba^{++}$, $Na^+$, $NH_4^+$
(*2*) $Ca^{++}$, $Mg^{++}$, $K^+$, $Na^+$
(*3*) $Sr^{++}$, $K^+(s)$, $NH_4^+(s)$

These solutions contain the following amounts of substance per liter of solution: (*1*) 26 g. $AlCl_3 \cdot 6H_2O$, 9 g. $MnCl_2 \cdot 4H_2O$, 4.5 g. $BaCl_2 \cdot 2H_2O$, 6.5 g. NaCl, 15 g. $NH_4Cl$, and 25 ml. of 5 *N* HCl; (*2*) 9 g. $CaCl_2 \cdot 2H_2O$, 21 g. $MgCl_2 \cdot 6H_2O$, 5 g. KCl, 6.5 g. NaCl, and 5 ml. of 5 *N* HCl; (*3*) 7.5 g. $SrCl_2 \cdot 6H_2O$, 2 g. KCl, 3 g. $NH_4Cl$, and 5 ml. of 5 *N* HCl.

Use 15 drops of the original solution to test for the presence of earlier groups, testing the solution after Group V for $Mg^{++}$, and removing fifth group metals when necessary before applying the flame tests for $K^+$ and $Na^+$.

*Solution 1.* (*a*) In testing for $Mg^{++}$ with $(NH_4)_2HPO_4$ a slight precipitate may be obtained, due to $Mn^{++}$ or $Ba^{++}$ incompletely removed in their proper groups. In such a case try the confirmatory test for $Mg^{++}$ by dissolving the precipitate in HCl, adding a drop of paranitrobenzene-azo-resorcinol, and treating with excess NaOH. If the precipitate obtained is not blue no $Mg^{++}$ is present.

(*b*) The flame test for $Na^+$ should be tried on the original solution and on the clear solution after Group V.

(*c*) Apply tests for $NH_4^+$ on the original solution. Use 2 drops of the original solution, add 5 drops of reagent NaOH, note odor and reaction of gases above the solution with moist red litmus paper, both with the solution cold and after heating nearly to boiling. Try boiling the alkaline solution and passing the gases into a few drops of Nessler's reagent.

*Solution 2.* (*a*) Treat a portion of the original solution with 2–3 drops of $NH_4OH$. A slight, finely divided precipitate is $CaCO_3$, due to $CO_3^{--}$ in the $NH_4OH$. If a moderate amount of flocculent precipitate is obtained this is probably $Mg(OH)_2$. In this latter case, take a fresh portion of the solution, add 2–3 drops of 5 *N* $NH_4Cl$ solution and then 2–3 drops of $NH_4OH$. Note that only a slight precipitate of $CaCO_3$ is now obtained.

(*b*) After precipitating Group V with $(NH_4)_2CO_3$, centrifuge and test for completeness of precipitation with this reagent, then add 1–2 drops of $(NH_4)_2C_2O_4$, warm and let stand a moment. A slight precipitate of $CaC_2O_4$ is usually obtained. If this appears sufficient to cause uncertainty in the direct precipitation test for $Mg^{++}$ with $(NH_4)_2HPO_4$, it should be removed and discarded, using the solution to test for $Mg^{++}$.

(*c*) When using the cobalt glass in the test for $K^+$, it is desirable to try a blank test on a solution of NaCl and compare the results. Occasionally the student mistakes the flash of deeper blue flame obtained through the cobalt glass from the NaCl solution, for the flash of violet color from the potassium flame.

*Solution 3.* (*a*) The fifth group precipitate should lead to a satisfactory precipitate of $SrSO_4$ with either 0.1 *N* $(NH_4)_2SO_4$ or $CaSO_4$ solution.

(*b*) If the flame test for $K^+$ appears uncertain in the solution after Group V, try evaporating the solution nearly to dryness and then apply the flame test on this more concentrated solution.

(*c*) Treat a portion of the original solution with excess NaOH, warm and test for $NH_3$ both by odor and by effect on moist red litmus paper. The tests are less pronounced than in the first solution but should be easily recognizable.

2. Delicacy of the tests for $Na^+$. Prepare a series of 8 test tubes containing decreasing amounts of NaCl, such that No. 1 contains 1 mg. of $Na^+$ per ml., No. 2 contains 0.5 mg. of $Na^+$ per ml., No. 3 contains 0.25 mg. of $Na^+$, etc. To each of the last four solutions add 2–3 drops of the magnesium uranyl acetate reagent and note the limit of precipitation of the sodium compound. Try the flame tests on the first four solutions and note the decreasing brightness and duration of the yellow color.

3. Delicacy of the flame test for $K^+$. Prepare a series of dilutions of KCl (see problem No. 2), starting with 4 mg. of $K^+$ per ml., and try the flame test for $K^+$. Clean the platinum wire after using on each solution before going to the next more dilute solution. Note the limit at which a positive test is obtained every time, and also the limit at which no test for $K^+$ is obtained in several attempts (with cleaned wire).

4. If the amount of solution picked up on a platinum wire is 0.001 ml., calculate the maximum amount of potassium that could be volatilized in the flame in the last solution in (3) in which a positive test for $K^+$ is regularly obtained.

5. Delicacy of the tests for $Mg^{++}$. Prepare two series of dilutions of $MgCl_2$ starting with 0.2 mg. of $Mg^{++}$ per ml. in tube No. 1, each successive tube containing half as much as the one that precedes it. To each tube in the first series add 2–3 drops of $NH_4Cl$, 2–3 drops of $NH_4OH$, and 1–2 drops of $(NH_4)_2HPO_4$. Stir if necessary to start crystallization. Note the limit of formation of $MgNH_4PO_4$. To each tube in the second series add 1 drop of paranitrobenzene-azo-resorcinol solution and 2–3 drops of NaOH solution. Note the limit of formation of recognizable blue precipitate. Compare the results in the two cases.

## *EQUILIBRIUM PROBLEMS IN GROUP VI*

Since Mg is the only metal of this group which forms a number of common, slightly soluble compounds, these problems all deal with this element.

I. Calculate the concentration of $PO_4^{---}$ supplied for the precipitation of $MgNH_4PO_4$. The conditions in the filtrate from Group V are: Volume is approximately 2 ml., the solution is rather strongly buffered with $NH_4^+$ and $NH_4OH$—both approximately 0.7 *M* $\left(0.9 \times \frac{1.5}{2}\right)$—and $[H_3O^+] = 5.6 \times 10^{-10}$. To this is added about 0.1 ml. each of $(NH_4)_2SO_4$ and $(NH_4)_2C_2O_4$ to remove traces of Group V metals; then about 0.1 ml. of 0.5 *N* $Na_2HPO_4$ to test for the presence of $Mg^{++}$. Total volume 2.3 ml. $K_{HPO_4^{--}} = 3.6 \times 10^{-13}$.

$$0.5\ N\ Na_2HPO_4 = 0.167\ M$$

$$\text{Concn. of } PO_4\text{—radical added } ([HPO_4^{--}] + [PO_4^{---}]) = 0.167 \times \frac{0.1}{2.3} = 0.0073$$

$$\frac{[H_3O^+] \times [PO_4^{---}]}{[HPO_4^{--}]} = 3.6 \times 10^{-13}$$

If

$$[H_3O^+] = 5.6 \times 10^{-10} \quad \frac{[PO_4^{---}]}{[HPO_4^{--}]} = \frac{3.6 \times 10^{-13}}{5.6 \times 10^{-10}} = \frac{6.4 \times 10^{-4}}{1}$$

$$[PO_4^{---}] = 7.3 \times 10^{-3} \times 6.4 \times 10^{-4} = 4.7 \times 10^{-6}$$

II. Calculate the concentration of $Mg^{++}$ required to saturate the solution if $[PO_4^{---}] = 4.7 \times 10^{-6}$, and $[NH_4^+] = 0.6$.

$$L_{MgNH_4PO_4} = 2.5 \times 10^{-13}$$

$$[Mg^{++}] \times [NH_4^+] \times [PO_4^{---}] = 2.5 \times 10^{-13}$$

$$[Mg^{++}] = \frac{2.5 \times 10^{-13}}{0.6 \times 4.7 \times 10^{-6}} = 8 \times 10^{-8}$$

III. Calculate the weight of $Mg^{++}$ that would be present in the clear solution after Group V if the total volume is 1.5 ml., and the solution is assumed to be just saturated (*a*) with $MgCO_3$, and (*b*) with $Mg(OH)_2$.

$$L_{MgCO_3} = 2.6 \times 10^{-5} \qquad L_{Mg(OH)_2} = 3 \times 10^{-10}$$

In the precipitation of Group V, $[CO_3^{--}] = 0.03$, $[OH^-] = 1.8 \times 10^{-5}$.

(*a*) If

$$[CO_3^{--}] = 0.03$$

$$[Mg^{++}] = \frac{2.6 \times 10^{-5}}{0.03} = 8.7 \times 10^{-4} \qquad \text{(At. wt. Mg = 24)}$$

$$\text{Wt. } Mg^{++} = (8.7 \times 10^{-4})(24)(1.5) = 0.03 \text{ mg. } Mg^{++}$$ *Ans. to (a)*

(*b*) If

$$[OH^-] = 1.7 \times 10^{-5}$$

$$[Mg^{++}] = \frac{3 \times 10^{-10}}{(1.8 \times 10^{-5})^2} \cong 1$$

$$\text{Wt. } Mg^{++} = (1)(24)(1.5) = 36 \text{ mg. } Mg^{++}$$ *Ans. to (b)*

Evidently there is little trouble to be feared from precipitation of $Mg(OH)_2$, but considerable amounts of $MgCO_3$ would precipitate in Group V if equilibrium conditions of the order suggested by these calculations are actually reached.

Direct experiments using 50 mg. of $Mg^{++}$ in 15 ml., plus 5 ml. each of 5 *N* $NH_4Cl$, 5 *N* $NH_4OH$, and 4 *N* $(NH_4)_2CO_3$ in the cold, gave no immediate precipitates of $MgCO_3$, and the solutions remained clear even on standing 1–2 hours. However, when similar solutions were prepared containing 5 mg. of $Ba^{++}$, $Sr^{++}$, or $Ca^{++}$ it was found that no immediate precipitation occurred in the cold with either $Ba^{++}$ or $Sr^{++}$. In the case of $Ca^{++}$ a fine, milky suspension was obtained, distinctly different in appearance from, and larger in amount than, the precipitate of $CaCO_3$ which forms in the absence of $Mg^{++}$. On heating these various solutions, with stirring, to incipient decomposition of the $(NH_4)_2CO_3$ (bubbles of $CO_2$ start to come off), a moderate precipitate was obtained in all cases: $Ba^{++} + Mg^{++}$, $Sr^{++} + Mg^{++}$, $Ca^{++} + Mg^{++}$, and $Mg^{++}$ alone. On cooling, filtering, and washing, the filtrate was tested first for incomplete precipitation of the Group V carbonates, using $(NH_4)_2SO_4$ to test for $Ba^{++}$ and $(NH_4)_2C_2O_4$ to test for $Sr^{++}$ and $Ca^{++}$. Rather faint tests were obtained, showing that fairly complete precipitation was accomplished in all three cases. Next, the filtrates were tested for $Mg^{++}$ by filtering and adding $Na_2HPO_4$ to the clear filtrates. Fairly bulky precipitates of $MgNH_4PO_4$ were obtained in all cases indicating that a considerable fraction of the $Mg^{++}$ had carried past Group V. Finally the precipitates obtained with the $(NH_4)_2CO_3$ were dissolved in acetic acid and tested for the individual metals of Group V and for $Mg^{++}$. Definite tests for $Ba^{++}$, $Sr^{++}$, and $Ca^{++}$ were obtained on the respective precipitates, and when $Na_2HPO_4$ was added to the final filtrate moderate precipitates of $MgNH_4PO_4$ were formed, the precipitate in this case being judged to be about 20–25% that found in the filtrate from Group V.

Similar experiments using 50 mg. of a Group V metal with only 5 mg. of $Mg^{++}$ showed that most of the $Mg^{++}$ remained in the filtrate from Group V and that the process of heating to incipient evolution of $CO_2$ and then cooling led to reasonably complete precipitation of Group V. Other experiments were tried, varying the amount of $NH_4Cl$ used from 2 ml. of the 5 *N* reagent up to 5 g. of the solid. In the former case Group V precipitated more readily, but considerably more $MgCO_3$ precipitated at the same time. When higher concentrations of $NH_4Cl$ were tried, somewhat less $MgCO_3$ precipitated but the Group V carbonates precipitated much more slowly. Further, in those cases where considerable $MgCO_3$ was carried down in Group V the precipitation of $SrSO_4$ by dilute $(NH_4)_2SO_4$ was interfered with seriously.

A further set of experiments on the precipitation of $MgCO_3$ by itself was run, in which, after heating to obtain the initial precipitation, the solutions were covered and then allowed to stand for varying lengths of time. After 2–3 hours the solutions appeared to be clear at first glance, but a closer examination showed the presence of some coarse, nearly transparent crystals on the bottom of the beaker. If at this time the solutions were stirred vigorously with a glass rod, a fairly copious, fine-grained precipitate was obtained. Or if the solutions were permitted to stand overnight, there was a considerable increase in the amount of the coarse crystals. In either case, on centrifuging and testing the clear solution with $Na_2HPO_4$, a reasonably good precipitate of $MgNH_4PO_4$ was obtained, although in some cases considerably over 50% of the $Mg^{++}$ was precipitated as $MgCO_3$.

In the light of the experiments just described it is evident that $MgCO_3$ will precipitate to some extent in Group V and that the retention of a reasonable amount of it in solution by use of $NH_4Cl$ is due mainly to the marked slowness with which equilibrium is reached under these conditions.

# II

## Arsenic Division of Group II

# Arsenic, Antimony, Tin

The arsenic division of Group II is precipitated by the use of $H_2S$ in the presence of HCl. It is separated from the copper division by the solubility of its sulfides in warm ammonium polysulfide. The metals included are As, Sb, and Sn. The common ions of these metals are $H_2AsO_3^-$, $H_2AsO_4^-$, $Sb^{+3}$, $SbCl_4^-$, $Sb(OH)_4^-$, $Sb^{+5}$, $SbCl_6^-$, $Sb(OH)_6^-$, $Sn^{++}$, $SnCl_4^{--}$, $Sn(OH)_3^-$, $Sn^{+4}$, $SnCl_6^{--}$, $Sn(OH)_5^-$.

### COMMON COMPOUNDS AND REACTIONS OF THE IONS OF As, Sb, AND Sn

**More Common Arsenic Compounds.** Arsenious chloride, $AsCl_3$, colorless liquid; arsenious sulfide, $As_2S_3$, yellow; arsenic sulfide, $As_2S_5$, yellow; arsenious oxide, $As_2O_3$, white; arsenic oxide (arsenic anhydride), $As_2O_5$, white; arsine, $AsH_3$, colorless gas; silver arsenite, $Ag_3AsO_3$, yellow; silver arsenate, $Ag_3AsO_4$, brown; lead arsenate, $Pb_3(AsO_4)_2$, white; copper arsenite (Paris green), $Cu_3(AsO_3)_2$, green; copper arsenate, $Cu_3(AsO_4)_2$, greenish blue; ferric arsenate, $FeAsO_4$, pale yellow; calcium arsenate, $Ca_3(AsO_4)_2$, white; magnesium ammonium arsenate, $MgNH_4AsO_4$, white; potassium arsenite, $K_4As_2O_5$, white; potassium arsenate, $K_2HAsO_4$, white; ammonium arsenite, $NH_4AsO_2$, white; ammonium arsenate, $(NH_4)_2HAsO_4$, white; sodium arsenite, $Na_2HAsO_3$, white; sodium arsenate, $Na_2HAsO_4$, white; ammonium molybdi-arsenate, $(NH_4)_3As(Mo_3O_{10})_4$, yellow.

**More Common Reactions of Arsenite Ion.** NaOH, $NH_4OH$, etc., do not affect $H_2AsO_3^-$; dilute solutions of the strong acids convert $H_2AsO_3^-$ to $H_3AsO_3$, moderately soluble but slightly ionized. $Pb(C_2H_3O_2)_2$ precipitates $Pb_3(AsO_3)_2$, white, soluble in $HNO_3$ and in NaOH; $AgNO_3$ precipitates $Ag_3AsO_3$, yellow, soluble in $HNO_3$ and in $NH_4OH$; $H_2S$ in a warm, acid solution precipitates $As_2S_3$, yellow, soluble in $HNO_3$ on heating (oxidation to $H_3AsO_4 + S$), in $NH_4OH$, NaOH, etc. (formation of $H_2AsO_3^-$ and $H_2AsS_3^-$), and in alkali sulfides and polysulfides (formation of $H_2AsS_3^-$ and $H_2AsS_4^-$). In neutral or alkaline solution $I_2$ readily oxidizes $H_2AsO_3^-$ to $H_2AsO_4^-$. In acid solution $HNO_3$ and the stronger oxidizing agents oxidize $H_3AsO_3$ to $H_3AsO_4$.

$SnCl_2$ in hot, concentrated HCl solution, reduces $H_3AsO_3$ to metallic As, flocculent, dark brown. Metallic Zn in warm dilute $H_2SO_4$ solution reduces $H_3AsO_3$ to arsine, $AsH_3$, a colorless gas, which decomposes on heating, with formation of a mirror of metallic arsenic, or which will form a black precipitate of metallic silver with $AgNO_3$. Arsine may also be obtained from $H_2AsO_3^-$ by the reducing action of Al and NaOH. The most characteristic reactions are (1) the formation of a yellow precipitate, $Ag_3AsO_3$, with $AgNO_3$ in neutral solution; and (2) the formation of $AsH_3$ with NaOH + Al, the $AsH_3$ being identified by its action on $AgNO_3$ solution.

**More Common Reactions of Arsenate Ion.** The common alkalis do not affect $AsO_4^{-3}$; dilute solutions of the strong acids convert $AsO_4^{-3}$ to acid ions, $HAsO_4^{--}$ and $H_2AsO_4^-$, the corresponding salts being generally soluble. $BaCl_2$ precipitates $BaHAsO_4$, white, soluble in HCl or $HNO_3$; $Pb(C_2H_3O_2)_2$ precipitates $Pb_3(AsO_4)_2$, white, soluble in $HNO_3$ or NaOH; $MgCl_2$ in $NH_4OH$ solution precipitates $MgNH_4AsO_4$, white, soluble in HCl and even in $HC_2H_3O_2$; $AgNO_3$ in neutral solution precipitates $Ag_3AsO_4$, brown, soluble in $HNO_3$ and in $NH_4OH$. $H_2S$ in hot, concentrated HCl solution precipitates $As_2S_5$, yellow, soluble in $HNO_3$ (oxidation to S°) and in alkali hydroxides and sulfides (formation of sulfoxyarsenates, $H_2AsO_2S_2^-$ and $H_2AsOS_3^-$ and of thioarsenate ion, $H_2AsS_4^-$). On acidifying such solutions $As_2S_5$ reprecipitates. Ammonium molybdate in warm $HNO_3$ solution precipitates ammonium molybdi-arsenate, $(NH_4)_3As(Mo_3O_{10})_4$, yellow, soluble in $NH_4OH$ or NaOH. In acid solution KI and other moderately strong reducing agents will reduce $H_3AsO_4$ to $H_3AsO_3$, whereas Zn + $H_2SO_4$ will reduce $H_3AsO_3$ or $H_3AsO_4$ to arsine, $AsH_3$, a colorless gas. The most characteristic reactions are: (1) the formation of a brown precipitate, $Ag_3AsO_4$, with $AgNO_3$ in neutral solution, and (2) the formation of a white precipitate, $MgNH_4AsO_4$, with $McCl_2$ in a cold $NH_4OH$ solution.

**More Common Antimony Compounds.** Antimonous chloride, $SbCl_3$, white; antimonic chloride, $SbCl_5$, colorless liquid; antimonous sulfide, $Sb_2S_3$, orange; antimonic sulfide, $Sb_2S_5$, orange; antimonous oxide, $Sb_2O_3$, white; antimony tetroxide, $Sb_2O_4$, white; antimony pentoxide, $Sb_2O_5$, yellow; antimonic acid, $H_3SbO_4$, white; antimonous oxychloride, SbOCl, white; stibine, $SbH_3$, colorless gas; ammonium thioantimonate, $(NH_4)_3SbS_4$, white; potassium acid antimonate, $KH_2SbO_4$, white; sodium antimonate, $NaSb(OH)_6$, white.

**Reactions of Antimonous Ion.** A solution of $SbCl_3$ on dilution with water forms a white precipitate, SbOCl, soluble in HCl, NaOH, or $H_2C_4H_4O_6$. $NH_4OH$, or NaOH, precipitates $Sb_2O_3$, white, soluble in HCl, and in NaOH (forming an antimonite, $Sb(OH)_4^-$). HCl changes $Sb^{+3}$ to $SbCl_4^-$. $H_2S$ in acid solution precipitates $Sb_2S_3$, orange, soluble in concentrated HCl, and in $(NH_4)_2S_2$ (formation of thio-antimonate ion, $H_2SbS_4^-$). In neutral or alkaline solution $I_2$ oxidizes $Sb(OH)_4^-$ to $Sb(OH)_6^-$, in acid solution hot $HNO_3$

and the stronger oxidizing agents oxidize $Sb^{+3}$ to $Sb^{+5}$. In dilute HCl solution Sn reduces $Sb^{+3}$ to metallic Sb, black; and in $H_2SO_4$ or HCl solution Zn reduces $Sb^{+3}$ in part to stibine, $SbH_3$, a colorless gas, which decomposes readily on heating, forming an antimony mirror. Tartaric acid forms a complex antimonyl tartrate ion, $SbOC_4H_4O_6^-$, which prevents the precipitation of SbOCl when the solution is diluted. The most characteristic reactions are (1) the precipitation of $Sb_2S_3$, orange, with $H_2S$ in acid solution, and (2) the precipitation of SbOCl, white, on dilution of $SbCl_3$ with water.

**Reactions of Antimonic Ion.** $NH_4OH$ or NaOH precipitates $SbO(OH)_3$, white, soluble in HCl and in NaOH (forming an antimonate). $H_2O$ added to a solution of $SbCl_5$ forms a precipitate, $SbOCl_3$, white, soluble in HCl, NaOH, or $H_2C_4H_4O_6$. $H_2S$ in acid solution precipitates $Sb_2S_5$, orange, soluble in concentrated HCl (formation of $SbCl_3$, $H_2S$, and S), and in $(NH_4)_2S$ (formation of thioantimonate ion, $H_2SbS_4^-$). In acid solution KI and other moderately strong reducing agents reduce $Sb^{+5}$ to $Sb^{+3}$; in dilute HCl solution $SnCl_2$ reduces $Sb^{+5}$ to $Sb^{+3}$; and in $H_2SO_4$ or HCl solution Zn reduces $Sb^{+5}$ in part to stibine, $SbH_3$, an unstable, colorless gas. Tartaric acid forms a complex tartrate with $Sb^{+5}$, which prevents the precipitation of $SbOCl_3$ when the solution is diluted. The most characteristic reactions are like those of $Sb^{+3}$, (1) the precipitation of $Sb_2S_5$, orange, with $H_2S$ in acid solution, and (2) the precipitation of $SbOCl_3$, white, on dilution of $SbCl_5$ with water.

**More Common Stannous Compounds.** Stannous chloride, $SnCl_2 \cdot 2H_2O$, white; stannous sulfate, $SnSO_4$, white; stannous sulfide, SnS, dark brown; stannous hydroxide, $Sn(OH)_2$, white; stannous oxide, SnO, black.

**Reactions of Stannous Ion.** $NH_4OH$ or NaOH precipitates $Sn(OH)_2$, white, soluble in HCl and in excess NaOH (forming a stannite, $Sn(OH)_3^-$). $H_2S$ in acid solution precipitates SnS, black, soluble in HCl and in $(NH_4)_2S_2$ (forming a thiostannate, $HSnS_3^-$). $HNO_3$ and even milder oxidizing agents, $I_2$, $HgCl_2$, $FeCl_3$, $CuSO_4$, etc., oxidize $Sn^{++}$ to $Sn^{+4}$. With excess $Sn^{++}$, $H_2SO_3$ is reduced to $H_2S$. The more electropositive metals Zn and Mg reduce $Sn^{++}$ to Sn°. The most characteristic reaction is the reduction of $HgCl_2$ to $Hg_2Cl_2$, white, by $SnCl_2$.

**More Common Stannic Compounds.** Stannic chloride, $SnCl_4$, colorless liquid; stannic sulfate, $Sn(SO_4)_2 \cdot 2H_2O$, white; ammonium chlorostannate (pink salt), $(NH_4)_2SnCl_6$, pink; stannic sulfide, $SnS_2$, yellow; stannic hydroxide (stannic acid), $SnO(OH)_2$, white; stannic oxide, $SnO_2$, white; stannic phosphate, $Sn_3(PO_4)_4$, white.

**Reactions of Stannic Ion.** $NH_4OH$ or NaOH precipitates $SnO(OH)_2$, white, soluble in HCl and in excess NaOH (forming stannate ion, $Sn(OH)_5^-$), insoluble in $HNO_3$. $H_2S$ in acid solution precipitates $SnS_2$, yellow, soluble in concentrated HCl and in $(NH_4)_2S$ (forming thiostannate ion, $HSnS_3^-$). Fe°, Ni°, and other metals in the intermediate position in the electromotive series reduce $Sn^{+4}$ to $Sn^{++}$. Zn°, Mg° and the more electropositive metals reduce

$Sn^{+4}$ to $Sn^\circ$. The most characteristic reactions are (1) the precipitation of $SnS_2$, yellow, with $H_2S$ in slightly acid solution, and (2) the reduction to $SnCl_2$ by $Fe^\circ$ in dilute HCl solution followed by the precipitation of $Hg_2Cl_2$, white, when $HgCl_2$ is added.

## REACTIONS OF ARSENIC DIVISION METALS IN THE SYSTEMATIC ANALYSIS OF EARLIER GROUPS

**At the Beginning of Group I.** Alkaline solutions containing $Sn(OH)_3^-$, $Sn(OH)_5^-$, $Sb(OH)_4^-$, or $Sb(OH)_6^-$ may give precipitates of the hydroxides, usually soluble in excess of the acid, when $HNO_3$ is added in preparing the solution for the precipitation of Group I. $H_2AsO_3^-$ changes to $H_3AsO_3$ but without precipitation or other visible change when the solution is acidified. On treatment with HCl for the precipitation of Group I, occasionally a precipitate of SbOCl is obtained, soluble in moderate excess of HCl.

**At the Beginning of Group II.** In neutralizing with $NH_4OH$, preparatory to making 0.25 *N* with HCl, Sn and Sb precipitate as hydroxides ($Sb^{+3}$ forms $Sb_2O_3$), the $Sn(OH)_2$ and $SnO(OH)_2$ redissolving as the HCl is added, but $Sb_2O_3$ and $SbO(OH)_3$ may only dissolve in part and in part be left as SbOCl and $SbOCl_3$. These latter precipitates change to the normal sulfides when $H_2S$ is passed into the solution. $H_3AsO_3$ changes to $H_2AsO_3^-$ and back to $H_3AsO_3$ when $NH_4OH$ is added, followed by HCl, no precipitate forming in either case. In the presence of various metals whose arsenates are insoluble, the corresponding arsenates may precipitate when $NH_4OH$ is added, redissolving when the solution is made 0.25 *N* with HCl.

## PREPARING THE SOLUTION FOR THE PRECIPITATION OF THE ARSENIC DIVISION OF GROUP II

The discussion given in connection with the copper division of Group II applies equally to the precipitation of the sulfides of Sn, Sb, and the lower valence of As. In the case of quinquivalent arsenic, precipitation with $H_2S$ takes place only slowly and indirectly in 0.25 *N* HCl solution. On making the solution strongly acid with HCl, however, precipitation of $As_2S_5$ may be carried out with a fair degree of success, although it is usually necessary to pass in $H_2S$ several times before the $As_2S_5$ is fully precipitated. Precipitation of Group II usually involves the two steps, (1) treatment with $H_2S$ in 0.25 *N* HCl solution followed by dilution and treatment again with $H_2S$ to test for completeness of precipitation, and (2) adjustment of the solution for effective precipitation of the higher valence of As, followed by further treatment with $H_2S$.

## PRECIPITATION AND ANALYSIS OF GROUP II, ARSENIC DIVISION (INCLUDING SEPARATION FROM THE COPPER DIVISION)

**Precipitation of Group II.** After the solution has been made 0.25 *N* with HCl, warm moderately (60°–80°) and pass in $H_2S$ for 2–3 minutes. Centrifuge, add 20 drops of water to the clear solution and pass in $H_2S$ again to test for completeness of precipitation. When it is evident that precipitation is complete, wash the precipitate and set it aside to be analyzed for both the copper and arsenic divisions of Group II. Evaporate the clear solution to 10 drops volume, add 5 drops of concentrated HCl, heat to boiling and pass in $H_2S$ for 2–3 minutes to precipitate $As_2S_5$. Heat again nearly to boiling and pass in $H_2S$ for 1–2 minutes to precipitate $As_2S_5$ further. Centrifuge, heat again nearly to boiling and pass in $H_2S$ once more to test for completeness of precipitation. If further precipitation occurs, pass in $H_2S$ for several minutes, centrifuge, and test again with $H_2S$. Repeat as often as necessary until no more precipitate is obtained. Wash the precipitate and set it aside to be examined directly for arsenic.

*Explanatory Notes.* (1) A white, granular or flocculent precipitate remaining when the solution has been made 0.25 *N* with HCl may be disregarded. BiOCl and SbOCl frequently appear at this point. They should be left in the solution and treated with $H_2S$, which will change them to the normal sulfides.

$$2SbOCl + 3H_2S = Sb_2S_3 + 2Cl^- + 2H_3O^-$$

However, a gelatinous or colored precipitate may be due to later group metals forming precipitates on neutralization ($Al(OH)_3$, $Fe(OH)_3$, $MnO_2$) and not redissolving completely in the amount of acid added. In such a case more HCl should be added 1 drop at a time, with stirring and warming, until the foreign precipitate dissolves.

(2) Since the two valences of arsenic show marked difference in readiness of precipitation as sulfides, it is desirable to precipitate the two separately as a convenient method of identifying the two forms of arsenic in the possible presence of each other. This is not a simple matter, however, since $As_2S_3$ precipitates somewhat slowly in a cold solution, whereas if the solution is very hot the monothioarsenic acid ($H_3AsO_3S$) formed by reaction of $H_2S$ with $H_3AsO_4$ decomposes at an appreciable rate into $H_3AsO_3$ + S, the former then precipitating as $As_2S_3$. However, a fair separation can be obtained by precipitating from a moderately hot solution and discontinuing the treatment with $H_2S$ when the solution develops a hazy yellowish opalescence with slow separation of a flocculent bright yellow precipitate. Under these conditions $H_3AsO_3$ will be completely removed as $As_2S_3$ and only minor amounts of $H_3AsO_4$ will be lost.

TABLE X. OUTLINE OF PROCEDURE FOR ARSENIC DIVISION

Ions of Cu-division + $SnCl_4^{--}$, $SnCl_6^{--}$, $SbCl_4^{-}$, $SbCl_6^{-}$, $H_3AsO_3$, $H_3AsO_4$

| | | | | |
|---|---|---|---|---|
| $H_2S$ (0.25 *N* HCl solution) | | | | |
| Cu-div. sulfides $SnS$ $SnS_2$ $Sb_2S_3$ $Sb_2S_5$ $As_2S_3$ | | | | $H_3AsO_3S$ |
| $(NH_4)_2S_2$ | | | | HCl (3 − 4N) + $H_2S$ |
| Cu-div. sulfides | $HSnS_3^{-}$ | $H_2SbS_4^{-}$ | $H_2AsS_4^{-}$ | $As_2S_5$ |
| Centrifuge and analyze by procedure for the copper division of Group II. (p. 97) | HCl (dilute) | | | $HNO_3$ |
| | $SnS_2$ | $Sb_2S_5$ | $As_2S_5$ | $H_3AsO_4$ |
| | HCl (concentrated) | | | $NH_4OH$ + $MgCl_2$ |
| | $SnCl_6^{--}$ | $SbCl_4^{-}$ | $As_2S_5$ | $MgNH_4AsO_4$ |
| | Divide into 2 parts | | $HNO_3$ | |
| | Fe | Sn-Ag couple | $H_3AsO_4$ | |
| | $SnCl_4^{--}$ | Sb | $NH_4OH$ + $MgCl_2$ | |
| | $HgCl_2$ | | $MgNH_4AsO_4$ | |
| | $SnCl_6^{--}$ + $Hg_2Cl_2$ | | | |

(3) When evaporating to 10 drops before adding more HCl to precipitate $As_2S_5$, a yellow precipitate may form. This should be left in the solution and separated with the $As_2S_5$.

(4) Occasionally the solution may contain sufficient nitrate ion to interfere seriously with the precipitation of $As_2S_5$ in the hot, strongly acid solution. A flocculent yellow precipitate of $As_2S_5$ obtained while treating with $H_2S$ may be converted largely to free sulfur by the HCl + $HNO_3$ during the process of centrifuging. In such a case the simplest procedure to remove the excess $HNO_3$ consists in adding 5–10 drops more of HCl and evaporating nearly to dryness ($3Cl^- + NO_3^- + 4H_3O^+ = Cl_2 + NOCl + 6H_2O$). The residue

may then be treated with 10 drops of 5 *N* HCl and subjected to treatment with $H_2S$.

(5) Another procedure sometimes employed in precipitating arsenic from the quinquivalent form consists in reducing to $H_3AsO_4$ with $H_2SO_3$ or KI and then obtaining $As_2S_3$. If $H_2SO_3$ is used, add sufficient excess to produce a marked odor of $SO_2$, boil for a few minutes to remove excess $H_2SO_3$, and then treat with $H_2S$. If KI is used add 1 drop of the usual KI solution, warm moderately, and treat with $H_2S$. By leaving the $I_2$ in the solution in this case it is reduced again to HI by the $H_2S$ and will reduce more $H_3AsO_4$ to $H_3AsO_3$ so that it is unnecessary to reduce all the $H_3AsO_4$ at the start.

$$H_3AsO_4 + 2I^- + 2H_3O^+ = H_3AsO_3 + I_2 + 3H_2O$$

$$I_2 + H_2S + 2H_2O = 2H_3O^+ + 2I^- + S$$

(6) The effect of HCl in promoting the precipitation of $As_2S_5$ is contrary to its usual behavior of interfering with the precipitation of sulfides. Experimental studies indicate that the precipitation of $As_2S_5$ involves the formation of mono- and dithio-arsenic acid followed by decomposition of the latter by $H_2S$ in the presence of the HCl.

$$H_3AsO_4 + H_2S = H_3AsO_3S + H_2O$$

$$H_3AsO_3S + H_2S = H_3AsO_2S_2 + H_2O$$

$$2H_3AsO_2S_2 + H_2S = As_2S_5 + 4H_2O$$

All these reactions take place more readily when the solution is strongly acid.

**Separation of the Arsenic Division from the Copper Division of Group II.** To the precipitate obtained in 0.25 *N* HCl solution add 5 drops of yellow ammonium sulfide, $(NH_4)_2S_2$, warm to 50°–60° (keep well below the boiling point) and let digest 1–2 minutes.

$$As_2S_3 + 2HS_2^- + HS^- + NH_4^+ = 2H_2AsS_4^- + NH_3$$

$$Sb_2S_3 + 2HS_2^- + HS^- + NH_4^+ = 2H_2SbS_4^- + NH_3$$

$$SnS_2 + HS^- = HSnS_3^-$$

Centrifuge, wash once or twice with a small amount of $(NH_4)_2S_2$ and then with hot 1% $NH_4NO_3$, discarding these washings. The precipitate contains the sulfides of the copper division metals and is analyzed according to the regular procedure as already given. The clear solution, containing ammonium thio-salts of As, Sb, and Sn, is analyzed for the arsenic division metals.

*Explanatory Notes.* (1) The reagent ammonium sulfide must contain some polysulfide in order to dissolve SnS and $Sb_2S_3$, which are not soluble in $(NH_4)_2S$, but are oxidized by the polysulfide and dissolve as $HSnS_3^-$ and

$H_2SbS_4^-$. However, CuS, which is very slightly soluble in $(NH_4)_2S$, dissolves to an appreciable extent in the polysulfide; therefore, the reagent should consist largely of the colorless sulfide with only a small amount of sulfur added to serve as oxidizing agent for the lower sulfides of Sn and Sb.

(2) Ammonium sulfide is an unstable reagent undergoing both oxidation ($2HS^- + O_2 + NH_4^+ = HS_2^- + NH_3 + 2H_2O$) and hydrolysis ($HS^- + NH_4^+ = H_2S + NH_3$). Therefore, it is desirable to test the reagent from time to time to be sure it will dissolve SnS or $Sb_2S_3$ readily but not CuS. If a satisfactory reagent is not available and only a small amount is needed, the following method of preparation will be found useful. Saturate 5 drops of 5 *N* $NH_4OH$ with $H_2S$, keeping the solution cool by placing it in a beaker of cold water. Add 5 drops of 5 *N* $NH_4OH$ and 2–3 drops of 3% $H_2O_2$.

$$NH_4OH + H_2S = HS^- + NH_4^+ + H_2O$$

$$2HS^- + H_2O_2 + NH_4^+ = HS_2^- + NH_3$$

(3) Ammonium sulfide is most effective when fairly concentrated.

(4) On washing the copper division sulfides after separation from the arsenic division, the solution frequently turns dark, containing some of the copper division sulfides in suspension. By washing first with dilute $NH_4NO_3$ this usually can be avoided.

**Reprecipitation of the Arsenic Division Sulfides and Separation of As from Sb and Sn.** To the solution containing the thio-salts of As, Sb, and Sn add diluted HCl (not directly from the reagent bottle, see Note 2 following), with stirring, until the solution is distinctly acid. The precipitate will consist of sulfides of the arsenic division metals mixed with some sulfur from excess $(NH_4)_2S_2$ ($HS_2^- + H_3O^+ = H_2S + \underline{S} + H_2O$).

Centrifuge, wash several times with hot water, and transfer to a crucible. Add 10 drops of concentrated HCl, heat to boiling, and keep barely at the boiling point for 1–2 minutes. Add 2–3 drops of water, pass in $H_2S$ a few seconds, and centrifuge. $As_2S_5$ is left practically unattacked whereas $Sb_2S_5$ and $SnS_2$ dissolve readily. Set the clear solution aside to test for Sb and Sn. Wash the precipitate once or twice with HCl, then thoroughly with hot water, and test for As.

*Explanatory Notes.* (1) The process of acidifying should be carried out at the hood rather than in the open laboratory, because the $H_2S$ given off is both unpleasant in odor and poisonous.

(2) If the acid were poured directly into the solution from the reagent bottle, the stock acid would be contaminated by the $H_2S$. The proper procedure is to pour 3–4 drops of 5 *N* HCl into a test tube, add 20 drops water, mix thoroughly, and then add this in small amounts at a time to the solution. Discard any excess not used. If more is needed, rinse the test tube out with distilled water before preparing a fresh mixture.

(3) Large excess of HCl is to be avoided since $SnS_2$ is appreciably soluble even in dilute HCl.

(4) If none of the arsenic division metals are present, a milky white precipitate of S is obtained when the solution is acidified. The sulfides of the arsenic division are bright-colored and flocculent, easily recognized in contrast to the S even when present in small amounts.

(5) Copper sulfide and HgS are slightly soluble in $(NH_4)_2S_2$, reprecipitating when the solution is acidified. At this point HgS is black, but CuS is brownish red (liver-colored), the reddish tinge sometimes suggesting Sb and causing time to be wasted in repeating tests when the confirmatory test for Sb is negative.

(6) After treatment of the precipitate with concentrated HCl, it is necessary to dilute slightly and pass in $H_2S$ to reprecipitate some $As_2S_5$. If too much water is added, some $Sb_2S_3$ may precipitate.

(7) The $As_2S_5$ should be washed first with HCl to avoid reprecipitation of Sb as $Sb_2S_3$.

**Confirmatory Tests for Arsenic.** Transfer the precipitate of $As_2S_5(+ S)$ to a crucible, add 5–10 drops of 5 *N* $HNO_3$, heat to boiling, and continue the heating for 2–3 minutes after visible reaction has ceased. This converts the $As_2S_5$ to $H_3AsO_4$. Dilute with 5–10 drops of water, centrifuge if necessary, and test for $H_3AsO_4$ in the solution.

(1) Add 3–5 drops $NH_4Cl$ solution and excess $NH_4OH$, then add 1 drop of $MgCl_2$ solution, cool, and stir to start crystallization. A white, granular precipitate, $MgNH_4AsO_4$, indicates $AsO_4^{-3}$.

(2) To a portion of the nitric acid solution add 1–2 drops of $AgNO_3$ solution and shake. Discard any white precipitate of AgCl, adding more $AgNO_3$ to the solution if necessary to insure excess. Tilt the test tube at an angle of 45–60°, and carefully pour in an upper half-inch layer of 5 *N* $NH_4OH$. In the neutral zone where the ammonium hydroxide makes contact with the $HNO_3$, a brown precipitate, $Ag_3AsO_4$, will form if $AsO_4^{-3}$ is present.

*Explanatory Notes.* (1) In dissolving $As_2S_5$ in $HNO_3$ the As may be largely reduced to $H_3AsO_3$ which will not respond to the magnesia-mixture test. Therefore it is necessary to boil the solution a few minutes longer to oxidize the $H_3AsO_3$ to $H_3AsO_4$.

(2) If $NH_4Cl$ is not added, or if too much $MgCl_2$ is used, a white precipitate of $Mg(OH)_2$ may be obtained. In case of doubt, centrifuge, dissolve the precipitate in 5 *N* HCl and treat with $H_2S$. A bright yellow precipitate of $As_2S_5$ indicates As.

(3) Magnesium ammonium arsenate is appreciably soluble in warm solutions and, even in the cold, forms supersaturated solutions from which precipitation takes place slowly. By stirring the solution with a glass rod so as to scratch the walls of the test tube somewhat, by shaking the solution vigorously, or by adding a few minute particles of the desired precipitate, this con-

dition of supersaturation can be overcome and the precipitate obtained readily.

(4) An alternative method of dissolving $As_2S_5$: Add 3–5 drops of 5 *N* $NH_4OH$ to the precipitate. $As_2S_5$ dissolves readily.

$$As_2S_5 + 4NH_4OH = HAsS_4^{--} + HAsO_3S^{--} + 4NH_4^+ + H_2O$$

Add to the clear solution 3–5 drops of $H_2O_2$ and boil gently 1–2 minutes. This oxidizes the sulfur in these compounds to sulfate ion, leaving As as $HAsO_4^{--}$ ready for testing.

$$HAsS_4^{--} + 8NH_3 + 16H_2O_2 = HAsO_4^{--} + 4SO_4^{--} + 8NH_4^+ + 12H_2O$$

$$HAsO_3S^{--} + 2NH_3 + 4H_2O_2 = HAsO_4^{--} + SO_4^{--} + 2NH_4^+ + 3H_2O$$

Add 3–5 drops $NH_4Cl$ and 1 drop $MgCl_2$, cool thoroughly, and stir to start precipitation. In this procedure sometimes a large number of fine bubbles of $O_2$ (from excess $H_2O_2$) form as the solution is stirred, producing an appearance much like a granular, white precipitate. However, this disappears on standing a moment (the bubbles rising to the surface and breaking), whereas a precipitate of $MgNH_4AsO_4$ will persist and even increase in amount.

**Confirmatory Tests for Antimony and Tin.** Evaporate the filtrate from $As_2S_5$ to 2–3 drops volume. Test a portion of this solution for Sb as follows: Put 1 drop of the solution on the surface of a silver coin that has been cleaned by moistening with $HNO_3$ and rinsing. Let stand a minute or two to make sure no stain develops from the action of the solution alone. Then drop onto the coin a small Λ-shaped piece of tin foil so that one end dips into the solution and the other touches the bare coin. If Sb is present, a brownish black stain will develop promptly on the surface of the coin.

Test the remainder of the solution for Sn as follows: Dilute with water to 5–6 drops, add 50 mg. Fe filings, warm until a steady evolution of $H_2$ takes place, let the reaction continue 3–4 minutes, then centrifuge, transferring the solution to a test tube containing 1–2 drops of $HgCl_2$ solution. A white precipitate of $Hg_2Cl_2$ will form if Sn is present, turning gray if the solution contains any considerable quantity of Sn.

*Explanatory Notes.* (1) The solution from $As_2S_5$ contains $H_2S$, which must be boiled out, otherwise it will form a black stain on the silver coin, interfering with the test for Sb.

(2) The test for Sb is made on only a drop of the solution. Unless the solution is first evaporated to a small volume the portion tested will contain only a small fraction of the Sb present. The delicacy of the test depends directly on the extent to which the volume of the solution is reduced.

(3) The tin foil forms a silver-tin couple with the coin and the current in the solution flows from Sn to Ag, causing the Sb to deposit on the surface of the coin.

(4) An alternative test, useful in recognizing moderate amounts of Sb, consists in diluting a portion of the solution with 5–10 drops of water, obtaining a white, flocculent precipitate of SbOCl. Concentrated $SnCl_4$ behaves somewhat similarly.

(5) While reducing $SnCl_6^{--}$ to $SnCl_4^{--}$, Sb forms a black flocculent precipitate of the free metal. This is a satisfactory test for moderate amounts of Sb, but cannot be used to identify very small amounts because free carbon is usually left as the Fe dissolves and has a similar appearance.

(6) Occasionally in moderately acid solutions the Sb deposits on the surface of the Fe as an adherent coating such that only Sb is exposed. Under such conditions the $SnCl_6^{--}$ is reduced very slowly and the test is commonly missed even when Sn is present. It is easy to recognize this condition by the marked decrease in rate of evolution of $H_2$. If this is observed, continue adding small amounts of Fe filings until all the Sb is reduced and $H_2$ comes off smoothly again. Let the reaction continue 2–3 minutes longer, centrifuge, and test for $SnCl_2$, with $HgCl_2$.

## ALTERNATIVE PROCEDURE FOR ARSENIC, ANTIMONY, AND TIN

The Marsh test, with its several modifications, constitutes the most accurate method of detecting very small amounts of As and Sb. The following procedure uses the Marsh apparatus and includes a test for Sn: Dissolve the sulfides of As, Sb, and Sn in HCl with the aid of small amounts of $NaClO_3$. Boil out any free $Cl_2$, filter to remove S, transfer to the Marsh apparatus, and test the gases evolved for $SbH_3$ and $AsH_3$: (1) By heating the hard glass tube and obtaining Sb and As mirrors, (2) by lighting the gases at the outlet tip and holding an evaporating dish in the flame, obtaining spots of metallic Sb and As, and (3) by passing the gases into $AgNO_3$ solution, filtering, and testing the filtrate for As and the precipitate for Sb. Treat the filtrate with HCl to precipitate excess $Ag^+$, filter and pass $H_2S$ into the filtrate, obtaining a bright yellow precipitate, $As_2S_3$, if As is present. To the precipitate which may contain Sb as $H_3SbO_3$, add 5 ml. of 5 *N* HCl, filter, partially neutralize with $NH_4OH$ and then treat with $H_2S$. An orange-colored precipitate, $Sb_2S_3$, forms if Sb is present.

In the Marsh apparatus Sn is reduced to the metal. This may be filtered out (along with Sb°, excess of Zn°, etc.), dissolved in HCl to form $SnCl_2$, and identified by adding $HgCl_2$ which forms a white precipitate of $Hg_2Cl_2$ if $SnCl_2$ is present.

The Marsh test is not suited for use by large classes and, even with individuals, should be used with considerable care, both on account of the poisonous nature of $AsH_3$ and $SbH_3$ and because of the danger of setting off explosive mixtures of $H_2$ and air in the apparatus. In the following material the procedures have not been changed to the semi-micro scale.

**The Marsh Apparatus.** The essential parts are an evolution flask, a purifying train, and a decomposition tube. The evolution flask is of the Erlenmeyer or Florence type, about 125 ml. in capacity, fitted with a rubber stopper having two holes through one of which passes a funnel (safety) tube reaching

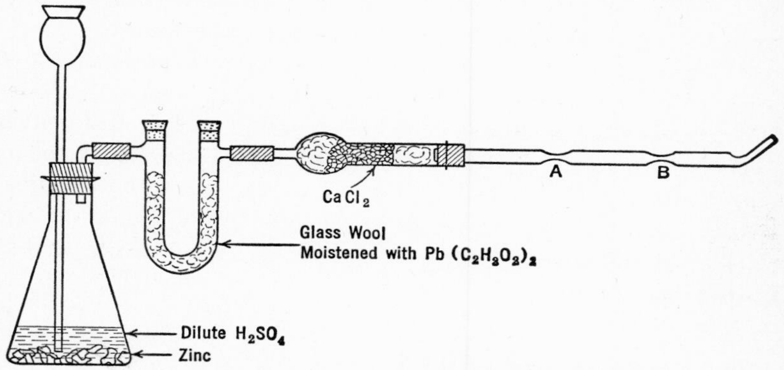


FIG. 4. Schematic Diagram of Marsh Test Apparatus.

nearly to the bottom of the flask; the other holds a 5–7 mm. glass tube bent to a right angle. This tube connects with a U-tube filled with glass wool that has been moistened (no excess liquid) with $Pb(C_2H_3O_2)_2$ solution to absorb any $H_2S$ evolved. Next comes a drying tube filled with about 8-mesh, anhydrous $CaCl_2$ or other suitable drying agent. Lastly a hard glass tube about 7 mm. in diameter by 25 cm. long is attached to the drying tube. This tube is constricted twice near the middle to about 2 mm. diameter, the distance between constrictions being 6–8 cm. The end of the tube is pulled out and turned up to form a tip suitable for burning the exit gases. A short piece of rubber tubing should be available for connecting this constricted end to a piece of ordinary glass tubing dipping into a test tube about two-thirds filled with a 2% solution of $AgNO_3$.

Fifteen grams of granulated zinc are placed in the flask with sufficient water to cover the end of the funnel tube and the stopper is fitted tightly in place. Dilute $H_2SO_4$(1:4) should now be added until a moderate evolution of hydrogen is obtained. If necessary, a few drops of $CuSO_4$ solution may be added to produce a more ready flow of hydrogen. The gas should be allowed to bubble through the $AgNO_3$ solution for several minutes and should produce no appreciable black precipitate or suspension, proving the system reasonably free from arsenic. Next add the solution to be tested, in small amounts at a time, through the funnel tube. If much arsenic (or antimony) is present there will be an almost immediate blackening of the $AgNO_3$ solution. If no test appears after 1–2 minutes the hard glass tube should be heated at A to a dull red (just below softening). Even with very small amounts of As or Sb, mirrors will form as the $AsH_3$ and $SbH_3$ decompose. $AsH_3$ is more stable than $SbH_3$, and therefore the arsenic mirror will appear beyond the flame whereas the antimony mirror will appear in front of the flame.

**Gutzeit Test for As on the Original Solution.** Place in a test tube 20–30 mg. of 20 mesh Zn and add 3–4 drops of 5 *N* $H_2SO_4$. Insert a plug of absorbent cotton in the tube (about half an inch above the surface of the liquid) and drop in a piece of moistened test paper ($AgNO_3$ or $HgCl_2$). Warm slightly if necessary to start the reaction and let run about 2 minutes. If reagents are satisfactory only a faint color should show on the test paper. Remove the cotton plug, add 2–3 drops of the solution to be tested, replace the cotton plug, and add a fresh piece of test paper. Leave for 2 minutes and compare the spots on the two pieces of test paper. If the second spot is darker than the first, the unknown contains arsenic or antimony.

## REPORTING ARSENIC DIVISION IONS IN AN UNKNOWN SOLUTION

**Arsenic.** The simplest procedure to distinguish between $H_2AsO_3^-$ and $H_2AsO_4^-$ consists in noting whether the arsenic precipitates as a sulfide in 0.25 *N* HCl solution or in the more strongly acid solution. In the former case report $H_2AsO_3^-$, in the latter case, $H_2AsO_4^-$; if As is found in both places, report both ions in the unknown. In using this procedure it should be remembered that small amounts of $H_3AsO_4$ may be converted to $As_2S_3$ if the treatment with $H_2S$ in 0.25 *N* HCl solution is unduly prolonged. If a strong test for $H_2AsO_4^-$ is obtained and only a slight test for $H_2AsO_3^-$, the latter may be due to the $H_3AsO_4$ and should be disregarded.

It should be noted that, although compounds such as $AsCl_3$ and $AsCl_5$ can be prepared, these undergo fairly complete hydrolysis in aqueous solution into $H_3AsO_3$ or $H_3AsO_4$ and HCl. Therefore the concentrations of $As^{+3}$ and $As^{+5}$ ions are negligibly small even in moderately acid solution.

**Antimony.** There is no simple test to identify either valence of antimony in the presence of the other. It is simplest, therefore, in unknowns to consider that the antimony is present in the trivalent form unless the solution contains a fairly strong oxidizing agent, such as $CrO_4^{--}$, $Cr_2O_7^{--}$, $MnO_4^{--}$, $MnO_4^-$, etc. Antimony is an amphoteric metal; if the solution is acid, report $Sb^{+3}$; if alkaline, report $Sb(OH)_4^-$; if the solution contains a strong oxidizing agent, the corresponding ions are $Sb^{+5}$ and $Sb(OH)_6^-$. In HCl solution the ions would be $SbCl_4^-$ or $SbCl_6^-$.

**Tin.** The direct test for the lower valence of Sn depends on its reducing action on $HgCl_2$. If the original solution is alkaline, acidify with HCl, adding 2–3 drops excess; if acid, add 2–3 drops of HCl, then add 1–2 drops of $HgCl_2$ and look for a white precipitate of $Hg_2Cl_2$ which slowly darkens if much $Sn^{++}$ is present. If this test is positive and the original solution is acid, report $Sn^{++}$; if alkaline, report $Sn(OH)_3^-$. There is no direct test for the higher valence of Sn so this is usually identified merely by finding Sn in the solution when the test for the lower valence of Sn is negative. In such a case report $Sn^{+4}$ if the solution is acid, $Sn(OH)_5^-$, if alkaline. In HCl solutions the ions would be $SnCl_4^{--}$ or $SnCl_6^{--}$.

## ARSENIC DIVISION METALS IN RELATION TO OTHER GROUPS

The behavior of the arsenic division metals in the precipitation of Group I and in preparing the solution for the precipitation of Group II has already been discussed in this chapter. The use of $(NH_4)_2S_2$ provides an effective separation from metals of other groups that may be carried down in Group II. Of the copper division sulfides, only HgS and CuS show appreciable solubility in $(NH_4)_2S_2$, the former very slight, but the latter fairly marked if the solution contains much of the polysulfide. On reprecipitating the arsenic division sulfides with dilute HCl, the CuS forms a brown- or liver-colored precipitate. It will dissolve, in part, in the concentrated HCl and may produce a reddish deposit of Cu in the test for Sb. This is not very serious, however, since even a small amount of Sb would form a brownish black deposit. The more serious feature is the possible failure to get a test for Cu in the copper division of Group II. If a considerable amount of $Fe^{+3}$ is present, when testing for the presence of Group II, the yellowish white precipitate of sulfur may possibly suggest $As_2S_3$ or $SnS_2$, but the regular procedure is sufficient to correct any error at this point. In precipitating Group II, $SnS_2$ and, to a lesser extent, $Sb_2S_3$ may fail to precipitate effectively if the solution is too strongly acid or contains excessive amounts of $Cl^-$. In this case these metals will form white precipitates in Group III and may be mistaken for Al at the start, but the confirmatory test with the Aluminon reagent is sufficient to distinguish Al from Sb or Sn. If quinquivalent arsenic is not fully removed in Group II, another type of irregularity may develop in Group III. With $H_3AsO_4$ present when the solution is made alkaline to precipitate Group III, arsenates of some of the later group metals, Mn, Ca, Mg, etc., may precipitate in Group III. The obvious remedy is to continue the treatment with $H_2S$ in the more strongly acid solution until it is certain that precipitation is complete.

## REACTIONS OF ARSENIC DIVISION METALS IN THE SYSTEMATIC ANALYSIS OF A SOLUTION

**Arsenic**

*Acidifying an alkaline solution with $HNO_3$*

$$H_2AsO_3^- + H_3O^+ = H_3AsO_3 + H_2O$$
$$HAsO_4^{--} + 2H_3O^+ = H_3AsO_4 + 2H_2O$$

*Adjusting the acidity for the precipitation of Group II*

$$H_3AsO_3 + NH_3 = H_2AsO_3^- + NH_4^+$$
$$H_2AsO_3^- + H_3O^+ = H_3AsO_3 + H_2O$$
$$H_3AsO_4 + NH_3 = H_2AsO_4^- + NH_4^+$$
$$H_2AsO_4^- + H_3O^+ = H_3AsO_4 + H_2O$$

*In Group II*

$$H_3AsO_3 + 3H_2S = \underline{As_2S_3} + 6H_2O$$
$$H_3AsO_4 + H_2S = H_3AsO_3S + H_2O$$
$$2H_3AsO_3S + 3H_2S\ (+\ \text{conc. HCl}) = \underline{As_2S_5} + 6H_2O$$
$$\underline{As_2S_3} + 2HS_2^- + HS^- = H_2AsS_4^- + HAsS_4^{--}$$
$$\underline{As_2S_5} + 3HS^- = H_2AsS_4^- + HAsS_4^{--}$$
$$2H_2AsS_4^- + 2H_3O^+ = \underline{As_2S_5} + 3H_2S + 2H_2O$$
$$\underline{3As_2S_5} + 10NO_3^- + 10H_3O^+ = 6H_3AsO_4 + 15S + 10NO + 6H_2O$$

1. $H_3AsO_4 + Mg^{++} + 3NH_3 = \underline{MgNH_4AsO_4} + 2NH_4^+$
2. $H_3AsO_4 + 3Ag^+ + 3NH_3 = \underline{Ag_3AsO_4} + 3NH_4^+$

*Marsh Test*

$$H_3AsO_3 + 3Zn + 6H_3O^+ = AsH_3 + 3Zn^{++} + 9H_2O$$
$$H_3AsO_4 + 4Zn + 8H_3O^+ = AsH_3 + 4Zn^{++} + 12H_2O$$
$$4AsH_3 + \text{heat} = \underline{As_4} + 6H_2$$
$$4AsH_3 + 3O_2 = \underline{As_4} + 6H_2O$$

*Gutzeit Test*

$$AsH_3 + 6Ag^+ + 9H_2O = \underline{6Ag} + H_3AsO_3 + 6H_3O^+$$

**Antimony**

*Acidifying an alkaline solution with $HNO_3$*

$$Sb(OH)_4^- + 4H_3O^+ + 4Cl^- = SbCl_4^- + 8H_2O$$

*Adjusting the acidity for the precipitation of Group II*

$$SbCl_4^- + 3NH_4OH = \underline{Sb(OH)_3} + 3NH_4^+ + 4Cl^-$$
$$\underline{Sb(OH)_3} + 3H_3O^+ + 4Cl^- = SbCl_4^- + 6H_2O$$

*In Group II*

$$2SbCl_4^- + 3H_2S + 6H_2O = \underline{Sb_2S_3} + 8Cl^- + 6H_3O^+$$
$$\underline{Sb_2S_3} + 2HS_2^- + HS^- = H_2SbS_4^- + HSbS_4^{--}$$

$$2H_2SbS_4^- + 2H_3O^+ = \underline{Sb_2S_5} + 3H_2S + 2H_2O$$
$$\underline{Sb_2S_5} + 6H_3O^+ + 8Cl^- = 2SbCl_4^- + \underline{2S} + 6H_2O + 3H_2S$$
$$2SbCl_4^- + 3Sn + 4Cl^- = \underline{2Sb} + 3SnCl_4^{--}$$

*Marsh Test*

$$2SbCl_4^- + 6Zn + 6H_3O^+ = 2SbH_3 + 8Cl^- + 6Zn^{++} + 6H_2O$$
$$2SbH_3 + \text{heat} = \underline{2Sb} + 3H_2$$
$$4SbH_3 + 3O_2 = \underline{4Sb} + 6H_2O$$

*Gutzeit Test*

$$SbH_3 + 6Ag^+ + 9H_2O = \underline{6Ag} + \underline{H_3SbO_3} + 6H_3O^+$$

**Tin**

*Acidifying an alkaline solution with $HNO_3$*

$$Sn(OH)_3^- + 3H_3O^+ + 4Cl^- = SnCl_4^{--} + 6H_2O$$
$$Sn(OH)_5^- + 5H_3O^+ + 6Cl^- = SnCl_6^{--} + 10H_2O$$

*Adjusting the acidity for the precipitation of Group II*

$$SnCl_4^{--} + 2NH_4OH = \underline{Sn(OH)_2} + 2NH_4^+ + 4Cl^-$$
$$\underline{Sn(OH)_2} + 2H_3O^+ + 4Cl^- = SnCl_4^{--} + 4H_2O$$
$$SnCl_6^{--} + 4NH_4OH = \underline{Sn(OH)_4} + 6Cl^- + 4NH_4^+$$
$$\underline{Sn(OH)_4} + 4H_3O^+ + 6Cl^- = SnCl_6^{--} + 8H_2O$$

*In Group II*

$$SnCl_4^{--} + H_2S + 2H_2O = \underline{SnS} + 4Cl^- + 2H_3O^+$$
$$SnCl_6^{--} + 2H_2S + 4H_2O = \underline{SnS_2} + 6Cl^- + 4H_3O^+$$
$$\underline{SnS} + HS_2^- = HSnS_3^-$$
$$\underline{SnS_2} + HS^- = HSnS_3^-$$
$$HSnS_3^- + H_3O^+ = \underline{SnS_2} + H_2S + H_2O$$
$$\underline{SnS_2} + 4H_3O^+ + 6Cl^- = SnCl_6^{--} + 2H_2S + 4H_2O$$
$$SnCl_6^{--} + Fe = SnCl_4^{--} + Fe^{++} + 2Cl^-$$
$$SnCl_4^{--} + 2HgCl_2 = SnCl_6^{--} + \underline{Hg_2Cl_2}$$
$$\underline{Hg_2Cl_2} + SnCl_4^{--} = \underline{2Hg} + SnCl_6^{--}$$

## SUMMARY AND REVIEW

Precipitation of Group II

1. Adjustment of acidity
   *A*. How adjusted?
   *B*. Why adjusted?
2. Actual precipitation
   *A*. Technique
   *B*. Color of As division sulfides
   *C*. Failure of $As^{v}$ to precipitate

(1) Action of $H_2S$ on $H_3AsO_4$
(2) Special procedure necessary
(*a*) Increasing $[H_3O^+]$
(*b*) Use of KI
(3) Detection of the As
*D*. Testing filtrate for completeness of precipitation
Why complete removal of As necessary?
3. Filtration
4. Washing the precipitate

Separation of As from Cu Division

1. Why use polysulfide?
*A*. Preparation of $(NH_4)_2S_2$
*B*. Technique
Why not boil?
*C*. Action on As division sulfides
*D*. Action on Cu division sulfides

Treatment of the Polysulfide Solution

1. Reprecipitation of sulfides
*A*. Why?
*B*. Why dilute HCl used?
*C*. Conclusion if precipitate white
2. Analysis of the precipitate
*A*. Separation of As
*B*. Detection of As
(1) Solution of $As_2S_5$
(2) Confirmatory tests
*C*. Detection of Sb
Coin test
*D*. Detection of Sn
(1) Reagents available for reduction to $Sn^{++}$
Effect on Sb
(2) Confirmatory tests

Valence Tests

1. For As, Sb, Sn
2. Ions possible in original solution
*A*. Acid
*B*. Ammoniacal
*C*. Alkaline with NaOH

Special Tests

1. Marsh
2. Gutzeit

## LABORATORY EXERCISES

1. Known solutions containing metals of Groups I–V.

(*1*) $BiCl_4^-$, $H_3AsO_3$, $SnCl_6^{--}$, $SbCl_4^-$, $Ca^{++}$
(*2*) $Cu(NH_3)_4^{++}$, $H_2AsO_4^-$
(*3*) $H_2AsO_3^-$, $Sb(OH)_4^-$, $Zn(OH)_3^-$

These solutions contain the following amounts of substance per liter: (*1*) 4 g. $BiCl_3$, 6.5 g. $K_4As_2O_5$, 7.5 g. $SnCl_4 \cdot 5H_2O$, 5 g. $SbCl_3$, 9 g. $CaCl_2 \cdot 2H_2O$, and 400 ml. of 5 *N* HCl; (*2*) 7.5 g. $CuCl_2 \cdot 2H_2O$, 6 g. $KH_2AsO_4$, 75 g. $NH_4Cl$, and 200 ml. of 5 *N* $NH_4OH$; (*3*) 6.5 g. $K_4As_2O_5$, 5 g. $SbCl_3$, 5 g. $ZnCl_2$, and 100 g. KOH.

Use 15 drops of the original solution. Make 0.25 *N* with HCl, warm moderately and precipitate with $H_2S$, testing in the usual way for completeness of precipitation. Evaporate the solution to 5–10 drops. Add 5 drops of concentrated HCl, heat, and precipitate again with $H_2S$. The precipitate obtained in 0.25 *N* HCl is examined for all metals of both divisions of Group II. That obtained in the strongly acid solution is tested only for As, the filtrate being examined for later group metals.

By testing a small portion of the precipitate obtained in dilute acid solution with $(NH_4)_2S_2$, centrifuging, and acidifying the clear solution with dilute HCl, one may judge whether or not it is necessary to treat the precipitate as a whole with this reagent. If a precipitate remains insoluble in $(NH_4)_2S_2$, and only a precipitate of $S^\circ$ is obtained from the clear solution, the arsenic division is absent and the main precipitate may be examined directly for the metals of the copper division. If the precipitate dissolves completely in $(NH_4)_2S_2$ only metals of the arsenic division are present and the main precipitate may be examined directly for them. If both divisions are present, then they must be separated by treatment with $(NH_4)_2S_2$.

*Solution 1.* (*a*) When this solution is made 0.25 *N* with HCl, a moderate precipitate remains that should be left in the solution while $H_2S$ is passed in. BiOCl, SbOCl, etc., will change to normal sulfides on treatment with $H_2S$.

(*b*) After testing for completeness of precipitation in 0.25 *N* HCl solution, the solution should give negative results when treated for the precipitation of $As_2S_5$. (If $As_2S_3$ is incompletely precipitated in the earlier operations it will form at this point.)

(*c*) The precipitate obtained in 0.25 *N* HCl solution should show the presence of both divisions of Group II. If the $Bi_2S_3$ becomes colloidal after treating with $(NH_4)_2S_2$, wash with 1% $NH_4NO_3$ solution.

(*d*) A slight precipitate is occasionally obtained in Group III due to incomplete precipitation of Sb and Sn in Group II.

*Solution 2.* (*a*) The precipitate obtained in 0.25 *N* HCl solution should contain none of the arsenic division if the temperature was kept well below boiling while treating with $H_2S$, and the latter was passed in for only a moderate time. If these conditions are not observed some $H_3AsO_4$ will be converted to $As_2S_3$.

(*b*) After CuS is completely precipitated and removed, warm the solution and pass in $H_2S$ again. Note that the solution slowly turns milky and a slight precipitate forms ($As_2S_3 + S^\circ$) due to secondary reactions of the $H_3AsO_4$. The appearance of this solution is fairly characteristic and should not be mistaken for sulfides that should precipitate in the 0.25 *N* HCl solution. When this effect is observed proceed directly with the precipitation of $As_2S_5$.

*Solution 3.* (*a*) In this solution the second group precipitate should dissolve completely in $(NH_4)_2S_2$, indicating the absence of copper division sulfides.

(*b*) If the $Sb_2S_3$ does not dissolve effectively in the available $(NH_4)_2S_2$, try the following procedure: To the precipitate add 5 drops of 5 *N* $NH_4OH$ and pass in $H_2S$

for 1–2 minutes (until the solution is nearly saturated with $H_2S$). Add $H_2O_2$, 1 drop at a time, shaking thoroughly after each addition, until the solution takes on a permanent light yellow color. The $Sb_2S_3$ dissolves readily under these conditions.

2. Other valence tests for arsenic. Try the action of Fehling's solution (alkaline copper tartrate) and of magnesia mixture ($NH_4Cl + NH_4OH + MgCl_2$) on separate solutions of $H_2AsO_3$ and $H_2AsO_4$. Apply heat when using Fehling's solution, keep cold and stir to start crystallization when using magnesia mixture.

3. Valence test for tin. To a test portion of $SnCl_2$ add a little $HgCl_2$. Note the formation of a white precipitate of $Hg_2Cl_2$, turning gray if excess of $SnCl_2$ is present. To 1 drop of $BiCl_3$ or $SbCl_3$ add several drops of $HgCl_2$. Note the possibility of precipitating BiOCl or SbOCl when testing for the presence of $Sn^{++}$. By adding 1–2 drops of HCl to the acid solution and using only a small amount of $HgCl_2$ this difficulty is easily avoided. If the solution is alkaline it must first be treated with excess HCl.

# 12

# The More Common Acid Radicals

## CHLORIDE, NITRATE, SULFATE, CARBONATE, AND SULFIDE

When testing for acid radicals it is not feasible to employ the same type of procedure as in the case of the metals. Reagents are available for the metals by which a systematic separation into groups can be developed through precipitation reactions. It will be recalled, however, that this was not a simple process involving only a somewhat random selection of group reagents from a fairly extensive and equally useful list. On the contrary, after the precipitation of Group I it was found necessary to resort to the use of weak electrolytes or largely hydrolyzed salts to obtain the effective control over the concentration of precipitant ion that is required to separate metals whose corresponding salts are all insoluble but which possess different orders of insolubility. On examining in some detail the solubility of the various salts of the fairly common acid radicals and the nature of the metallic ions by which precipitation might be effected, it becomes obvious that the division of acid radicals into groups cannot be effected by employing the same principles that were involved in the case of the metals. Further, the systematic analysis of a possible group precipitate of acid radicals cannot be carried out satisfactorily by the simple dissolving and reprecipitation procedures that proved successful earlier.

## COMMON COMPOUNDS AND REACTIONS OF CHLORIDE, NITRATE, SULFATE, CARBONATE, AND SULFIDE RADICALS

**More Common Chlorides.** All of the metals form chlorides, of which the following are insoluble in water: $AgCl$, white; $Hg_2Cl_2$, white; $PbCl_2$, white, slightly soluble; $CuCl$, white. The following are soluble only in the presence of free $HCl$, undergoing hydrolysis with the precipitation of basic salts when the salt is treated with water in sufficient amount, especially on heating: $BiCl_3$, $SbCl_3$, and $SnCl_2$; less pronounced precipitation occurs in the cases of $SnCl_4$, $CuCl_2$, $FeCl_2$, $FeCl_3$, and $ZnCl_2$. The non-metals (except F and $As^{V}$) form chlorides, most of which are largely hydrolyzed by water into $HCl$ and the corresponding free acid of the non-metal. Thus $PCl_3$ is hydrolyzed practically completely into $HCl$ and $H_3PO_3$. $AsCl_3$ shows similar behavior.

**Reactions of Chloride Ion.** $AgNO_3$ precipitates AgCl, white, insoluble in $HNO_3$, soluble in $NH_4OH$, slightly transposed by 5 *N* NaOH into brown $Ag_2O$. Mercuric ion combines with chloride ion to form the slightly ionized but soluble $HgCl_2$, thus lowering the concentration of chloride ion to such an extent as to dissolve $PbCl_2$ readily and even AgCl slightly. With high concentration of chloride ion a number of chlorides are converted to complex negative ions, $AgCl_2^-$, $PbCl_3^-$, $CdCl_3^-$, $BiCl_4^-$, $SnCl_6^{--}$, $SbCl_4^-$, etc. $KMnO_4$ and other strong oxidizing agents in acid solution oxidize $Cl^-$ to free $Cl_2$. Concentrated $H_2SO_4$, on heating, converts $Cl^-$ to HCl which may be volatilized from the solution at 170°–180°C. The most characteristic reaction is the precipitation of AgCl by $AgNO_3$ in the presence of a moderate amount of $HNO_3$, followed by dissolving in $NH_4OH$ and reprecipitation with excess of $HNO_3$.

**More Common Nitrates.** The metals generally form nitrates, soluble in water. In the cases of As, $Sn^{iv}$, and $Sb^{v}$ no nitrates exist, while $Fe(NO_3)_2$ and $Sn(NO_3)_2$ are unstable, especially if heated, the metals undergoing oxidation at the expense of the nitrate radical. The non-metals do not form nitrates. The nitrates of those metals whose hydroxides are relatively insoluble in water undergo hydrolysis to a corresponding extent, precipitation occurring in the cases of $Hg_2(NO_3)_2$, $Hg(NO_3)_2$, and $Bi(NO_3)_3$, and to a slight extent in the case of $Fe(NO_3)_3$ unless free nitric acid is present.

**Reactions of Nitrate Ion.** There are no simple precipitation reactions, although bismuth, mercurous, and mercuric nitrates form precipitates of basic salts on heating with water. In acid solution nitrate ion is an oxidizing agent of moderate strength, being reduced to varying states according to the temperature, concentration of reagents, and strength of reducing agents used. With mild reducing agents, such as Cu or Hg, used in hot, strongly acid solutions, $N_2O_3$ is the main reduction product; with somewhat stronger reducing agents, such as Pb, Fe, $Fe^{++}$, etc., the main reduction product is NO. At lower temperatures, and with strong reducing agents, the nitrogen is reduced still further to an ammonium salt. Under ordinary conditions hydrogen is obtained in only minor amount from $HNO_3$. When $FeSO_4$ is used as the reducing agent in the presence of concentrated $H_2SO_4$, the NO formed combines with excess of the $FeSO_4$, producing a deep brown-colored, soluble, unstable ion, $Fe \cdot NO^{++}$. In alkaline solution the nitrate ion is reduced less readily, but in the presence of NaOH metallic Al reduces it fairly rapidly to $NH_3$. If this reaction is interrupted too quickly, the nitrogen may be largely in an intermediate stage of reduction, such as nitrite ion or hyponitrite. The most characteristic reactions are the formation of the brown color with $FeSO_4$ in the presence of $H_2SO_4$, and the formation of $NH_3$ on reduction with NaOH + Al.

**More Common Sulfates.** All of the metals form sulfates, of which the following are insoluble in water: mercurous sulfate, $Hg_2SO_4$, white; lead sulfate, $PbSO_4$, white; barium sulfate, $BaSO_4$, white; and strontium sulfate, $SrSO_4$, white. Silver sulfate,

$Ag_2SO_4$, and calcium sulfate, $CaSO_4$, are slightly soluble. None of the non-metals forms sulfates, except the hydrides of nitrogen [$(NH_4)_2SO_4$, etc.], and of carbon (dimethyl sulfate, $(CH_3)_2SO_4$, etc.). There are also such compounds as nitrosylsulfuric acid, $NO \cdot HSO_4$, and sulfuryl chloride, $SO_2Cl_2$, this latter being a derivative of sulfuric anhydride, $SO_3$, with two atoms of chlorine taking the place of one atom of oxygen.

**Reactions of Sulfate Ion.** Barium chloride (and other soluble barium salts supplying $Ba^{++}$) precipitates $BaSO_4$, white, insoluble in dilute HCl or $HNO_3$, slightly soluble in the more concentrated acids, partly transposed to $BaCO_3$ by boiling with a concentrated $Na_2CO_3$ solution. $SrCl_2$ precipitates $SrSO_4$, white, similar to $BaSO_4$ but slightly more soluble in water and in acids and transposed more completely by boiling with $Na_2CO_3$. $CaCl_2$ precipitates $CaSO_4$, white, slightly soluble in water, moderately soluble in strong HCl or $HNO_3$, readily transposed by $Na_2CO_3$ into $CaCO_3$. $Pb(NO_3)_2$ precipitates $PbSO_4$, white, slightly soluble in 5 *N* HCl or $HNO_3$, soluble in excess NaOH, forming $Pb(OH)_3^-$ and $SO_4^{--}$, soluble in concentrated $NH_4C_2H_3O_2$, forming $Pb(C_2H_3O_2)_2$ and $Pb(C_2H_3O_2)_3^-$, and transposed to $PbCO_3$ by boiling with $Na_2CO_3$. $Hg_2(NO_3)_2$ precipitates $Hg_2SO_4$, white, transposed by HCl to $Hg_2Cl_2$, soluble on boiling with $HNO_3$ or HCl + $HNO_3$ through oxidation to a mercuric salt, converted by $NH_4OH$ to a black mixture of $Hg^\circ$ and $Hg_2(NH_2)_2SO_4$, transposed by boiling with NaOH or $Na_2CO_3$ to black $Hg_2O$. $AgNO_3$ (in solutions of moderate to high concentration) precipitates $Ag_2SO_4$, white, slightly soluble in water and in $HNO_3$ transposed by HCl to AgCl, soluble in $NH_4OH$, and converted to $Ag_2O$, dark brown, by NaOH or boiling $Na_2CO_3$. In addition to these precipitation reactions, $Bi_2(SO_4)_3$, $Sb_2(SO_4)_3$, and $Sn(SO_4)_2$, and to a slight extent $CuSO_4$ and $FeSO_4$ on heating, undergo hydrolysis with precipitation of basic sulfates. Sulfate ion is unusually stable, not being affected by common reducing agents although in hot, concentrated acid solution the more powerful reducing agents yield various reduction products ranging from $H_2SO_3$ to $H_2S$. Thus the attempt to prepare HI by distillation from a mixture of KI and $H_2SO_4$ at ordinary pressure produces considerable $I_2$ and $SO_2$; also metallic zinc with hot concentrated $H_2SO_4$ causes the formation of $H_2SO_3$, $H_2S$ and $S^\circ$. On heating in a reducing atmosphere on carbon, sulfates are reduced to sulfides. Sulfate ion does not form complexes in dilute aqueous solution though under certain conditions double sulfates, such as $K_2SO_4 \cdot Al_2(SO_4)_3 \cdot 24H_2O$ and the rest of the alums, may be formed by crystallization. The most characteristic reaction of sulfate ion is the precipitation of $BaSO_4$ by $BaCl_2$ or $Ba(NO_3)_2$ in the presence of dilute HCl or $HNO_3$.

**More Common Carbonates.** All of the metals form carbonates except As, Sb, Al and Cr. In the cases of $Sn^{+4}$, $Fe^{+3}$, $Cr^{+3}$ and $Al^{+3}$, the hydroxides, precipitated by the action of $Na_2CO_3$ on soluble salts of these metals, usually contain small amounts of adsorbed carbonate ion but hardly sufficient to warrant calling these precipitates basic carbonates. Only the alkali carbonates are soluble in water.

**Reactions of Carbonate Ion.** $CaCl_2$ precipitates $CaCO_3$, white, soluble in $HC_2H_3O_2$, HCl, and $HNO_3$, insoluble in $NH_4OH$ or NaOH. $BaCl_2$ precipitates $BaCO_3$, white, soluble in $HC_2H_3O_2$, HCl, and $HNO_3$, insoluble in $NH_4OH$ or NaOH. $Pb(NO_3)_2$ precipitates $PbCO_3 \cdot xPb(OH)_2$, white, soluble in $HC_2H_3O_2$ and $HNO_3$, insoluble in $NH_4OH$, soluble in NaOH. Since $H_2CO_3$ is a weak, unstable acid, and $CO_2$ is only slightly soluble in water, the common acids react with small amounts of the insoluble carbonates and with moderate concentrations of carbonate ion with evolution of $CO_2$.

Further, since $HCO_3^-$ is a very weak acid, all the soluble carbonates undergo significant hydrolysis, $(NH_4)_2CO_3$ being largely hydrolyzed into $NH_3$ and $HCO_3^-$, whereas $Na_2CO_3$ is moderately hydrolyzed into $OH^-$ and $HCO_3^-$. Thus it is impossible to introduce much carbonate ion into a solution without adding hydroxyl ion at the same time. This makes it easy to understand why some of the metals ($Fe^{+3}$, $Sn^{+4}$, $Sb^{+3}$, $Cr^{+3}$, $Al^{+3}$) whose hydroxides are fairly insoluble, precipitate as hydroxides rather than as carbonates, and why most of the other metals form basic rather than normal carbonates when their soluble salts are treated with $Na_2CO_3$ solution. In the case of Fe it is interesting to note that the lower valence forms a carbonate whereas the higher valence forms the hydroxide, corresponding to the fact that $Fe(OH)_2$ is more soluble than $Fe(OH)_3$. The most characteristic reaction of carbonate ion is the formation of $CO_2$ with dilute acids, the $CO_2$ being identified by passing into $Ca(OH)_2$ or $Ba(OH)_2$ solution, producing a white precipitate of $CaCO_3$ or $BaCO_3$ which may be centrifuged, washed, and caused to effervesce by treating with a few drops of $HC_2H_3O_2$.

**More Common Sulfides.** All of the metals form sulfides, the alkali sulfides being readily soluble in water, BaS, SrS, CaS, and MgS slightly soluble, and the others insoluble. $Al_2S_3$ and $Cr_2S_3$ are hydrolyzed to the corresponding hydroxides on treatment with water. Many of the non-metals form sulfides, of which the most important are $CS_2$, a colorless liquid, insoluble in water, and excellent solvent for $I_2$, S, etc.; $P_4S_3$, yellow, used in the manufacture of matches; and $S_2Cl_2$, a red liquid, used in vulcanizing rubber.

**Reactions of Sulfide Ion.** $AgNO_3$ precipitates $Ag_2S$, black, soluble in $HNO_3$, insoluble in $NH_4OH$. $Pb(C_2H_3O_2)_2$ precipitates PbS, black, soluble in HCl and in $HNO_3$, insoluble in NaOH. $CdCl_2$ precipitates CdS, yellow, soluble in HCl and in $HNO_3$, insoluble in $NH_4OH$. Since $H_2S$ is a weak acid, slightly soluble in water, dilute HCl will react with small amounts of ZnS, MnS, FeS, etc., and with moderate concentrations of sulfide ion or acid sulfide ion with evolution of $H_2S$. Sulfide ion is a moderately strong reducing agent; therefore, when hot $HNO_3$ is used as a solvent for the less soluble sulfides, the important product is free sulfur instead of $H_2S$. With excess of strong oxidizing agents the $S^\circ$ is slowly oxidized further to $H_2SO_4$. The sulfides of As, Sb, and Sn (and HgS less readily) dissolve in moderate concentrations of $(NH_4)_2S_x$ or $Na_2S_x$ with the formation of the corresponding thio anions, thioarsenate ion, $H_2AsS_4^-$ thioantimonate ion, $H_2SbS_4^-$, and thiostannate ion, $HSnS_3^-$ (HgS dissolves in $Na_2S + NaOH$ to form $HgS_2^{--}$). The most characteristic reactions of sulfide ion are the evolution of $H_2S$ with HCl, the $H_2S$ being identified by odor or by forming a black stain of PbS on lead acetate paper, the formation of a black precipitate of PbS with $NaPb(OH)_3$ in the presence of NaOH, and the formation of a yellow precipitate of CdS with $Cd(NH_3)_4Cl_2$ in the presence of $NH_4OH$.

## ANALYSIS OF SOLUTIONS FOR $Cl^-$, $NO_3^-$, $SO_4^{--}$, $CO_3^{--}$, AND $S^{--}$

As noted at the beginning of this chapter, it is not feasible to divide the acid radicals into precipitation groups for systematic examination as in the case of the metals. It becomes necessary, therefore, to proceed more directly with individual tests for the different acid radicals. When only a small number of acid radicals are involved, it is a fairly simple matter to devise a series of tests that can be used quite directly and simply. This is the situation in the case of the more common acid radicals now being discussed. When the list is extended, however, the procedures become more complex because interferences of various sorts arise, until in some cases the identification of a particular acid radical may be a fairly complicated matter. For example, the identification of $Cl^-$ in a mixture of $Cl^-$, $NO_3^-$, and $SO_4^{--}$ is carried out very simply by acidifying a portion of the solution with $HNO_3$ and adding a little $AgNO_3$. Chloride ion is the only one of the three that will give a white precipitate under these conditions. But if $S^{--}$ or $I^-$ is present, a black precipitate of $Ag_2S$ or a light yellow precipitate of AgI will form under the above conditions. To remove $S^{--}$ before testing for $Cl^-$, the solution is acidified slightly and boiled for 1 or 2 minutes (until the test for $H_2S$ in the vapors is negative). To remove $I^-$ requires oxidation under not too strong oxidizing conditions (to avoid conversion of $Cl^-$ to $Cl_2$) and boiling until the $I_2$ is all volatilized. Further, if $ClO_3^-$ were present along with $I^-$, the procedure used to remove $I^-$ might introduce appreciable amounts of $Cl^-$ by reduction of $ClO_3^-$.

$$6I^- + ClO_3^- + 6H_3O^+ = 3I_2 + Cl^- + 9H_2O$$

Therefore, a preliminary separation of $Cl^-$ from $ClO_3^-$ would be necessary before a satisfactory test for $Cl^-$ could be applied.

The list of acid radicals that introduce complications into the test for $Cl^-$ is by no means exhausted by the cases just considered. The latter are sufficient, however, to emphasize the fact that one may need to know a good deal about the chemistry of the other acid radicals that may be present in order to devise a procedure that will identify effectively a particular acid radical for which there is no simple, highly characteristic reaction.

In the description of methods of analysis for the more common acid radicals it will be assumed at first that only these acid radicals may be present. Later, as some of the other acid radicals are considered, it will be pointed out in detail the extent to which they make necessary the introduction of other preliminary or supplementary procedures.

**Chloride.** To 2 drops of the original solution add 1 drop excess of $HNO_3$ (first neutralize with $HNO_3$ if the solution is alkaline), then add a drop of $AgNO_3$ solution and look for a curdy white precipitate of AgCl. If the amount of $Cl^-$ is small, the solution may turn slightly milky without the formation of visible particles of AgCl.

$$Cl^- + Ag^+ = AgCl$$

*Interferences.* If $SO_4^{--}$ is present in large amount and too much $AgNO_3$ is added, a white, coarsely crystalline precipitate, $Ag_2SO_4$, may form. If $S^{--}$ is present, a black precipitate of $Ag_2S$ will obscure the test for $Cl^-$. In such a case the $S^{--}$ may be removed before testing for $Cl^-$ by acidifying with dilute $H_2SO_4$ and boiling until the vapors no longer give a black stain with lead acetate paper. Or, the original solution may be treated with excess of $AgNO_3$, the mixed precipitate of AgCl and $Ag_2S$ filtered, washed, and extracted with dilute $NH_4OH$ (AgCl is soluble in $NH_4OH$, but $Ag_2S$ is not), and the ammoniacal solution acidified with $HNO_3$ (AgCl reprecipitates as in the test for $Ag^+$ in the analysis of Group I metals).

**Nitrate. Brown Ring Test.** To 2 drops of the original solution add cautiously, with shaking, 4–5 drops of concentrated $H_2SO_4$. Cool thoroughly, then hold the test tube at an angle of 40°–45° from the vertical and carefully pour in 3–4 drops of a fresh solution of $FeSO_4$, letting this form an upper layer in the test tube. Without mixing, cool the solution under running water and look for a brown ring, $FeSO_4 \cdot NO$, in the zone separating the two layers.

$$NO_3^- + 3Fe^{++} + 4H_3O^+ = NO + 3Fe^{+3} + 6H_2O$$

$$NO + Fe^{++} = Fe \cdot NO^{++}$$

**Nitrate. Ammonia Test.** To 2 drops of the original solution add 5 drops of 3 $N$ NaOH, warm and test for $NH_3$ with moist red litmus paper. If the test is positive (derived from $NH_4^+$ in the solution), transfer the solution to a small crucible, add 8–10 drops of $H_2O$ and boil until the $NH_3$ is removed. Place the solution in a small test tube, dilute to about 10 drops if necessary, add a small piece of coarse Al-wire, insert a cotton plug to about a half inch above the surface of the solution, and warm until there is a rapid evolution of $H_2$. Place a piece of moist red litmus paper in the tube and let the reaction continue for 3–5 minutes. If $NO_3^-$ is present it will be reduced slowly to $NH_3$, turning the litmus paper blue.

$$3NO_3^- + 8Al + 5OH^- + 18H_2O = 3NH_3 + 8Al(OH)_4^-$$

*Interferences.* Of the acid radicals considered in this first list, none interfere seriously with either of the above tests for a nitrate, although if a sulfide or carbonate is present it may be desirable to remove these before using the brown ring test in order to avoid disturbances due to evolution of gases during the test. To remove sulfide and carbonate, acidify slightly with $H_2SO_4$ and boil for 1–2 minutes.

**Sulfate.** To 2 drops of the original solution add 1 drop of 5 *N* HCl (if alkaline neutralize first with HCl, if strongly acid, neutralize first with $NH_4OH$), then add 1 drop of $BaCl_2$ solution and look for a white finely divided precipitate of $BaSO_4$.

*Interferences.* It is necessary to acidify an alkaline solution to prevent the precipitation of $BaCO_3$ white, when $BaCl_2$ is added. However, if the solution is strongly acid there is serious interference with the delicacy of the test for $SO_4^{--}$. With high concentration of $NO_3^-$ it is possible to obtain a white precipitate of $Ba(NO_3)_2$ if too much $BaCl_2$ is added. On acidifying an alkaline solution containing a sulfide, a milky precipitate of free S° is usually obtained, due to presence of some polysulfide formed by oxygen from the air.

$$4HS^- + O_2 = 2HS_2^- + 2OH^-$$

$$HS_2^- + H_3O^+ = H_2S + S + H_2O$$

**Carbonate. Effervescence Test.** To 2 drops of the original solution add 1–2 drops of 5*N* HCl. If a moderate or large amount of $CO_3^{--}$ is present, there will be a distinct formation of bubbles of $CO_2$ in the solution.

$$CO_3^{--} + 2H_3O^+ = H_2CO_3 + 2H_2O$$

$$H_2CO_3 = H_2O + CO_2$$

**Carbonate. Barium Hydroxide Test.** This starts like the effervescence test, but in this case the $CO_2$ is identified by its reaction with $Ba(OH)_2$. Place 2–3 drops of the original solution in a centrifuge tube and add 1–2 drops of 5 *N* HCl. If effervescence is noted, the $CO_2$ as a heavy gas accumulates in the tube above the solution. Squeeze the bulb of a dropper tube and insert the tube so the tip is 2–3 mm. above the surface of the solution; then release the bulb so as to draw some of the $CO_2$ into the tube. Place 1–2 drops of $Ba(OH)_2$ solution in a clean centrifuge tube, insert the tip of the tube below the surface of this solution and slowly squeeze the bulb to force the $CO_2$ into the reagent. A white precipitate, $BaCO_3$, will form if moderate amounts of $CO_3^{--}$ are present in the original solution.

$$CO_2 + Ba^{++} + 2OH^- = \underline{BaCO_3} + H_2O$$

If the amount of $CO_3^{--}$ is too small to show effervescence, the $CO_2$ which slowly diffuses from the solution may be identified as follows: Pick up 2–3 drops of $Ba(OH)_2$ solution in a dropper tube, insert the tube so the tip is about 3–4 mm. from the surface of the acidified solution, and then squeeze the bulb very gently so as to force part of a drop out of the tip. (Keep the tip centered in the test tube so the $Ba(OH)_2$ solution is not lost on the wall of the test tube.) A white film will form slowly (half a minute) on the surface of the $Ba(OH)_2$ solution if $CO_3^{--}$ is present in the unknown.

**Sulfide.** Place 2–3 drops of the solution in a small test tube, add 1 drop of 5 *N* HCl and insert a narrow strip of filter paper which has been treated with a small drop of $Pb(C_2H_3O_2)_2$ solution. A brown to black stain of PbS will form in a few seconds if sulfide is present.

$$HS^- + H_3O^+ = H_2S + H_2O$$

$$H_2S + Pb(C_2H_3O_2)_2 = \underline{PbS} + 2HC_2H_3O_2$$

**Alternative Tests for Sulfide.** (1) Place a drop of the solution in a depression on the test plate, add 2 drops of 3 *N* NaOH, and then add some $Pb(OH)_3^-$ solution (prepared by adding 2–3 drops of NaOH to 1 drop of $Pb(NO_3)_2$ solution). A black precipitate of PbS indicates a sulfide.

$$HS^- + Pb(OH)_3^- = \underline{PbS} + H_2O + 2OH^-$$

(2) Treat a drop of the solution with 2 drops of 5 *N* $NH_4OH$ and then add a little $Cd(NH_3)_4^{++}$ solution (prepared by adding 2–3 drops of $NH_4OH$ to 1 drop of $CdCl_2$ solution). A yellow precipitate of CdS will form if sulfide is present.

$$HS^- + Cd(NH_3)_4^{++} = \underline{CdS} + NH_4^+ + 3NH_3$$

*Interferences.* The only common interference with the evolution of $H_2S$ in the first method occurs when the solution contains certain acid radicals that become strong enough oxidizing agents in acid solution to cause oxidation of $H_2S$ to S°. In slightly acid solution $NO_3^-$ does not cause trouble, but if the solution is made strongly acid the oxidizing power of the $NO_3^-$ may be increased sufficiently to bring about this oxidation.

$$2NO_3^- + 2H_3O^+ + 3H_2S = 3S^\circ + 2NO + 6H_2O$$

## *LABORATORY EXERCISES*

1. Known solutions containing the more common acid radicals.

(*1*) $Cl^-$, $NO_3^-$, $SO_4^{--}$
(*2*) $NO_3^-$, $CO_3^{--}$, $HS^-$
(*3*) $Cl^-$, $SO_4^{--}$, $CO_3^{--}$, $HS^-$

These solutions contain the following amounts of substance per liter of solution: (*1*) 8.3 g. NaCl, 30 g. $NaNO_3$, and 22 g. $Na_2SO_4$; (*2*) 30 g. $NaNO_3$, 119 g. $Na_2CO_3\cdot$

$10H_2O$, 39 g. $Na_2S \cdot 9H_2O$, and 25 ml. of 5 *N* NaOH; (*3*) 8.3 g. NaCl, 22 g. $Na_2SO_4$, 119 g. $Na_2CO_3 \cdot 10H_2O$, 39 g. $Na_2S \cdot 9H_2O$, and 25 ml. of 5 *N* NaOH.

Use 2–3 drops of the original solution to test for each of the acid radicals covered in this chapter.

2. Prepare a series of $Na_2CO_3$ solutions as follows: (a) 10 drops of $Na_2CO_3$ test solution (10 mg. C per ml.) in test tube No. 1; (b) 10 drops of $Na_2CO_3$ test solution plus 10 drops of $H_2O$, mix, place 10 drops of the solution in test tube No. 2, and dilute the remainder with 10 drops of $H_2O$; (c) place 10 drops of the diluted solution from (b) in test tube No. 3, and dilute the remainder with 10 drops of $H_2O$, (d) place 10 drops of the diluted solution from (c) in test tube No. 4, and dilute the remainder with 10 drops of $H_2O$, (e) place 10 drops of the diluted solution from (d) in test tube No. 5. To each solution in order add 1 drop of 5 *N* HCl, mix, and note the limit of the effervescence test. Try the $Ba(OH)_2$ test (p. 215) on any tubes which fail to show effervescence. Results?

# 13

# Other Common Acid Radicals

## SULFITE, PHOSPHATE, OXALATE, BROMIDE, IODIDE, AND CHLORATE RADICALS

As indicated in the previous chapter, when testing for most of the acid radicals the number of preliminary separations or special precautions needed usually increases with the number of acid radicals present. In the present chapter it will be assumed that the solution may contain any of the more common acid radicals as well as the ones now added. The procedures will be described in sufficient detail to give satisfactory tests for moderate or small amounts of each of the acid radicals in the presence of moderate amounts of any of the others. The special problem of the identification of very small amounts of one substance in the presence of large amounts of another will not be discussed specifically.

## COMMON COMPOUNDS AND REACTIONS OF SULFITE, PHOSPHATE, OXALATE, BROMIDE, IODIDE, AND CHLORATE RADICALS

**More Common Sulfites.** All of the metals except As form sulfites, of which only those of the alkali metals, $NH_4^+$, and $Mg^{++}$ are readily soluble in water. None of the non-metals form simple sulfites, although there are basic radicals, such as $NH_4^+$, that permit the formation of corresponding sulfites.

**Reactions of Sulfite Ion.** $BaCl_2$ precipitates $BaSO_3$, white, soluble in 5 $N$ HCl, insoluble in $HC_2H_3O_2$, transposed by $Na_2CO_3$ into $BaCO_3 + Na_2SO_3$. $AgNO_3$ precipitates $Ag_2SO_3$, white, unstable (breaking down into $Ag^\circ + H_2SO_4$), soluble in $HNO_3$. In acid solution $H_2SO_3$ is a moderately strong reducing agent, being oxidized readily by $I_2$, $Br_2$, $Fe^{+3}$, $Cu^{++}$, etc., to $H_2SO_4$. With strong reducing agents, such as $SnCl_2$, $H_2SO_3$ is reduced to $H_2S$. A number of metals whose sulfites are listed as slightly soluble to insoluble fail to precipitate readily as sulfites, either through supersaturation effects or because of complexes formed with excess of the sulfite reagent. With HCl or dilute $H_2SO_4$, sulfite ion forms $H_2SO_3$, slightly ionized and unstable. On heating this solution $SO_2$ is given off. The most characteristic reaction is the oxidation to $SO_4^{--}$ by bromine followed by precipitation of $BaSO_4$ with $BaCl_2$ in the presence of HCl.

**More Common Phosphates.** All of the metals except As and Sb form phosphates, of which only those of the alkalis and $NH_4^+$ are soluble in water. None of the non-metals form simple phosphates, although there are basic radicals, such as $NH_4^+$, that permit the formation of corresponding phosphates.

**Reactions of Phosphate Ion.** $AgNO_3$ precipitates $Ag_3PO_4$, yellow, soluble in $HNO_3$ and in $NH_4OH$. $BaCl_2$ precipitates $Ba_3(PO_4)_2$, white, soluble in HCl, moderately soluble in $HC_2H_3O_2$. $MgCl_2$, in the presence of $NH_4OH$, precipitates $MgNH_4PO_4$, white, soluble in HCl and in $HC_2H_3O_2$, slightly soluble in hot water. $(NH_4)_2MoO_4$, in warm, moderately acid $HNO_3$ solution, precipitates $(NH_4)_3P(Mo_3O_{10})_4$, yellow, insoluble in $HNO_3$, soluble in NaOH. A fresh solution of $SnCl_4 \cdot 5H_2O$, in dilute HCl solution, precipitates $Sn_3(PO_4)_4$, white. $FeCl_3$ in $NaC_2H_3O_2 + HC_2H_3O_2$ solution precipitates $FePO_4$, yellow, soluble in HCl. There are no common oxidation-reduction reactions. The most characteristic reaction is the precipitation of $(NH_4)_3P(Mo_3O_{10})_4$, yellow, by $(NH_4)_2MoO_4$ in $HNO_3$ solution.

**More Common Oxalates.** All of the metals except As and Sb form oxalates, of which only the alkalis and $Fe^{+3}$ are soluble in water, although there are a number of double or complex oxalates that are soluble. None of the non-metals form simple oxalates, although there are positive radicals, such as $NH_4^+$, that permit the formation of corresponding oxalates.

**Reactions of Oxalate Ion.** $AgNO_3$ precipitates $Ag_2C_2O_4$, white, granular, soluble in 5 *N* $HNO_3$ and in $NH_4OH$, insoluble in $HC_2H_3O_2$. $CaCl_2$ precipitates $CaC_2O_4$, white, soluble in HCl or $HNO_3$, insoluble in $HC_2H_3O_2$, transposed by $Na_2CO_3$ largely to $CaCO_3$ and $Na_2C_2O_4$. A number of metals, notably Zn and Mg, whose oxalates are listed as insoluble, fail to precipitate readily as oxalates, either through supersaturation effects or because of complexes formed with excess $C_2O_4^{--}$. HCl, or dilute $H_2SO_4$, converts $C_2O_4^{--}$ to $H_2C_2O_4$, slightly ionized, but fairly stable. With hot concentrated $H_2SO_4$, $H_2C_2O_4$ is decomposed: $H_2C_2O_4 = H_2O + CO_2 + CO$. In acid solution $H_2C_2O_4$ is a mild reducing agent being oxidized by $KMnO_4$, aqua regia, and other strong oxidizing agents to $CO_2$:

$$5H_2C_2O_4 + 2MnO_4^- + 6H_3O^+ = 2Mn^{++} + 10CO_2 + 14H_2O$$

In neutral or alkaline solution $C_2O_4^{--}$ is readily oxidized to $CO_3^{--}$ by $Cl_2$ or $Br_2$. The most characteristic reactions are the precipitation of $CaC_2O_4$, white, by 0.1 *N* $CaCl_2$ solution in the presence of $HC_2H_3O_2$; the oxidation to $CO_2$ by $KMnO_4$ in hot $HNO_3$ solution; and the separation from other reducing agents by precipitation as $CaC_2O_4$ and boiling with 5 *N* $HNO_3$, followed by decolorization of dilute $KMnO_4$ solution.

**More Common Bromides.** All of the metals form bromides, of which the following are insoluble in water: AgBr, white; $Hg_2Br_2$, white; $HgBr_2$, white (slightly soluble); $PbBr_2$, white (slightly soluble); CuBr, white. The following are soluble only in the presence of free HBr (or HCl), undergoing hydrolysis with the precipitation of basic salts when treated with water in sufficient amount, especially if the solution is heated: $BiBr_3$, $SbBr_3$, and $SnBr_2$; less pronounced precipitation occurs in the cases of $SnBr_4$, $CuBr_2$, $FeBr_2$, $FeBr_3$ and $ZnBr_2$. The non-metals (except Cl, $Sb^{v}$ and $As^{v}$) form bromides, most of which are largely hydrolyzed by water into HBr and the corresponding free acid of the non-metal. Thus $PBr_3$ is hydrolyzed practically completely into HBr and $H_3PO_3$.

**Reactions of Bromide Ion.** $AgNO_3$ precipitates AgBr, pale yellow, insoluble in $HNO_3$, slightly soluble in $NH_4OH$, not transposed by 5 *N* NaOH into $Ag_2O$. Mercuric ion combines with bromide ion to form the slightly ionized and slightly soluble $HgBr_2$, thus lowering the concentration of bromide ion to such an extent as to dissolve $PbBr_2$ readily and to prevent the ready oxidation of bromide ion to $Br_2$ by $KMnO_4$ in cold, dilute $HNO_3$ solution. With high concentration of bromide ion a number of bromides are converted to complex negative ions, $AgBr_2^-$, $PbBr_3^-$, $BiBr_4^-$, $SnBr_6^{--}$, $SbBr_4^-$, etc. Bromine dissolves readily in a concentrated bromide solution forming $Br_3^-$. $Ca(ClO)_2$, $KMnO_4$, and other strong oxidizing agents, including $Cl_2$ in acid solution, oxidize $Br^-$ to free bromine. Concentrated $H_2SO_4$ on boiling at reduced pressure converts $Br^-$ to HBr, which may be volatilized from the solution. At ordinary atmospheric pressure the boiling $H_2SO_4$ is partly reduced to $SO_2$ with corresponding oxidation of some of the $Br^-$ to $Br_2$. The most characteristic reaction is the oxidation of $Br^-$ to $Br_2$ by $Ca(ClO)_2$ in dilute HCl solution, followed by extraction with $CCl_4$, the $Br_2$ forming a straw to golden-brown solution in the $CCl_4$ layer.

**More Common Iodides.** All of the metals (except $Sb^{v}$, $As^{v}$) form iodides, of which the following are insoluble in water: AgI, yellow; $Hg_2I_2$, greenish yellow; $HgI_2$, red; $PbI_2$, yellow (slightly soluble in hot water); $BiI_3$, brownish black; CuI, white. The non-metals form iodides, most of which are largely hydrolyzed by water into HI and the corresponding free acid of the non-metal. Thus $PI_3$ is hydrolyzed practically completely into HI and $H_3PO_3$ (one of the common methods of preparing HI). In ICl, however, the iodine is the positive element in the salt and the chlorine the negative element; therefore, on hydrolysis one would expect to obtain HCl and HIO. Actually the latter changes to a mixture of $I_2$ and $HIO_3$ so the equation for the hydrolysis is as follows:

$$5ICl + 9H_2O = 2I_2 + IO_3^- + 5Cl^- + 6H_3O^+$$

**Reactions of Iodide Ion.** $AgNO_3$ precipitates AgI, light yellow, insoluble in $HNO_3$ or $NH_4OH$, not transposed to $Ag_2O$ by 5 *N* NaOH. $Pb(NO_3)_2$ precipitates $PbI_2$, yellow, slightly soluble in hot water, soluble in 5 *N* $HNO_3$ on heating (oxidation of $I^-$ to $I_2$), slightly soluble in HCl (formation of complex ion, $PbCl_3^-$), soluble in concentrated $NH_4C_2H_3O_2$ solution [formation of the complex ion, $Pb(C_2H_3O_2)_3^-$]. $Hg(NO_3)_2$ precipitates $HgI_2$, red, slightly soluble in HCl (formation of complex ion $HgCl_4^{--}$) slowly soluble in $HNO_3$ or aqua regia (oxidation of $I^-$ to $I_2$), readily soluble in KI (formation of the complex ion $HgI_4^{--}$). With high concentration of iodide ion a number of iodides are converted to complex negative ions, $HgI_4^{--}$, $CdI_4^{--}$, $BiI_4^-$, etc. Iodine dissolves readily in a concentrated $I^-$ solution forming $I_3^-$. $FeCl_3$, $CuSO_4$, $NaNO_2$, and other mild oxidizing agents, in slightly acid solution, oxidize $I^-$ to free $I_2$. Strong oxidizing agents such as $Ca(ClO)_2$, $KMnO_4$, and $Cl_2$, when used in excess, oxidize $I^-$ to $IO_3^-$; therefore in using such reagents to test for $I^-$ it is necessary to employ very limited amounts of the reagent when the amount of $I^-$ may be small. Concentrated $H_2SO_4$, on boiling at reduced pressure, converts $I^-$ to HI, which may be volatilized from the solution. At ordinary atmospheric pressure the boiling $H_2SO_4$ would oxidize the $I^-$ largely to $I_2$. The most characteristic reaction is the oxidation of $I^-$ to $I_2$ by $Fe(NO_3)_3$ in $HNO_3$ solution, followed by extraction with $CCl_4$, the $I_2$ forming a pink to violet solution in the $CCl_4$ layer.

**More Common Chlorates.** All of the metals, except Sb and As, form chlorates, which are slightly to readily soluble in water. The following are soluble only in the presence of free acid, undergoing hydrolysis with precipitation of basic salts when treated with water in sufficient amounts, especially when heated: $Hg(ClO_3)_2$, $Bi(ClO_3)_3$, and $Sn(ClO_3)_4$. None of the non-metals form simple chlorates, although there are basic radicals, such as $NH_4^+$, that permit the formation of corresponding chlorates.

**Reactions of Chlorate Ion.** There are no simple precipitation reactions involving the formation of chlorates. In acid solution $ClO_3^-$ is a fairly strong oxidizing agent readily oxidizing $Fe^{++}$ to $Fe^{+3}$, and in 5 *N* HCl solution oxidizing $SbCl_4^-$ and $H_3AsO_3$ to $SbCl_6^-$ and $H_3AsO_4$, respectively. In the presence of mineral acid (HCl, $HNO_3$, $H_2SO_4$, etc.), $I^-$ and $Br^-$ are oxidized to $I_2$ and $Br_2$ and with excess of $ClO_3^-$ partial oxidation of $I_2$ to $IO_3^-$ takes place. In hot strong $HNO_3$ solution $Mn^{++}$ is oxidized to $MnO_2$. In neutral or alkaline solution the oxidizing power of $ClO_3^-$ is considerably diminished, $I^-$ and $ClO_3^-$ forming a stable mixture. $H_2SO_3$ reduces $ClO_3^-$ readily in the cold to $Cl^-$. The most characteristic reaction is the reduction of $ClO_3^-$ to $Cl^-$ by $H_2SO_3$ followed by precipitation of AgCl with $AgNO_3$ in a solution moderately acid with $HNO_3$.

## ANALYSIS FOR $SO_4^{--}$, $SO_3^{--}$, $CO_3^{--}$, $PO_4^{-3}$, AND $C_2O_4^{--}$

**Sulfate.** Using a portion of the original solution apply the test with $BaCl_2$ in the presence of HCl as previously described (see p. 215).

*Interferences.* $BaSO_3$ and, less readily, $BaC_2O_4$ precipitate with $BaCl_2$ in dilute HCl solution, whereas if the solution is too strongly acid there is marked decrease in the sensitivity of the test for $SO_4^{--}$.

**Sulfite.** If $SO_4^{--}$ is present, treat 2–3 drops of the original solution with 1 drop excess of 5 *N* HCl (neutralize with $NH_4OH$ if acid, or with HCl if alkaline), then add $BaCl_2$ solution 1 drop at a time, with shaking, until precipitation is complete (this precipitates the $SO_4^{--}$ and may precipitate some $SO_3^{--}$). Centrifuge, test the clear solution with a drop of $BaCl_2$ to make certain that precipitation of $BaSO_4$ is complete, then add 5 drops of bromine water, warm, and look for a white precipitate of $BaSO_4$.

$$H_2SO_3 + Ba^{++} + Br_2 + 5H_2O = BaSO_4 + 2Br^- + 4H_3O^+$$

*Interferences.* Since this test involves the oxidation of $H_2SO_3$ to $H_2SO_4$, it is to be expected that other lower states of oxidation of sulfur will behave similarly. In most cases the oxidation does not proceed as readily as with $H_2SO_3$, but it does take place readily enough so that the test is not characteristic unless steps are taken to separate $SO_3^{--}$ from other lower states of oxidation of sulfur. The only other state being considered in this book is $S^{--}$. If $S^{--}$ were stable in aqueous solution, it would be simple to precipitate $S^{--}$ with $Cd(NH_3)_4Cl_2$ in ammoniacal solution, centrifuge, and test the clear solution for $SO_3^{--}$. Actually, however, atmospheric oxidation may yield polysulfide, thiosulfate, etc., and in such cases the isolation of $SO_3^{--}$ by this procedure is incomplete. Further, a solution containing $SO_3^{--}$ and $S^{--}$ is unstable when acidified, undergoing such reactions as the following:

$$5H_2SO_3 + 5H_2S = H_2S_5O_6 + 5S + 9H_2O$$

$$H_2SO_3 + 2H_2S = 3S + 3H_2O$$

This may cause trouble in some of the other tests for acid radicals that must be carried out in acid solution. Therefore, the practice is frequently adopted of not putting both $SO_3^{--}$ and $S^{--}$ in the same solution in making up unknowns.

**Carbonate.** Using a portion of the original solution, apply the test with dilute HCl, identifying the $CO_2$ evolved with $Ba(OH)_2$ solution, according to the directions on p. 215.

*Interferences.* Of the additional acid radicals now being considered, $SO_3^{--}$ will interfere with the $Ba(OH)_2$ test, giving a white precipitate of $BaSO_3$. In the absence of an oxalate the $SO_3^{--}$ can be oxidized to $SO_4^{--}$ by adding a drop excess of $KMnO_4$ solution, then the solution is acidified and tested for $CO_2$ with $Ba(OH)_2$ solution.

If both $SO_3^{--}$ and $C_2O_4^{--}$ are present, 2–3 drops of the original solution may be treated with 2–3 drops of $BaCl_2$ reagent and centrifuged. Test for completeness of precipitation with $BaCl_2$; then discard the clear solution. The precipitate will be a mixture of $BaSO_3$, $BaC_2O_4$, and $BaCO_3$. Add a drop of $BaCl_2$ reagent, then 2 drops of 5 $N$ $HC_2H_3O_2$, stir to mix the precipitate with the reagent and test for $CO_2$ above the solution with a drop of $Ba(OH)_2$.

**Phosphate.** To 2–3 drops of the original solution add 1–2 drops excess of $HNO_3$ (neutralize with $HNO_3$ if alkaline, or with $NH_4OH$ if strongly acid), then add 10 drops of $(NH_4)_2MoO_4$ solution, warm to 60°–80°C. (keep below boiling), and look for the formation of a bright yellow precipitate $(NH_4)_3P(Mo_3O_{10})_4$.

$$H_3PO_4 + 12HMoO_4^- + 3NH_4^+ + 9H_3O^+ = (NH_4)_3P(Mo_3O_{10})_4 + 21H_2O$$

**Alternative Test.** To 2–3 drops of the original solution add 2–3 drops of $NH_4Cl$ solution, 1–2 drops excess of $NH_4OH$, and 1 drop of $MgCl_2$ solution. Keep cold and stir with a glass rod to start crystallization. A white crystalline precipitate, $MgNH_4PO_4$ indicates $PO_4^{-3}$. This test is confirmed by centrifuging, washing, dissolving the precipitate in 5 $N$ $HNO_3$ and applying the ammonium molybdate reaction.

*Interferences.* In the ammonium molybdate test various reducing agents, especially $H_2SO_3$, $H_2S$, and HI among the other acid radicals, may produce dark colors, blue and brown, by reduction of the molybdate (and formation of $I_2$ and thiomolybdates in the cases of HI and $H_2S$). This interferes with the direct recognition of the ammonium molybdi-phosphate as a yellow precipitate. On prolonged digestion the $HNO_3$ present usually reoxidizes the molybdenum and causes the disappearance of the interfering colors, but it requires much less time to precipitate any $PO_4^{-3}$ as $MgNH_4PO_4$ by the alternative procedure, and then centrifuge, wash, dissolve this precipitate in 5 $N$ $HNO_3$ and apply the ammonium molybdate test. This separates the phosphate from any interfering reducing agents and makes the formation of the yellow precipitate especially satisfactory.

If the solution is heated too strongly, there may be some decomposition of the reagent with formation of a light yellow precipitate of molybdic acid. This may be mistaken for a test for $PO_4^{-3}$, but may be avoided effectively by keeping the temperature below 80°C. Arsenic in the form of $H_3AsO_4$ gives the same type of precipitate with $(NH_4)_2MoO_4$ or $MgCl_2 + NH_4Cl + NH_4OH$ as $PO_4^{-3}$. Therefore, these tests can be used for $PO_4^{-3}$ only when $AsO_4^{-3}$ is known to be absent. Since Mg salts are generally white, the Mg mixture test is less characteristic than the $(NH_4)_2MoO_4$ reaction and should be supplemented by the latter.

**Oxalate.** To 2–3 drops of the original solution add 1 drop excess of $HC_2H_3O_2$ (if acid originally, neutralize first with $NH_4OH$, if alkaline, neutralize with $HC_2H_3O_2$), then add 5 drops of saturated $CaSO_4$ solution (or 5 drops of 0.1 $N$ $Ca(NO_3)_2$) and look for a white, finely divided precipitate of $CaC_2O_4$.

**Alternative Tests.** (1) Take 2–3 drops of the original solution, if acid neutralize with $NH_4OH$, then add 3–4 drops of $CaCl_2$ reagent, mix thoroughly, centrifuge, and test for completeness of precipitation with another drop of $CaCl_2$. Discard the clear solution and wash the precipitate twice with distilled water. Dissolve the precipitate in 3 drops of 5 $N$ $HNO_3$, transfer the solution to a small crucible, add 3–4 drops of $H_2O$, and heat on the hot plate just to boiling. Add water to keep up the volume and let the reaction continue about a minute. Let cool slightly; then add 1 drop of $Mn(NO_3)_2$ solution and 1 drop of very dilute $KMnO_4$ solution (reagent $KMnO_4$ diluted 1:50). If oxalate is present the permanganate color will disappear.

$$C_2O_4^{--} + Ca^{++} = \underline{CaC_2O_4}$$

(separation from soluble reducing agents)

$$\underline{CaC_2O_4} + 2H_3O^+ + NO_3^- = Ca^{++} + H_2C_2O_4 + 2H_2O + NO_3^-$$

(boiling oxidizes any $H_2SO_3$ and removes $HNO_2$)

$$5H_2C_2O_4 + 2MnO_4^- + 6H_3O^+ = 2Mn^{++} + 10CO_2 + 14H_2O$$

(2) Take 2–3 drops of the original solution, if alkaline acidify with $HNO_3$ adding 1 drop excess, and then boil for 1 minute to remove any $CO_2$ from $CO_3^{--}$. Transfer the solution to a small test tube, add 1 drop of $Mn(NO_3)_2$ solution and 2 drops of $KMnO_4$ reagent, and test for $CO_2$ in the space above the solution with a drop of $Ba(OH)_2$. (The oxidation of oxalate to $CO_2$ by $KMnO_4$ is a slow reaction at room temperature unless $Mn^{++}$ is present to catalyze the reaction.)

*Interferences.* None of the other acid radicals considered give precipitates with a dilute solution of $Ca^{++}$ in the presence of $HC_2H_3O_2$. If the solution is too strongly acid (HCl or $HNO_3$, etc.), $CaC_2O_4$ fails to precipitate; if neutral or alkaline, $CaSO_3$, $CaCO_3$, $Ca_3(PO_4)_2$, etc., may precipitate. In an unknown in which various metals may be present it is important not to be misled by a precipitate formed by the acid radical of the Ca salt (e.g., $CaSO_4$ might precipitate $BaSO_4$ instead of $CaC_2O_4$). In the test involving decolorization of $KMnO_4$ the final reaction is a simple case of oxidation-reduction. Obviously there are many reducing agents that will decolorize a $KMnO_4$ solution: $H_2SO_3$, $HNO_2$, HCl, etc.; therefore, preliminary steps are required to separate $C_2O_4^{--}$ from other possible reducing agents before the test can be used. Precipitation of $CaC_2O_4$ in neutral or acetic acid solution separates $C_2O_4^{--}$ from many reducing agents whose Ca salts are soluble. Dissolving the precipitate in $HNO_3$ and boiling a few minutes oxidizes any $H_2SO_3$ to $H_2SO_4$ ($CaSO_3$ may precipitate in neutral or alkaline solution) and removes any $HNO_2$ formed or present from decomposition in the $HNO_3$ used. Oxalate ion is a mild enough reducing agent so that it is not oxidized appreciably by boiling for a short time with 5 $N$ $HNO_3$. In the $CO_2$ test for $C_2O_4^{--}$, since $CO_3^{--}$ and $C_2O_4^{--}$ are the only forms of carbon-containing radicals being considered, the removal of $CO_2$ from $CO_3^{--}$, followed by oxidation and production of more $CO_2$, becomes a test for $C_2O_4^{--}$. There are, of course, other carbon compounds, such as formaldehyde ($CH_2O$), formic acid (HCOOH), etc., that also yield $CO_2$ on oxidation with $KMnO_4$.

## ANALYSIS FOR $S^{--}$, $I^-$, $Br^-$, $Cl^-$, $ClO_3^-$, AND $NO_3^-$

**Sulfide.** Using a portion of the original solution, apply the test with $NaPb(OH)_3$ or $Cd(NH_3)_4Cl_2$ as previously described (see p. 216).

*Interferences.* There are no interferences with these tests. However, if $S^{--}$ is present it interferes with the direct tests for $I^-$ and $Br^-$ since these involve oxidation to $I_2$ and $Br_2$, and $S^{--}$ will use up an equivalent amount of the oxidizing agent. In the absence of $ClO_3^-$ and $NO_3^-$, $S^{--}$ may be removed by acidifying slightly with $H_2SO_4$ and boiling a few minutes until the fumes from the solution no longer produce a dark stain of PbS on lead acetate paper. If $ClO_3^-$ or $NO_3^-$ is present (or not known to be absent) it is best to use the general procedure for halides described in the next paragraphs.

**Chlorate and Halides.** To 5 drops of original solution (neutralized with $HNO_3$ if ammoniacal) add a drop of $AgNO_3$ solution. If a precipitate forms add more $AgNO_3$, 1 drop at a time, with shaking, until precipitation is complete. Centrifuge, wash, and reserve the solution to test for $ClO_3^-$. Transfer the precipitate to a test tube, add 5 drops of 5 *N* $HNO_3$ and heat to boiling. Of the various precipitates that may have formed with the $AgNO_3$ ($Ag_2S$, AgI, AgBr, AgCl, $Ag_2C_2O_4$, $Ag_3PO_4$, $Ag_2SO_3$, $Ag_2CO_3$, $Ag_2O$), only AgI, AgBr and AgCl are insoluble in hot $HNO_3$, although a residue of $S°$ will be left by $Ag_2S$. If a greenish-yellow, yellow, or white, flocculent or curdy precipitate is left, set aside to test for AgI, AgBr, and AgCl. Meanwhile test the reserved clear solution for $ClO_3^-$ as follows: Acidify with $HNO_3$, adding 2–3 drops excess. Add 1 drop of $AgNO_3$ solution to insure the presence of excess $Ag^+$. If a precipitate forms, centrifuge and treat the clear solution with a little more $AgNO_3$. Then add to the solution 1 drop of $H_2SO_3$ solution (or 1 drop of 0.5 *N* $NaHSO_3$). A white precipitate of AgCl indicates the presence of $ClO_3^-$ in the original solution.

$$ClO_3^- + 3H_2SO_3 + 3H_2O = Cl^- + 3HSO_4^- + 3H_3O^+$$

$$Cl^- + Ag^+ = AgCl$$

To test the reserved precipitate for $I^-$, $Br^-$, and $Cl^-$, use the following procedure: wash the precipitate 2–3 times with distilled water, transfer to a test tube or small beaker, add 5 drops of $H_2O$, 2 drops of $H_2SO_4$, and 50 mg. of granulated zinc. Shake frequently and let stand 3–5 minutes for displacement of Ag by Zn.

$$2AgI + Zn° = 2Ag° + 2I^- + Zn^{++}$$

$$2AgBr + Zn° = 2Ag° + 2Br^- + Zn^{++}$$

$$2AgCl + Zn° = 2Ag° + 2Cl^- + Zn^{++}$$

Centrifuge and either use the persulfate method to test for $I^-$, $Br^-$, and $Cl^-$ in the clear solution or divide the solution into two parts, testing for $I^-$ and $Br^-$ in one portion by the hypochlorite method and for $Cl^-$ in the other portion after removing $I^-$ and $Br^-$ by the persulfate procedure.

**Persulfate Method for $I^-$, $Br^-$, and $Cl^-$.** Neutralize the solution with $NH_4OH$, add 2 drops 3 *N* $NH_4C_2H_3O_2$ and 5 drops of 5 *N* $HC_2H_3O_2$, and transfer the solution to a small crucible (No. 000). Dilute to approximately 3 ml. with water, add about 20 mg. of $K_2S_2O_8$ (2–3 small pieces the diameter of the lead in a pencil). Heat just to boiling on the hot plate and stir to dissolve the $K_2S_2O_8$. If $I^-$ is present it will be oxidized to $I_2$ as the solution becomes hot, producing a tan color in the solution. The $I_2$ may be further identified by placing a few drops of the solution in a test tube, cooling, adding a drop of $CCl_4$, and shaking to extract the $I_2$. The $CCl_4$ layer will show a pink color with $I_2$. Keep just at the boiling point until the $I_2$ color disappears (largely volatilized as $I_2$, although a little will be oxidized to $IO_3^-$). Add $H_2O$ from time to time as the solution evaporates. Add 1–2 more crystals of $K_2S_2O_8$ and note whether any more color develops. If it does, heat again until colorless and repeat the test. When the $I_2$ is all gone remove from the hot plate, add 5 drops of 5 *N* $HNO_3$, stir, and heat again to boiling. If $Br^-$ is present it will be oxidized to $Br_2$, giving a yellow to tan color. The $Br_2$ may be further identified by extracting a few drops of the solution with a drop of $CCl_4$, giving a tan color to the $CCl_4$ layer. Heat until colorless and test for completeness of oxidation of $Br^-$ by adding a little more $K_2S_2O_8$. When the $Br_2$ is all gone, transfer the solution to a small beaker, cool, and add 1 drop of diluted $AgNO_3$ (1:10). If $Cl^-$ is present a marked opalescence will show in the solution.

In the acetic acid solution only $I^-$ is oxidized,

$$2I^- + S_2O_8^{--} = I_2 + 2SO_4^{--}$$

and in the dilute $HNO_3$ solution the $Br^-$ is oxidized,

$$2Br^- + S_2O_8^{--} + 2H_3O^+ = Br_2 + 2HSO_4^- + 2H_2O$$

but the oxidation of $Cl^-$ is so slow that a reasonable amount of this will still be left after the $Br_2$ is removed.

**Hypochlorite Method for $I^-$ and $Br^-$.** Place the solution in a small test tube and dilute with water to about 10 drops. Add 1 drop of diluted NaClO reagent (side shelf reagent diluted about 1:20) and a small globule of $CCl_4$, shake thoroughly, then let stand a moment and note the color of the $CCl_4$ layer. A pink color indicates $I_2$. If the color is tan instead of pink, $Br^-$ was present but no $I^-$.

$$2I^- + ClO^- + 2H_3O^+ = I_2 + Cl^- + 3H_2O$$

$$2Br^- + ClO^- + 2H_3O^+ = Br_2 + Cl^- + 3H_2O$$

If $I^-$ is present add reagent NaClO a drop at a time, mixing thoroughly after each addition. After the $I^-$ has been oxidized to $I_2$, excess NaClO will oxidize this further to $IO_3^-$.

$$I_2 + 5ClO^- + 3H_2O = 2IO_3^- + 5Cl^- + 2H_3O^+$$

As the $I_2$ color disappears the $Br^-$ is then oxidized and the tan color of $Br_2$ will show in the $CCl_4$ layer.

**Persulfate Method for $Cl^-$ When $I^-$ or $Br^-$ Is Present.** Place the solution in a small crucible, add 5 drops of 5 *N* $HNO_3$, dilute to about 3 ml., and add 20–30 mg. of $K_2S_2O_8$. Heat to boiling and keep hot until colorless. Let cool slightly and test for completeness of removal of $I^-$ and $Br^-$ by adding 2–3 small pieces of $K_2S_2O_8$ and heating again. When no further color shows, transfer the solution to a small beaker, cool, and add 1 drop of diluted $AgNO_3$ (1:10). If $Cl^-$ is present a marked opalescence will be seen. In this procedure more $I_2$ is oxidized to $IO_3^-$ than in the acetic solution described above. As a result there may be a transient precipitation of white $AgIO_3$ as the drop of $AgNO_3$ is added. However this will redissolve when the solution is mixed if the $AgNO_3$ is properly diluted.

**Nitrate.** If neither $I^-$ nor $Br^-$ is present, a portion of the original solution may be tested directly for $NO_3^-$ by either the brown ring or the ammonia test as previously described (p. 214). If either $I^-$ or $Br^-$ is present, the ammonia test may be used without interference, but for the brown ring test the following preliminary procedure should be used: To 2–3 drops of the original solution add 0.5 *N* $AgClO_4$ (see Note 5 following) solution, 1 drop at a time, shaking after each addition, until no further precipitate forms. Then, without filtering, add 1 *N* HCl one drop at a time, with shaking, until no further precipitate forms. Centrifuge and use the clear solution in the usual way for the brown ring test. The $AgClO_4$ precipitates $I^-$ and $Br^-$ as AgI and AgBr (along with a number of other Ag salts), and the HCl removes any excess of $Ag^+$ that might form a brown color of $Ag^\circ$ and thus interfere with the test for $NO_3^-$.

*Explanatory Notes.* (1) In the absence of halides the test for $ClO_3^-$ may be made directly by acidifying with $HNO_3$, adding 3–5 drops excess, then adding 1–2 drops of $AgNO_3$ solution and reducing any $ClO_3^-$ to $Cl^-$ with 1 drop of $H_2SO_3$. A white precipitate, AgCl, indicates $ClO_3^-$. If the precipitate is granular instead of curdy, add 3–4 drops more of $HNO_3$ and heat to dissolve any $Ag_2SO_3$, occasionally obtained by not having sufficient $HNO_3$ present and by adding a large excess of $Na_2SO_3$ ($Na_2SO_3 + HNO_3 = NaHSO_3 + NaNO_3$, $NaHSO_3 + 2AgNO_3 = Ag_2SO_3 + NaNO_3 + HNO_3$).

(2) If $ClO_3^-$ is absent the tests for halides may be made on the original solution (after removing $S^{--}$ with dilute $H_2SO_4$ and boiling), using the procedure described above (p. 226) after the silver halides have been converted to soluble zinc halides. In this case it is necessary to remove sulfide first

since it is a stronger reducing agent that $I^-$ or $Br^-$ and would interfere with their ready detection by the procedure given.

(3) Many other oxidizing agents may be used to test for $I^-$ besides the one recommended, but a hypochlorite is the only convenient one to use if one wishes to oxidize the $I_2$ to $HIO_3$ and obtain a test for $Br^-$ on the same solution.

(4) If, in the hypochlorite test for $Br^-$ in a solution containing $I^-$, the amount of $I_2$ liberated is so great that it forms a crystalline precipitate, the oxidation to $HIO_3$ is a little slow. In such a case it is simpler to filter, thus removing the crystalline $I_2$ and the $CCl_4$ globule; then add 1 drop of $CCl_4$ to the filtrate and continue the treatment with $Ca(ClO)_2$.

(5) $Ag_2SO_4$ may be used instead of $AgClO_4$, but it is so much less soluble that a fairly large volume must be used to remove moderate or large amounts of $I^-$ or $Br^-$.

(6) The interference of $I^-$ and $Br^-$ with the brown ring test for a nitrate lies in the fact that the $FeSO_4$ reagent always contains some $Fe_2(SO_4)_3$, and the latter, in the presence of strong $H_2SO_4$, will oxidize $I^-$ and $Br^-$ to $I_2$ and $Br_2$, whose colors might be mistaken for the test for $NO_3^-$.

$$2I^- + 2Fe^{+3} = I_2 + 2Fe^{++}$$

$$2Br^- + 2Fe^{+3} = Br_2 + Fe^{++}$$

The latter reaction occurs to only a small extent in cold solution even in the presence of concentrated $H_2SO_4$.

## ANALYSIS FOR METALS AND ACID RADICALS IN THE PRESENCE OF EACH OTHER

The procedures that have been described thus far have dealt separately with the metals and acid radicals. There are several cases, however, in which the systematic separation of the metallic groups might be seriously affected by the presence of certain acid radicals; and there are some instances in which the tests for particular acid radicals would be interfered with by the presence of certain metals.

In testing for acid radicals in a solution that may contain metals the following general procedure is commonly used: Add concentrated $Na_2CO_3$ solution until the solution is alkaline, then add 10–15 drops excess, heat nearly to boiling and let stand for several minutes with frequent shaking. Centrifuge and discard the precipitate. The solution is then tested for acid radicals in the usual way with some care taken to avoid trouble due to the high concentration of $CO_3^{--}$ thus added.

This procedure assumes that the carbonates of the common metals are sufficiently insoluble to precipitate in place of salts of the other acid radicals.

There are a few cases such as $CaC_2O_4$ in which some of the acid radical may be lost, but, ordinarily, sufficient will remain in solution to permit normal identification.

In the general scheme of analysis for the metals the two most common acid radicals to cause trouble are oxalate and phosphate. So long as the solution is distinctly acid various metal ions may be present along with these acid radicals; but, on neutralizing the solution, the corresponding salts will precipitate. Since the solution is kept acid while precipitating the first two groups, no difficulty will be encountered in Groups I and II. But when the solution is neutralized for the precipitation of Group III or made more strongly alkaline for the precipitation of Group IV, insoluble oxalates and phosphates of later group metals may precipitate. Since this difficulty is not encountered until the third group is precipitated, it is customary to test the solution from Group II for the presence of phosphate and oxalate and, if either test is positive, to introduce proper supplementary procedures to remove the corresponding acid radical before precipitating with $NH_4OH$.

To remove oxalate radical the simplest procedure consists in adding to the solution 15–20 drops of nitrohydrochloric acid, heating to boiling, and letting evaporate slowly (5–10 minutes) to dryness. The oxalate is slowly oxidized to $CO_2$.

$$3H_2C_2O_4 + 2NO_3^- + 2H_3O^+ = 6CO_2 + 2NO + 6H_2O$$

The residue may then be taken up with a little $HNO_3$ and tested once more for oxalate radical. Repeat the treatment with nitrohydrochloric acid if necessary.

To remove phosphate radical the most direct procedure consists in precipitating with $SnCl_4$. This reagent is prepared by dissolving 0.5 g. of the crystallized salt in cold water immediately before use. The precipitation of $Sn_3(PO_4)_4$ is carried out as follows: After removing $H_2S$ from the filtrate from Group II, dilute to 5 ml., add 5 drops of $(NH_4)_2HPO_4$ reagent if the test for phosphate radical was slight (stannic phosphate precipitates better when a moderate amount is being formed), add $NH_4OH$ carefully until the precipitate that forms will barely redissolve on shaking, then add 2 drops of 5 $N$ HCl. Heat to boiling, add 3 drops of the $SnCl_4$ solution, let digest a moment, then centrifuge, and test 1 drop of the solution for $PO_4^{-3}$ with $(NH_4)_2MoO_4$. If the test is still positive, add 1 drop more of the $SnCl_4$ solution and repeat, continuing as necessary until the test for $PO_4^{-3}$ is negative. Centrifuge and discard the precipitate. To the clear solution add 3 drops of 5 $N$ HCl, precipitate the Sn with $H_2S$, centrifuge, discard the precipitate and analyze the solution for Groups III–VI.

## *LABORATORY EXERCISES*

1. Known solutions containing the common acid radicals.

(*1*) $SO_4^{--}$, $C_2O_4^{--}$, $HS^-$, $I^-$, $Br^-$
(*2*) $SO_4^{--}$, $SO_3^{--}$, $I^-$, $Cl^-$, $NO_3^-$
(*3*) $C_2O_4^{--}$, $HAsO_4^{--}$, $CO_3^{--}$, $Br^-$, $ClO_3^-$
(*4*) $HPO_4^{--}$, $HAsO_4^{--}$, $I^-$, $NO_3^-$, $ClO_3^-$

These solutions contain the following amounts of substance per liter of solution: (*1*) 22 g. $Na_2SO_4$, 28 g. $Na_2C_2O_4$, 38 g. $Na_2S \cdot 9H_2O$, 6.6 g. KI, and 7.5 g. KBr; (*2*) 22 g. $Na_2SO_4$, 39 g. $Na_2SO_3 \cdot 7H_2O$, 6.6 g. KI, 8.3 g. NaCl, and 30 g. $NaNO_3$; (*3*) 28 g. $Na_2C_2O_4$, 12 g. $KH_2AsO_4$, 119 g. $Na_2CO_3 \cdot 10H_2O$, 7.5 g. KBr, 17 g. $KClO_3$, and 25 ml. of 5 *N* NaOH; (*4*) 21 g. $(NH_4)_2HPO_4$, 12 g. $KH_2AsO_4$, 6.6 g. KI, 30 g. $NaNO_3$, and 17 g. $KClO_3$.

Use small portions of the original solution to test for each of the acid radicals covered in this chapter. In addition to the regular tests for acid radicals present, special attention should be paid to irregularities that might develop in testing for the acid radicals not present. Several suggestions are made in the following notes:

(*a*) In numbers *1*, *3*, and *4* try the test for $Cl^-$ after the other halides have been removed.

(*b*) In numbers *1*, *2*, and *4* try both the brown ring and the ammonia tests for $NO_3^-$. Be sure to get satisfactory results in all cases.

(*c*) In number *2*, acidify with HCl and treat with $H_2S$ as if looking for $AsO_4^{-3}$. Note the precipitation of S° due to the oxidizing action of the solution.

(*d*) In numbers *3* and *4* precipitate $HAsO_4^{--}$ and $HPO_4^{--}$ with excess of Mg-mixture, centrifuge, wash, dissolve in HCl, remove As with $H_2S$ and test the clear solution for $H_3PO_4$.

# 14

# Qualitative Examination of Simple Dry Unknowns

## METALS AND ALLOYS

In this chapter the problem of identifying individual metals and of determining the metals present in mixtures of finely divided metals and in simple alloys will be discussed. The metals covered will include only those found in the ordinary groups of qualitative analysis and, at present, tests for the common non-metallic constituents (C, S, P, and Si) will be omitted. The procedures recommended for routine examination are capable of recognizing minor constituents down to the order of 0.5%. If one wishes to identify metals present in smaller proportions than this, it will usually be necessary to modify the scheme at least to the extent of starting with a larger sample for analysis and occasionally introducing preliminary operations by which the minor constituents may be separated from the main bulk of the major constituents by fractional precipitation or other appropriate means.

The general procedure suggested is to test small portions of the material separately with HCl, $HNO_3$, and HCl + $HNO_3$ to discover the most convenient and effective solvent; next, to dissolve a fair sample of the material in the reagent or reagents suggested by the preliminary tests, and then to carry out a systematic analysis of the resulting solution or solutions by the methods already developed for the common metals. Such a study should make it a simple matter to identify all the constituents which are present to the extent of 2–3%, and with reasonable care may even give satisfactory results down to a somewhat lower range, as above suggested. If it is desired to conduct a search for other minor constituents whose amounts may be even lower than this, the preliminary information now available as to the major composition of the unknown should make it fairly simple to work out special schemes for concentrating suspected minor constituents so that their identification will be made easier. The detailed discussion of this problem is considered to be outside the scope of this text.

## GENERAL PROCEDURE FOR METALS AND ALLOYS

Preliminary tests with common acids. Place 5 mg. of the material in a test tube, add 5 drops of 5 *N* HCl, warm moderately and note whether or not reaction takes place readily as shown by the evolution of $H_2$ at temperatures distinctly below boiling. If reaction occurs, continue the treatment until it is certain whether or not the material will dissolve completely in this acid. If complete solution is obtained, it is unnecessary to proceed further with the preliminary tests.

If the material does not dissolve effectively in HCl, test a fresh portion in the same way with 5 drops of 5 *N* $HNO_3$. In this case the evolution of oxides of nitrogen and the development of brown fumes may be taken as evidence that reaction is taking place. If the material will dissolve completely in $HNO_3$, this acid may be used to dissolve the larger sample for actual analysis.

If neither HCl nor $HNO_3$ proves to be an effective solvent, sometimes the metallic unknown may be dissolved in a mixture of the two. Try a fresh 5 mg. portion with a mixture of 2 drops of 5 *N* $HNO_3$ and 4 drops of 5 *N* HCl. In this case, as heat is applied, $Cl_2$ and NO may be evolved merely from the interaction of the two acids. If, however, the gases are evolved at the surface of the metal, the latter is probably dissolving, and in the course of a few minutes it is possible to ascertain if the metal will dissolve completely.

In some cases the metal or alloy may not dissolve readily in the 5 *N* acids, but will dissolve reasonably well if higher concentrations are employed. It is best, however, to try the more dilute acids first and only use the stronger acids if the former prove ineffective. When the stronger acids are to be tried, the following concentrations are the ones most commonly employed:

11–12 *N* HCl (the usual concentrated acid);

7.5 *N* or 10 *N* $HNO_3$ (the concentrated acid diluted either with an equal volume of water, or with half its volume of water);

3 parts by volume of concentrated HCl with 2 parts by volume of 5 *N* $HNO_3$.

If necessary, continue the preliminary tests using these more concentrated acids in the same manner as the dilute acids were tried until an effective solvent has been found or until the list has been exhausted. In carrying out each of the tests keep a careful record of the extent to which reaction appears to take place and the nature of the final residue left. When no single solvent can be found, it is frequently possible to use a second solvent to dissolve the residue left by a first solvent, and thus obtain complete solution of the alloy. In this case the two solutions are best kept apart and analyzed separately for the metals they contain.

The residues left after the reaction of a given solvent is complete may be classified as follows:

(*a*) After HCl: metals below hydrogen in the electromotive series (Cu, As, Sb, Bi, Hg, Ag), usually a dark flocculent residue;

(*b*) After $HNO_3$: metals of the arsenic division of Group II (Sn converted to $H_2SnO_3$, Sb converted to $H_3SbO_4$, and As in the presence of Sn as $Sn_3(AsO_4)_4$), white flocculent or very finely divided suspensions; also Cr, Al, and even Fe, which may become passive with $HNO_3$;

(*c*) After HCl + $HNO_3$: chlorides of Ag and Pb, and of Hg if the mercury is not fully oxidized to the mercuric state; and occasionally Sn and Sb as under (*b*), when excess of $HNO_3$ is used and the reaction continued long enough to convert the HCl + $HNO_3$ to essentially a solution of $HNO_3$ ($3Cl^- + NO_3^- + 4H_3O^+ = Cl_2 + NOCl + 6H_2O$);

(*d*) After any of the acids there may be left a flocculent residue of carbon or silicic acid, or a mixture of the two. This is usually dark in color and resembles the metallic residue insoluble in HCl.

These residues may be gotten into solution by proper use of the other acids or by certain special procedures. Thus the metals insoluble in HCl can be dissolved in $HNO_3$, except Sb, which is soluble in HCl + $HNO_3$. Stannic acid, etc., insoluble in $HNO_3$, can be filtered out, washed, and dissolved by boiling several minutes with concentrated HCl and then diluting moderately with water. Or it may be digested with a concentrated $Na_2S$ solution, a small residue of sulfides of other metals separated and discarded, and the sulfides of Sn, Sb, and As reprecipitated with cold dilute HCl and subjected to regular examination by the procedure used in the arsenic division of Group II. The residue insoluble in HCl + $HNO_3$, insofar as it consists of AgCl, $PbCl_2$, or $Hg_2Cl_2$, may be gotten into solution by reducing to the metallic form with metallic zinc in the presence of dilute $H_2SO_4$, centrifuging, washing, and dissolving the free metals in $HNO_3$. The formation of stannic acid, etc., in HCl + $HNO_3$ may be avoided by using excess of HCl. The residue consisting of carbon or silicic acid is insoluble in the common acids but should not be discarded until it has been subjected to the above treatments so as to dissolve any metallic constituents that may be present.

## DISSOLVING A REGULAR SAMPLE FOR ANALYSIS

On the basis of the preliminary tests, the procedure to be employed should be fairly clear. If HCl was effective on the small sample, use the same reagent to dissolve the larger portion. If HCl was ineffective but $HNO_3$ or HCl + $HNO_3$ gave a satisfactory solution, use whichever one of these seemed to work best. In case more than one solvent must be used the preliminary tests will tell which one to use first and suggest how the residue should be treated. If the material is not finely divided, it may react so slowly with the reagent that the student becomes impatient. It is important, however, to carry each reaction to an end. In all cases the treatment with the first solvent is as follows:

Place a 50 mg. sample of the unknown in a small crucible, add 15–20 drops of the selected solvent, cover with a watch glass to avoid undue evaporation if the reaction is slow, heat moderately until the reaction is taking place at a reasonable rate and continue the process until the reaction is complete. Remove the watch glass, let the solution evaporate to a volume of approximately 5 drops, dilute with water to 50 drops, centrifuge if necessary, and place the clear solution in a tincture bottle labelled with the identifying mark of the unknown and the name of the acid used as solvent. If in the use of $HCl + HNO_3$ a white precipitate appears on dilution, this may be BiOCl or SbOCl. In such a case decant the clear solution into a tincture bottle, dissolve the residue in a few drops of HCl and add this to the main solution. The excess acid thus used will probably be sufficient to prevent further hydrolysis.

If HCl was used as the solvent and a slight dark residue remains, wash this residue, transfer to a small crucible, add 5 drops of 5 *N* $HNO_3$, cover with a watch glass and boil gently for 2–3 minutes. Centrifuge if necessary and discard the residue, testing the solution for metals insoluble in HCl.

If $HNO_3$ was used as the solvent and a white, finely divided residue remains, use one of the following procedures on this residue:

(*a*) Wash the residue, transfer to a crucible, add 10 drops of concentrated HCl, cover with a watch glass, boil gently 2–3 minutes, and then add 25–30 drops of water. $H_3SbO_4$ will dissolve on boiling with HCl and will stay in solution on diluting if the water is added in moderate amount. Stannic acid, $H_2SnO_3$, and stannic arsenate, $Sn_3(AsO_4)_4$, will not dissolve in concentrated HCl but are converted to complex chlorides that dissolve when water is added. In this case no apparent change takes place until the solution is diluted.

(*b*) Wash the residue, transfer to a crucible, add 10 drops of 3 *N* $Na_2S$, warm moderately (well below boiling) for 1–2 minutes, then centrifuge, wash with diluted $Na_2S$, dissolve the precipitate in $HNO_3$, and combine this solution with the main $HNO_3$ solution. Treat the $Na_2S$ solution with cold, dilute HCl, 1 drop at a time until slightly acid; centrifuge, wash, and analyze this precipitate for As, Sb, and Sn according to the regular procedure for these metals.

If $HCl + HNO_3$ was used (keeping HCl in excess to avoid the precipitation of $H_2SnO_3$, etc.), any residue of Group I chlorides may be dissolved as follows: Centrifuge, wash, add 5 drops of water, 1 drop of conc. $H_2SO_4$, and 20–30 mg. of 20 mesh zinc. Warm slightly, and let stand 4–5 minutes with occasional shaking. Centrifuge, wash, discard the solution, dissolve the precipitate in $HNO_3$, centrifuge if necessary to remove carbon and $H_2SiO_3$, and analyze the solution for Ag, Pb, and Hg (including a test for Pb in Group II).

## REACTIONS OF THE METALS WITH THE COMMON ACIDS

Hydrochloric acid dissolves the metals above hydrogen in the electromotive series, i.e., all except Ag, Hg, Bi, Cu, Sb, and As, although the reaction is slow with coarse pieces of Co, Ni, Pb, and Cd. The typical reaction is represented by the following equation: $Zn^\circ + 2H_3O^+ = Zn^{++} + H_2 + 2H_2O$. With HCl, tin and iron are oxidized to their lower valences, forming $SnCl_2$ and $FeCl_2$, respectively. In the case of alloys containing a large amount of a metal insoluble in HCl, this metal may exert a protective action on the more electropositive metals so that the latter will not dissolve in the HCl.

Nitric acid dissolves all the common metals except Al, Cr, Sn, and Sb (and As in the presence of much Sn). In the case of the first two metals, in finely divided form reaction may take place fairly well, but coarse pieces do not dissolve as well as in HCl. With Sn and Sb reaction takes place readily, but insoluble white precipitates are formed—$H_2SnO_3$ and $H_3SbO_4$. The typical reaction where dissolving takes place with the 5 *N* acid is represented by the following equation:

$$3Cu + 2NO_3^- + 8H_3O^+ = 3Cu^{++} + 2NO + 12H_2O$$

In the case of As the reaction is commonly written as follows:

$$3As + 5NO_3^- + 5H_3O^+ = 3H_3AsO_4 + 5NO + 3H_2O$$

Alloys running high in Al or Cr do not dissolve effectively in $HNO_3$ unless in finely divided form. In these alloys the other metals present may thus be prevented from dissolving. Nitric acid regularly oxidizes the metals to the higher salt-forming valence; thus Fe forms $Fe(NO_3)_3$ rather than $Fe(NO_3)_2$; but in the cases of As and Hg the oxidation to $H_3AsO_4$ and $Hg(NO_3)_2$ will be incomplete unless the action of the reagent is continued for a little while after the metals are completely dissolved.

Hydrochloric and nitric acids, used together, dissolve all the common metals except Ag and Pb, these latter being acted upon fairly readily but converted to AgCl and $PbCl_2$. A small amount of $PbCl_2$ will stay in solution, and very small amounts of Ag are occasionally overlooked because of the fact that AgCl is appreciably soluble in the presence of a high concentration of chloride ion, forming $AgCl_3^{--}$. As in the case of $HNO_3$, the higher salts are formed rather than the lower salts; $FeCl^{++}$ and $SnCl_6^{--}$, instead of $Fe^{++}$ and $SnCl_4^{--}$. The typical reaction is shown in the following equation:

$$3Sb + 18Cl^- + 5NO_3^- + 20H_3O^+ = 3SbCl_6^- + 5NO + 30H_2O$$

In the case of As, however, the compound formed is $H_3AsO_4$ and the equation is similar to that given under $HNO_3$.

### *PROBLEMS AND LABORATORY EXERCISES ON METALS AND ALLOYS*

1. Try the action of HCl, $HNO_3$, and HCl + $HNO_3$ on each of the following (use first the 5 *N* reagents and then try the higher concentrations suggested on p. 232 for those cases in which the dilute acids react slowly):

Al (coarse, smooth wire), Fe, Sb, Cu, bronze turnings, brass turnings, lead amalgam.

2. Write the equations for all the reactions that take place in 1.
3. Outline a method for dissolving an alloy of Ag–Ni–Sb, and write the equations for the reactions involved.
4. Explain why Al dissolves less readily in $HNO_3$ than in HCl.
5. Explain why HCl does not dissolve the Zn in a sample of brass.

## SIMPLE NON-METALLIC DRY UNKNOWNS

Since metals and alloys have already been considered, the materials now under discussion will be limited to oxides, hydroxides, acids, and salts.

Some of these materials are soluble in water; some may require acids or special reagents to prepare solutions for analysis. In the dissolving process reactions may occur which must be recognized by definite test or observation in order to identify the material of which the original unknown consists.

**Three types of oxides may be distinguished:** (1) Basic oxides, soluble in water to give an alkaline solution, or soluble in acids by simple neutralization; (2) acidic oxides, soluble in water to give an acid solution, or soluble in bases by simple neutralization; (3) higher oxides insoluble in water or in non-reducing acids, but soluble in HCl, or in $HNO_3$ if a reducing agent is present. The three types may be illustrated by (1) CaO, CuO; (2) $CrO_3$, $As_2O_3$; (3) $PbO_2$.

Calcium oxide is slightly soluble in water giving the alkaline solution known as lime water.

$$CaO + H_2O = Ca^{++} + 2OH^-$$

CuO is insoluble in water, but dissolves in HCl.

$$CuO + 2H_3O^+ = Cu^{++} + 3H_2O$$

$CrO_3$ is soluble in water, giving an acid solution.

$$CrO_3 + 2H_2O = H_3O^+ + HCrO_4^-$$

$As_2O_3$ is slightly soluble in water, but dissolves more readily in $NH_4OH$ or NaOH.

$$As_2O_3 + 2NH_4OH + H_2O = 2NH_4^+ + 2H_2AsO_3^-$$

$PbO_2$ is insoluble in water, but dissolves in HCl, or in $HNO_3 + H_2O_2$.

$$PbO_2 + 3Cl^- + 4H_3O^+ = PbCl^+ + Cl_2 + 6H_2O$$

$$PbO_2 + H_2O_2 + 2H_3O^+ = Pb^{++} + O_2 + 4H_2O$$

In stating that the materials dissolve as indicated it must not be concluded that these reactions always take place rapidly. Not infrequently time, reagents, and unknown all are wasted by the impatience of the analyst who fails to carry the most effective solvent reaction to completion.

**Two types of hydroxides may be distinguished:** Those soluble in water to give an alkaline solution, e.g., $NaOH$; and those soluble in acids by neutralization, e.g., $Zn(OH)_2$.

$$Zn(OH)_2 + 2H_3O^+ = Zn^{++} + 4H_2O$$

**Four types of salts may be distinguished:** (1) Normal salts, such as $CuSO_4$ and $BaCO_3$, which do not contain hydrogen or hydroxyl radical, although by hydrolysis they may form acid, alkaline, or neutral solutions; (2) acid salts, such as $NaHCO_3$ and $Na_2HPO_4$, which do contain hydrogen radical, although by hydrolysis such materials may form neutral or alkaline as well as acid solutions; (3) basic salts, such as $BiONO_3$ and $MgOHCl$, which contain hydroxyl radical, although by hydrolysis such materials may form neutral or acid as well as alkaline solutions; and (4) double salts, such as $MgNH_4PO_4$ and $KAl(SO_4)_2 \cdot 12H_2O$, which may be normal, acid, or basic in composition, but which, in addition, have two positive radicals other than hydrogen or, in a few cases, two negative radicals other than hydroxyl.

In analyzing materials of the above types it is necessary to dissolve them and apply confirmatory tests for the constituent materials. In the dissolving process reactions may occur with the formation of products whose recognition is necessary if the original material is to be identified. Typical reactions of the common solvents are considered in the following paragraphs.

## REACTIONS OF WATER AS SOLVENT

1. Hydrolysis of normal salt to give acid reaction (with or without precipitation of hydroxide or basic salt).

*Examples:*

$AlCl_3$ dissolves readily in water, giving a distinctly acid solution, but with negligible precipitation of $Al(OH)_3$.

$BiCl_3$ reacts readily with water, giving a strongly acid solution, but with almost complete precipitation of the bismuth as $BiOCl$.

2. Hydrolysis of normal salt to give basic reaction (with or without precipitation of acid or acid salt).

*Examples:*

$Na_2CO_3$ dissolves readily in water, giving a clear, distinctly alkaline solution.

$NaAlO_2$ reacts readily with water, giving a strongly alkaline solution, but with moderate precipitation of the aluminum as $H_3AlO_3$ [$Al(OH)_3$].

3. Hydrolysis of acid salt to give a basic reaction.

*Example:*

$NaHCO_3$ dissolves readily in water, and if heat is applied undergoes sufficient hydrolysis to cause loss of $CO_2$ as a gas. When the solution is cooled it is found to react distinctly alkaline. ($NaHCO_3$, dissolved in cold water, reacts practically neutral.)

4. Hydrolysis of a basic salt to give an acid reaction.

*Examples:*

BiOCl on boiling with water is converted to a slight extent into $Bi(OH)_3$ and HCl.

$Cr(OH)_2NO_3$ dissolves in water, giving an acid reaction.

5. Hydration of a basic or acidic oxide to form the corresponding base or acid.

*Examples:*

CaO reacts with water to form $Ca(OH)_2$;

$As_2O_5$ reacts with water to form $H_3AsO_4$.

6. During the preparation of the water solution loss of volatile reaction products of hydrolysis may occur.

*Example:*

$CO_2$, $H_2S$, and $NH_3$ may be formed by hydrolysis of carbonates, sulfides, and certain ammonium salts to a sufficient extent to escape from the solution when the latter is heated. In a few extreme cases these materials may be overlooked unless tests are applied while treating with water or fairly promptly thereafter.

## REACTIONS OF HCl AS A SOLVENT

Assuming that any simple, dry unknown will be tested with water first and dissolved in that solvent if possible, it is only necessary to include at this point the reactions of HCl with substances insoluble or slightly soluble in water. In the case of substances which dissolve largely in water, with slight precipitation by hydrolysis, this situation will be recognized by the decrease in volume of the solid, and it will be sufficient ordinarily to analyze the aqueous solution. With substances such as $BiCl_3$, which hydrolyze to such an extent that the volume of the flocculent precipitate may be approximately that of the original salt, it will be desirable both to examine the water solution and to dissolve the residue in HCl and analyze this solution to distinguish between such possibilities as $BiCl_3$ and BiOCl.

1. Neutralization of hydroxides, oxides, and basic salts.

*Examples:*

$Cu(OH)_2$, ZnO, and BiOCl are all insoluble in water, but dissolve readily in HCl. The equations are as follows:

$$Cu(OH)_2 + 2H_3O^+ = Cu^{++} + 4H_2O$$

$$ZnO + 2H_3O^+ = Zn^{++} + 3H_2O$$

$$BiOCl + 3Cl^- + 2H_3O^+ = BiCl_4^- + 3H_2O$$

2. Formation of a slightly ionized acid (which may or may not be stable).
*Examples:*

$CaCO_3$, ZnS, and $MgNH_4PO_4$ are all insoluble in water, but dissolve readily in HCl. The equations are as follows:

$$CaCO_3 + 2H_3O^+ = Ca^{++} + CO_2 + 3H_2O$$

$$ZnS + 2H_3O^+ = Zn^{++} + H_2S + 2H_2O$$

$$MgNH_4PO_4 + 2H_3O^+ = Mg^{++} + NH_4^+ + H_2PO_4^- + 2H_2O$$

3. Reduction of certain strong oxidizing agents.
*Examples:*

$MnO_2$, $Co_2O_3$, and to a lesser extent $PbCrO_4$, are all insoluble in water, but dissolve on boiling with strong HCl, the latter being oxidized to $Cl_2$. The equations are as follows:

$$MnO_2 + 2Cl^- + 4H_3O^+ = Mn^{++} + Cl_2 + 6H_2O$$

$$Co_2O_3 + 2Cl^- + 6H_3O^+ = 2Co^{++} + Cl_2 + 9H_2O$$

$$2PbCrO_4 + 8Cl^- + 16H_3O^+ = 2PbCl^+ + 3Cl_2 + 2Cr^{+++} + 24H_2O$$

(Reduction in the case of $PbCrO_4$ may be incomplete.)

4. Formation of complex chlorides. To a minor extent such compounds as $PbI_2$, CuCl, and even AgCl dissolve in strong HCl solutions.

$$PbI_2 + 3Cl^- = PbCl_3^- + 2I^-$$

$$CuCl + Cl^- = CuCl_2^-$$

$$AgCl + Cl^- = AgCl_2^-$$

5. During the dissolving in HCl, volatile reaction products may be formed which should be identified by direct tests while the reactions are taking place. These include especially $CO_2$ from carbonates, $H_2S$ from sulfides, $Cl_2$ from reaction with strong oxidizing agents, and $SO_2$ from sulfites.

6. It will be noted that HCl is not an effective solvent for compounds of the first group metals even though reaction takes place readily. The insolubility of the chlorides of these metals makes it desirable to avoid the use of HCl in such cases.

## REACTIONS OF $HNO_3$ AS A SOLVENT

The introductory statement under HCl concerning the precipitates formed by hydrolysis of salts applies equally well to the use of $HNO_3$.

1. Neutralization of hydroxides, oxides, and basic salts: To the extent to which these dissolve in $HNO_3$ without oxidation the reactions are similar to those given under HCl. It may be noted that BiOCl dissolves in $HNO_3$ by neutralization ($BiOCl + 2H_3O^+ = Bi^{+3} + Cl^- + 3H_2O$) giving a solution in which the test for chloride may be obtained. In a similar way $BiONO_3$ is soluble in HCl as well as in $HNO_3$.

2. Formation of a slightly ionized acid: Except in those cases in which $HNO_3$ may act as an oxidizing agent (covered under 3, following) this phase of the reactions of $HNO_3$ is the same as that of HCl.

3. Oxidation of reducing agents.

*Examples:*

NiS, $Fe_3O_4$, and CuI are soluble in $HNO_3$, the following equations indicating the reactions:

$$3NiS + 2NO_3^- + 8H_3O^+ = 3Ni^{++} + 2NO + 3S + 12H_2O$$

$$3Fe_3O_4 + NO_3^- + 28H_3O^+ = 9Fe^{+3} + NO + 42H_2O$$

$$6CuI + 4NO_3^- + 16H_3O^+ = 6Cu^{++} + 3I_2 + 4NO + 24H_2O$$

4. During the dissolving in $HNO_3$ volatile reaction products may be formed, which should be identified by direct test or observation while the reactions are taking place. These include especially $CO_2$ from carbonates, $NO_2$ (brown fumes indicating reduction of some of the $HNO_3$), and $I_2$ (violet vapors as the $I_2$ volatilizes from the boiling solution).

5. $HNO_3$ is not an effective solvent for compounds of Sn and Sb even though reaction may take place readily. Under ordinary conditions of reaction such compounds are converted to the white precipitates, $(H_2SnO_3)_x$ and $SbO(OH)_3$ (the latter slightly soluble in water).

## REACTIONS OF $HCl + HNO_3$ AS A SOLVENT

The reactions of aqua regia combine to some degree the reactions of the two acids when used separately, in some cases dissolving individual substances better than either acid by itself, in other cases proving less effective than one or the other of the two acids would be.

1. Neutralization of oxides, hydroxides, and basic salts, and formation of slightly ionized acids. These reactions are the same as with the individual acids insofar as no oxidation, reduction, or complex formation takes place. In such cases only a single equation is required:

$$Cu(OH)_2 + 2H_3O^+ = Cu^{++} + 4H_2O$$

$$Ni_3(PO_4)_2 + 4H_3O^+ = 3Ni^{++} + 2H_2PO_4^- + 4H_2O$$

2. Oxidation of reducing agents. The same reducing agents will be oxidized by aqua regia as by $HNO_3$, the equations for these reactions being the same as with $HNO_3$. In those oxidations in which $HCl + HNO_3$ are more effective than $HNO_3$ alone, the usual explanation is found in the formation of complex chlorides. However, there are some cases in which oxidation by $Cl_2$ (from interaction of HCl and $HNO_3$) appears to be more effective than by $HNO_3$. In the treatment of insoluble iodides with aqua regia, there is more extensive oxidation than with $HNO_3$ by itself, significant amounts of the iodine being oxidized to iodic acid. Also, on prolonged digestion in a hot solution, oxalic acid is oxidized to carbon dioxide. The following equations indicate typical reactions:

$$3As_2S_5 + 10NO_3^- + 10H_3O^+(+ Cl^-) = 6H_3AsO_4 + 15S + 10NO + 6H_2O$$

$$3HgS + 2NO_3^- + 12Cl^- + 8H_3O^+ = 3HgCl_4^{--} + 2NO + 3S + 12H_2O$$

$$3Cu(AsO_2)_2 + 4NO_3^- + 10H_3O^+ = 3Cu^{++} + 6H_3AsO_4 + 4NO + 6H_2O$$

$$3Fe_3O_4 + NO_3^- + 28H_3O^+ = 9Fe^{+3} + NO + 42H_2O$$

$$3Hg_2I_2 + 14NO_3^- + 24Cl^- + 20H_3O^+ = 6HgCl_4^{--} + 14NO + 6IO_3^- + 30H_2O$$

$$3SnS + 4NO_3^- + 18Cl^- + 16H_3O^+ = 3SnCl_6^{--} + 3S + 4NO + 24H_2O$$

$$3CaC_2O_4 + 2NO_3^-(+ Cl^-) + 8H_3O^+ = 3Ca^{++} + 6CO_2 + 2NO + 12H_2O$$

Note that in dissolving compounds of Sn and Sb with aqua regia it is important to use considerable excess of HCl in order to avoid possible precipitation of $(H_2SnO_3)_x$ or $H_3SbO_4$ when evaporating to remove excess of acid.

$$3Sb_2S_5 + 10NO_3^- + 36Cl^- + 40H_3O^+ = 6SbCl_6^- + 15S + 10NO + 60H_2O$$

but:

$$SbCl_6^- + 2NO_3^- + 3H_3O^+ = H_3SbO_4 + 2NO + 3Cl_2 + 3H_2O$$

3. Reduction of oxidizing agents: The presence of HCl in the mixture means that practically the same oxidizing agents may be reduced in the dissolving process as would be reduced by the HCl alone. The reaction takes place less readily, however, than it would in the latter case.

$$MnO_2 + 2Cl^- + 4H_3O^+(+ NO_3^-) = Mn^{++} + Cl_2 + 6H_2O$$

In such a case it would be impossible to recognize the oxidizing action of the dry unknown since $Cl_2$ would also be evolved through the action of $HNO_3$ on the HCl.

$$3Cl^- + NO_3^- + 4H_3O^+ = Cl_2 + NOCl + 6H_2O$$

## SPECIAL REACTIONS FOR SUBSTANCES INSOLUBLE IN ACIDS

These substances, as far as the range of this book is concerned, may be divided into three groups: insoluble sulfates, insoluble halides, and ignited oxides. For each group there is available a fairly simple procedure that may be tried if the acids fail.

**Insoluble Sulfates.** The fact that these substances do not dissolve in HCl or in $HNO_3$ is explained by the strength of sulfuric acid. Since this compound is highly ionized, there is no effective lowering of concentration of negative ion by the hydrogen ion introduced. Thus, since the nitrates and chlorides are generally highly ionized, no significant chemical dissolving of the sulfates will occur. Therefore, it becomes necessary to resort to some procedure that will separate the metal from the sulfate radical. This may be done by boiling for a little while (10–15 minutes) with a concentrated solution of sodium carbonate. This converts the insoluble sulfates into carbonates, which are insoluble in water but readily soluble in dilute $HNO_3$. Even barium sulfate, the least soluble of the sulfates, is converted to the carbonate to an extent of greater than 50%, if the reaction is continued for a reasonable time.

$$BaSO_4 + CO_3^{--} = BaCO_3 + SO_4^{--}$$

If necessary, the sodium carbonate solution, containing sulfate ion, may be carefully decanted (or separated more completely by centrifuging) and the residue boiled with a fresh portion of sodium carbonate solution. The first sodium carbonate solution is used to test for sulfate radical, the final residue is dissolved in $HNO_3$ and this solution examined for metals whose sulfates are insoluble.

$$BaCO_3 + 2H_3O^+ = Ba^{++} + 3H_2O + CO_2$$

**Insoluble Halides.** In these cases, as with the insoluble sulfates, the lack of effective dissolving in the dilute acids is due to the fact that the hydrogen halides (HI, HBr, and HCl) are strong acids, so there is no significant lowering of concentration of negative ion when the hydrogen ion is added. However, with the more concentrated acids other reactions may occur in certain cases which may result finally in a dissolving of the insoluble halide. Thus, with $HNO_3$ or aqua regia all the insoluble iodides and bromides except those of Ag are slowly oxidized to $I_2$, $HIO_3$, and $Br_2$, and mercurous and cuprous salts are oxidized to $Hg^{++}$ and $Cu^{++}$. The general procedure suggested for separating halide from metal in the case of insoluble halides depends upon the fact that the metals which form insoluble halides are relatively much more noble than zinc; therefore if the insoluble halides are treated with metallic zinc, in the presence of dilute $H_2SO_4$, the zinc will, in the course of a few minutes, reduce the other metals to the metallic state, with corresponding accumulation of the halide radicals in solution as halide ions.

$$2AgI + Zn^{\circ} = 2Ag^{\circ} + Zn^{++} + 2I^{-}$$

The excess zinc and the other free metals may then be filtered out and the filtrate examined in the ordinary way for the individual halides.

**Ignited Oxides.** The hydroxides of the metals dissolve readily in acids, but on being heated are converted to oxides which dissolve less readily in acids. In the case of $Fe_2O_3$, $Al_2O_3$, $Cr_2O_3$, $SnO_2$, and NiO (commonly referred to as the ignited oxides), after prolonged heating at high temperatures, the material dissolves so slowly in HCl that the process becomes very tedious even at best. In this situation fusion of the dry material with sodium pyrosulfate, $Na_2S_2O_7$, may be tried, the acid anhydride, $SO_3$, at higher temperature than can be obtained in aqueous solution, combining with the basic oxide to form a sulfate.

$$Na_2S_2O_7 = Na_2SO_4 + SO_3$$

$$Fe_2O_3 + 3SO_3 = Fe_2(SO_4)_3$$

This treatment is reasonably effective for $Fe_2O_3$, $Al_2O_3$, and $Cr_2O_3$, much less so for $SnO_2$ and NiO. The procedure commonly used for $SnO_2$ is ignition at 400°–500°C. with a mixture of $Na_2CO_3$ and S°, forming $Na_2SnS_3$ ($2SnO_2 + 2Na_2CO_3 + 9S = 2Na_2SnS_3 + 3SO_2 + 2CO_2$). After cooling and extracting with water, the solution may be examined for Sn by the method used with the solution in $(NH_4)_2S_x$ after separating the As-division from the Cu-division in Group II. In the case of NiO probably the simplest method of attack is by reduction to the free metal through heating strongly in a current of hydrogen ($NiO + H_2 = Ni + H_2O$). The resulting metal is soluble in $HNO_3$. This latter procedure may also be used for $SnO_2$, the resulting Sn dissolving in HCl or HCl + $HNO_3$.

## PROCEDURE FOR STUDY OF SIMPLE NON-METALLIC DRY UNKNOWNS

1. Test small portions (5 mg.) separately with 5–10 drops of $H_2O$, HCl, $HNO_3$, and aqua regia, heating if necessary. Note the extent of dissolving in each solvent, and the formation of gaseous reaction products which should be identified as part of the evidence concerning the composition of the dry unknown.

2. If the substance dissolves completely in water or any of the common acids, prepare a solution using 30–50 mg. of the dry unknown, using the solvent which worked best in the preliminary tests, and applying tests for gaseous reaction products while the unknown is dissolving.

3. Analyze the solution for metals and acid radicals (other than those of the reagents used as solvents).

4. Prepare a list of substances that would account for the following observed facts: (*a*) method of dissolving, (*b*) reaction products observed during the dissolving process, (*c*) cations and anions found in the solution.

5. Devise and carry out further tests as necessary to distinguish between individual members in this list.

6. If the substance cannot be dissolved effectively by any of the above solvents, apply further special tests on the unknown as follows:

(*a*) Place 5 mg. in a crucible, add 10 drops of 3 *N* $Na_2CO_3$ solution, heat to boiling, and keep just at the boiling point for 5–10 minutes. Centrifuge, wash, and test the solubility of the precipitate in 5 *N* $HNO_3$.

$$\underline{BaSO_4} + CO_3^{--} = \underline{BaCO_3} + SO_4^{--}$$

(*b*) Place 5 mg. in a test tube, add 5 drops of water, 1–2 drops of $H_2SO_4$ and 20 mg. of 20-mesh metallic zinc. Warm slightly and let stand with occasional shaking for 5 minutes. Centrifuge, wash, and test the solubility of the residue in 5 *N* $HNO_3$.

$$2AgBr + Zn^\circ = 2Ag^\circ + Zn^{++} + 2Br^-$$

$$3Ag^\circ + 4H_3O^+ + NO_3^- = 3Ag^+ + NO + 6H_2O$$

(*c*) Place 5 mg. in a crucible. Add 0.1–0.2 g. of $Na_2S_2O_7$, and heat gently over an open flame until the $Na_2S_2O_7$ melts. Raise the temperature gradually until $SO_3$ fumes are definitely recognized; then cover with a watch glass and continue heating at this last temperature for 5–10 minutes. Finally raise the temperature until the mass fumes strongly; then remove the flame and let cool. When fairly cool, add 5 drops of concentrated $H_2SO_4$, warm cautiously until the fusion mass dissolves, and let cool to below 100°C. Add 25–30 drops of distilled water. If a fine residue still persists, boil gently for 2–3 minutes to complete the solution.

$$3Na_2S_2O_7 + Fe_2O_3 = 3Na_2SO_4 + Fe_2(SO_4)_3$$

7. If one of the special procedures is required, use the one which worked best in the preliminary tests, carrying 10–20 mg. of the unknown through this procedure. In the case of insoluble sulfates or halides, the residue after reaction with $Na_2CO_3$ or with Zn and $H_2SO_4$ is separated, washed, dissolved in $HNO_3$ and this solution tested for the various metals concerned. The

$Na_2CO_3$ (or $Zn + H_2SO_4$) solution is examined for the corresponding acid radicals. In the case of fusion with $Na_2S_2O_7$ the final solution is tested for those metals whose strongly heated oxides are fairly inert toward aqueous acids.

**Tests to Be Applied During the Dissolving Process.** When using water as the solvent, particularly if the solution is boiled, tests for $NH_3$, $CO_2$, and $H_2S$ may be obtained occasionally as a result of hydrolysis. Ammonia is recognized by odor or by turning moist red litmus paper blue. Carbon dioxide is identified by passing the gas into a solution of $Ca(OH)_2$, obtaining a white precipitate of $CaCO_3$. Hydrogen sulfide is detected by noting the odor or by the black stain of PbS given to moist lead acetate paper by the escaping gas.

When using HCl as the solvent, tests for $CO_2$, $H_2S$, $SO_2$, and $Cl_2$ should be applied, positive tests showing the presence of a carbonate, sulfide, sulfite, and strong oxidizing agent, respectively. Sulfur dioxide is recognized by its characteristic odor. Chlorine is identified in this particular case by testing the gases coming off with a piece of filter paper moistened with KI solution, a brown stain of free iodine being considered a test for $Cl_2$.

When using $HNO_3$ as the solvent, a test for $CO_2$ should be made; also one should look for brown fumes of $NO_2$, evidence that some reducing agent is being oxidized by the $HNO_3$. Many reducing agents will produce this effect: sulfides, sulfites, iodides (if not too insoluble), stannous salts, ferrous salts, arsenites, etc. Of these, sulfides are oxidized to free sulfur, usually dark and spongy, which may be lifted out with a glass rod, rinsed and burned to $SO_2$ of characteristic odor; iodides and bromides may be oxidized to $I_2$ (violet vapor) and $Br_2$ (brown fumes). These latter may be dissolved in $CCl_4$, with production of violet- or brown-colored solution, respectively.

When using $HCl + HNO_3$ as the solvent, a test for $CO_2$ should be made. Various oxidations may occur, which are not easy to recognize because of the action of HCl and $HNO_3$ with each other. Free sulfur, $I_2$ and $Br_2$ may be identified as suggested under nitric acid, and the final solution may contain $H_2SO_4$ and $HIO_3$, derived from sulfide or sulfite, and iodide, respectively. To test for $HIO_3$, treat with $FeSO_4$ and extract with $CCl_4$. $HIO_3$ is thus reduced to $I_2$ which imparts a pink to violet color to the $CCl_4$.

## SUPPLEMENTARY STUDIES

After a simple, dry unknown has been dissolved and the solution (or solutions) analyzed for metals and acid radicals, there may still be some question as to which of several substances one has in hand. In such a case it is frequently possible to devise some supplementary test to distinguish between these different substances. Several typical situations are covered in the following discussion.

**A. Hydrates or Anhydrous Substances.** The most obvious test to distinguish between a hydrate and an anhydrous substance consists in placing 10–15 mg. of the material in a dry test tube, then holding the test tube in a horizontal position, warming the closed end cautiously to 110°–120°C. and looking for moisture condensing on the cool portion of the tube. The majority of the common salts having water of crystallization lose much of this at temperatures slightly over 100°C. Thus $Na_2CO_3 \cdot H_2O$ changes to the anhydrous salt at 100°, $CuSO_4 \cdot 5H_2O$ loses 4 molecules of $H_2O$ at 110°, $CaSO_4 \cdot 2H_2O$ loses 1.5 molecules of $H_2O$ at 128°; but $CaSO_4 \cdot 0.5H_2O$ requires 163° to change to the anhydrous $CaSO_4$, and $CuSO_4 \cdot H_2O$ loses $H_2O$ only at 250°C. or above. These latter temperatures are in the range at which the less stable acids, hydroxides, and acid and basic salts decompose. $H_2C_2O_4$ decomposes at 186°, $Pb(OH)_2$ at 145°, $H_4As_2O_7$ at 206°, $NaHCO_3$ at 270°, $Al(OH)_3$ at 300°, $HAsO_3$ at 358°, etc. From these data it will be evident that the results of this test will require interpretation in the light of the particular substances between which one is trying to distinguish. It is necessary also to draw a somewhat arbitrary line between water of hydration or constitution and incidental hygroscopic moisture. If a given substance forms no definite hydrate, the amount of moisture observed is usually quite small as compared with that obtained even from a mono-hydrate.

Another point of difference between a hydrate and an anhydrous substance may be found frequently in their colors. $Cu(OH)_2$ is blue, CuO black; $Cd(OH)_2$ is white, CdO brown; $CuSO_4 \cdot 5H_2O$ is blue, $CuSO_4$ grayish white, etc. On the other hand, ZnO and $Zn(OH)_2$ are both white, as are $BaCl_2$ and $BaCl_2 \cdot 2H_2O$ and $Na_2CO_3$, $Na_2CO_3 \cdot H_2O$, and $Na_2CO_3 \cdot 10H_2O$.

**B. Acid, Normal, and Basic Salts.** In the case of salts insoluble in water there is no simple qualitative test to distinguish between an acid salt and a normal salt or a basic salt. $Ca_3(PO_4)_2$ and $CaHPO_4$ are both insoluble in water, as are $MgCO_3 \cdot 3H_2O$, $3MgCO_3 \cdot Mg(OH)_2 \cdot 3H_2O$, and BiOCl. In some cases decomposition by heating may be employed, as suggested under A, with identification of water as a reaction product. A more general type of test might consist in treating the unknown with a normal salt which would react by double decomposition to form a normal salt as a reaction product. Thus $CaHPO_4$ would react slowly with $AgNO_3$ to form $Ag_3PO_4$, $Ca(NO_3)_2$, and $HNO_3$. $PbSO_4 \cdot PbO$ would react with $Na_2S$ forming PbS, $Na_2SO_4$, and NaOH. In cases of this sort, after taking care to avoid any interference that might result from excess of the reagent, the acidity or alkalinity of the resulting aqueous solution would serve to show the nature of the unknown salt.

Usually there is a difference in solubility of acid, normal, and basic salts, the acid salts commonly being more soluble and the basic salts less soluble than the normal salts. Frequently, the acid salt is moderately soluble whereas the normal salt is insoluble; or the normal salt is moderately soluble whereas the basic salt is insoluble. Thus $Ca(H_2PO_4)_2$ is soluble in water, $CaHPO_4$ and $Ca_3(PO_4)_2$ are insoluble; $MgCl_2$ is soluble in water, $Mg_2OCl_2$ is insoluble. In a few cases, where both the acid salt and the normal salt are distinctly soluble, the normal salt may be more soluble than the acid salt; for example, $KHCO_3$ and $NaHCO_3$ are less soluble than $K_2CO_3$ and $Na_2CO_3$, respectively. In cases where there is a sufficient difference in solubility so that one may be dissolved in water whereas the other requires acid or other solvents, the method of dissolving furnishes a definite means of distinguishing the two substances.

In cases where the substances being considered are both soluble in water, the reaction of the resulting solution toward litmus, in conjunction with the dissociation constants of the corresponding acid and base, will permit a fairly clear distinction between the two. Thus $Na_2CO_3$, a salt derived from a strong base and a very weak acid, dissolves in water to give a moderately alkaline solution; $NaHCO_3$, a salt derived from a strong base and a moderately weak acid, dissolves in water to give a faintly alkaline solution. (In this case the solution must be kept cool at all times since $NaHCO_3$ decomposes to form $Na_2CO_3$ at elevated temperatures.) $Na_2C_2O_4$, a salt derived from a strong base and a fairly strong acid, dissolves in water to give essentially a neutral solution. $NaHC_2O_4$, an acid salt derived from a strong base and a fairly strong acid, dissolves in water and undergoes secondary ionization to give a moderately acid solution. $FeCl_3$, a normal salt derived from a very weak base and a strong acid, dissolves in water to give a moderately acid solution, etc.

**C. Oxides or Hydroxides and Insoluble Normal or Basic Salts.** In this case the chief point to be emphasized is the need of testing the unknown for the acid radical of any acid used to prepare a solution for analysis. For example, both $Bi(OH)_3$ and $BiOCl$ are white compounds, and in the routine procedure both would be dissolved in HCl and the resulting solutions analyzed. Obviously, a test for $Cl^-$ in the HCl solution would have no significance. It would be necessary to treat the unknowns in such a way as to identify the chloride radical present in the second case. This might be done by dissolving a separate portion of the unknown in $HNO_3$ instead of HCl and using the solution for the test in question. Similarly, $BiONO_3$ should be dissolved in HCl in order that the nitrate radical may be identified. It is also possible in many cases to boil the unknown for a short time with concentrated $Na_2CO_3$ solution, forming the corresponding hydroxide or carbonate of the metal as a precipitate, but dissolving the negative radical ($2BiOCl + CO_3^{--} = Bi_2O_2CO_3 + 2Cl^-$). On centrifuging, the test for the acid radical may be obtained in the clear solution. Also, it is possible to treat salts of the less electro-positive metals with metallic zinc in the presence of dilute $H_2SO_4$ or HCl, thus reducing the metal to the free state but getting the acid radical in solution so that it may be identified. This procedure is especially suited to $PbCl_2$, $PbBr_2$, $PbI_2$, CuI, $HgI_2$, etc., which may be dissolved in oxidizing acids, but with oxidation of the acid radical during the dissolving process.

An isolated case that occasionally causes trouble is found in trying to identify $Br^-$ in $HgBr_2$. This compound, slightly soluble in water, like $HgCl_2$ is very slightly ionized so that in the presence of $HNO_3$ or $H_2SO_4$ the common oxidizing agents do not convert the $Br^-$ to $Br_2$. If HCl or $Cl^-$ is added, however, the $Hg^{++}$ is converted to a complex ion, $HgCl_4^{--}$, which makes the $Br^-$ available for oxidation.

**D. Use of Common Indicators to Distinguish Between the Normal and Acid Sodium (or Potassium) Salts of the Common Acids.** Having identified the acid radical by the ordinary chemical test, the problem of deciding whether the salt in question is a normal salt or an acid salt—and of distinguishing between the acid salts if more than one type is formed—can be attacked by the use of a few common indicators and correlating the data thus obtained with the ionization constants of the acids in question. For this purpose four indicators are commonly used: phenolphthalein, litmus paper, methyl red and methylene blue, and methyl orange.

Phenolphthalein is colorless in solutions with a pH less than 8.3. At 8.3 a faint pink starts to show, developing to a light red at a pH of 8.7, and a bright red at 9 or higher. Thus only those salts which hydrolyze to give a concentration of $OH^-$ of $10^{-5}$ or greater will show a bright red color when 1–2 drops of phenolphthalein are added to the dilute aqueous solution. These include $K_2S$, $K_3PO_4$, $K_2CO_3$, KHS, $K_3AsO_4$, and $K_2HPO_4$.

Litmus paper is put out in two colors, red and blue. The blue will change to red if placed in contact with a solution having a pH of 6 or less, and the red litmus paper will turn blue if placed in contact with a solution having a pH of 8 or higher. Solutions between these two values have little effect on either color of litmus paper. Thus dilute aqueous solutions of salts which hydrolyze to only a negligible extent, or in which the dissociation of an acid anion offsets its hydrolysis, will show a neutral reaction toward litmus. This includes such salts as $KNO_3$, KCl, KBr, KI, $K_2SO_4$, and $K_2HAsO_4$.

Methyl red plus methylene blue shows a light purple color in solutions having a pH of 4.6 or less, steel gray in the range from pH 4.8 to 5.4, and green at a pH of 5.6 or higher. Thus those acid salts in which the acid anions are moderately weak acids will supply sufficient $H_3O^+$ by direct dissociation to give a neutral or acid reaction toward this indicator. This includes such salts as $K_2Cr_2O_7$, $KH_2PO_4$, $KHSO_3$, $KH_2AsO_4$, $KHC_2O_4$ and $KHSO_4$.

Methyl orange gives a light red color in solutions with a pH of less than 3.8, a salmon pink (light orange) in the range from pH 3.8 to 4.2, and yellow when the pH is greater than 4.2. Thus, only those acid salts in which the acid anion undergoes fairly significant dissociation with small or no hydrolysis will show an acid reaction with methyl orange. These cases include $KHSO_3$, $KH_2AsO_4$, $KHC_2O_4$, and $KHSO_4$.

In trying these tests a small portion of the salt (5–10 mg.) is placed in a small beaker, covered with 5–10 ml. of water and then stirred without heating for a short time with a stirring rod to prepare the solution for testing. It is unnecessary to dissolve all the salt for these tests. Next add 1 drop of phenolphthalein solution. If solution remains colorless, test its reaction with red litmus paper. If no change, try the action on blue litmus. If blue litmus changes to red, divide the solution into two equal parts testing one with 1 drop of methyl red plus methylene blue, and the other with 1 drop of methyl orange. If at any stage other indications are obtained (e.g., solution is red or pink with phenolphthalein, red litmus turns blue, or blue litmus does not turn red), it is unnecessary to go further with the tests since one may know in advance how they would turn out, namely, alkaline indications by the later indicators.

In the one case of attempting to distinguish between a carbonate and a bicarbonate it is important to use a freshly prepared solution and to avoid heating the solution. Otherwise there may be sufficient loss of $CO_2$ from the solution of a bicarbonate to shift the pH so that a red color will show with phenolphthalein.

The explanation of the procedure just given in terms of the reactions of the anions of the salt in dilute aqueous solution involves calculations based on the water constant and the ionization constants of the several acids. In the case of normal salts, hydrolysis is the only reaction which needs to be considered, the net reaction being represented by one of the equations:

$$A^- + H_2O = HA + OH^- \tag{1}$$

$$A^{--} + H_2O = HA^- + OH^- \tag{2}$$

$$A^{---} + H_2O = HA^{--} + OH^- \tag{3}$$

If HA, $HA^-$, or $HA^{--}$ is a strong acid, hydrolysis will not take place and the solution will have a pH of 7 (or nearer 6 if one takes $CO_2$ from the air into account). Thus the sodium or potassium salts of $HNO_3$, HCl, HBr, and HI undergo no hydrolysis.

As the ionization constants of HA, $HA^-$, or $HA^{--}$ become smaller, the reactions with water take place to increasing extents and the resulting solutions become more and more alkaline. At the one extreme stands $HSO_4^-$ with an ionization constant of $3 \times 10^{-2}$; at the other, $HS^-$ with an ionization constant of $1 \times 10^{-15}$; whereas $K_{HSO_3^-}$ lies in between at $5 \times 10^{-6}$. The hydrolysis of $Na_2SO_4$, $Na_2SO_3$, and $Na_2S$ in 0.01 *M* solutions will now be calculated.

**A. Hydrolysis of 0.01 *M* $Na_2SO_4$**

$$SO_4^{--} + H_2O \rightleftarrows HSO_4^- + OH^-$$

$$K_{HSO_4} = 3 \times 10^{-2} \qquad K_W = 1 \times 10^{-14}$$

$$[SO_4^{--}] = 0.01 - x = 0.01$$

$$[HSO_4^-] = x$$

$$[OH^-] = 1 \times 10^{-7} + x$$ (Since in this case the $[OH^-]$ supplied by direct dissociation of water probably cannot be neglected.)

$$\frac{[H_3O^+] \times [SO_4^{--}]}{[HSO_4^-]} = 3 \times 10^{-2}$$

$$[H_3O^+] \times [OH^-] = 1 \times 10^{-14}$$

substituting 0.01 for $[SO_4^{--}]$ and $\dfrac{1 \times 10^{-14}}{1 \times 10^{-7} + x}$ for $[H_3O^+]$

$$\frac{1 \times 10^{-14} \times 0.01}{(x + 1 \times 10^{-7})(x)} = 3 \times 10^{-2}$$

$$3 \times 10^{-2}x^2 + 3 \times 10^{-9}x = 1 \times 10^{-14}$$

$$x^2 + 1 \times 10^{-7}x = \tfrac{1}{3} \times 10^{-14}$$

$$(x + 0.5 \times 10^{-7}) = \sqrt{\tfrac{1}{3} \times 10^{-14} + (0.5 \times 10^{-7})^2}$$

$$= 0.764 \times 10^{-7}$$

$$x = 0.764 \times 10^{-7} - 0.5 \times 10^{-7}$$

$$= 0.264 \times 10^{-7} = [HSO_4^-]$$

$$[OH^-] = 1.264 \times 10^{-7}$$

$$[H_3O^+] = \frac{1 \times 10^{-14}}{1.264 \times 10^{-7}} = 0.79 \times 10^{-7}$$

$$pH = 7.10$$

Assuming $[HSO_4^-] = [OH^-]$

$$[OH^-] = \frac{[H_3O^+] \times 0.01}{3 \times 10^{-2}} = \frac{1 \times 10^{-14}}{[H_3O^+]}$$

$$[H_3O^+] = \sqrt{\frac{3 \times 10^{-16}}{0.01}} = \sqrt{3 \times 10^{-14}} = 1.75 \times 10^{-7}$$

(which means, merely, that the $[OH^-]$ formed by hydrolysis is less than that supplied by dissociation of water).

**B. Hydrolysis of 0.01 *M* $Na_2S$**

$$K_{HS^-} = 1 \times 10^{-15} \qquad K_W = 1 \times 10^{-14}$$

$$S^{--} + H_2O = HS^- + OH^-$$

In this case,

$$[HS^-] = [OH^-]$$

$$[S^{--}] = 0.01 - [HS^-] = 0.01 - [OH^-]$$

$$\frac{[H_3O^+] \times [S^{--}]}{[HS^-]} = 1 \times 10^{-15}$$

$$[H_3O^+] \times [OH^-] = 1 \times 10^{-14}$$

Substituting $[OH^-]$ for $[HS^-]$, $\frac{1 \times 10^{-14}}{[H^+]}$ for $[OH^-]$, and $0.01 - [OH^-]$ for $[S^{--}]$,

$$\frac{[H_3O^+]^2 \times \left(0.01 - \frac{1 \times 10^{-14}}{[H_3O^+]}\right)}{1 \times 10^{-14}} = 1 \times 10^{-15}$$

$$0.01[H_3O^+]^2 - 1 \times 10^{-14}[H_3O^+] = 1 \times 10^{-29}$$

$$[H_3O^+]^2 - 1 \times 10^{-12}[H_3O^+] = 1 \times 10^{-27}$$

$$[H_3O^+] - 0.5 \times 10^{-12} = \sqrt{0.25 \times 10^{-24} + 1 \times 10^{-27}}$$

$$= 0.501 \times 10^{-12}$$

$$[H_3O^+] = 1.001 \times 10^{-12}$$

i.e., pH $\cong$ 12 and $Na_2S$ is 99.9% hydrolyzed in 0.01 *M* solution.

**C. Hydrolysis of 0.01 *M* $Na_2SO_3$**

$$K_{HSO_3^-} = 5 \times 10^{-6} \qquad K_W = 1 \times 10^{-14}$$

$$SO_3^{--} + H_2O = HSO_3^- + OH^-$$

$$[SO_3^{--}] \cong 0.01$$

$$[HSO_3^-] = (OH^-)$$

$$\frac{[H_3O^+] \times 0.01}{[OH^-]} = 5 \times 10^{-6}$$

$$[OH^-] = \frac{0.01[H_3O^+]}{5 \times 10^{-6}} = \frac{1 \times 10^{-14}}{[H_3O^+]}$$

$$[H_3O^+] = \sqrt{\frac{1 \times 10^{-14} \times 5 \times 10^{-6}}{0.01}} = \sqrt{5 \times 10^{-18}}$$

$$= 2.24 \times 10^{-9}$$

In this case it may be demonstrated that $[SO_3^{--}] = 0.01$.

$$[HSO_3^-] = \frac{1 \times 10^{-14}}{2.24 \times 10^{-9}} = 4.46 \times 10^{-6}$$

$$[SO_3^{--}] = 0.01 - 4.46 \times 10^{-6} \cong 0.01$$

$$\text{Extent of hydrolysis} = \frac{4.46 \times 10^{-6}}{0.01} = 4.46 \times 10^{-4} = 0.04\%$$

In the case of acid salts the final condition in the solution depends on the interplay of three different reactions:

(1) Direct dissociation of the acid anion.

(2) Possible hydrolysis of the acid anion to form a weak acid.

(3) Neutralization of $H_3O^+$ and $OH^-$ liberated by reactions (1) and (2).

The extent to which the first reaction takes place is determined by the ionization constant of the acid anion, and the extent to which the second reaction takes place is determined by the water constant and the ionization constant of the acid formed by hydrolysis. If reactions (1) and (2) take place to a sufficient extent to liberate appreciable amounts of $H_3O^+$ and $OH^-$, then these will combine to form water and carry the other two reactions along in equivalent amounts. As an example of a case in which all three effects must be considered, one may calculate the pH of 0.01 *M* $NaHCO_3$.

1st reaction:

$$HCO_3^- + H_2O = H_3O^+ + CO_3^{--} \qquad K_{HCO_3} = 5 \times 10^{-11}$$

2nd reaction:

$$HCO_3^- + H_2O = H_2CO_3 + OH^- \qquad K_{H_2CO_3} = 3 \times 10^{-7}$$

3rd reaction:

$$H_3O^+ + OH^- = 2H_2O \qquad K_W = 1 \times 10^{-14}$$

Considering the first reaction by itself:

$$\frac{[H_3O^+] \times [CO_3^{--}]}{[HCO_3^-]} = 5 \times 10^{-11}$$

$$[H_3O^+] = \sqrt{5 \times 10^{-13}} = 7.1 \times 10^{-7}$$

Considering the second reaction by itself:

$$\frac{[H_3O^+] \times [HCO_3^{--}]}{[H_2CO_3]} = 3 \times 10^{-7}$$

If

$$[HCO_3^-] = 0.01$$

$$[H_2CO_3] = [OH^-]$$

$$[H_3O^+] \times [OH^-] = 1 \times 10^{-14}$$

$$[OH^-] = \frac{0.01[H_3O^+]}{3 \times 10^{-7}} = \frac{1 \times 10^{-14}}{[H_3O^+]}$$

$$[H_3O^+] = \sqrt{\frac{3 \times 10^{-7} \times 1 \times 10^{-14}}{0.01}} = \sqrt{3 \times 10^{-19}}$$

$$= 5.5 \times 10^{-10}$$

$$[OH^-] = \frac{1 \times 10^{-14}}{5.5 \times 10^{-10}} = 1.8 \times 10^{-5}$$

Since $[H_3O^+] \times [OH^-]$ is much greater than $K_W$, a significant neutralization reaction will occur which will carry the two other reactions along together. This permits the three equations to be combined into a single net reaction:

$$HCO_3^- + H_2O = H_3O^+ + CO_3^{--}$$

$$HCO_3^- + H_2O = H_2CO_3 + OH^-$$

$$H_3O^+ + OH^- = 2H_2O$$

Adding and cancelling:

$$2HCO_3^- = H_2CO_3 + CO_3^{--}$$

On this basis, in the final solution $(H_2CO_3) = (CO_3^{--})$ and the calculation of the concentration of $H_3O^+$ is made by using the combined constant $K_{1,2H_2CO_3} = 3 \times 10^{-7} \times 5 \times 10^{-11} \cong 15 \times 10^{-18}$

$$\frac{[H_3O^+]^2 \times [CO_3^{--}]}{[H_2CO_3]} = 15 \times 10^{-18}$$

But since $[H_2CO_3] = [CO_3^{--}]$

$$[H_3O^+] = \sqrt{15 \times 10^{-18}} = 3.9 \times 10^{-9}$$

As an example of a case in which only the first reaction takes place to a significant extent one may calculate the pH of a 0.01 *M* solution of $KHSO_4$.

1st reaction:

$$HSO_4^- + H_2O = H_3O^+ + SO_4^{--}$$

2nd reaction:

$$HSO_4^- + H_2O = H_2SO_4 + OH^- \text{ (does not take place)}$$

3rd reaction:

Does not take place

$$\frac{[H_3O^+] \times [SO_4^{--}]}{[HSO_4^-]} = 3 \times 10^{-2}$$

$$[H_3O^+] = [SO_4^{--}]$$

$$[HSO_4^-] = 0.01 - [H_3O^+]$$

$$\frac{[H_3O^+] \times [H_3O^+]}{0.01 - [H_3O^+]} = 3 \times 10^{-2}$$

$$[H_3O^+]^2 + 3 \times 10^{-2}[H_3O^+] = 3 \times 10^{-4}$$

$$[H_3O^+] + 1.5 \times 10^{-2} = \sqrt{3 \times 10^{-4} + 2.25 \times 10^{-4}}$$

$$[H_3O^+] = (2.29 - 1.5) \times 10^{-2}$$

$$= 0.79 \times 10^{-2}$$

Whence

$$pH = 2.10$$

In the intermediate range between $HCO_3^-$ and $HSO_4^-$ there are cases in which the second and third reactions take place to some extent but not sufficiently to warrant the assumption that reactions (1) and (2) are practically equal. For example, consider the case of $NaHC_2O_4$.

$$K_{H_2C_2O_4} = 4 \times 10^{-2} \qquad K_{HC_2O_4^-} = 5 \times 10^{-5}$$

1st reaction:

$$HC_2O_4^- + H_2O = H_3O^+ + C_2O_4^{--}$$

2nd reaction:

$$HC_2O_4^- + H_2O = H_2C_2O_4 + OH^-$$

If one calculates the $[H_3O^+]$ on the assumption that these two reactions are taking place to approximately equal extents:

$$[H_3O^+] = \sqrt{4 \times 10^{-2} \times 5 \times 10^{-5}} = \sqrt{2 \times 10^{-6}} = 1.42 \times 10^{-3}$$

But if one calculates the $[H_3O^+]$ that would be obtained by direct dissociation of $HC_2O_4^-$ in 0.01 *M* solution:

$$[H_3O^+] = \sqrt{1 \times 10^{-2} \times 5 \times 10^{-5}} = \sqrt{5 \times 10^{-7}} = 7.1 \times 10^{-4}$$

Since $7.1 \times 10^{-4}$ is smaller than $1.42 \times 10^{-3}$, and since the effect of the second and third reactions must lower the concentration of $H_3O^+$ derived from the first reaction, it is evident that the first calculation was based on a false premise.

In the case of acid salts of the general types $HA^{--}$ and $H_2A^-$, the reactions involve the same types as those just considered, but care must be taken to use the correct constants for the calculations. This may be shown by reference to $Na_2HPO_4$ and $NaH_2PO_4$.

$$HPO_4^{--} + H_2O = H_3O^+ + PO_4^{---} \qquad (K_{HPO_4^{--}} = 3.6 \times 10^{-13})$$

$$HPO_4^{--} + H_2O = H_2PO_4^- + OH^- \qquad (K_{H_2PO_4^-} = 2 \times 10^{-7})$$

$$[H_3O^+] = \sqrt{3.6 \times 10^{-13} \times 2 \times 10^{-7}} = \sqrt{7.2 \times 10^{-20}}$$

$$= 2.66 \times 10^{-10}$$

Whence

$$pH = 9.57$$

$$H_2PO_4^- + H_2O = H_3O^+ + HPO_4^{--} \qquad (K_{H_2PO_4^-} = 2 \times 10^{-7})$$

$$H_2PO_4^- + H_2O = H_3PO_4 + OH^- \qquad (K_{H_3PO_4} = 1 \times 10^{-2})$$

Assuming the two reactions take place in equivalent amounts:

$$[H_3O^+] = \sqrt{1 \times 10^{-2} \times 2 \times 10^{-7}} = \sqrt{20 \times 10^{-10}} = 4.47 \times 10^{-5}$$

For 0.01 *M* $NaH_2PO_4$, direct dissociation yields:

$$[H_3O^+] = \sqrt{1 \times 10^{-2} \times 2 \times 10^{-7}} = \sqrt{20 \times 10^{-10}} = 4.47 \times 10^{-5}$$

The fact that these two values for $[H_3O^+]$ are identical for 0.01 *M* $H_2PO_4^-$ indicates that in this solution the main reaction is direct dissociation of the acid anion and that hydrolysis, with neutralization, must take place to a very minor extent so that the actual concentration of $H_3O^+$ will be only slightly less than this figure.

From calculations of these various types the following table has been constructed.

TABLE XI. pH OF 0.01 *M* SOLUTIONS OF SODIUM SALTS OF THE COMMON ACIDS

| *Salt* | *pH of 0.01 M Solution* |
|---|---|
| $Na_2S$ | 12 |
| $Na_3PO_4$ | 11.88 |
| $Na_2CO_3$ | 11.12 |
| $NaHS$ | 11.00 |
| $Na_3AsO_4$ | 10.61 |
| $Na_2HPO_4$ | 9.57 |
| $Na_2SO_3$ | 8.66 |
| $NaHCO_3$ | 8.41 |
| $Na_2SO_4$ | 7.10 |
| $NaNO_3$ | 7.00 |
| $NaCl$ | 7.00 |
| $NaBr$ | 7.00 |
| $NaI$ | 7.00 |
| $NaH_2PO_4$ | 4.35 |
| $NaHSO_3$ | 3.7 |
| $NaHC_2O_4$ | 3.2 |
| $NaHSO_4$ | 2.1 |

## LABORATORY EXERCISES

1. Try the action of HCl, $HNO_3$, and HCl + $HNO_3$ on each of the following (use first the 5 *N* reagents and then try the higher concentrations suggested for those cases in which the dilute acids are not effective): $CaCO_3$, $Fe(OH)_3$ (freshly precipitated), AgBr (freshly precipitated), cinnabar (red HgS).

2. Place about 5 mg. of $BaSO_4$ in a crucible, add 20 drops of 3 *N* $Na_2CO_3$, cover with a watch glass, heat to boiling and keep just at the boiling point for 5 minutes. Centrifuge, wash, and test the solubility of a portion of the residue in dilute HCl. If the residue does not dissolve completely, return it to the crucible, repeat the treatment with $Na_2CO_3$, and test again with HCl.

3. Place about 5 mg. of $Cr_2O_3$ in a crucible. Add 0.2 g. of $Na_2S_2O_7$, cover with a watch glass and heat carefully to quiet fusion. (At first considerable frothing may occur from decomposition of $NaHSO_4$ present: $2NaHSO_4 = Na_2S_2O_7 + H_2O$.) Keep in a fused condition for 5–10 minutes, then raise the temperature until moderate fumes of $SO_3$ appear. After 2–3 minutes let cool. Add 5 drops of concentrated $H_2SO_4$, heat until the salts dissolve, let cool again, and pour into 25–30 drops of distilled water. Note whether any of the $Cr_2O_3$ has dissolved. Has the reaction been complete?

4. Treat 5 drops of $AgNO_3$ solution with a slight excess of KBr, centrifuge and wash. To the precipitate add 5–10 drops of water, 1 drop of conc. $H_2SO_4$, and 20 mg. of granular zinc (about 20 mesh). Let stand with occasional stirring for 4–5 minutes, centrifuge, and wash thoroughly. Test the clear solution for $Br^-$ and test the residue for complete solubility in $HNO_3$. To the $HNO_3$ solution add a drop of HCl. Result?

# 15

# Complex Dry Unknowns

These are mixtures of several of the following types of material: free metals, acids, basic oxides or hydroxides, higher oxides, salts (acid, normal, basic). The same solvents are used as in the case of the simple dry unknowns, but various interactions may occur when water is added to the mixture, so that it is impossible to determine the substances present in the original system by the ordinary chemical reactions unless some mechanical scheme of separation into a series of simple dry unknowns can be introduced as a preliminary step. In the absence of such a scheme, the procedure adopted here consists in treating the complex mixture with water; centrifuging, analyzing the water solution for cations and anions which are then reported as such; and finally trying, so far as chemical reactions permit, to determine the substances present in the residue left insoluble in water.

## REACTIONS DURING PREPARATION OF THE WATER SOLUTION

In connection with simple non-metallic dry unknowns attention was called to the variety of ways in which these substances may behave when treated with water. In the case of complex dry unknowns, these reactions will be supplemented by the various possible interactions that may take place when several simple substances are brought together in the presence of water. An extensive review of reactions in aqueous solutions is involved in attempting to summarize the possibilities.

**1. Precipitation of Metathesis.** Two soluble salts such as sodium chloride and silver nitrate may be mixed in the original unknown. In the absence of water they do not react at ordinary temperature, but when water is added they dissolve and then react to form a precipitate of silver chloride. If two or more ions are introduced that may form precipitates with another ion, the least soluble compound may be expected to precipitate first, then the others in order. Thus if a limited amount of silver nitrate is mixed with excess of both sodium iodide and sodium chloride, the precipitate, after equilibrium has been established, will be silver iodide—not silver chloride or a mixture of the two.

**2. Precipitation by Hydrolysis.** In the case of soluble salts of the weaker acids, such as sodium sulfide or sodium carbonate, hydrolysis takes place to such an extent that the water solution is fairly alkaline. When a mixture of sodium carbonate and ferric chloride is treated with water, there are present carbonate, bicarbonate, and hydroxyl ions as possible reagents to precipitate the ferric ion. Under such conditions the relative solubility of the different compounds in the presence of these varying concentrations of reagents determines which shall form as a precipitate. In the cases of $Fe^{+3}$, $Al^{+3}$, $Cr^{+3}$, $Sn^{+4}$, $Sb^{+3}$, and $Sb^{+5}$, the precipitates with soluble carbonates are hydroxides rather than carbonates ($Sb^{+3}$ forms $Sb_2O_3$). With soluble sulfides only $Al^{+3}$ and $Cr^{+3}$ still precipitate as hydroxides rather than sulfides.

**3. Neutralization Reactions.** Oxalic acid, arsenious oxide, potassium acid sulfate, and ferric chloride are typical substances that dissolve in water to form acid solutions. Sodium hydroxide, calcium oxide, and potassium carbonate are typical substances that dissolve in water to form basic solutions. When dry unknowns containing substances from these two lists are treated with water, neutralization occurs and the resulting solution will be acid, neutral, or alkaline according to the proportions in which the two types are mixed. In the cases of metals whose hydroxides are amphoteric, the reaction of an alkaline solution may go so far as to dissolve compounds which are insoluble in water, placing the corresponding anions in the water solution. Thus the solution prepared with water from a mixture containing a large amount of sodium carbonate and a small amount of aluminum chloride will contain more or less of the aluminum as aluminate ion.

**4. Oxidation-reduction Reactions.** Soluble oxidizing and reducing agents may form a stable dry mixture, but when water is added the usual oxidation-reduction reactions will occur, conditioned by the proportions in which the reagents are present and the acidity or alkalinity of the solution. If the solution is moderately acid (because of the presence of $KHSO_4$, *et al.*), a large range of oxidation-reduction reactions may occur, involving such reducing agents as stannous salts, sulfides, sulfites, ferrous compounds, iodides, bromides, chlorides, arsenites, oxalates, antimonous salts, mercurous salts, manganous salts, etc., and such oxidizing agents as red lead, permanganates, chlorates, dichromates, chromates, manganese dioxide, ferric salts, cupric salts, arsenates, antimonic salts, silver salts, etc. If the solution is alkaline (because of the presence of $Na_2CO_3$, *et al.*), a much more limited range of oxidation-reduction reactions may occur. Permanganates are readily reduced to manganese dioxide (in acid solution the reduced product is usually manganous ion) by such reagents as stannous salts, sulfides, sulfites, ferrous salts, arsenites, manganous salts, etc.; chlorates and chromates are reduced somewhat less readily by these same reagents; and arsenic, copper, antimony, bismuth, and silver compounds, if not too insoluble, may be reduced to the free metal by a stannous salt.

**5. Formation of Complexes.** Several reactions are available by which substances insoluble in water are dissolved through the formation of complex ions. Thus a mixture of potassium iodide and mercuric chloride might be expected to form the bright red precipitate of mercuric iodide, but if excess of potassium iodide is present the precipitate dissolves readily with formation of the colorless mercuric iodide ion, $HgI_4^{--}$. This reaction may occur in acid, neutral or alkaline solution. Bismuth also forms a complex iodide ion, $BiI_4^-$, but only in acid solution. If the solution contains too little free acid, a red precipitate, bismuth oxy-iodide, BiOI, may form.

A second type of mixture that behaves in this general way may be made with alkali sulfide and salts of the arsenic division metals. With small amounts of sodium sulfide the sulfides of arsenic, antimony, and tin may precipitate, dissolving in excess of sodium sulfide to form thio-anions containing the metals. Stannic chloride with excess of sodium sulfide will form thiostannate ion, $HSnS_3^-$, found in the water solution, and misbehaving to the extent of forming a precipitate of stannic sulfide when nitric acid is added to acidify the alkaline solution as the first step in the systematic analysis for metals. However, the only metals of Groups I, II, and IV that might be present in such a solution are arsenic, antimony, tin, and mercury (with high concentration of sulfide ion mercuric sulfide forms a complex ion, $HgS_2^{--}$); hence, the solution may be acidified directly with HCl, the precipitate being examined for mercury and the arsenic division metals, the filtrate being treated first with HCl and $H_2S$ to insure complete removal of arsenic, and then examined for Groups III, V, and VI. In the case of the sulfides of arsenic, which are soluble in alkalis—even in ammonium hydroxide—a mixture containing considerable excess of sodium carbonate will form oxy-thio arsenites or arsenates which will be found in the water solution. This case is not readily distinguished from the previous one, except that the former will show a marked test for sulfide ion in the water solution.

A third type of mixture involves the use of an ammonium salt and sodium or potassium carbonate to produce ammonium hydroxide in the aqueous solution. With such a mixture it is possible to find silver, copper, cadmium, etc., in the water solution in the form of complex ammonia ions. It is also possible with such a mixture to convert mercuric salts to white precipitates of the mercuric amines ($HgNH_2Cl$, etc.), and mercurous salts to black precipitates of the corresponding mercuric amine and metallic mercury. In the presence of iodide ion, mercuric salts may even be converted to the reddish-brown precipitate that is obtained with ammonia and Nessler's reagent.

It is obvious that a complex mixture may contain substances such that more than one of these various reactions may take place. In such a case it is necessary to have available information as to relative solubility, relative strength as oxidizing or reducing agents, relative stability of complex ions, etc., in order to say which of several reactions competing for a particular reagent will occur most readily and which least readily. It is only from such facts that one may recognize the range of variations in composition of water solution and residue that may result from varying the proportions in which the same components are mixed.

## PROCEDURES FOR COMPLEX DRY UNKNOWNS

**Preparation of Water Solution.** Place 50 mg. of the well-mixed sample in a beaker or crucible, add 1–2 ml. of water, cover with a watch glass, heat to boiling and apply tests for $CO_2$, $H_2S$, $NH_3$, etc., which may be given off because of reactions occurring when the water is added. Keep the solution hot for 4–5 minutes, stirring occasionally. Let the solution cool, centrifuge if necessary, wash 2–3 times with cold water and place the clear solution in a 5 ml. tincture bottle labelled "Water Solution of Dry No. —." This solution is set aside to be tested later for the various cations and anions.

**Preliminary Tests with Acids.** If the dry unknown does not dissolve completely in water, transfer a 5 mg. test portion of the residue to a test tube, add 5 drops of 5 *N* HCl and note whether or not the residue dissolves. Heat if necessary and look for evidence of reaction products ($CO_2$, $H_2S$, $Cl_2$, $H_2$) that may be identified later when dissolving a larger portion for actual analysis. If the test portion dissolves completely in HCl, this acid is selected as the solvent for the main portion of the residue. If HCl does not dissolve the sample completely, place another 5 mg. test portion in a clean test tube and try the action of 5 drops of 5 *N* $HNO_3$, heat and note possible formation of $CO_2$, $S°$, $I_2$, etc., which may be identified later when treating the main portion of the residue with this acid. If the second test portion dissolves completely in $HNO_3$ (except for possible $S°$), this acid is used for the treatment of the rest of the residue. If neither HCl nor $HNO_3$ separately proves to be an effective solvent, a third test portion is treated with a mixture of 3 drops of 5 *N* HCl and 2 drops of 5 *N* $HNO_3$. Heat to boiling and note possible evolution of $CO_2$. Continue the reaction in each of the above cases long enough to make certain that the material will not dissolve in the solvent being tried before proceeding to the next one. Occasionally the materials may dissolve rather slowly in what is actually the best solvent for the given case. If there is real doubt as to whether the materials are still dissolving, it may be desirable to centrifuge, wash, add a fresh portion of the acid in question, continue the treatment 4–5 minutes longer, and then evaporate a little of the fresh acid solution to dryness and look for a residue as evidence that the solvent is still effective.

If none of the three preliminary tests indicates a satisfactory solvent, it may still be possible in certain cases to dissolve the residue by successive treatment with the different acids without resorting to special procedures such as treatment with Zn° and dilute $H_2SO_4$, boiling with concentrated $Na_2CO_3$ solution, or fusion with $Na_2S_2O_7$. Thus a mixture of $Ag_2CO_3$ and $Sb_2O_5$ might be dissolved by treating first with $HNO_3$ to dissolve the $Ag_2CO_3$; then, after centrifuging and washing, the residue of $Sb_2O_5$ could be dissolved by boiling with HCl. It is unnecessary to waste more of the residue on a preliminary trial of this procedure. Instead, proceed directly to treat the rest of the material insoluble in water with acids.

**Dissolving the Residue in Acids.** If the preliminary tests showed HCl to be an effective solvent, use this acid on the main sample. If HCl was unsatisfactory but $HNO_3$ dissolved the test portion, use this acid on the main sample. If a mixture of the two proved most effective, use this combination in the ratio of 2–3 parts of HCl to 1 part of $HNO_3$. If no single solution in the acids could be prepared, treat the residue from the water solution first with $HNO_3$, then centrifuge, wash, and treat the residue with HCl, and, if a residue still remains, centrifuge, wash, and treat it with HCl + $HNO_3$. The separate solutions should be kept for analysis. Any residue left insoluble in these acids is tested by one or more of the special procedures, as suggested under the discussion of simple dry unknowns.

In treating the residue with a given acid, place the residue in a crucible with 15–20 drops of the selected acid, heat if necessary, and apply tests for such significant reaction products as may be given off from the solution. If the material does not dissolve readily, cover with a watch glass and let the reaction continue for 10–15 minutes if necessary, keeping the solution near the boiling point. After the reaction with a given acid is complete, centrifuge if necessary, evaporate the solution to a volume of 5 drops to remove any large excess of acid, then dilute to 30–35 drops and place in a tincture bottle labelled with the name of the acid used and the identifying number of the unknown. If more than one acid solution is prepared, these are placed in separate tincture bottles and analyzed individually.

**Special Procedures for Substances Insoluble in Acids.** One or more of the three procedures described under the dissolving of simple dry unknowns may be used effectively for practically all cases. There is a slight advantage in using them in the following order: (*a*) boil with concentrated $Na_2CO_3$ solution, (*b*) treat with metallic Zn and dilute $H_2SO_4$, (*c*) fuse with $Na_2S_2O_7$.

**(a) $Na_2CO_3$ Treatment.** Place the residue in a crucible, add 15–20 drops of 3 *N* $Na_2CO_3$ solution, cover with a watch glass, and boil gently for 5–10 minutes. Centrifuge, wash, reserve the clear solution to test for $SO_4^{--}$ and $CrO_4^{--}$, and try dissolving the residue in 5 drops of 5 *N* $HNO_3$. If the residue does not dissolve completely, it may be boiled a second time with $Na_2CO_3$ solution before using the next procedure, since $BaSO_4$ is not fully transposed to $BaCO_3$ in a single treatment. The resulting $HNO_3$ solution should be filtered if necessary and tested for Pb, Ba, Sr, and Ca.

**(b) $Zn^\circ + H_2SO_4$ Treatment.** Wash residue from (*a*) and transfer it to a test tube. Add 5 drops of $H_2O$, 1 drop of concentrated $H_2SO_4$ and 15–20 mg. of granulated zinc (about 20 mesh), warm slightly until there is a moderate evolution of $H_2$, and let stand with occasional shaking for 5 minutes. Centrifuge and wash. Set the clear solution aside to test for $I^-$, $Br^-$, and $Cl^-$, and treat the residue with 10–15 drops of 5 *N* $HNO_3$. The excess of Zn and any free metals formed by the reducing action of the Zn will dissolve, leaving as a residue such inert materials as the ignited oxides. Filter if necessary and analyze the solution for Ag and possibly Hg and Cu.

**(c) $Na_2S_2O_7$ Fusion.** Wash the residue left insoluble in $HNO_3$ after treatment with $Zn^\circ + H_2SO_4$, place in a small crucible and dry at 100°–150°. Add 0.3 g. of $Na_2S_2O_7$ and heat cautiously over the open flame of a Bunsen burner. When the mass is in a state of quiet fusion, cover with a watch glass and raise the temperature until there is a moderate evolution of $SO_3$ fumes. Maintain at this temperature for 5–10 minutes, then let cool. Add 5 drops of concentrated $H_2SO_4$ and heat cautiously again to complete solution of the solid mass. Let cool moderately, then pour into 25–30 drops of cold water. If the solution is not clear, pour it back into the crucible and let digest near the boiling point for 20–30 minutes until the anhydrous sulfates dissolve. Place in a tincture bottle labelled "Solution after fusion with $Na_2S_2O_7$," and analyze for metals that form insoluble ignited oxides.

## REPORTING COMPLEX DRY UNKNOWNS

In keeping with the method of analysis described above, the report on complex dry unknowns is divided into four parts: (A) "Water Solution," (B) "Residue Insoluble in Water," (C) "Solvent(s) for Residue," and (D) "Gases Escaping During the Dissolving Process."

**A. Water Solution.** This part should include a list of the positive and negative ions that show the form in which the elements identified are present in the water solution. Further, if significant amounts of $CO_2$, $H_2S$, or $NH_3$ were evolved in preparing the water solution and these are not present in the solution itself, they should be reported as gases given off. In connection with this part of the report it should be noted that a considerable range of reactions may occur in preparing the water solution. The water solution may be acid, neutral, or alkaline. In the latter case any aluminum present should be reported as $Al(OH)_4^-$ instead of $Al^{+3}$. The solution may contain free $NH_4OH$, in which case copper, cadmium, etc., should be reported as complex ammonia ions. The solution may contain excess of sulfide ion along with metals of the arsenic division, indicating that the latter are present as thioanions. Similarly, iodide ion in a solution containing Hg or Bi means that the latter should be reported as $HgI_4^{--}$ and $BiI_4^-$.

**B. Residue Insoluble in Water.** This part of the report should include (1) an outline of the method of getting the material into solution, (2) a statement of any significant gases identified while treating the material with acids, and (3) a list of chemical substances which, if present in the residue, would account for all the available facts, including the physical appearance of the residue, the method of dissolving employed, and all the positive chemical tests obtained.

## *LABORATORY EXERCISES*

1. Place 50 mg. of a mixture of $Na_2CO_3$, $Ba(NO_3)_2$, and $AgNO_3$ (ratio by weight 7:2:1) in a crucible. Add 2 ml. of water, cover with a watch glass, keep at boiling point for 3–5 minutes. Cool, centrifuge, and wash. Test portions of the water solution (*a*) for $Ag^+$ by adding a drop of 5 *N* HCl, and (*b*) for $Ba^{++}$ by adding a drop of $H_2SO_4$. Test portions of the residue insoluble in water for solubility in HCl, $HNO_3$, and HCl + $HNO_3$. Note effervescence during the reaction with the different acids. Prepare a report for the mixture as a dry unknown.

2. Place 50 mg. of a mixture of $K_2CO_3$, $KMnO_4$, and $As_2O_3$ (ratio by weight 7:1:2) in a crucible and treat with water as in (1). Test the residue for solubility in HCl, $HNO_3$, and HCl + $HNO_3$, noting absence of effervescence, but evolution of $Cl_2$ with HCl. Dissolve a portion of the residue in HCl, evaporate nearly to dryness to remove $Cl_2$, add 5 drops of 5 *N* HCl, heat, and pass in $H_2S$. Is As present in the residue? Examine the water solution for the presence of Mn ($Mn^{++}$ or $MnO_4^-$), $H_2AsO_3^-$, and $HAsO_4^{--}$. Prepare a report for the mixture as a dry unknown.

3. Write the equations for the reaction involved in preparing the water solution of the dry mixture in (2).

# Appendix

## TYPE QUESTIONS ILLUSTRATED AND DISCUSSED

These examples are taken from Group I and the copper division of Group II, since this type of material may well be introduced fairly early in the course.

### FIRST TYPE QUESTION

**Write Formulas for Names and Names for Formulas.** In answering this type of question two things are called for: first, a knowledge of formulas and valences of radicals; second, a knowledge of the principles of nomenclature. In its simpler form this may be used from the beginning of the course, whereas the more complex form may be used to good advantage by way of review toward the end.

**Examples:**

(*a*) Write the formulas corresponding to the following names:

1. Silver ammonia sulfate.
2. Sodium plumbite.
3. Mercuric amino chloride.

(*b*) Write the names corresponding to the following formulas:

1. $Cd(NH_3)_4CrO_4$.
2. $Na_2Cu(CN)_3$
3. $KBiI_4$

**Answers:**

(*a*) 1. $[Ag(NH_3)_2]_2SO_4$.
2. $NaPb(OH)_3$
3. $HgNH_2Cl$.

(*b*) 1. Cadmium ammonia chromate.
2. Sodium cuprocyanide.
3. Potassium bismuth iodide.

## SECOND TYPE QUESTION

**Outline a Method of Analysis.** This covers only the chemical basis of the process, including formulas for reagents used, formulas for main products, and separations obtained. Descriptive details, such as quantities used and conditions required, are intentionally omitted from the answer, since these are specifically covered in the next type of question.

**Example:**

Outline the method of analysis for Group I, starting with a neutral or acid solution.

**Answer:**

| | | |
|---|---|---|
| $Ag^+$ | $Hg_2^{++}$ | $Pb^{++}$ |
| | $HCl$ | |
| $\underline{AgCl}$ | $\underline{Hg_2Cl_2}$ | $\underline{PbCl_2}$ |
| | Hot water | |
| $\underline{AgCl}$ | $\underline{Hg_2Cl_2}$ | $PbCl_2$ |
| $NH_4OH$ | | 1. $H_2SO_4 \rightarrow \underline{PbSO_4}$ |
| $Ag(NH_3)_2Cl$<br>1. $HNO_3 \rightarrow \underline{AgCl}$<br>2. $KI \rightarrow \underline{AgI}$ | $\underline{NH_2Hg_2Cl}$ | 2. $KI \rightarrow \underline{PbI_2}$<br>3. $K_2Cr_2O_7 \rightarrow \underline{PbCrO_4}$ |

## THIRD TYPE QUESTION

**Describe a Method of Analysis.** In this case the ground covered is the same as in the preceding type of question, but with all the manipulative details added that are necessary in actually carrying out the analysis in the laboratory. Since the answer should be written out very fully, such a question should cover only a narrow field. One of the chief sources of trouble in the laboratory is the haphazard use of reagents and the failure to establish proper conditions. Few of the books in qualitative analysis describe the methods fully; therefore it is not surprising if difficulty is encountered in giving complete answers to questions of this type which emphasize the importance of intelligent control of operations in the laboratory as opposed to a routine following of directions.

**Example:**

Describe the method of separating lead from mercury in Group II.

**Answer:**

The precipitates of PbS and HgS are transferred to a small crucible using approximately 5 drops of distilled water. (If larger amounts of water are required, let the precipitate settle and pour off the excess.) Add 5 drops of 5 *N* $HNO_3$, cover with a watch glass and heat just to vigorous boiling, remove the flame after 10–15 seconds, and let stand a moment; then transfer to a centrifuge tube, centrifuge, and wash the precipitate twice with a few drops of water. The mercury will be in the centrifuge tube in the form of HgS, and the lead will be in the clear solution as $Pb(NO_3)_2$.

## FOURTH TYPE QUESTION

**Write the Successive Forms for a Metal.** The phrase "successive forms" is used to ask for two things: First, a list of the reagents that affect a metal during the regular, systematic analysis of a solution; and, second, the formulas for the compounds of the metal that result from the action of these reagents. The two lists should be given in parallel columns. For metals in later groups it will be assumed that the solution is a general unknown in which the earlier groups are to be precipitated before the one is reached in which the metal belongs. To the extent to which reactions take place in the separations from earlier groups, these should be included in the list.

**Example:**

Write the successive forms for mercury starting with mercuric nitrate in the original solution.

**Answer:**

| | |
|---|---|
| | $Hg(NO_3)_2$ |
| HCl | $HgCl_4^{--}$ |
| $NH_4OH$ | $HgNH_2Cl$ |
| HCl (0.25 *N*) | $HgCl_4^{--}$ |
| $H_2S$ | HgS |
| HCl + $HNO_3$ | $HgCl_4^{--}$ |
| (1) $SnCl_2$ | $Hg_2Cl_2 \rightarrow Hg^\circ$ |
| (2) Cu° | Hg° |

## FIFTH TYPE QUESTION

**Write the Analytical Equations for a Metal.** This covers the same ground as successive forms, except that balanced equations for the reactions should be given.

**Example:**

Write the analytical equations for copper starting with cupric ammonia nitrate in the original solution.

**Answer:**

$$Cu(NH_3)_4^{++} + 4H_3O^+ = Cu^{++} + 4NH_4^+ + 4H_2O$$

$$Cu^{++} + 2NH_4OH = \underline{Cu(OH)_2} + 2NH_4^+$$

$$\underline{Cu(OH)_2} + 2H_3O^+ = Cu^{++} + 4H_2O$$

$$Cu^{++} + H_2S + 2H_2O = \underline{CuS} + 2H_3O^+$$

$$3\underline{CuS} + 2NO_3^- + 8H_3O^+ = 3Cu^{++} + 3\underline{S} + 2NO + 12H_2O$$

$$Cu^{++} + 4NH_3 = Cu(NH_3)_4^{++}$$

$$Cu(NH_3)_4^{++} + 4HC_2H_3O_2 = Cu^{++} + 4NH_4^+ + 4C_2H_3O_2^-$$

$$2Cu^{++} + Fe(CN)_6^{-4} = \underline{Cu_2Fe(CN)_6}$$

## SIXTH TYPE QUESTION

**Explain an Analytical Procedure.** When answering such a question the student is expected to show, first, that he understands the practical analytical significance of the procedure and, second, that he knows the chemistry on which the process is based. Both should be given in some detail.

**Example:**

Explain why one evaporates to fumes of $SO_3$ in the separations in Group II.

**Answer:**

At this point $H_2SO_4$ has been added to precipitate lead as $PbSO_4$ in separating this metal from bismuth, copper, and cadmium. However, the solution contains a moderate amount of $HNO_3$, which was used to dissolve the sulfides originally, and $PbSO_4$ is slightly soluble in $HNO_3$. This $HNO_3$ may be removed by evaporating the solution until fumes of $SO_3$ start to appear, because $HNO_3$ boils out at a temperature of about 130°C. while the decomposition of the $H_2SO_4$ only commences at about 160–180°C. Thus, if $SO_3$ fumes appear, one may be sure that the $HNO_3$ has been removed. The solution may then be cooled and poured into 20 drops of distilled water to precipitate the $PbSO_4$ without interference from the $HNO_3$.

## SEVENTH TYPE QUESTION

**Discuss an Analytical Procedure.** This type of question is similar to the preceding one, except that it is used more commonly with reference to procedures that do not fully accomplish their objectives. In this case, therefore, the answer should show not only the purpose of the procedure and the chemistry involved, but also the extent to which the procedure fails, the chemistry involved in the failure, and any special precautions or modifications that will make it more satisfactory.

**Example:**

Discuss the ammonium hydroxide separation of silver and mercury in Group I.

**Answer:**

Ammonium hydroxide is used in Group I on a mixed precipitate of silver and mercurous chlorides, the silver chloride reacting to form a soluble compound [$Ag(NH_3)_2Cl$], while the mercurous chloride reacts to form substances which still leave the mercury in an insoluble condition ($Hg_2NH_2Cl$, partly decomposed into $HgNH_2Cl + Hg$). The separation is not quantitative, however, because of a secondary reaction in which the finely divided metallic mercury reduces some of the silver to free metal which is insoluble in ammonium hydroxide. With moderate amounts of silver and mercury present, sufficient silver chloride will dissolve in the ammonium hydroxide to give a satisfactory qualitative test for silver; but with a small amount of silver and a large amount of mercury present the silver chloride may be reduced so completely that not enough will dissolve in the ammonium hydroxide to give a test for silver. Under such conditions the ammonium hydroxide separation fails completely and must be replaced by another procedure or supplemented by testing the black precipitate for silver.

## EIGHTH TYPE QUESTION

**Trace the Effect of an Irregularity in Separations.** It requires little experience for the chemist to learn that it is not always easy in the laboratory to obtain the separations that look simple on paper. In this type of question the student is expected to apply his knowledge of the chemistry of the given metal to trace its progress through the further reactions to which it is exposed because of its incomplete separation at the proper point.

**Example:**

Trace the effect of incomplete removal of $HNO_3$ when precipitating lead as $PbSO_4$.

**Answer:**

If sufficient $HNO_3$ is left in solution and the amount of lead present is quite small, one may fail to obtain a precipitate of $PbSO_4$ and thus miss the lead entirely. With larger amounts of lead present, partial precipitation of lead as $PbSO_4$ may take place, but some may be left in solution. If lead is not fully removed as $PbSO_4$, one may obtain a white precipitate of $Pb(OH)_2$ when adding $NH_4OH$ to precipitate $Bi(OH)_3$, and some of the lead may carry through to give a black precipitate of PbS when testing for cadmium with $H_2S$. The lead does not interfere with the confirmatory test for bismuth, although a yellow precipitate of $PbI_2$ may be obtained which would need to settle out or be removed by centrifuging in judging the color of the solution. In the case of cadmium, a further separation from lead would need to be carried out before a satisfactory test could be obtained.

## NINTH TYPE QUESTION

**Give the Ions Not Eliminated by Exploratory Tests.** In this type of exercise certain information will be given about a solution as to color, reaction toward litmus, odor, and behavior with certain reagents. The student is expected to tell which metals of a given group may be present by writing the formulas of the possible ions.

**Example:**

If the original solution is acid and gives no precipitate with KI, what ions of Group I and the copper division of Group II may be present?

**Answer:**

$Cd^{++}$, and possibly $BiCl_4^-$ (if the solution contains sufficient $Cl^-$ to prevent the precipitation of $BiI_3$ or BiOI).

## TENTH TYPE QUESTION

**Give Methods of Separating Two Metals in One Operation.** In this exercise two metals are given as solid compounds or as ions in solution and the task is to name reagents that will convert one metal to a soluble, the other to an insoluble substance, so that the process of centrifuging and washing will complete the separation of the given metals. Following each reagent should be given the formulas of substances produced with proper indication as to which is soluble, which insoluble. In each case give all the separations that can be accomplished by the use of common reagents.

**Example:**

Give the common methods of separating Ag and Pb in one operation starting with $Ag^+$ and $Pb^{++}$.

**Answer:**

(*a*) Treat with excess $NH_4OH$; $Ag^+$ forms $Ag(NH_3)_2{}^+$ (soluble), $Pb^{++}$ forms $Pb(OH)_2$ (insoluble).
(*b*) Treat with excess NaOH; $Ag^+$ forms $Ag_2O$ (insoluble), $Pb^{++}$ forms $Pb(OH)_3{}^-$ (soluble).
(*c*) Treat with excess of very dilute HCl; $Ag^+$ forms AgCl (insoluble), $Pb^{++}$ remains as such in solution.
(*d*) Treat with excess of moderately dilute $H_2SO_4$; $Ag^+$ remains in solution as such, $Pb^{++}$ forms $PbSO_4$ (insoluble).

## ELEVENTH TYPE QUESTION

**Give Methods of Testing Directly for One Metal When Certain Other Metals Are Present.** This is the problem of repeating the test for a given metal when the first test is uncertain. Assuming that the tests for the other metals are correct, it is frequently possible to devise short cuts to settle the doubtful case that will be distinctly more direct and time saving than to repeat the routine method of analysis. To do this it is necessary to have a ready knowledge of the reactions of common reagents with the various metals. (In the laboratory when such tests have been run it is very much worthwhile to return to the regular systematic procedure and study this to try to discover the cause of the earlier difficulty.)

**Example:**

Give a method of testing as directly as possible for cadmium when lead and copper are the only other metals present in the solution.

**Answer:**

Make the solution nearly neutral (less than 0.25 *N* with acid), and pass in $H_2S$ until precipitation is complete. Centrifuge (PbS, CuS, and any CdS), wash thoroughly, and transfer the precipitate to a small crucible. Add about 10 drops of 5 *N* $H_2SO_4$, and boil gently for about half a minute. Only the CdS dissolves under these conditions. Centrifuge, nearly neutralize the clear solution with $NH_4OH$, and pass in $H_2S$ for a short time. If cadmium is present, a yellow precipitate of CdS will be obtained.

## TWELFTH TYPE QUESTION

**Formulate and Explain a Chemical Reaction Involving the Dissolving or Formation of a Precipitate.** To formulate a reaction is to write a series of equations representing (*a*) the aqueous solution of each separate reagent, (*b*) the primary reaction occurring as the reagents are brought together, (*c*) any secondary reactions brought about as a result of disturbances in equilibrium by the primary reaction and (*d*) write the equation for the net reaction occurring.

To explain a reaction is to state in words such facts as the order of solubility, extent of dissociation, strength as oxidizing or reducing agent, etc., of the various reagents used and products formed so that the suggested mechanism of the reaction will appear reasonable.

To illustrate this case four examples will be given.

**Examples:**

1. Formulate and explain the dissolving of $AgCl$ in $NH_4OH$.

**Answer:**

(*a*) Formulation:

$$AgCl$$

$$AgCl \rightleftarrows Ag^+ + Cl^-$$

$$NH_3 + H_2O \rightleftarrows NH_4^+ + OH^-$$

$$NH_4OH$$

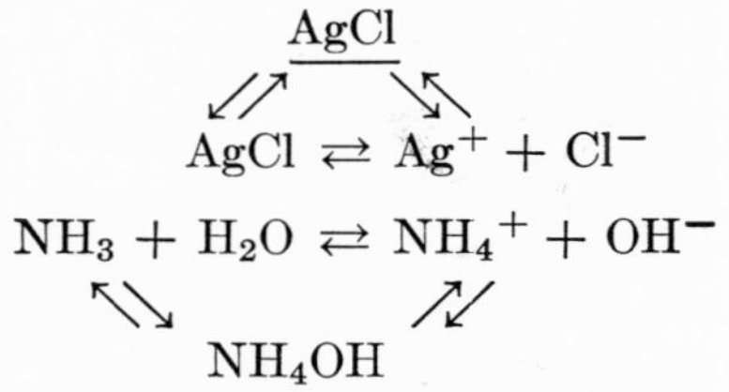

$$Ag^+ + 2NH_3 \rightleftarrows Ag(NH_3)_2^+$$

Net reaction: $AgCl + 2NH_3 = Ag(NH_3)_2^+ + Cl^-$

(*b*) Explanation:

Silver chloride is very slightly soluble in water, the amount in solution consisting largely of silver and chloride ions and very little molecular silver chloride. Ammonium hydroxide is a weak base, slightly ionized into ammonium and hydroxyl ions, but quite unstable, largely decomposed into ammonia and water. Silver ammonia ion is a very slightly ionized material, the extent of dissociation being so low that when a moderate concentration of $NH_3$ is added to a saturated aqueous solution of $AgCl$ there will be effective combination of $NH_3$ with $Ag^+$, lowering the concentration of silver ion and thus causing the solution to become unsaturated with respect to silver chloride so that more of the precipitate in contact with the solution will dissolve. These processes continue until the precipitate is completely dissolved or until equilibrium is reached with the solution saturated and some precipitate still remaining. In dissolving the silver chloride the silver is converted to $Ag(NH_3)_2^+$ and the negative radical goes into solution as $Cl^-$.

2. Formulate and explain the precipitation of silver chloride on adding nitric acid to a solution of silver ammonia chloride.

**Answer:**

(*a*) Formulation:

$$Ag(NH_3)_2Cl \rightleftarrows Ag(NH_3)_2^+ + Cl^-$$

$$Ag(NH_3)_2^+ \rightleftarrows Ag^+ + 2NH_3$$

$$\begin{array}{c} NH_3 + H_2O \rightleftarrows NH_4^+ + OH^- \\ \searrow\!\!\nwarrow \quad \nearrow\!\!\swarrow \\ NH_4OH \end{array}$$

$$HNO_3 + H_2O = H_3O^+ + NO_3^-$$

$$H_3O^+ + NH_3 = NH_4^+ + H_2O$$

$$Ag^+ + Cl^- \rightleftarrows \underline{AgCl}$$

Net reaction:

$$Ag(NH_3)_2^+ + 2H_3O^+ + Cl^- = \underline{AgCl} + 2NH_4^+ + 2H_2O$$

(*b*) Explanation:

Silver ammonia chloride is very largely ionized into silver ammonia ion and chloride ion. Silver ammonia ion is very slightly dissociated into silver ion and ammonia. Ammonia combines to a moderate extent with water to form ammonium hydroxide which is slightly ionized into ammonium and hydroxyl ions. In the actual solution a considerable amount of ammonium hydroxide is present, introducing a fairly high concentration of $NH_3$ which represses the ionization of $Ag(NH_3)_2^+$ into silver ion and ammonia. Therefore the concentration of silver ion is very low, but the concentration of chloride ion is relatively large. Nitric acid is very largely ionized. Hydronium ion combines with the $NH_3$ forming ammonium ion. As the concentration of ammonia is thus lowered the equilibrium between silver ammonia ion and silver ion and ammonia is disturbed seriously, causing a marked increase in the concentration of silver ion. The solubility product of silver chloride is very low. As the concentration of silver ion increases in the presence of a moderate concentration of chloride ion already in the solution, a condition is reached in which the product of concentrations of silver and chloride ions is greater than the solubility product of silver chloride. This means that the solution is supersaturated with respect to silver chloride, and therefore a precipitate of silver chloride may be obtained. In the precipitation of the silver chloride the ammonia is converted to $NH_4^+$ by the $H_3O^+$, permitting the $Ag^+$ and $Cl^-$ to combine and precipitate as AgCl.

3. Formulate and explain the dissolving of copper sulfide in nitric acid.

**Answer:**

(*a*) Formulation:

$$\underline{CuS}$$

$$\swarrow\!\!\nearrow \qquad \nwarrow\!\!\searrow$$

$$CuS \rightleftarrows Cu^{++} + S^{--}$$

$$HNO_3 + H_2O \rightleftarrows H_3O^+ + NO_3^-$$

$$2H_3O^+ + S^{--} \rightleftarrows H_2S + 2H_2O$$

$$3H_2S + 2NO_3^- + 2H_3O^+ = \underline{3S} + 2NO + 6H_2O$$

Net reaction:

$$\underline{3CuS} + 8H_3O^+ + 2NO_3^- = 3Cu^{++} + 2NO + 3S + 12H_2O$$

(*b*) Explanation:

Copper sulfide is extremely insoluble in water. To the extent to which it dissolves it is quite fully ionized into cupric and sulfide ions. Nitric acid is a strong acid, essentially completely ionized to hydronium and nitrate ions. Hydrogen sulfide is a weak electrolyte, and therefore the hydronium ions combine with sulfide ions to form hydrogen sulfide; but the original concentration of sulfide ion was so low that in spite of this reaction the copper sulfide is still fairly insoluble. However, in hot, acid solution, the nitrate ion is a strong oxidizing agent and hydrogen sulfide is a strong reducing agent; accordingly, as heat is applied, the hydrogen sulfide is oxidized to free sulfur by the nitrate ion. As this occurs, further combining of $H_3O^+$ and $S^{--}$ takes place and the concentration of sulfide ion is reduced to so low a value that all the copper sulfide will dissolve. In this dissolving the sulfur is oxidized to free sulfur, the copper goes into solution as $Cu^{++}$, and the nitrate ion is reduced to NO.

4. Formulate and explain the precipitation of cadmium sulfide on passing $H_2S$ into a solution of cadmium ammonia sulfate.

**Answer:**

(*a*) Formulation:

$$Cd(NH_3)_4SO_4 \rightleftarrows Cd(NH_3)_4^{++} + SO_4^{--}$$

$$Cd(NH_3)_4^{++} \rightleftarrows Cd^{++} + 4NH_3$$

$$\begin{array}{ccc} NH_3 + H_2O & \rightleftarrows & NH_4^{+} + OH^{-} \\ \nwarrow\!\searrow & & \nearrow\!\swarrow \\ & NH_4OH & \end{array}$$

$$H_2S + H_2O \rightleftarrows H_3O^{+} + HS^{-}$$

$$HS^{-} + H_2O \rightleftarrows H_3O^{+} + S^{--}$$

$$H_3O^{+} + OH^{-} \rightleftarrows 2H_2O$$

$$Cd^{++} + S^{--} \rightleftarrows \underline{CdS}$$

Net reaction:

$$Cd(NH_3)_4^{++} + H_2S = \underline{CdS} + 2NH_4^{+} + 2NH_3$$

(*b*) Explanation:

Cadmium ammonia sulfate is a typical strong electrolyte, practically completely ionized into cadmium ammonia ions and sulfate ions. Cadmium ammonia ion is very slightly ionized into cadmium ion and ammonia, the excess $NH_3$ from the $NH_4OH$ in the solution decreasing very much the extent of dissociation of the complex ion. Hydrogen sulfide is normally very slightly ionized into $H_3O^{+}$ and $HS^{-}$, and very much less into $H_3O^{+}$ and $S^{--}$. However, the ammonium hydroxide present furnishes sufficient $OH^{-}$ so that the $H_2S$ is largely neutralized to $HS^{-}$ and the ionization of $HS^{-}$ is increased considerably, although it still remains very slight. The solubility product of cadmium sulfide is very small, so that, in spite of the low concentrations of $Cd^{++}$ and $S^{--}$ brought together, their product exceeds the solubility product of cadmium sulfide, and precipitation takes place. As the concentrations of $Cd^{++}$ and $S^{--}$ are thus lowered, further progressive dissociation of cadmium ammonia ion and of bisulfide ion takes place so that precipitation continues until the cadmium is quite fully removed from the solution. In this precipitation the cadmium is converted to cadmium sufide, and the ammonia from the complex ion is partly changed to $NH_4^{+}$ in the neutralization of the $H_2S$ and partly accumulates in the solution as $NH_3$.

## PROBLEMS

**Group I**

1. What metals are in Group I? Why? Name and give formulas for the ions of Group I metals.

2. Could $NH_4Cl + HNO_3$ be substituted for HCl in the precipitation of Group I? Explain.

3. Describe the method of precipitating Group I and testing for completeness of precipitation when the original solution is alkaline.

4. When precipitating Group I, why add an excess of the reagent? Why avoid a large excess?

5. Why wash the Group I precipitate? What wash solutions should be used? Why?

6. Why extract the Group I precipitate with hot water? Describe the operation.

7. Starting with the Group I precipitate, outline the regular method for its analysis.

8. Give balanced equation for each final, confirmatory test for each metal in Group I.

9. Which of the three final tests for Pb is the most delicate in (*a*) acid solution, (*b*) neutral solution? Explain in each case.

10. Arrange the final tests for Pb in Group I in order of increasing delicacy. Describe a laboratory experiment demonstrating the correctness of the order given.

11. If $PbCl_2$ is precipitated in Group I, what errors in technic would result in a negative dichromate test?

12. The following equation is frequently found on student papers. Although balanced, it is obviously wrong. Explain.

$$Hg_2Cl_2 + NH_4OH\ (xs) = NH_2Hg_2Cl + HCl + H_2O$$

13. Why does AgCl dissolve in ammonia water?

14. Account for the formation of a precipitate of AgCl upon the addition of $HNO_3$ in the final test for silver.

15. What is the function of $HNO_3$ in the final test for silver? What other reagents could be used to accomplish the same result?

16. In the final test for Ag why must an excess of $HNO_3$ be added? How tell when an excess is present?

17. When a solution contains relatively a large amount of $Hg_2^{++}$ and a small amount of $Ag^+$, the final test for $Ag^+$ may fail entirely. What happens to the $Ag^+$?

18. Give three important requirements that a group reagent must meet. Show wherein $Cl^-$, as the Group I reagent, does or does not meet these requirements.

19. If a solution contains 5 mg. of $Ag^+$ per milliliter, what is the normality?

20. If a solution contains 5 mg. of $Ag^+$ per milliliter, calculate the number of milliliters of 5 *N* HCl that would be equivalent to 15 ml. of this solution.

21. If 15 ml. of a solution containing 100 mg. of $Hg_2^{++}$ is treated with 1.5 ml. of 5 *N* HCl, calculate the concentration of $Cl^-$ in the resulting solution. *Ans.* 0.424 *N*.

22. A 15-ml. sample of a Group I unknown contains 100 mg. of $Ag^+$. How many milliliters of 5 *N* HCl would be required to precipitate the silver? *Ans.* 0.18 ml.

23. How many milliliters of 1.5 *N* $NH_4Cl$ would be required to precipitate 0.25 g. of Ag as AgCl?

24. If 5 ml. of a solution containing 10 mg. per milliliter of $Pb^{++}$ were treated with a slight excess of $K_2CrO_4$, how many grams of $PbCrO_4$ would be obtained, assuming complete conversion?

**Group II, Copper Division**

1. Name the metals in Group II, Copper Division. Divide their ions into three classes: those existing in (*a*) acid solution, (*b*) NaOH solution, (*c*) $NH_4OH$ solution.

2. Describe the method for precipitating Group II starting with the filtrate from Group I.

3. Explain why the solution is made 0.25 *N* with HCl before treating with $H_2S$.

4. Explain why the solution should be diluted in testing for completeness of precipitation of Group II.

5. What difference would it make if the acidity when precipitating Group II were (*a*) too high, (*b*) too low?

6. Which is the more satisfactory to use for the precipitation of Group II, gaseous $H_2S$ or a saturated aqueous solution? Give reasons.

7. "One of the most pernicious habits of the beginner in qualitative analysis is failure to make sure that every reaction in a series has accomplished its purpose." Apply to the separations in Group II, Copper Division.

8. What is the effect of excess hydrogen ion on the precipitation of $Pb^{++}$ as PbS? Explain.

9. Describe the washing of a Group II precipitate. Give reason for each operation and method for determining when satisfactorily performed.

10. Starting with the Group II precipitate, outline the regular method for its analysis. Give balanced equation for each final, confirmatory test.

11. Write the analytical equations for Hg starting with $Hg(NO_3)_2$ in the original solution. (Note that the reactions occurring when the solution is treated with HCl for the precipitation of Group I and when the solution is being made 0.25 *N* with HCl before precipitating Group II should be included.)

12. Starting with an original solution containing $Cu(NH_3)_4SO_4$ and $Cd(NH_3)_4SO_4$ before the precipitation of Group I, give (*a*) the successive forms for Cu and (*b*) the analytical equations for Cd.

13. What precautions should be taken when separating HgS from the other Group II sulfides?

14. Occasionally a black residue is left when treating the Group II sulfides precipitate with $HNO_3$. This residue gives no test for $Hg^{++}$. Give three possible reasons.

15. Compare the action of hot 2 *N* $HNO_3$ on CuS and HgS. Explain.

16. How does one detect Hg in (*a*) Group I, (*b*) Group II?

17. Explain why 3–4 drops of $SnCl_2$ are added in the final test for Hg, whereas only 1 drop of $K_2Cr_2O_7$ is used to test for Pb.

18. Why are Pb and Hg in both Group I and II?

19. If $Pb^{++}$ is not precipitated in Group I, what errors in technic would result in the positive iodide test?

20. If a large amount of $Hg^{++}$ is present, $Ag^+$ may not precipitate as AgCl in Group I. Explain.

21. Mercuric sulfide is the only Group II sulfide insoluble in hot 2 *N* $HNO_3$. Explain.

22. Why is concentrated $H_2SO_4$ used when separating Pb in Group II?

23. What precautions are necessary in the separation of Pb in Group II?

24. Why evaporate to fumes of $SO_3$ when separating Pb in Group II? What precautions are necessary in handling the residue from the standpoint of (*a*) personal safety, (*b*) re-solution of bismuth?

25. When sufficient lead is present to give a good precipitate in Group I, often no precipitate is obtained in Group II in spite of the fact that $PbCl_2$ is soluble to the extent of about 10 g. per liter. Explain.

26. What precautions are necessary if KI is used for the detection of Pb in Group II?

27. Lead sulfate dissolves in concentrated $NH_4C_2H_3O_2$ but not in concentrated $HC_2H_3O_2$. Explain. The solution obtained usually will not give the KI test for Pb. Explain. Addition of $HNO_3$ or HCl after KI may cause the precipitation of $PbI_2$. Explain.

28. Why may the iodide test for Pb in Group II be unsatisfactory if (*a*) the $PbSO_4$ is not properly washed, (*b*) the KI is added to the acetate solution of $PbSO_4$?

29. Explain the separation of Pb from Bi in Group II.

30. Cupric sulfide dissolves readily in hot 2 *N* $HNO_3$ but not in HCl of the same concentration. Explain.

31. Describe a final test for Cd in the presence of Cu. State specifically why the procedure is successful.

32. Explain the use of NaCN in the test for Cd in Group II.

33. Frequently a black precipitate is obtained when making the final test for Cd. Explain. What steps should be taken to verify the presence or absence of Cd?

34. Outline the method of analysis for Hg, Pb, and Bi in Group II, starting with the sulfides precipitated.

35. Outline the method of analysis for Hg, Cu, and Cd in Group II, starting with the sulfides precipitated.

36. Write the analytical equations for Cu starting with $Cu(NH_3)_4(NO_3)_2$ in the original solution. (Note that the reactions occurring when the alkaline solution is acidified with $HNO_3$ and when the solution is made 0.25 *N* with HCl before precipitating Group II should be included. However, $Cu(NO_3)_2$ does not undergo significant reaction with HCl in Group I.)

37. Give balanced molecular equation for one final test for each element in Group II.

38. Explain the common ion effect in connection with (*a*) the use of 0.25 *N* HCl when precipitating Group II with $H_2S$; (*b*) the use of 2 drops of concentrated $H_2SO_4$ when precipitating Pb as $PbSO_4$; (*c*) the use of 3 *N* $NH_4C_2H_3O_2$ to dissolve $PbSO_4$.

39. Write the formulas of the ions of the metals of Group I and the copper division of Group II that might be present (*a*) in an acid solution, (*b*) in an ammoniacal solution, (*c*) in a solution alkaline with NaOH.

40. If 1.5 drops excess of concentrated $H_2SO_4$ is used in precipitating Pb, how many drops of 5 *N* $NH_4OH$ will be needed merely to neutralize the solution when separating Bi from Cu and Cd. (Consult table on reagents in appendix for data on $H_2SO_4$.) *Ans.* 10.8 drops.

41. How might Ag be detected in Group II if it escapes precipitation in Group I?

42. A certain unknown solution covering only Group I–II metals was colorless and acid to litmus. Addition of a few drops or an excess of KI gave no visible action. What ions of Group I–II metals could be present in the original solution?

43. How many milliliters of pure $H_2S$ at STP would be required to precipitate 75 mg. of $Bi^{+++}$ as $Bi_2S_3$? *Ans.* 12.1 ml.

44. How many milliliters of $H_2S$ gas would be required to precipitate 75 mg. of Cu as CuS? (Assume: (*a*) $H_2S$ is 90% pure; (*b*) amount of gas wasted is 50%; (*c*) temperature is 20°C.; (*d*) pressure is 740 mm.) *Ans.* 64.7 ml.

45. A solution containing 75 mg. of $Cu^{++}$ is treated with $H_2S$ and the CuS after filtration and washing is dissolved in hot 2 *N* $HNO_3$. (*a*) How many milliliters of the acid would be required assuming the ratio of $3CuS:8HNO_3$? (*b*) How many milliliters of $H_2S$ would be evolved assuming that it is measured at STP?

46. How many milliliters of 36 *N* $H_2SO_4$ are required to precipitate 75 mg. of Pb as $PbSO_4$?

47. How many milliliters of $H_2S$ (at STP) would be required to precipitate 100 mg. of $Pb^{++}$ as PbS? *Ans.* 10.82 ml.

48. How many milliliters of the ordinary reagent $HNO_3$ would be required to dissolve 100 mg. of CuS? (Is the $HNO_3$ 5 *N* in this oxidation reaction?) *Ans.* 0.56 ml.

49. How many milliliters of 5 *N* $NH_4OH$ will be required to neutralize every milliliter excess of concentrated $H_2SO_4$ used to precipitate Pb in Group II? *Ans.* 7.2 ml.

**Group II, Arsenic Division**

1. Outline the method of analysis for the arsenic division of Group II, starting with the sulfides precipitated.
2. Give formula for the product formed by each Group II, Arsenic Division metal when treated with hot 5 *N* $HNO_3$.
3. Discuss the interference of $HNO_3$ with the precipitation of $As_2S_5$ in strong HCl solution.
4. Explain the use of KI to assist in precipitating arsenic from $H_3AsO_4$ with $H_2S$.
5. Name all the metals in Group II. Divide their ions into three classes, those existing in (*a*) acid solution, (*b*) NaOH solution, (*c*) ammoniacal solution.
6. In general any metal that can be precipitated as the sulfide from an acid solution is more readily precipitated from one that is alkaline. Arsenic is an exception. It cannot be precipitated as the sulfide from an alkaline solution. Explain.
7. Why is ammonium polysulfide used instead of the monosulfide for dissolving the sulfides of As, Sb, and Sn? Is this reagent entirely satisfactory? Explain.
8. Give formula and name for the compound formed when $(NH_4)_2S_2$ reacts with each of the following: $As_2S_3$, $As_2S_5$, SnS, $SnS_2$, $Sb_2S_3$, $Sb_2S_5$.
9. Explain the separation of Hg from Sb in Group II.
10. Describe the magnesia mixture test for arsenic starting with a precipitate of $As_2S_5$.
11. Give two methods for precipitating $As^{V}$ in Group II.
12. Describe the Gutzeit test covering (*a*) chemistry, including balanced equation for each reaction; (*b*) apparatus with sketch; (*c*) procedure; (*d*) precautions; (*e*) interferences.
13. An alloy consisting of Zn (99%) and As (1%) was dissolved in HCl and the solution analyzed. The analyst reported "Pure zinc." Account for his error.
14. What is Fehling's solution? For what is it used in this division?
15. Describe the Marsh test for arsenic.
16. Describe a method for distinguishing between arsine and stibine.
17. Give the reaction of $Sn^{++}$ in the Marsh flask. How might the Sn be identified?
18. Write the analytical equations for antimony starting with antimonous chloride in the original solution.
19. Explain the method of distinguishing between the different ions of tin.
20. Describe the coin test for Sb. Include precautions and interferences.
21. How distinguish SbOCl from BiOCl?
22. Write the successive forms for Sn starting with sodium stannite in the original solution.
23. In the final test for Sn metallic iron is used to reduce the $SnCl_6^{--}$ to $SnCl_4^{--}$. Would any of the following metals be equally satisfactory: Al, Cu, Zn, Mg? Explain in each case.
24. Starting with an original solution containing $Sn(OH)_3^-$ before precipitation of Group I, give the analytical equations for Sn.
25. Formulate and explain the dissolving of $SnS_2$ in $(NH_4)_2S$.
26. Formulate and explain the precipitation of $As_2S_5$ on adding HCl to a solution of $NH_4H_2AsS_4$.
27. Formulate and explain the dissolving of $SnS_2$ in HCl.
28. Formulate and explain the precipitation of $Hg_2Cl_2$ on adding $HgCl_2$ to a solution of $SnCl_2$.
29. Calculate the number of milliliters of 3.5 *N* $(NH_4)_2S$ necessary to dissolve 100 mg. of Sn precipitated as $SnS_2$. Explain why 5 ml. of the reagent are used and any excess water first poured off. *Ans.* 0.48 ml.

**Group III**

1. What effect has the Group II reagent on each Group III ion found in acid solution? Give balanced equation for each reaction.
2. When, how, why reduce $Cr_2O_7^{--}$?
3. Starting with the Group III precipitate, outline the regular method for its analysis.
4. Why add $NH_4Cl$ before $NH_4OH$ when precipitating Group III?
5. Frequently Fe is precipitated in Group II. Explain. Show how avoided. Indicate where the Fe would interfere in the Group II analysis.
6. Start with the clear solution from Group II and give, in order, the steps in the preparation for an actual precipitation of Group III down to and including the washing of the precipitate.
7. Starting with the Group III precipitate, give specific directions for the separation and detection of Al.
8. Why is it impossible to use $NaCl + NaOH$ instead of $NH_4Cl + NH_4OH$ for the precipitation of Group III?
9. Addition of sufficient $NH_4Cl$ to a hot solution of $Al(OH)_4^-$ or $Cr(OH)_4^-$ will give a precipitate of the corresponding hydroxide. Explain.
10. Account for the fact that $Al(OH)_3$ dissolves in NaOH but not in $NH_4OH$.
11. Describe the (*a*) Aluminon test for Al, (*b*) vanishing blue test for Cr. Emphasize precautions and interferences.
12. Give in tabular form (*a*) five reagents that will distinguish $Fe^{++}$ from $Fe^{+3}$, (*b*) the formula, (*c*) form, and (*d*) color for each product.
13. Same as in problem 12 for $Cr^{+3}$ and $Cr_2O_7^{--}$.
14. Starting with an original solution containing $Na_2CrO_4$, before the precipitation of Group I, give the successive forms for Cr.
15. Starting with an original solution of $FeCl_3$ before the precipitation of Group I, give the analytical equations for Fe.
16. How may the following conversions be effected?

(*a*) $Cr^{+3}$ to $Cr_2O_7^{--}$
(*b*) $Cr(OH)_4^-$ to $CrO_4^{--}$
(*c*) $Al(OH)_4^-$ to $Al^{+3}$
(*d*) $Fe^{++}$ to $Fe^{+3}$
(*e*) $Cr^{+3}$ to $CrO_4^{--}$
(*f*) $CrO_4^{--}$ to $Cr_2O_7^{--}$

17. If chromium is found in an unknown solution, how does one ascertain the ionic form in the original sample?
18. Account for the precipitation of $Cr(OH)_3$ when $Na_2CO_3$ is added to a solution of $CrCl_3$.
19. Is $Fe(OH)_2$ a stronger or weaker base than $Fe(OH)_3$? Is this the usual relation for compounds of two valences of the same metal or is it a special case?
20. Name the metals of Groups I, II, and III. List all their ions existing in acid solution and give the color of each ion.
21. Considering only the metals in Groups I, II, and III, list all their ions existing in alkaline solution. Give the color of each ion.
22. Formulate and explain the precipitation of $Fe(OH)_3$ on adding $NH_4OH$ in slight excess to a solution of $FeCl_3$ which contains a high concentration of $NH_4Cl$.
23. Formulate and explain the dissolving of $Al(OH)_3$ in NaOH.
24. Formulate and explain the precipitation of $Al(OH)_3$ on adding $NH_4Cl$ in excess to a solution of $NaAl(OH)_4$.
25. Formulate and explain the dissolving of $Cr(OH)_3$ in $NaOH + H_2O_2$.
26. How many milliliters of 5 *N* $NH_4OH$ would be required to precipitate 75 mg. of $Fe^{+3}$ according to the ratio $Fe^{+3}:3NH_4OH$?

27. Calculate the concentration of $NH_4OH$ resulting from the addition of 0.1 ml. of 5 *N* $NH_4OH$ to 25 ml. of a neutral solution. *Ans.* 0.02 *N*.

28. Calculate the number of milligrams of Cr that will be oxidized from $Cr(OH)_3$ to $Na_2CrO_4$ by 1 ml. of 3% $H_2O_2$ in the presence of excess NaOH. *Ans.* 30.8 mg.

29. Calculate the number of milliliters of 5 *N* NaOH equivalent to 1 g. of $NH_4Cl$. *Ans.* 3.7 ml.

30. How many milliliters of 5 *N* $NH_4OH$ would be required to precipitate 100 mg. of $Fe^{+3}$ as $Fe(OH)_3$? *Ans.* 1.07 ml.

31. How much 5 *N* $NH_4OH$ would be required to precipitate 100 mg. of $Fe^{+3}$ as $Fe(OH)_3$ assuming that 3 ml. of the base are required to neutralize the acid initially present?

32. How much 5 *N* HCl would be required to dissolve 200 mg. of $Fe(OH)_3$?

33. A 100-ml. solution containing 100 mg. of Cr as $K_2Cr_2O_7$ has a pH of 0.6. What is the pH after addition of enough $H_2S$ to reduce the chromium: $K_2Cr_2O_7 + 3H_2S + 8HCl = Cr^{+3} + \cdots$.

34. How many milliliters of reagent 5 *N* $HNO_3$ would be required to dissolve 100 mg. of FeS? ($Fe^{+3} + S + NO$) *Ans.* 0.92 ml.

35. How many milliliters of 5 *N* $HNO_3$ would be required to dissolve 0.5 g. of iron assuming that no excess of acid is required? *Ans.* 7.15 ml.

**Group IV**

1. Write the formulas, names, colors, and conditions of stability for the ions of the fourth group metals.

2. Starting with the Group IV precipitate, outline the regular method for its analysis. Give balanced equation for each final, confirmatory test.

3. State the conditions set up for the precipitation of Group IV that determine the concentration of sulfide ion.

4. Why is a black precipitate in Group IV not proof that Co or Ni is present?

5. Discuss the concentrations of $NH_4Cl$ and of $NH_4OH$ necessary to prevent the precipitation of fourth group metals in Group III.

6. Explain why a permanganate should be reduced before the precipitation of Group II.

7. Explain why $H_2S$ should be removed from the filtrate from Group II before precipitating Group III.

8. Although Mn is considered a Group IV metal, it is frequently more or less completely precipitated in Group III. Explain. How is Mn detected in Group III?

9. Give specific directions for the separation of $Mn^{++}$ from $Zn^{++}$ in Group IV.

10. Discuss the separation of CoS and NiS from ZnS and MnS by dilute HCl.

11. Starting with the Group IV precipitate give specific directions for the separation and detection of Zn. Emphasize precautions and interferences.

12. Sulfide ion is used as the reagent for both Group II and IV. Explain.

13. Give three confirmatory tests for cobalt.

14. Describe the thiocyanate test for Co. Indicate the necessary precautions.

15. Give four methods of oxidizing $Mn^{++}$ to $MnO_4^-$. Include balanced equation for each.

16. Formulate and explain the precipitation of CoS in Group IV.

17. Formulate and explain the dissolving of NiS in $HCl + HNO_3$.

18. Formulate and explain the precipitation of ZnS on passing $H_2S$ into a solution of $NaZn(OH)_3$.

19. Write the successive forms for Mn, starting with sodium manganate in the original solution.

20. Write the analytical equations for Zn, starting with zinc ammonia nitrate in the original solution.

21. Write equations for $H_2O_2$ acting (*a*) as an oxidizing agent, (*b*) as a reducing agent.

22. A certain acid solution containing only ions of Groups I–IV thus far considered gave no precipitate upon addition of excess of $Na_2CO_3$. What ions of Groups I–IV metals might be present? What might be the color of the original solution?

23. Can $Mn^{++}$ be detected in the presence of other Group IV metals? If so, how? If not, why not?

24. How many milliliters of 5 *N* HCl would be required to dissolve 75 mg. of Mn in the form of $MnO_2$?

25. How many milliliters of $H_2S$ would be required to precipitate 75 mg. of Mn as MnS assuming STP and pure $H_2S$?

26. If 100 ml. of a solution contains 100 mg. of Mn as $KMnO_4$ and is 0.25 *N* with respect to $H_3O^+$, what would be the acidity after reduction of the $MnO_4^-$ with $H_2S$?

27. How many milliliters of 1 *N* HCl would be used up in dissolving 75 mg. of Zn present as ZnS?

28. If 100 mg. of ZnS were treated with excess HCl, how many milliliters of $H_2S$ (at STP) would be evolved?

**Group V**

1. Starting with the Group V precipitate, outline the regular method for its analysis. Give balanced equation for each final confirmatory test involving precipitation.

2. Why remove any large excess of ammonium salts before precipitating Group V?

3. State the conditions set up for the precipitation of Group V that determine the concentration of carbonate ion.

4. Account for the precipitation of $BaCrO_4$ when $K_2Cr_2O_7$ is added to a solution of $BaCl_2$. After equilibrium has been established, what would be the effect on the system of the following: HCl, NaCl, $Na_2SO_4$, NaOH?

5. How can Ca be separated from Sr in Group V when (*a*) the amounts are equal, (*b*) only a small amount of Sr is present?

6. Explain the separation of and tests for Sr and Ca. A mere description of *how* to do it is inadequate.

7. Group V ions may be lost in Groups II, III, and IV. Explain in each case.

8. $CaCO_3$ will dissolve in a solution of $NH_4Cl$ but not NaCl. Explain.

9. Explain the difference in completeness of precipitation of $BaCrO_4$ with $K_2Cr_2O_7$ from $BaCl_2$ and from $Ba(C_2H_3O_2)_2$.

10. Discuss the effectiveness of the $(NH_4)_2SO_4$ precipitation of $Sr^{++}$ in the presence of $Ca^{++}$.

11. Give specific directions for performing a flame test.

12. Calcium oxalate dissolves readily in HCl but is insoluble in acetic acid. Explain. (Hint: Compare the extent of ionization of the three acids.)

13. If an unknown solution covering all groups gives a green flame test, is it proof that $Ba^{++}$ is present? Explain.

14. If lime water, $Ca(OH)_2$, is treated with $CO_2$, a precipitate of $CaCO_3$ appears. When an excess of $CO_2$ is added, the precipitate disappears. Explain.

15. Formulate and explain the precipitation of $BaCO_3$ in Group V.

16. Formulate and explain the dissolving of $CaCO_3$ in $HC_2H_3O_2$.

17. Formulate and explain the precipitation of $BaCrO_4$ when $K_2Cr_2O_7$ is added to a solution containing $Ba(C_2H_3O_2)_2$.

## Group VI

1. Give specific directions for the detection of $Mg^{++}$ (*a*) in the Group IV filtrate after removal of excess $NH_4^+$, (*b*) in the Group V filtrate.
2. A solution of $MgCl_2$ yields a precipitate of $Mg(OH)_2$ upon addition of $NH_4OH$. If $NH_4Cl$ is added before the $NH_4OH$, no precipitation occurs. Explain.
3. Why is $MgCO_3$ not precipitated in Group V?
4. Explain the use of the cobalt glass in the test for potassium.
5. Describe a precipitation test for (*a*) Na, (*b*) K.
6. Magnesium carbonate will dissolve in a hot solution of $NH_4NO_3$. Explain.
7. Give equations showing the action of $Na_2HPO_4$ on $Mg^{++}$ in (*a*) acid solution, (*b*) neutral solution, (*c*) ammoniacal solution.
8. Mention three methods for the detection of $NH_4^+$ and give the essential equations.
9. Give directions for the preparation of an empirical solution of NaCl such that 1 ml. is equivalent to 1 mg. of $Ag^+$.
10. How many milliliters of $CO_2$ at STP can be obtained from 100 mg. of $CaCO_3$? Would this volume be sufficient to saturate 50 ml. of $H_2O$ at 20°C.?
11. What is Nessler's reagent? How is it prepared?
12. Describe (*a*) a direct test for ammonia, (*b*) an indirect test.
13. Do any of the following interfere with the flame test for potassium: Na, Sr, Ca, Ba, Cu?
14. How does one test a "cobalt glass" to be sure that it is suitable for the detection of potassium?

## Acids

1. (*a*) Describe the ammonia test for $NO_3^-$. Include the chemistry (balanced molecular equations), apparatus (sketch), manipulations, precautions, and interferences. (*b*) Same for the brown ring test.
2. Give balanced molecular equation for the final confirmatory reaction in the detection of $CO_3^{--}$, $S^{--}$, $SO_4^{--}$, $NO_3^-$.
3. How detect each ion in the following combinations: (*a*) $Cl^-$ and $S^{--}$, (*b*) $NO_3^-$ and $S^{--}$, (*c*) $SO_4^{--}$ and $CO_3^{--}$, (*d*) $S^{--}$ and $CO_3^{--}$, (*e*) $NO_3^-$, $CO_3^{--}$, and $NH_4^+$.
4. Which is the better reagent for the detection of $CO_3^{--}$, lime water or baryta water? Explain.
5. Which is the more reliable method for detection of $H_2S$, lead acetate paper or the odor? Explain.
6. How test each of the following for the acid radical: AgCl, CuS, $CaCO_3$, $BaSO_4$, $BiONO_3$? Note that the first step is to dissolve the salt.
7. Compare the effervescence tests for $CO_3^{--}$ and $S^{--}$. How may the gases be identified if evolved together?
8. Outline a procedure for the detection of $SO_4^{--}$, $SO_3^{--}$, and $S^{--}$ when in one solution.
9. Outline a procedure for the detection of $C_2O_4^{--}$, $PO_4^{-3}$, $AsO_4^{-3}$, and $Cl^-$ when in one solution.
10. Outline a procedure for the detection of $I^-$, $Br^-$, $NO_3^-$, and $ClO_3^-$ when in one solution.
11. How detect $Cl^-$, $I^-$, $S^{--}$, $PO_4^{-3}$, and $C_2O_4^{--}$ when present in one solution?
12. Describe the hypochlorite test for $Br^-$ and $I^-$. Emphasize precautions and give molecular equation for each essential reaction.
13. Describe the persulfate method for the separation and detection of $Cl^-$, $Br^-$, and $I^-$.

14. Can a nitrite be used in place of sulfite for the reduction of $ClO_3^-$ in the test for that ion? Does either reducing agent have any advantages over the other?

15. Describe the test for $SO_3^{--}$ in a solution containing $SO_4^{--}$.

16. Explain the interference of $I^-$ with (*a*) the ammonium molybdate test for $PO_4^{-3}$, (*b*) the brown ring test.

17. Explain the interference of $ClO_3^-$ with the test for halides.

18. Explain the interference of $Br^-$ with the brown ring test for a nitrate.

19. Discuss the interference of $ClO_3^-$ with the brown ring test and ammonia test for a nitrate.

20. The formula for commercial ammonium molybdate is $(NH_4)_6Mo_7O_{24}$. Complete and balance the following equation:

$$Ca(H_2PO_4)_2 + (NH_4)_6Mo_7O_{24} + HNO_3 = Ca(NO_3)_2 + H_2O + (NH_4)_3P(Mo_3O_{10})_4$$

21. Formulate and explain the precipitation of $BaSO_4$ on adding $Br_2$ to a solution containing $BaCl_2$, $H_2SO_3$, and HCl.

22. Formulate and explain the precipitation of $CaCO_3$ on passing $CO_2$ into a solution of $Ca(OH)_2$.

23. Formulate and explain the precipitation of AgCl on adding $H_2SO_3$ to a solution containing $AgNO_3$, $KClO_3$, and $HNO_3$.

24. Write the equation for the final reaction involved in the identification of each of the following acid radicals: (*a*) sulfate, (*b*) oxalate, (*c*) carbonate, (*d*) phosphate, (*e*) arsenate, (*f*) sulfide, (*g*) iodide, (*h*) bromide, (*i*) chloride, (*j*) nitrate, (*k*) chlorate, (*l*) sulfite.

25. Write the equations for the oxidation of $I^-$ to $I_2$ and for the oxidation of $I_2$ to $HIO_3$ by $Ca(ClO)_2$.

26. Give in tabular form (*a*) five reagents that will distinguish $Cl^-$ from $I^-$, (*b*) the formula for the halogen product in each case, (*c*) the color and form of each halogen product.

27. Using phosphate, oxalate, and arsenate, explain how each would interfere in the regular procedure for analysis beyond Group III. Give directions for the removal of each to avoid the interference.

28. If 0.02 mg. of $I_2$ is the minimum amount of free iodine that can be recognized readily by extraction with $CCl_4$, calculate the number of milliliters of a solution containing 1 g. NaClO in 100 ml. (1% solution) which would be required to oxidize this amount of $I^-$ to $I_2$. *Ans.* 0.0006.

29. If excess NaClO will oxidize $I_2$ to $HIO_3$, calculate the amount of iodine that would be left as free iodine if 0.05 ml. of a solution containing 5 g. of NaClO in 100 ml. (5% solution) is added to a solution containing 2 mg. of $I^-$. *Ans.* 0.71 mg.

30. Calculate the number of milligrams of $C_2O_4^{--}$ needed to decolorize 0.05 ml. of (*a*) 0.5 *N* $KMnO_4$, (*b*) 0.1 *N* $KMnO_4$. *Ans.* (*a*) 1.1 mg., (*b*) 0.22 mg. Note that the sensitivity of this test for $C_2O_4^{--}$ is increased by using the smaller amount of reagent.

**Dry Samples**

1. Give the chemical name for the substance of which each of the following is chiefly or entirely composed: baking soda, blue vitriol, calomel, gypsum, brass, pencil lead, a dime, Epsom salts, green vitriol, corrosive sublimate.

2. What single test will distinguish (*a*) $CaCO_3$ from $CaC_2O_4$, (*b*) $CuCl_2$ from $NiCl_2$, (*c*) FeS from CuS, (*d*) $K_2Cr_2O_7$ from $(NH_4)_2Cr_2O_7$?

3. A certain unknown is a mixture of either $KHSO_4$ and Zn or $KHSO_4$ and ZnO. Describe one test applicable directly to a portion of the original sample that would decide the question.

4. Analysis of a certain dry unknown indicated that it was a mixture of approximately equal amounts of $NaHCO_3$ and $MgCl_2$. Give three simple tests that might be applied directly to the original sample to verify the tentative conclusions.

5. Labels have fallen from the bottles containing the following dry salts: $Pb_3O_4$, $MnO_2$, CuS, FeS, $BaCO_3$, and $BaSO_4$. How restore each label if only distilled water and HCl are available as reagents?

6. Labels have fallen from the bottles containing the following dry salts: BiOCl, $BiCl_3$, $HgCl_2$, $Hg_2Cl_2$, and CuS. How restore each label if only distilled water and dilute $NH_4OH$ are available as reagents?

7. An alloy is believed to contain Zn (at least 75%) with Bi, Sb, and Sn in amounts less than 10% each. How dissolve and test as directly as possible for each of the four metals?

8. Tabulate the behavior of $H_2O$, HCl, $HNO_3$, and aqua regia as solvents for the following substances:

| | |
|---|---|
| $As_2O_3$ | $Al_2O_3$ (ignited) |
| $H_2C_2O_4 \cdot 2H_2O$ | $ZnCO_3$ |
| CuO | $Hg_2Cl_2$ |
| $MnO_2$ | $BiCl_3$ |
| $Pb_3O_4$ | SnS |
| $Fe_3O_4$ | $BaSO_4$ |

9. Write equations for all the reactions of solvent with solid in the cases listed in question 8.

10. Outline several differences between $Na_2CO_3$ and $NaHCO_3$ that might be used as a means of distinguishing between the two substances.

11. Outline a method of distinguishing between $Bi_2O_3$, $Bi(OH)_3$, BiOCl, and $BiCl_3$.

12. State a series of facts that could be made the basis of a scheme to distinguish between PbO, $Pb(OH)_2$, $Pb_3O_4$, and $PbO_2$.

13. Describe the tests to be made while dissolving a dry unknown in HCl.

14. Describe the tests to be made while dissolving a dry unknown in $HNO_3$.

15. Compare the amount of information obtained from tests applied during the dissolving process when the three reagents HCl, $HNO_3$, and aqua regia are used as solvents.

16. Explain the difference in the effectiveness of the common acids as solvents in the following cases: (*a*) $Hg_2Cl_2$ and AgCl, (*b*) $HgI_2$ and AgI, (*c*) $Hg_2SO_4$ and $BaSO_4$.

17. Explain a laboratory method for distinguishing between the different substances in each of the following cases:

| | |
|---|---|
| (*a*) $CuSO_4 \cdot 5H_2O$ or $CuSO_4$ | (*e*) $Mg_2OCl_2$ or $MgCl_2$ |
| (*b*) $BaCl_2 \cdot 2H_2O$ or $BaCl_2$ | (*f*) SbOCl or $SbCl_3$ |
| (*c*) MgO or $Mg(OH)_2$ | (*g*) $Na_2C_2O_4$ or $NaHC_2O_4$ |
| (*d*) $Bi_2O_3$, BiOCl, or $BiONO_3$ | (*h*) $Na_3PO_4$, $Na_2HPO_4$, or $NaH_2PO_4$ |

18. Outline laboratory procedures to distinguish as directly as possible between the two substances in each of the following cases:

| | |
|---|---|
| (*a*) $HgCl_2$ and $Hg_2Cl_2$ | (*f*) $HgCl_2$ and $HgBr_2$ |
| (*b*) CuS and CuO | (*g*) $BaCrO_4$ and $PbCrO_4$ |
| (*c*) Fe and $Fe_3O_4$ | (*h*) HgO and $HgI_2$ |
| (*d*) FeS and $MnO_2$ | (*i*) $K_2Cr_2O_7$ and $(NH_4)_2Cr_2O_7$ |
| (*e*) $Pb_3O_4$ and $PbO_2$ | (*j*) FeS and CuS |

19. What happens when each of the following dry mixtures is boiled in water:

(*a*) $FeCl_3$ and FeS
(*b*) $FeCO_3$ and $NH_4NO_3$
(*c*) $CuCO_3$ and $NH_4Al(SO_4)_2 \cdot 12H_2O$
(*d*) $SrCO_3$ and $Fe_2(SO_4)_3$
(*e*) $NH_4Cl$ (excess), $PbCO_3$ and ZnS

20. *Practice Exercise in Reporting Complex Dry Unknowns.* In each of the following cases assume that the mixture as given has been studied in the laboratory according to the directions given for complex dry unknowns, and on the basis of your general chemical knowledge make out the report as if it had been based on the laboratory examination. Since the report in a given case will depend on the proportions in which the materials are mixed as well as on the substances present initially, it will be assumed that the materials are mixed in equivalent proportions for such reactions as occur in the preparation of the water solution unless indications are given to the contrary, such as (*xs*) and (*s*), meaning large excess and small amount, respectively.

*Illustration.* Make out a report of the following complex dry unknown: $Na_2CO_3$ (*xs*), $AlCl_3$, Cu.

(*a*) Ions in water solution: $Na^+$, $CO_3^{--}$, $Cl^-$, $Al(OH)_4^-$
(*b*) Substances in residue: $Al(OH)_3$, $Cu^\circ$
(*c*) Solvent for residue: $HNO_3$
(*d*) Gases escaping during the dissolving process: $CO_2$ from *a*, $NO_2$ during solution of *b*

---

(1) $NaNO_3$, $Fe_2O_3$
(2) $AgNO_3$, NaCl
(3) $(NH_4)_2CO_3$
(4) Ca
(5) $AgNO_3$, $Na_2CO_3$ (*xs*)
(6) $CaCl_2$, $Na_2CO_3$ (*xs*)
(7) $Na_2CO_3$ (*xs*), $Hg_2(NO_3)_2$
(8) $Na_2CO_3$, $K_2Cr_2O_7$
(9) $Na_2CO_3$ (*xs*), $HgCl_2$
(10) $Na_2CO_3$ (*xs*), $AlCl_3$
(11) $(NH_4)_2SO_4$, $BaCO_3$
(12) $AgNO_3$, Al
(13) $AgNO_3$, $Na_2CO_3$ (*xs*), Al
(14) ZnS, $NH_4Cl$ (*xs*)
(15) $NH_4Cl$, $MgCO_3$
(16) $NaHSO_4$, $BaCO_3$
(17) $NaHCO_3$, $MgCl_2$
(18) $Na_2CO_3$, Al
(19) $Na_2CO_3$, Cu
(20) $As_2O_3$
(21) $Na_2CO_3$, $As_2O_3$
(22) $Na_2CO_3$, $As_2S_3$
(23) $Na_2CO_3$ (*xs*), $Fe_2(SO_4)_3$
(24) $BaCl_2$, $K_2Cr_2O_7$
(25) $NaHSO_4$ (*xs*), $NaNO_3$, $FeSO_4$
(26) $Na_2CO_3$, $Zn(NO_3)_2$, $FeSO_4$
(27) $KHSO_4$ (*xs*), $As_2O_3$, $KMnO_4$
(28) $Na_2CO_3$ (*xs*), $As_2O_3$, $KMnO_4$
(29) $KHSO_4$ (*xs*), $As_2O_3$, Zn
(30) $NH_4Cl$ (*xs*), Mg
(31) $NaHSO_4$ (*xs*), $K_2Cr_2O_7$, $FeSO_4$
(32) $FeSO_4$, $KMnO_4$
(33) $NH_4Cl$ (*xs*), $BaCO_3$, $Al_2O_3$
(34) $KAl(SO_4)_2 \cdot 12H_2O$, $Na_2CO_3$
(35) $CuSO_4$, $NaHSO_4$ (*xs*), Al
(36) $NaHSO_4$ (*xs*), $As_2O_3$, Al
(37) $Na_2CO_3$ (*xs*), $NH_4Cl$, $AgNO_3$
(38) $Fe(NH_4)_2(SO_4)_2$
(39) $NaHSO_4$ (*xs*), $K_2CrO_4$, $FeSO_4$
(40) $K_2CO_3$ (*xs*), SbOCl, Bi
(41) $NaHSO_4$ (*xs*), $MgCO_3$, FeS
(42) $NaHSO_4$ (*xs*), $BaCO_3$, $Al_2O_3$
(43) $NaHSO_4$ (*xs*), $CuCO_3$, FeS
(44) $Na_2CO_3$ (*xs*), $CuBr_2$, $KAl(SO_4)_2$
(45) $Na_2CO_3$ (*xs*), $ZnSO_4$, $K_2Cr_2O_7$
(46) $Na_2CO_3$, $NiSO_4$ (*s*), $FeCl_3$, $NH_4Cl$ (*xs*)
(47) $Na_2S$ (*xs*), $SnCl_4$ (*s*)
(48) $KHSO_4$ (*xs*), $CaCO_3$ (*s*), $BaCrO_4$
(49) KI (*xs*), $HgCl_2$ (*s*), $AgNO_3$
(50) $NaHSO_4$ (*xs*), KI, $BaCrO_4$

(a) Give molecular equations for all reactions taking place when preparing the water solutions in each of the above problems.

21. Balance the following equation and calculate the proportions in which the three substances should be mixed to correspond to this reaction:

$$Na_2CO_3 + SbOCl + KMnO_4 + H_2O = H_3SbO_4 + MnO_2 + KCl + NaCl + CO_2$$

22. Balance the following equation and calculate the proportions in which the three substances should be mixed to correspond to this reaction:

$$K_2Cr_2O_7 + FeSO_4 \cdot (NH_4)_2SO_4 \cdot 6H_2O + KHSO_4 = Cr_2(SO_4)_3 + Fe_2(SO_4)_3 + (NH_4)_2SO_4 + K_2SO_4 + H_2O$$

23. Show the variety of reports that might be obtained by a laboratory study of mixtures, in varying proportions, of the following salts:

$$K_2CO_3, \quad NH_4NO_3, \quad AgNO_3, \quad AlCl_3$$

24. Show the variety of reports that might be obtained by a laboratory study of mixtures, in varying proportions, of the three salts, KI, $HgCl_2$, and $AgNO_3$.

## GENERAL REVIEW EQUATIONS

### Oxidation-reduction Reactions

1. Describe the oxidation-number for balancing the following equations:

(a) $KMnO_4 + CH_2O + HCl = MnCl_2 + KCl + CH_2O_2 + H_2O$
(b) $Fe(NO_3)_3 + FeSO_4 + H_2SO_4 = Fe_2(SO_4)_3 + FeSO_4 \cdot NO + H_2O$
(c) $Zn(NO_3)_2 + NaOH + Al = NH_3 + NaZn(OH)_3 + NaAl(OH)_4 + H_2O$
(d) $Sb_2S_5 + HCl = SbCl_3 + H_2S + S$
(e) $Na_2Cr_2O_7 + H_2SO_4 + H_2O_2 = CrO_5 + Na_2SO_4 + H_2O$

2. Describe the ion-electron method for balancing the following equations:

(a) $KMnO_4 + HNO_3 + H_2O_2 = Mn(NO_3)_2 + KNO_3 + O_2 + H_2O$
(b) $Mn(NO_3)_2 + HNO_3 + Pb_3O_4 = HMnO_4 + Pb(NO_3)_2 + H_2O$
(c) $Cr(OH)_3 + OH^- + H_2O_2 = CrO_4^{--} + H_2O$
(d) $As_2S_3 + (NH_4)_2S_2 + (NH_4)_2S = (NH_4)_3AsS_4$
(e) $K_2C_2O_4 + HNO_3 + KMnO_4 = KNO_3 + Mn(NO_3)_2 + CO_2 + H_2O$
(f) $FeI_2 + HCl + Ca(ClO)_2 = FeCl_3 + HIO_3 + CaCl_2 + H_2O$
(g) $Mg(NO_3)_2 + NaOH + Al + H_2O = NH_3 + NaAl(OH)_4 + Mg(OH)_2$

### Net Reactions

Write the net reaction for each of the following:

1. Precipitation of $PbCl_2$ in Group I.
2. Reaction between $K_2Cr_2O_7$ and $PbCl_2$.
3. Interaction of $Hg_2Cl_2$ and $NH_4OH$.
4. Dissolving AgCl in $NH_4OH$.
5. Addition of $HNO_3$ to $Ag(NH_3)_2Cl$ to form AgCl.
6. Precipitation of AgI on adding KI to $Ag(NH_3)_2Cl$.
7. Neutralization of $HgCl_2$ with $NH_4OH$.
8. Precipitation of CuS in Group II.

9. Dissolving $Bi_2S_3$ in $HNO_3$.
10. Dissolving HgS in nitro-hydrochloric acid.
11. Precipitation of $PbSO_4$ on evaporation of $Pb(NO_3)_2$ with $H_2SO_4$.
12. Dissolving $PbSO_4$ in ammonium acetate.
13. Formation of $PbCrO_4$ from $K_2Cr_2O_7$ and lead acetate.
14. Interaction of bismuth sulfate and $NH_4OH$.
15. Dissolving $Bi(OH)_3$ in HCl.
16. Potassium iodide test for Bi.
17. Reduction of $Bi(OH)_3$ by $NaSn(OH)_3$.
18. Conversion of $Cu(NH_3)_4SO_4$ to $Na_2Cu(CN)_3$ by NaCN.
19. Interaction of $H_2S$ and $Cd(NH_3)_4SO_4$.
20. Action of $H_2S$ in a solution containing $Na_2Cd(CN)_4$, $(NH_4)_2SO_4$, and $NH_4OH$ to form CdS.
21. Formation of $As_2S_3$ on interaction of $H_2S$ and $H_3AsO_3$.
22. Dissolving $Sb_2S_3$ in $(NH_4)_2S_2$.
23. Reaction of dilute HCl and ammonium thiostannate to form $SnS_2$.
24. Solution of $As_2S_5$ in $HNO_3$.
25. Precipitation of $Ag_3AsO_4$ in the "brown ring test for As."
26. Dissolving $Sb_2S_5$ in concentrated HCl.
27. Precipitation of Sb in the silver coin test.
28. Reduction of $H_2SnCl_6$ by Fe.
29. Mercuric chloride test for Sn.
30. Interaction of $K_2Cr_2O_7$, HCl, and $H_2S$.
31. Reaction of $K_2Cr_2O_7$, HCl, and $NaNO_2$.
32. Reduction of $FeCl_3$ with $H_2S$.
33. Oxidation of $FeCl_2$ by HCl and $NaNO_2$.
34. Precipitation of $Al(OH)_3$ in Group III.
35. Dissolving $Al(OH)_3$ in NaOH.
36. Interaction of $Cr(OH)_3$, NaOH, and $H_2O_2$.
37. Reaction of $K_2CrO_4$ with $HNO_3$.
38. Acidification of $NaAl(OH)_4$ with $HNO_3$.
39. Interaction of $NaAl(OH)_4$ and $NH_4Cl$.
40. Dissolving $Fe(OH)_3$ in $H_2SO_4$.
41. Interaction of $Na_2CrO_4$, $HNO_3$, and $H_2O_2$.
42. Reaction of KCNS with ferric sulfate.
43. Formation of ferric ferrocyanide from ferric sulfate and $K_4Fe(CN)_6$.
44. Acidification of $K_2MnO_4$ with $HNO_3$.
45. Addition of excess $HNO_3$ to $Ni(NH_3)_6Cl_2$.
46. Acidification of $NaZn(OH)_3$ with $HNO_3$.
47. Interaction of $KMnO_4$, HCl, and $H_2S$.
48. Reduction of $KMnO_4$ with HCl and $NaNO_2$.
49. Precipitation of MnS in Group IV.
50. Formation of CoS in Group IV.
51. Dissolving ZnS in HCl.
52. Interaction of NaOH, bromine water, and $MnCl_2$ to form $MnO_2$.
53. Dissolving $MnO_2$ in $HNO_3$ and $H_2O_2$.
54. Periodate test for Mn.
55. Formation of ZnS from $H_2S$ and $NaZn(OH)_3$.
56. Dissolving CoS in nitro-hydrochloric acid.
57. Thiocyanate test for Co.
58. Dioxime test for Ni.
59. Precipitation of $CaCO_3$ in Group V.

60. Dissolving $SrCO_3$ in acetic acid.
61. Formation of $BaCrO_4$ from $K_2Cr_2O_7$ and barium acetate.
62. Precipitation of $BaSO_4$ from a solution of $BaCl_2$ treated with $H_2SO_4$.
63. Separation of $SrSO_4$ upon addition of $(NH_4)_2SO_4$ to an acetic acid solution of strontium acetate.
64. Formation of $BaSO_4$ when bromine water is added to a solution containing $BaCl_2$, HCl, and $H_2SO_3$.
65. Precipitation of $CaCO_3$ when $CO_2$ is passed into a solution of $Ca(OH)_2$.
66. Interaction of $KMnO_4$, $Na_2C_2O_4$, and $HNO_3$ in a warm solution.
67. Formation of $MgNH_4PO_4$ in a solution of $MgCl_2$, $Na_2HPO_4$, $NH_4Cl$, and $NH_4OH$.
68. Precipitation of ammonium molybdi-phosphate on adding $(NH_4)_2MoO_4$ to a nitric acid solution of ammonium phosphate.
69. Formation of PbS in the lead acetate test for $H_2S$.
70. Oxidation of iodide to iodine when an HCl solution of KI is treated with $Ca(ClO)_2$.
71. Removal of $I_2$ by addition of $Ca(ClO)_2$ in the test for bromide.
72. Brown ring test for nitrate.
73. Ammonia test for nitrate.
74. Precipitation of AgCl upon interaction of $H_2SO_3$, $AgNO_3$, $HNO_3$, and $NaClO_3$.
75. Formation of AgCl when a chlorate is treated with $HNO_3$ and $NaNO_2$.

## PROBLEMS

### Normal and Empirical Solutions

1. One liter of a concentrated (28%) solution of $NH_3$ weighs 900 g. What is its normality?
2. How much concentrated ammonia solution (problem 1) and how much water should be mixed to produce 250 ml. of 5 $N$ solution?
3. How much water should be added to 500 ml. of concentrated ammonia solution to produce a 5 $N$ solution?
4. If concentrated ammonia water is 15 $N$, how many liters of $NH_3$, at STP, have been dissolved in 1 liter of water to produce such a solution?
5. A solution contains 40% HCl and its density is 1.2. What is the normality?
6. How many milliliters of 70% $HNO_3$ (density 1.42) would be required for 100 ml. of 5 $N$ solution? *Ans.* 31.7 ml.
7. Concentrated $H_2SO_4$ assays 94% and has a density of 1.84. How many milliliters will be required for 250 ml. of 5 $N$ solution? *Ans.* 35.4 ml.
8. The solubility of $H_2S$ in water is 437 ml. per 100 ml. at 0°C. 760 mm. Calculate the (*a*) molarity and (*b*) normality for neutralization.
9. If 90 ml. of $CO_2$ will dissolve in 100 ml. of $H_2O$ at 20°C., what is the molarity of the resulting solution?
10. A solution of $HNO_3$ contains 25 g. of the acid per liter. Calculate (*a*) the normality of the solution when used to neutralize a base, (*b*) the normality of the solution when used to oxidize $Fe^{++}$ to $Fe^{+++}$.
11. A solution of $K_2Cr_2O_7$ contains 15 g. of the salt per liter. Calculate (*a*) the molar concentration of the solution, (*b*) the normality when used to precipitate $Pb^{++}$ as $PbCrO_4$, (*c*) the normality when used to oxidize $Fe^{++}$ to $Fe^{+++}$.
12. Calculate the normality of a 3% $H_2O_2$ (3 g. in 100 ml.) solution when used to dissolve $MnO_2$ in an acid solution. ($MnO_2 + H_2O_2 + 2H_3O^+ = Mn^{++} + 4H_2O + O_2$)

13. Calculate the concentration of $NH_4OH$ resulting from the addition of 0.1 ml. of 5 *N* $NH_4OH$ to 25 ml. of a neutral solution.

14. Calculate the normality of a solution of HCl if 1 ml. is equivalent to 5 mg. of $Ag^+$.

15. Calculate the normality of a solution of $H_2SO_4$ if 1 ml. will give a precipitate of 20 mg. of $BaSO_4$.

16. Calculate the extent to which 5 *N* HCl should be diluted to prepare a solution in which 1 ml. is equivalent to 10 mg. of $Ag^+$.

17. If a solution contains 5 mg. of $Ag^+$ per ml., calculate the volume of 5 *N* HCl that would be equivalent to 15 ml. of this solution.

18. If 15 ml. of a solution containing 100 mg. of $Hg_2^{++}$ is treated with 1.5 ml. of 5 *N* HCl, calculate the concentration of $Cl^-$ in the resulting solution. *Ans.* 0.424 *N*.

19. Composition of the reagent $(NH_4)_2S_x$. Treat 150 ml. of 15 *N* $NH_4OH$ with $H_2S$ to saturation (forms $NH_4HS$), add 250 ml. of 15 *N* $NH_4OH$ and 10 g. of S. When the S is dissolved, dilute to 1 liter. Neglecting hydrolysis, calculate the molar concentrations of $(NH_4)_2S_2$, $(NH_4)_2S$, and $NH_4OH$ in this solution.

*Ans.* $(NH_4)_2S_2$ = 0.31 *M*, $(NH_4)_2S$ = 1.94 *M*, and $NH_4OH$ = 1.5 *M*.

20. Calculate the concentration of $H_3O^+$ in the solution after 50 mg. of Fe, precipitated as $Fe(OH)_3$, has dissolved in 20 ml. of 0.25 *N* HCl. *Ans.* $H_3O^+$ = 0.115 *N*.

21. Calculate the number of milliliters of 3% $H_2O_2$ used up in dissolving 75 mg. of $MnO_2$ in $HNO_3 + H_2O_2$.

**Boiling and Freezing Points**

The molar elevation of boiling point of water is 0.52 degrees on the centigrade scale. The molar depression of freezing point of water is 1.86 degrees on the centigrade scale.

1. What is the molecular weight of a compound 3.2 g. of which elevates the boiling point of 1 liter of water 0.018°C.? *Ans.* 92.

2. What is the molecular weight of a compound 7.355 g. of which depresses the freezing point of 1 liter of water 0.04°C.? *Ans.* 342.

3. How many grams of dextrose would be required to raise the boiling point of 2 liters of water to 102°C.? *Ans.* 1386 g.

4. How many grams of dextrose ($C_6H_{12}O_6$) would be required to lower the freezing point of 5 liters of water to −5°C.? *Ans.* 2419 g.

5. What concentration of methyl alcohol in water would give a mixture freezing at −10°C.? *Ans.* 14.7%.

6. If 6 g. of AB in 50 ml. of $H_2O$ forms a solution boiling at 100.345°C., what is the apparent molecular weight of AB?

7. If 58.46 g. of NaCl in 1000 g. of water forms a solution freezing at −3.42°C., what is the apparent extent of ionization?

8. Calculate the apparent extent of dissociation of the compound AB (mol. wt. 75) if 3.75 g. in 100 g. of water gives a solution freezing at −1.023°C. *Ans.* 10%.

9. If 74.56 g. of KCl in 1000 g. of water forms a solution boiling at 100.97°C., what is the apparent extent of ionization?

10. If AB is 20% ionized in 0.5 *M* solution, at what temperature will the mixture freeze?

11. The compound AB is 25% ionized in 0.3 *M* solution. At what temperature will the mixture boil?

**Ionization Constants**

1. If 0.5 *N* $HNO_2$ is 3% ionized, what is the dissociation constant K?

2. The compound AB is 2% ionized in 0.3 *M* aqueous solution. Calculate the ionization constant.

3. What is the fraction of acetic acid dissociated in 0.4 *M* solution?
4. If AB is 1% ionized in 0.1 *M* solution, what is the $[B^-]$ in 0.5 *M* solution?
5. Calculate the extent of ionization of HCN at each of the following dilutions: 0.01 *N*, 0.1 *N*, 1.0 *N*. $K_{HCN} = 7 \times 10^{-10}$.
6. Calculate $K_i$ for the acid HB if it is 0.05% ionized in 0.1 *M* solution. *Ans.* $2.51 \times 10^{-8}$.
7. Calculate the extent of ionization of 0.1 *M* $NH_4OH$.
8. Calculate the extent of ionization of 0.01 *M* $NH_4OH$.
9. Calculate $[OH^-]$ in 0.1 *M* $NH_4OH$ containing sufficient $NH_4Cl$ to make the $[NH_4^+]$ total 1 *M*.
10. Calculate the concentration of AC, a strong electrolyte, that must be present in a 0.1 *M* solution of AB to make $B^- = 1 \times 10^{-4}$ if $K_{AB} = 1 \times 10^{-5}$.
11. Calculate $S^{--}$ in a solution in which $H_3O^+$ is 0.2 and $H_2S = 0.1$.

$$K_{H_2S} = 1 \times 10^{-7}, \quad K_{HS^-} = 1 \times 10^{-15}$$

12. What fraction of the $H_2S$ absorbed in a solution would be changed to $HS^-$ if the final concentration of $H_3O^+$ is (*a*) $1 \times 10^{-6}$, (*b*) $1 \times 10^{-7}$, (*c*) $1 \times 10^{-8}$?
13. If a reagent AB is 1% ionized in 0.1 *M* solution, what concentration of $B^-$ would be present in 0.5 *M* solution? In 0.01 *M* solution?

**Hydrogen Ion Concentration, pH**

1. If the F.P. of 0.01 *M* HAc is −0.0194°C., what is the pH of the solution?
2. If $K_{HAc} = 1.8 \times 10^{-5}$, what normality of HAc would be required for a solution of pH 3.5?
3. If 500 ml. of $NH_3$ (at STP) is dissolved in $H_2O$ and the volume made up to 1 liter, what will be the pH of the solution? $K_{NH_4OH} = 1.8 \times 10^{-5}$. *Ans.* 10.8.
4. What concentration of $HC_2H_3O_2$, expressed in grams per liter, would be required for a solution of pH 3.5? *Ans.* 0.336 g./l.
5. A 0.01 *M* solution of $HC_2H_3O_2$ is 4.3% ionized. What is the pH?
6. Calculate the pH of 0.01 *M* $NH_4OH$. $K_{NH_4OH} = 1.8 \times 10^{-5}$.
7. Calculate the pH of 0.1 *M* $NH_4OH$. $K_{NH_4OH} = 1.8 \times 10^{-5}$.
8. If a 0.01 *M* solution of acetic acid freezes at −0.0194°C., what is (*a*) $K_{HAc}$, (*b*) pH of a 0.5 *M* solution?
9. The dissociation constant for the acid $HC_2H_3O_2$ is $1.8 \times 10^{-5}$. What is the pH of 0.5 *N* solution?
10. Into 1000 ml. of 0.2 *M* $NH_4OH$ solution is passed 2,240 ml. of HCl gas. What is the pH of the resulting solution? *Ans.* 9.26.
11. What is the pH of a solution 0.1 *M* with respect to $NH_4OH$ and 0.5 *M* with regard to $NH_4Cl$ (100% ionized)? *Ans.* 8.56.
12. A solution of pH 7.6 is desired. What $[NH_4OH]$ and $[NH_4Cl]$ will be required? Assume the salt 100% ionized.
13. Calculate the pH of 0.1 *M* acetic acid before and after the addition of an equal volume of 0.1 *M* sodium acetate (100% ionized). *Ans.* 2.87 before, 4.74 after.
14. What is the pH of a solution 0.1 *M* with respect to both acetic acid and sodium acetate? $K_{HAc} = 1.8 \times 10^{-5}$.
15. If 100 ml. of 0.1 *M* NaOH is added to 150 ml. of 0.2 *M* acetic acid, what is the final pH? *Ans.* 4.45.
16. How many grams of $NaC_2H_3O_2$ should be added to 500 ml. of a 0.1 *M* acetic acid to give a solution of pH 4.5? (Ignore any volume change due to addition of the salt.)
17. A 0.01 *M* solution of $NH_4OH$ is 4.2% ionized. Calculate the pH before and after adding enough $NH_4Cl$ to make the $(NH_4^+)$ equal to 1 *M*.

18. If equal volumes of 0.4 *M* acetic acid and 1 *M* NaAc (100% ionized) are mixed, what is the pH of the resulting solution? *Ans.* 5.14.

19. Calculate the pH when equivalent amounts of a 0.096 *N* solution of a monobasic acid ($K_A = 3 \times 10^{-5}$) and 0.096 *N* NaOH are mixed.

20. Calculate the pH of a solution obtained by mixing 50 ml. of 1.4 *N* HCl with 90 ml. of 1.4 *N* BOH, a monoacid base ($K_B = 4.5 \times 10^{-7}$).

21. A solution containing 100 mg. of Cr as $K_2Cr_2O_7$ in 100 ml. has a pH of 0.6. What is the pH after addition of enough $H_2S$ to reduce the Cr to $Cr^{+++}$.

$$(Cr_2O_7^{--} + 3H_2S + 8H_3O^+ = 2Cr^{+++} + 3S + 15H_2O)$$

*Ans.* pH = 0.75.

22. If 450 ml. of $CO_2$ are absorbed in 100 ml. of 0.25 *M* $Ba(OH)_2$, what is the approximate pH of the final solution?

**Hydrolysis**

The hydrolysis constant for an ion which hydrolyzes to give a basic solution is the water constant divided by the ionization constant of the weak acid formed.

$$K_{hydr.\ B^-} = \frac{K_W}{K_{HA}}.$$

The hydrolysis constant for an ion which hydrolyzes to give an acid solution is the water constant divided by the ionization constant of the weak base formed.

$$K_{hydr.\ A^+} = \frac{K_W}{K_{BOH}}.$$

1. Derive the formula for $[H_3O^+]$ in a given solution of $NH_4Cl$ starting with $K_{hydr.} = \frac{K_W}{K_{NH_4OH}}$.

2. Derive the formula for $[OH^-]$ in a given solution of $NaC_2H_3O_2$ starting with $K_{hydr.} = \frac{K_W}{K_{HAc}}$.

3. How many grams of $NH_4Cl$ must be added to 500 ml. of $H_2O$ to produce a concentration of $H_3O^+$ of $1 \times 10^{-5}$?

4. If one assumes that $NH_4^+$ is a weak acid which dissociates to yield $H_3O^+$ and $NH_3$ ($K_{NH_4^+} = 5.6 \times 10^{-10}$), what concentration of $NH_4^+$ would be needed to produce a concentration of $H_3O^+$ of $1 \times 10^{-5}$?

5. If $Na_2C_2O_4$ hydrolyzes according to the equation $C_2O_4^{--} + H_2O = HC_2O_4^- + OH^-$, what is the concentration of $OH^-$ in a 0.1 *M* solution of the salt?

6. If $Fe^{+++}$ hydrolyzes according to the equation $Fe^{+++} + 2H_2O = FeOH^{++} + H_3O^+$, what will be the concentration of $H_3O^+$ in 0.1 *M* solution of $Fe^{+++}$? $K_{FeOH^{++}} = 2.5 \times 10^{-12}$.

7. Will $Mg(OH)_2$ precipitate when equal volumes of 0.1 *M* $MgCl_2$ and 0.1 *M* KCN are mixed? $L_{Mg(OH)_2} = 3 \times 10^{-10}$, $K_{HCN} = 7 \times 10^{-10}$.

8. If equal volumes of *N* $NH_4OH$ and *N* HCl are mixed, what will be the concentration of $H_3O^+$ in the resulting solution?

9. If $(NH_4)_2CO_3$ is 0.3 *M* in a solution in which the final concentrations of $NH_4^+$ and $NH_4OH$ are 0.75 *M* and 1.5 *M*, respectively, what fraction of the $CO_3^{--}$ would be hydrolyzed to form $HCO_3^-$?

10. (*a*) Calculate the concentration of $OH^-$ in a 0.5 *M* solution of $Na_2CO_3$. (*b*) What percentage of the $CO_3^{--}$ is hydrolyzed?

11. Calculate the concentration of $OH^-$ in a 0.5 *M* solution of $Na_2S$.

**Solubility Products**

1. Assuming the solubility of AgCl is 1.5 mg. per liter, what is the solubility product?

2. The solubility of $SrSO_4$ is 0.11 g./l. Calculate the solubility product.

3. A saturated solution of $BaCO_3$ contains 20 parts per million. Calculate $L_{BaCO_3}$.

4. Calculate the solubility product of $A_2B$ if the solubility is $2.5 \times 10^{-3}$ grams per liter and the molecular weight is 125.

5. If 0.1 g. of $PbI_2$ will just saturate 147 ml. of $H_2O$ at 25°C., what is the solubility product of $PbI_2$? (Neglect the possible formation of some $PbI^+$).

6. A 420-ml. sample of satd. $Mg(OH)_2$ solution was evaporated to dryness and ignited. The MgO weighed 6.7 mg. Calculate the solubility product of $Mg(OH)_2$.

7. If the solubility product of PbS is $3.4 \times 10^{-28}$, calculate the solubility of PbS in water, assuming water is an inert solvent.

8. $L_{Cu(IO_3)_2} = 1.4 \times 10^{-7}$. Calculate $Cu^{++}$ and $IO_3^-$ in a saturated solution in water.

9. If the solubility product of $Cr(OH)_3$ is $2.9 \times 10^{-29}$, derive a formula for calculating the solubility in terms of moles of $Cr(OH)_3$ per liter.

$$\textit{Ans.}\quad M = \sqrt[4]{\frac{L_{Cr(OH)_3}}{27}} = \sqrt[4]{\frac{2.9 \times 10^{-29}}{27}}.$$

10. Express the formula for the solubility product of $Ba_3(PO_4)_2$ in terms of $Ba^{++}$ in the saturated aqueous solution. *Ans.* $L = \frac{4}{9}[Ba^{++}]^5$.

11. If $[Ba^{++}] = 0.25$, what $[SO_4^{--}]$ would be required to saturate the solution with respect to $BaSO_4$?

12. Calculate the concentration of $CO_3^{--}$ needed to saturate a 0.2 *M* solution of $MgCl_2$ with $MgCO_3$.

13. What $[OH^-]$ is necessary to saturate a 0.01 *M* solution of $Mg^{++}$ with $Mg(OH)_2$?

14. If $[Pb^{++}] = 0.01$, what $[PO_4^{---}]$ would be necessary to give a saturated solution of $Pb_3(PO_4)_2$? $L_{Pb_3(PO_4)_2} = 1.5 \times 10^{-32}$.

15. A certain solution of $Na_2CO_3$ is 0.09 *M*. How many drops of 0.01 *N* $Ca(OH)_2$ (0.05 ml. each) should be added to 10 ml. of the solution to produce saturation with respect to $CaCO_3$? $L_{CaCO_3} = 1.7 \times 10^{-8}$.

16. How many milligrams of $Ag^+$ will be left in 20 ml. of a solution containing 0.5 ml. of 5 *N* HCl in excess of that needed to precipitate Group I?

17. (*a*) Given $L_{Al(OH)_3} = 8.5 \times 10^{-33}$, at what pH will $Al(OH)_3$ start to precipitate from a solution containing 10 mg. $Al^{+++}$ per liter?

(*b*) Same for $Fe^{+++}$, $L_{Fe(OH)_3} = 1.3 \times 10^{-38}$.
(*c*) Same for $Cr^{+++}$, $L_{Ca(OH)_3} = 2.9 \times 10^{-29}$.
(*d*) Same for $Fe^{++}$, $L_{Fe(OH)_2} = 3.6 \times 10^{-19}$.

18. How many milligrams of $Mg^{++}$ can be present in 1 liter of a solution 0.01 *M* with respect to $CO_3^{--}$?

19. Calculate the effectiveness of the separation of Al from Mn when $[OH^-] = 1 \times 10^{-6}$. $L_{Al(OH)_3} = 8.5 \times 10^{-33}$, $L_{Mn(OH)_2} = 5 \times 10^{-13}$.

20. Fifteen milliliters of a neutral solution containing 50 mg. of $Ag^+$ is treated with 0.5 ml. of 5 *N* HCl. Calculate the (*a*) grams of AgCl formed, (*b*) grams of $Ag^+$ left in solution, (*c*) normality of the solution with respect to $H_3O^+$.

*Ans.* (*a*) 0.066 g. AgCl. (*b*) $1.28 \times 10^{-9}$ g. $Ag^+$. (*c*) 0.16 *N*.

21. A solution contains $Mn^{++}$ and $Mg^{++}$ each 0.1 *M*. Calculate the concentration of $Mn^{++}$ left on treatment with $OH^-$ when the solution is just saturated with $Mg(OH)_2$. $L_{Mn(OH)_2} = 5 \times 10^{-13}$ $L_{Mg(OH)_2} = 3 \times 10^{-10}$.

**General Equilibrium Problems**

1. Calculate the extent to which $A$ and $B$ will react to form $C$ and $D$ if the reagents are each molar at the start and the equilibrium constant is 100.

2. If the equilibrium constant in the reaction $A + B = C + D$ is $1 \times 10^{-4}$, what is the final concentration of each substance if at the start $A = B = 1$ and $C = D = 0$?

3. Calculate the extent to which $A$ and $B$ will react to form $C$ and $D$ if equal volumes of 1 $M$ $A$ and 2 $M$ $B$ are mixed and the equilibrium constant is 100.

*Ans.* Approx. 99% of the $A$ will be used up.

4. Set up the basis for calculating the extent of reaction between $A$ and $B$ if the original concentrations in the system are $A = 0.5\ M$, $B = 1.0\ M$, $C = 1.5\ M$, and $D = 2.0\ M$ if the equilibrium constant is 30.

5. Show mathematically that the $[OH^-]$ in a mixture of $a$ moles of $NH_4OH$ and $b$ moles of $NH_4Cl$ (100% ionized) is independent of dilution (except at extreme dilution).

6. Calculate the concentration of $S^{--}$ in a solution in which the final concentration of $OH^-$ is $1 \times 10^{-5}$ if $[H_2S] + [HS^-] + [S^{--}] = 0.1$. $K_W = 1 \times 10^{-14}$, $K_{H_2S} = 1 \times 10^{-7}$, $K_{HS^-} = 1 \times 10^{-15}$.

7. What fraction of the $S^{--}$ added to a solution would be changed to $HS^-$ if the final concentration of $OH^-$ in the solution is (*a*) 0.1 $M$, (*b*) $1 \times 10^{-3}$ $M$?

8. If $K_{1H_2S} = 1 \times 10^{-7}$ and $K_{HS^-} = 1 \times 10^{-15}$, calculate the ratio $[H_2S]:[HS^-]:[S^{--}]$ in a solution in which $[H_3O^+] =$ (*a*) $10^{-5}$ $N$, (*b*) $10^{-7}$ $N$, (*c*) $10^{-9}$ $N$.

*Ans.* (*a*) $1:10^{-2}:10^{-12}$. (*b*) $1:1:10^{-8}$. (*c*) $1:100:10^{-4}$.

9. If $[H_2S] + [HS^-] + [S^{--}] = 0.2\ N$ in a solution in which $[NH_4^+] = 3$ and $[NH_4OH] = 1$, calculate $[S^{--}]$. $K_{1H_2S} = 1 \times 10^{-7}$, $K_{HS^-} = 1 \times 10^{-15}$, $K_{NH_4OH} = 1.8 \times 10^{-5}$, $K_W = 1 \times 10^{-14}$. *Ans.* $[S^{--}] = 5.9 \times 10^{-8}$.

10. If in a solution $[H_2CO_3] + [HCO_3^-] + [CO_3^{--}] = 0.1$, at what $[OH^-]$ will $[CO_3^{--}]$ be 0.01? $K_{H_2CO_3} = 3 \times 10^{-7}$, $K_{HCO_3} = 5.3 \times 10^{-11}$?

*Ans.* $[OH^-] = 2.1 \times 10^{-5}$.

11. If in a solution $[H_2CO_3] + [HCO_3^-] + [CO_3^{--}] = 0.1$ and $[NH_4^+] = 0.2$, what $[NH_4OH]$ must be present in order that $[CO_3^{--}] = 0.01$? *Ans.* $[NH_4OH] = 0.233\ M$.

12. A certain solution is 0.001 $M$ with $NH_4OH$. If it could be made 0.01 $M$ with respect to $Zn^{++}$ without change in volume, would the solubility product of $Zn(OH)_2$ be exceeded? $K_{NH_4OH} = 1.8 \times 10^{-5}$, $L_{Zn(OH)_2} = 4 \times 10^{-18}$.

13. Calculate the concentration of $NH_4OH$ that will make a 0.1 $M$ $MnCl_2$ solution containing $NH_4Cl$ (2 $N$, completely ionized) just saturated with $Mn(OH)_2$. $K_{NH_4OH} = 1.8 \times 10^{-5}$, $L_{Mn(OH)_2} = 5 \times 10^{-13}$.

14. Calculate the concentration of $NH_4Cl$ needed to prevent the precipitation of $Mg(OH)_2$ in a solution that is 0.25 $M$ with respect to $Mg^{++}$ and 0.5 $M$ with respect to $NH_4OH$. $K_{NH_4OH} = 1.8 \times 10^{-5}$, $L_{Mg(OH)_2} = 3 \times 10^{-10}$.

15. If the solubility product of $Mg(OH)_2$ is $3 \times 10^{-10}$, calculate the concentration of $Mg^{++}$ that must be present in 0.1 $M$ $NH_4OH$ solution in order to saturate the solution with $Mg(OH)_2$. $K_{NH_4OH} = 1.8 \times 10^{-5}$.

16. Calculate the concentration of $CO_3^{--}$ in a solution that is 3 $M$ with respect to $NH_4Cl$, $M$ with respect to $NH_4OH$, and 0.02 $M$ with respect to $HCO_3^-$. $K_{NH_4OH} = 1.8 \times 10^{-5}$, $K_{HCO_3} = 5.3 \times 10^{-11}$.

If this solution were made 0.1 $N$ with respect to $Ca^{++}$ would $CaCO_3$ precipitate? $L_{CaCO_3} = 1.7 \times 10^{-8}$.

17. Calculate the $[CO_3^{--}]$ in a solution which is 2 $N$ with respect to $NH_4Cl$, 0.5 $N$ with respect to $NH_4OH$, and in which $[H_2CO_3] + [HCO_3^-] + [CO_3^{--}] = 0.2$.

18. Calculate the concentration of $CO_3^{--}$ in a molar solution of $NH_4OH$ that has absorbed half its volume of $CO_2$ from the air. (The main reaction of the $CO_2$ is $CO_2 + NH_4OH = HCO_3^- + NH_4^+$. A secondary reaction occurs, $HCO_3^- + NH_4OH = NH_4^+ + H_2O + CO_3^{--}$.) $K_{NH_4OH} = 1.8 \times 10^{-5}$, $K_{HCO_3^-} = 5.3 \times 10^{-11}$.

*Ans.* $[CO_3^{--}] = 0.016\ M$.

19. How much $NH_4Cl$ (100% ionized) must be added to a 0.1 *M* solution of $Mg^{++}$ to prevent precipitation of $Mg(OH)_2$ when the solution is made 0.1 *M* with respect to $NH_4OH$? $L_{Mg(OH)_2} = 3 \times 10^{-10}$, $K_{NH_4OH} = 1.8 \times 10^{-5}$.

20. Calculate the solubility of $CaCO_3$ in water (*a*) neglecting hydrolysis, and (*b*) taking hydrolysis into account. $L_{CaCO_3} = 1.7 \times 10^{-8}$, $K_{HCO_3^-} = 5.3 \times 10^{-11}$, $K_W = 1 \times 10^{-14}$.

21. Show by calculation that a precipitate of $CaCO_3$ should form if 1 ml. $CO_2$ (at STP) is absorbed in 5 ml. of 0.02 *N* $Ca(OH)_2$. $L_{CaCO_3} = 1.7 \times 10^{-8}$, $K_{HCO_3^-} = 5.3 \times 10^{-11}$.

*Ans.* $[Ca^{++}] = 0.01$. $[CO_3^{--}] = 8.2 \times 10^{-3}$. $[Ca^{++}] \times [CO_3^{--}] > 1.7 \times 10^{-8}$.

22. Show by calculation that a precipitate of $CaCO_3$ might form if 5 ml. of $CO_2$ (at STP) are absorbed in 5 ml. of 0.02 *N* $Ca(OH)_2$. $L_{CaCO_3} = 1.7 \times 10^{-8}$, $K_{H_2CO_3} = 3 \times 10^{-7}$, $K_{HCO_3^-} = 5.3 \times 10^{-11}$.

*Ans.* $[Ca^{++}] = 0.01$. $[CO_3^{--}] = 2.6 \times 10^{-6}$. $[Ca^{++}] \times [CO_3^{--}] \cong 1.7 \times 10^{-8}$.

23. Show by calculation that no precipitate of $CaCO_3$ should form if 7 ml. of $CO_2$ (at STP) are absorbed in 5 ml. of 0.02 *N* $Ca(OH)_2$. $L_{CaCO_3} = 1.7 \times 10^{-8}$, $K_{HCO_3^-} = 5.3 \times 10^{-11}$, $K_{H_2CO_3} = 3 \times 10^{-7}$.

*Ans.* $[Ca^{++}] = 0.01$. $[CO_3^{--}] = 1.6 \times 10^{-6}$. $[Ca^{++}] \times [CO_3^{--}] < 1.7 \times 10^{-8}$.

24. (*a*) Calculate the solubility of MnS in molar HCl, assuming no loss of $H_2S$ from the solution. (*b*) What is the final concentration of $H_3O^+$? (*c*) If the solubility of $H_2S$ at 1 atm. pressure is 0.1 mole per liter, what pressure would be required to prevent the escape of $H_2S$ from the solution?

*Ans.* (*a*) $[Mn^{++}] \cong 0.5$. (*b*) $[H_3O^+] = 1.9 \times 10^{-4}$. (*c*) 5 atm. pressure.

25. (*a*) Calculate the solubility of MnS in molar acetic acid, assuming no loss of $H_2S$ from the solution. $K_{HAc} = 1.8 \times 10^{-5}$, $L_{MnS} = 7 \times 10^{-16}$, $K_{H_2S} = 1 \times 10^{-7}$, $K_{HS^-} = 1 \times 10^{-15}$. (*b*) What will be the final pH of the solution? (*c*) What percentage of the acetic acid is used up in the reaction?

*Ans.* (*a*) $[Mn^{++}] = 0.1323$. (*b*) pH = 4.3. (*c*) 26.46%.

26. (*a*) Calculate the solubility of $CaC_2O_4$ in *M* HCl. $L_{CaC_2O_4} = 2.5 \times 10^{-9}$, $K_{H_2C_2O_4} = 0.04$, $K_{HC_2O_4^-} = 5 \times 10^{-5}$. (*b*) What will be the final concentration of $H_3O^+$? (*c*) What will be the final ratio $[H_2C_2O_4]:[HC_2O_4^-]:[C_2O_4^{--}]$?

*Ans.* (*a*) $[Ca^{++}] = 0.034$. (*b*) $[H_3O^+] = 0.932$. (*c*) $[H_2C_2O_4]:[HC_2O_4^-]:[C_2O_4^{--}]::1:0.042:2.3 \times 10^{-6}$.

27. Calculate the solubility of ZnS in 1 *N* HCl, assuming no loss of $H_2S$ from the solution. $L_{ZnS} = 2.4 \times 10^{-25}$, $K_{H_2S} = 1 \times 10^{-7}$, $K_{HS^-} = 1 \times 10^{-22}$.

## *REVIEW QUESTIONS*

1. Starting with any group precipitate, outline the regular method for its analysis.
2. Starting with an original solution before removal of Group I, give the successive forms for any metal considered in this course.
3. Starting with an original solution before removal of Group I, give the analytical equations for any metal considered in this course.
4. List all of the metal ions considered in this course and divide them into three groups, viz., those existing in (*a*) acid solution, (*b*) NaOH solution, (*c*) $NH_4OH$ solution.
5. In a general unknown, explain the method of adjusting the solution for the precipitation of each group (*a*) assuming that no earlier groups were present, and (*b*) assuming that earlier groups were present and have been removed.

6. Give reasons for (*a*) adjustment of acidity before precipitation of Group II, (*b*) addition of $NH_4Cl$ before $NH_4OH$ when precipitating Group III, (*c*) removal of ammonium salts before precipitation of Group V, (*d*) reduction of $Cr_2O_7^{--}$ and $MnO_4^-$ before adjusting the acidity in Group II.

7. If any particular ion is precipitated too soon or in a later group, how may it be detected? For example, Fe in Group II or in Group IV, Mg in Group III, Cu in Group IV.

8. If any particular ion is precipitated too soon or in a later group, how may it interfere with any regular tests in that group? For example, Bi in Group I, Ni in Group II, Pb in Group III, Fe in Group IV.

9. Give balanced equations for the final confirmatory tests for each metal.

10. Define concentration. Mention three ways in which concentration is usually expressed and show how to convert from any one form to the others.

11. How many grams of $H_2C_2O_4 \cdot 2H_2O$ would be required to make 500 ml. of a solution (*a*) molar, (*b*) normal for neutralization, (*c*) normal for oxidation-reduction, (*d*) empirical, such that 1 ml. is equivalent to 1 mg. of $CaCO_3$.

12. What is (*a*) Law of Mass Action, (*b*) Le Chatelier's Theorem, (*c*) Kinetic Molecular Theory, (*d*) Avogadro's Theory, (*e*) Arrhenius' Theory?

13. Summarize the experimental basis and give the main assumptions of the theory of electrolytic dissociation.

14. Mention four different methods for experimentally determining the extent of ionization of a compound.

15. Upon what factors does the concentration of an ion depend?

16. Why is the dilution effect large in the case of a weak electrolyte and small in the case of a strong electrolyte (at moderate concentrations)?

17. Show how the Law of Mass Action explains (*a*) the dilution effect for weak electrolytes, (*b*) the common ion effect for weak electrolytes, and (*c*) the common ion effect for slightly soluble substances.

18. What is common ion effect? Give five examples encountered in this course and show its importance in each case.

19. Using the solubility product principle, discuss the delicacy of the three final tests for Pb in Group I.

20. Using the solubility product and chemical equilibrium principles, account for the (*a*) insolubility of HgS in hot 2 *N* $HNO_3$, (*b*) dissolving of $CaCO_3$ in acetic acid, (*c*) insolubility of $CaC_2O_4$ in acetic acid, (*d*) nonprecipitation of $Mg(OH)_2$ in Group III.

21. "Fundamentally, qualitative analysis is based upon ionization constants and solubility products." Explain in each case.

22. "Qualitative analysis is essentially a process of elimination." Explain.

23. Why are the metals divided into groups in qualitative analysis? What is the basis for this division?

24. Give the important requirements that a group reagent must meet. In view of these requirements, discuss (*a*) HCl as a Group I reagent, (*b*) $H_2S$ as a Group II reagent, (*c*) $NH_4OH$ as a Group III reagent.

25. What problems arise in washing a precipitate?

26. Considering only the metals covered in this course, which would be precipitated in Group I and which in Group II if dilute $H_2SO_4$ were used as the Group I reagent and $NH_4OH$, excess, as the Group II reagent?

27. List the chemical facts that would be known concerning an element if it is found in Group IV in the present scheme of Qualitative Analysis.

28. "The question of the presence of an ion can be answered only in a relative way because the decision depends upon the delicacy of the test employed." Discuss.

29. Give three criteria by which a qualitative test may be judged satisfactory or unsatisfactory.

30. What conclusions are justified when one confirmatory test is positive and another is negative?

31. What is meant by the terms "delicate test," "characteristic test," and "specific test"? Give an example of each.

32. The addition of an excess of reagent (*a*) may or (*b*) may not increase the sensitivity of a test, or (*c*) may decrease the sensitivity. Give examples of each and explain briefly.

33. Tests may be divided into four main groups: precipitation, color, gas, flame. Upon what factors does the sensitivity of each class depend?

34. What three requirements must be met in order to obtain a precipitation test?

35. Briefly describe a laboratory method for ascertaining the sensitivity of a test.

36. In the analysis of a general review unknown, a white precipitate was obtained for Group III. List seven possibilities.

37. Give the formula for each colored ion covered in this course. Divide these into three groups, those stable in: (*a*) acid solution, (*b*) NaOH solution, (*c*) $NH_4OH$ solution.

38. Give the formula and name of each colored ion that may exist in an ammoniacal solution.

39. Give the formula and color of each colored ion in this course that may exist in an acid solution.

40. List all the ions of the metals of Groups II–IV that might be present in a solution containing excess of NaOH.

41. List all the ions of the metals of Groups II–IV that might be present in an ammoniacal solution.

42. List all the ions of the metals of Groups II–IV that might be present in a solution containing $Sn(OH)_3^-$.

43. List all the ions of the metals of Groups II–IV that would not be found in a solution containing $Sn^{++}$.

44. How does the thiocyanate test for Co differ from the thiocyanate test for Fe?

45. An original solution was acid and colored. Addition of excess $NH_4OH$ changed the color but gave a clear solution. What ions of Groups I–IV metals could be present in the original solution?

46. An original solution was acid and colored. Addition of NaOH gave a precipitate which dissolved in excess of the reagent. What ions of Groups I–IV metals might be present? Which metals would be absent?

47. An original solution was acid and colorless. Addition of a slight excess of $NH_4OH$ gave no precipitate. What ions of Groups I–IV metals could be present?

48. An ammoniacal solution was given out for analysis. When HCl was added to one portion and $H_2S$ to another, no precipitate was obtained in either case. What ions of Groups I–III might be in the original solution?

49. Using the common reagents, outline methods for separating two metals in one operation; i.e., if both are in solution give a reagent that will precipitate one and not the other, or if both are present as solids (free metals or compounds), give a reagent that will dissolve one and not the other. Give formulas of main products and tell which is insoluble.

50. How separate in one operation (*a*) $Cu^{++}$ from $Cd^{++}$, (*b*) $AsO_4^{-3}$ from $Sn^{+4}$, (*c*) $Ag^+$ from $Bi^{+3}$, (*d*) $Fe^{+3}$ from $Cr^{+3}$, (*e*) HgS from $Ag_2S$, (*f*) $Cr_2O_7^{--}$ from $SO_4^{--}$?

51. Give in tabular form five reagents that would distinguish between $Fe^{++}$ and $Fe^{+++}$. In each case give formula, color, and state of product. Same for (*b*) $Cr^{+++}$ and $Cr_2O_7^{--}$, (*c*) $Co^{++}$ and $Ni^{++}$, (*d*) $AsO_4^{-3}$ and $AsO_3^{-3}$.

52. A certain solution contains $Al^{+++}$, $Ag^{+}$, and $Ba^{++}$. Show how to separate these ions using only $H_2S$, $H_2SO_4$, and NaOH.

53. Show how to separate $Pb^{++}$, $Al^{+++}$, $Ni^{++}$, and $Zn^{++}$ using any three reagents.

54. A certain solution contains $Ca^{++}$, $Al^{+++}$, and $Hg^{++}$. Show how to separate these ions using only the three reagents $NH_4OH$, HCl, and $H_2S$.

55. Mention one test used in this course for the detection of (*a*) a compound, not an ion; (*b*) an ion by use of extraction (immissible solvent); (*c*) a gas; (*d*) $NH_4^+$ by precipitation.

56. In making the usual test for each of the following, what major interferences must be considered:

(*a*) $ClO_3^-$.
(*b*) Gutzeit test for As.
(*c*) Coin test for Sb.
(*d*) $NH_3$ test for $NO_3^-$.
(*e*) Brown ring test for $NO_3^-$.

57. What metals are insoluble in, or but slightly attacked by, (*a*) HCl, (*b*) $HNO_3$?

58. Divide all sulfides considered in this course into four groups: (*a*) water soluble; (*b*) water insoluble, HCl soluble; (*c*) HCl insoluble, $HNO_3$ soluble; (*d*) soluble only in $HCl + HNO_3$.

59. What is the action of $H_2O$, HCl, and $HNO_3$ on Ag, Cu, Mg, $Pb_3O_4$, $Fe_2O_3$, $MnO_2$, $Cu_2I_2$, $Sn_3(AsO_3)_2$, and $Sb_2O_3$?

60. How dissolve each of the following: $Pb_3O_4$, As, Al, Sb, Cu? Give balanced equation in each case.

61. A certain precipitate consists of $Al(OH)_3$, CuS, and AgCl in equal amounts. How can they be separated if only HCl, $HNO_3$, $NH_4OH$, and NaOH are available as reagents?

62. Excess $Na_2CO_3$ was added to separate solutions of $Fe^{++}$, $Fe^{+++}$, $Cr^{+++}$, $Cr_2O_7^{--}$, $Hg^{++}$, $Zn^{++}$, and $Ba^{++}$. Give formula for product and color in each case.

## STUDENT CHECK LIST OF EQUIPMENT

Desk No.______ Name____________________

The following is a list of the material which should be in the desk at the beginning of the course, and which must be replaced in the desk by the student before he turns in his desk at the end of the semester. If material is missing from the desk at the beginning of the semester, the student should make a list of the missing articles and ask the instructor to verify and sign the list. The material will be replaced without charge if the list is presented to the dispensing stand immediately at the beginning of the course. The student should note carefully the directions for turning in laboratory desks.

4. beakers, 50 ml.
1 bottle, 8 oz. Polyethylene
1 rubber stopper #2, 1 hole
1 foot 5 mm. glass tubing
1 burner, Micro
1 burner, Bunsen
1 burner tubing, rubber 4 ft.
1 cobalt glass, 50 mm.
3 crucibles, #0
3 crucible covers #0
1 cylinder, grad. 10 ml.
1 flask Erlenmeyer, 250 ml.
1 lock on desk
3 micro slides
1 rubber stopper 1-hole #6
1 spatula, nickel
1 spot plate 89 × 109
1 test tube, 15 cm., Pyrex
12 tubes, centrifuge (plain) 3 ml.
1 pair tongs, crucible iron
4 vials, Opti-clear K-3
2 watch glasses, 50 mm.

The following material, which is not returnable for credit, may be purchased at the dispensing room. This nonreturnable material should be removed from your desk at the end of the semester.

1 brush, centrifuge tube
2 crucibles #000, Form 230
1 foot glass rod, 3 mm.
2 feet glass tubing, 7 mm.
1 box labels #223
2 litmus paper, red and blue
1 box matches
6 medicine droppers
1 pipe cleaner
1 sponge
1 box wipettes
1 wiping cloth

## REAGENTS

For some years past the aqueous reagents for use in qualitative chemical analysis at the University of Michigan have been made up on the normality basis. Thus a normal solution of KOH should contain 56.1 g. of the compound per liter of solution; but the available solid usually contains about 10% of moisture; therefore it is directed to weigh out $56.1 \times \frac{10}{9}$, or 62.3 g. of the solid, dissolve in water, and dilute to 1 liter, for a normal solution. In the case of reagents that may be used either as precipitating agents or as oxidants or reductants, the normality is figured in terms of the precipitation reaction. Thus a normal solution of $K_2Cr_2O_7$ would contain $\frac{294.2}{4}$ g. per liter, since this reagent is used to precipitate metals as chromates, and the valence of the chromate radical is 2. For a reagent that is used solely as an oxidant or reductant, the normality is figured in terms of that reaction. Hence, $KMnO_4$ is used as an oxidant, commonly undergoing five units of reduction per molecule; therefore a normal solution would contain $\frac{158}{5}$ g. per liter.

In addition to reagents, there should be available a set of test solutions, which the student may use to become familiar with the analytical behavior of the various metals and acid radicals, or to check up on reagents which may be open to suspicion. These test solutions are made up on an empirical basis, the concentration of the solution being so adjusted that 1 ml. of the solution contains 10 mg. of the metal or non-metal under consideration. This is a solution of sufficient concentration so that 3–5 drops will be ample to study an ordinary reaction, and the solution may easily be diluted tenfold or a hundredfold to cover the lower concentrations commonly encountered.

The solutions used by the assistant in preparing unknowns for analysis commonly contain 50 mg. of metal or non-metal per ml. Known volumes of these are placed in a 250-ml. tincture bottle, excess acid or alkali added as necessary for particular ions, the bottle then filled with water and well shaken. The student is given a 15-ml. sample for analysis.

Many of the salts are commercially available in more than one degree of hydration. Thus sodium carbonate may be had as the anhydrous salt, $Na_2CO_3$; as the monohydrate, $Na_2CO_3 \cdot H_2O$; and as the decahydrate, $Na_2CO_3 \cdot 10H_2O$. In the tables only one of the more common forms has been used as the basis of calculation. If one of the other hydrates is being used, the quantities must be correspondingly modified. In case of doubt as to the actual composition of the basic material it may be necessary to resort to some type of quantitative analysis. If the anhydrous salt is fairly stable, it may be possible to ignite a weighed portion of the salt to the anhydrous condition to determine the actual amount of water present. In other cases it may be easier to use some simple gravimetric or volumetric method to determine the per cent of metal or non-metal present.

| *Acids* | *Normality* |
|---|---|
| Acetic, conc. (sp. gr. 1.05, 99.5%) | 17.4 |
| Acetic, dil., 287 ml. of the conc. acid per liter | 5.0 |
| Hydrochloric, conc. (sp. gr. 1.18, 36%) | 11.6 |
| Hydrochloric, dil., 431 ml. of the conc. acid per liter | 5.0 |
| Nitric, conc. (sp. gr. 1.42, 72%) | 16.2 |
| Nitric, dil., 309 ml. of the conc. acid per liter | 5.0 |
| Sulfuric, conc. (sp. gr. 1.84, 96%) | 36.0 |
| Sulfuric, dil., 139 ml. of the conc. acid, pour carefully into 500 ml. $H_2O$, cool, and dilute to 1 liter | 5.0 |

| *Hydroxides* | |
|---|---|
| Ammonium hydroxide, conc. (sp. gr. 0.90, 28.4% $NH_3$) | 15.0 |
| Ammonium hydroxide, dil., 333 ml. of conc. $NH_4OH$ per liter | 5.0 |
| Barium hydroxide, $Ba(OH)_2 \cdot 8H_2O$, 63 g. per liter, satd. soln. (filter off $BaCO_3$ and protect from $CO_2$ of the air) | 0.4 |
| Calcium hydroxide, $Ca(OH)_2$, 1.5 g. per liter, satd. soln. (use some excess, filter off $CaCO_3$ and protect from $CO_2$ of the air) | 0.04 |
| Potassium hydroxide, KOH (90%), dissolve 311 g. of the sticks in water and dilute to 1 liter | 5.0 |
| Sodium hydroxide, NaOH (90%), dissolve 222 g. of the sticks in water and dilute to 1 liter | 5.0 |

*Special Liquids and Solutions*

Aluminon solution, 1.0 g. of the ammonium salt of aurin tricarboxylic acid, dissolve in $H_2O$ and dilute to 1 liter. (0.1% solution.)

Amyl alcohol, $C_5H_{11}OH$.

Carbon tetrachloride, $CCl_4$.

Dimethyl dioxime, $C_4H_8N_2O_2$. Dissolve 10 g. in ethyl alcohol, and dilute with alcohol to 1 liter. (1% solution.)

Dipyridyl reagent. Dissolve 5 g. $\alpha,\alpha'$-dipyridyl and 2.92 g. $FeSO_4 \cdot 7H_2O$ in 1 liter of water and add 200 g. of KI. After thorough shaking the precipitate is filtered off. If solution becomes turbid on standing it may be filtered.

Ether, $(C_2H_5)_2O$.

Fehling's solution:

A (blue part). Dissolve 34.7 g. of $CuSO_4 \cdot 5H_2O$ in water and dilute to 500 ml.

B (colorless part). Dissolve 173 g. of Rochelle salts and 50 g. of NaOH in water and dilute to 500 ml.

Mix equal amounts of the two parts for use.

Formaldehyde, $CH_2O$. Dilute 125 ml. of the concentrated reagent (40% solution) with water to 1 liter (5% solution).

Hydrogen peroxide, $H_2O_2$. Use the commercial 3% solution.

*Special Liquids and Solutions (Cont.)* *Normality*

Magnesia mixture. Dissolve 52 g. of $MgCl_2 \cdot 6H_2O$ and 134 g. of $NH_4Cl$ in water, add 350 ml. of conc. $NH_4OH$, and dilute to 1 liter. Use only the freshly filtered reagent.

Nessler's reagent. Dissolve 50 g. of KI in 50 ml. of water, add saturated $HgCl_2$ solution (60 g. per liter) in small amounts at a time, with shaking, until a slight permanent precipitate forms, then add 200 ml. of 5 *N* NaOH and dilute to 1 liter. Let settle, then draw off the clear liquid.

Paranitrobenzene-azo-resorcinol. Dissolve 0.01 g. in 1 liter of *N* NaOH. Use the clear solution.

*Solid Reagents*

Aluminum, metal, Al. Smooth coarse turnings, or No. 8 or No. 12 wire.
Ammonium chloride, $NH_4Cl$.
Ammonium thiocyanate, $NH_4CNS$.
Borax, $Na_2B_4O_7 \cdot 10H_2O$.
Copper, metal. Wire or turnings (for Hg test).
Iron, metal. Powder (for Sn test).
Microcosmic salt, $NaNH_4HPO_4 \cdot 4H_2O$
Potassium acid antimonate, $KH_2SbO_4$ (for Na test).
Potassium chlorate, $KClO_3$.
Potassium nitrate, $KNO_3$.
Potassium persulfate, $K_2S_2O_8$.
Sodium bicarbonate, $NaHCO_3$.
Sodium pyrosulfate (sodium acid sulfate fused), $Na_2S_2O_7$
Stannic chloride, $SnCl_4 \cdot 5H_2O$ (for $PO_4^{-3}$ removal).
Stannous chloride, $SnCl_2 \cdot 2H_2O$ (for As test).
Tin, metal, Sn. Foil (for Sb test).
Zinc, metal, Zn. 20 mesh.

*Salt Solutions*

Ammonium acetate, $NH_4C_2H_3O_2$, dissolve 231 g. of the salt in water and dilute to 1 liter. 3 *N*

Ammonium carbonate, coml. salt is a mixture of $NH_4HCO_3$ and $NH_4NH_2CO_2$. Dissolve 157 g. of the salt in 400 ml. of 5 *N* $NH_4OH$ and dilute to 1 liter. 4 *N*

Ammonium chloride, $NH_4Cl$, dissolve 268 g. of the salt in 900 ml. of water and dilute to 1 liter. 5 *N*

Ammonium molybdate, $(NH_4)_2MoO_4$ (the coml. salt is the para molybdate, $(NH_4)_6Mo_7O_{24}$), dissolve 42 g. of $MoO_3$ (85%) in a mixture of 70 ml. of conc. $NH_4OH$ and 140 ml. of water; after solution is complete, add very slowly, with vigorous stirring, a mixture of 250 ml. of conc. $HNO_3$ and 500 ml. of water; then dilute to 1 liter. 0.5 *N*

Ammonium oxalate, $(NH_4)_2C_2O_4 \cdot H_2O$, dissolve 35.5 g. of the salt in water and dilute to 1 liter. 0.5 *N*

Ammonium sulfate, $(NH_4)_2SO_4$, dissolve 132 g. of the salt in water and dilute to 1 liter (conc. reagent, to ppt. Sr before testing for Ca). 2.0 *N*

Ammonium sulfate, $(NH_4)_2SO_4$, dissolve 6.6 g. of the salt in water and dilute to 1 liter (dilute reagent, to test for Sr in the presence of Ca). 0.1 *N*

Ammonium sulfide, yellow, $(NH_4)_2S_x$, treat 150 ml. of conc. $NH_4OH$ with $H_2S$ until saturated, keeping the solution cold; add 250 ml. of conc. $NH_4OH$ and 10 g. of washed sulfur, shake to dissolve the latter and dilute to 1 liter. (On standing, the concentration of $(NH_4)_2S_2$ increases and that of $(NH_4)_2S$ and $NH_4OH$ decreases). { $(NH_4)_2S_2$ = 0.6 *N*; $(NH_4)_2S$ = 3.9 *N*; $NH_4OH$ = 1.5 *N* }

| *Salt Solutions (Cont.)* | *Normality* |
|---|---|
| Barium chloride, $BaCl_2 \cdot 2H_2O$, dissolve 61 g. of the salt in water and dilute to 1 liter. | 0.5 *N* |
| Calcium chloride, $CaCl_2 \cdot 6H_2O$, dissolve 55 g. of the salt in water and dilute to 1 liter. | 0.5 *N* |
| Calcium hypochlorite, $Ca(ClO)_2$ (65%), treat 50 g. of the salt with water and dilute to 1 liter. Filter or decant when ready to use the reagent. | 1.0 *N* |
| Calcium sulfate, $CaSO_4 \cdot 2H_2O$, satd. soln., treat 3.0 g. of the salt with 1 liter of water, shake occasionally over a period of several hours, then filter or decant. | 0.03 *N* |
| Cupric sulfate, $CuSO_4 \cdot 5H_2O$, dissolve 124.8 g. of the salt in water, add 2–3 ml. of $H_2SO_4$, and dilute to 1 liter. (Normality is calculated as an oxidant.) | 0.5 *N* |
| Ferric chloride, $FeCl_3 \cdot 6H_2O$, dissolve 135.2 g. of the salt in water containing 50 ml. of 5 *N* HCl, and dilute to 1 liter. (Normality is calculated as an oxidant.) | 0.5 *N* |
| Ferric sulfate, $Fe_2(SO_4)_3 \cdot 9H_2O$, dissolve 140.5 g. of the salt in sufficient 5 *N* $H_2SO_4$ to make 1 liter. (Normality is calculated as an oxidant.) | 0.5 *N* |
| Ferrous sulfate, $FeSO_4 \cdot 7H_2O$, dissolve 139 g. of the salt in water containing 50 ml. of 5 *N* $H_2SO_4$, and dilute to 1 liter. (Normality is calculated as a reductant.) | 0.5 *N* |
| Lead acetate, $Pb(C_2H_3O_2)_2 \cdot 3H_2O$, dissolve 95 g. of the salt in water and dilute to 1 liter. | 0.5 *N* |
| Magnesium uranyl acetate, to 100 g. of uranyl acetate, $UO_2(C_2H_3O_2)_2 \cdot 2H_2O$, add 100 g. of glacial acetic acid, stir, and add 400 ml. of water. To 300 g. of $Mg(C_2H_3O_2)_2 \cdot 4H_2O$ add 200 ml. of water. Heat both solutions to the boiling point, keeping them hot until both are practically clear, then pour the Mg solution into the other. Let cool slightly and dilute to 1 liter. Let stand overnight and filter. | $UO_2(C_2H_3O_2)_2$ = 0.47 *N*<br>$Mg(C_2H_3O_2)_2$ = 2.8 *N*<br>$HC_2H_3O_2$ = 1.7 *N* |
| Mercuric chloride, $HgCl_2$, dissolve 68 g. of the salt in water and dilute to 1 liter. | 0.5 *N* |
| Potassium cyanide, KCN, dissolve 33 g. of the salt in water and dilute to 1 liter. | 0.5 *N* |
| Potassium dichromate, $K_2Cr_2O_7$, dissolve 73.5 g. of the salt in water and dilute to 1 liter. (Normality is calculated as precipitant.) | 0.5 *N* |
| Potassium ferricyanide, $K_3Fe(CN)_6$, dissolve 55 g. of the salt in water and dilute to 1 liter. | 0.5 *N* |
| Potassium ferrocyanide, $K_4Fe(CN)_6 \cdot 3H_2O$, dissolve 212 g. of the salt in water and dilute to 1 liter. (Concentrated reagent used to remove Ca in testing for Sr.) | 2.0 *N* |
| Potassium ferrocyanide, $K_4Fe(CN)_6 \cdot 3H_2O$, dissolve 53 g. of the salt in water and dilute to 1 liter. | 0.5 *N* |
| Potassium iodide, KI, dissolve 83 g. of the salt in water and dilute to 1 liter. | 0.5 *N* |
| Potassium permanganate, $KMnO_4$, dissolve 15.8 g. of the salt in water and dilute to 1 liter. After standing for several days syphon off the clear solution, or filter through a Gooch crucible or its equivalent. (Normality is calculated as an oxidant.) | 0.5 *N* |
| Potassium thiocyanate, KCNS, dissolve 49 g. of the salt in water and dilute to 1 liter. | 0.5 *N* |
| Silver nitrate, $AgNO_3$, dissolve 42.5 g. of the salt in water and dilute to 1 liter. | 0.25 *N* |
| Silver perchlorate, $AgClO_4$, dissolve 52 g. of the salt in water and dilute to 1 liter. | 0.25 *N* |
| Sodium acetate, $NaC_2H_3O_2 \cdot 3H_2O$, dissolve 408 g. of the salt in water and dilute to 1 liter. | 3.0 *N* |
| Sodium carbonate, $Na_2CO_3$, dissolve 159 g. of the salt in water and dilute to 1 liter. | 3.0 *N* |
| Sodium cobaltinitrite, $Na_3Co(NO_2)_6$, dissolve 67.3 g. of the salt in water and dilute to 1 liter. (Or the solution may be prepared as follows: Dissolve 48.5 g. of $Co(NO_3)_2 \cdot 6H_2O$ in 100–150 ml. of water; dissolve 81 g. of $NaNO_2$ in | 0.5 *N* |

| *Salt Solutions (Cont.)* | *Normality* |
| --- | --- |
| 100–150 ml. of water; mix the two solutions with stirring; add 19.5 ml. of glacial acetic acid, stir thoroughly, dilute to 1 liter, shake, let stand a few days and filter.) | |
| Sodium cyanide, NaCN, dissolve 24.5 g. of the salt in water and dilute to 1 liter. | 0.5 *N* |
| Sodium hypochlorite, NaClO, use the solution sold under the trade names Oxol, Roman Cleanser, or Chlorox, at most grocery stores. | 5% |
| Sodium phosphate (secondary), $Na_2HPO_4 \cdot 12H_2O$, dissolve 60 g. of the salt in water and dilute to 1 liter. | 0.5 *N* |
| Sodium sulfide, $Na_2S \cdot 9H_2O$, dissolve 120 g. of the salt in water and dilute to 1 liter. | 1.0 *N* |
| Sodium sulfite, $Na_2SO_3 \cdot 7H_2O$, dissolve 63 g. of the salt in water and dilute to 1 liter. | 0.5 *N* |
| Stannous chloride, $SnCl_2 \cdot 2H_2O$, treat 56 g. of the salt with 100 ml. of conc. HCl, let stand overnight, then dilute to 1 liter. | 0.5 *N* |

## TEST SOLUTIONS

These solutions are made up in such a way that 1 ml. contains 10 mg. of the metal or non-metal. The test solutions for the metals are arranged in the order of the groups; those for the non-metals are arranged alphabetically, the various acid radicals of each non-metal being listed in the order of increasing oxidation-number of the non-metal.

### METALS

| Metal | Formula of Dry Salt | Grams of Salt per Liter of Soln. | Special Precautions in Preparing the Soln. |
|---|---|---|---|
| Lead | $Pb(NO_3)_2$ | 16.0 | Use 5 ml. of 5 *N* $HNO_3$ |
| Mercury (ous) | $Hg_2(NO_3)_2 \cdot 2H_2O$ | 14.0 | Use 150 ml. of 5 *N* $HNO_3$ |
| Silver | $AgNO_3$ | 15.8 | |
| Mercury (ic) | $HgCl_2$ | 13.5 | |
| | $Hg(NO_3)_2$ | 16.2 | Use 50 ml. of 5 *N* $HNO_3$ |
| | $HgSO_4$ | 14.8 | Use 50 ml. of 5 *N* $H_2SO_4$ |
| Bismuth | $BiCl_3$ | 15.1 | Dissolve in 400 ml. of 5 *N* HCl and dilute to 1 liter |
| | $Bi(NO_3)_3 \cdot 5H_2O$ | 23.2 | Dissolve in 500 ml. of *N* $HNO_3$ and dilute to 1 liter |
| Copper | $CuCl_2 \cdot 2H_2O$ | 26.8 | Use 5 ml. of 5 *N* HCl |
| | $Cu(NO_3)_2 \cdot 3H_2O$ | 38.0 | Use 5 ml. of 5 *N* $HNO_3$ |
| | $CuSO_4 \cdot 5H_2O$ | 39.3 | Use 5 ml. of 5 *N* $H_2SO_4$ |
| Cadmium | $CdCl_2 \cdot 2H_2O$ | 19.4 | Use 5 ml. of 5 *N* HCl |
| | $Cd(NO_3)_2 \cdot 4H_2O$ | 27.4 | Use 5 ml. of 5 *N* $HNO_3$ |
| | $3CdSO_4 \cdot 8H_2O$ | 22.8 | Use 5 ml. of 5 *N* $H_2SO_4$ |
| Arsenic (ous) | $As_2O_3$ | 13.2 | Dissolve in hot water containing 15–20 ml. of 5 *N* HCl, and dilute to 1 liter |
| | $K_4As_2O_5$ | 25.8 | |
| (ic) | $As_2O_5$ | 15.3 | Dissolve in hot water, adding a little HCl if necessary to form a clear solution; then dilute to 1 liter |
| | $KH_2AsO_4$ | 24.0 | |

METALS (Continued)

| Metal | Formula of Dry Salt | Grams of Salt per Liter of Soln. | Special Precautions in Preparing the Soln. |
|---|---|---|---|
| Antimony (ous) | $SbCl_3$ | 18.7 | Dissolve in 400 ml. of 5 *N* HCl and dilute to 1 liter |
| (ic) | $SbCl_5$ | 24.5 | Dissolve in 500 ml. of 5 *N* HCl and dilute to 1 liter |
| Tin (ous) | $SnCl_2 \cdot 2H_2O$ | 19.0 | Treat the salt with 100 ml. of conc. HCl, let stand overnight, then dilute to 1 liter. Filter if necessary |
| (ic) | $SnCl_4 \cdot 5H_2O$ | 29.5 | Dissolve in 400 ml. of 5 *N* HCl and dilute to 1 liter |
| Iron (ous) | $Fe(NH_4)_2(SO_4)_2 \cdot 6H_2O$ | 70.3 | Use 25 ml. of 5 *N* $H_2SO_4$ |
| (ic) | $FeCl_3 \cdot 6H_2O$ | 48.4 | Use 50 ml. of 5 *N* HCl |
| | $Fe(NO_3)_3 \cdot 9H_2O$ | 72.4 | Use 50 ml. of 5 *N* $HNO_3$ |
| Aluminum | $AlCl_3 \cdot 6H_2O$ | 89.5 | Use 25 ml. of 5 *N* HCl |
| | $Al(NO_3)_3 \cdot 9H_2O$ | 138.4 | Use 25 ml. of 5 *N* $HNO_3$ |
| | $Al_2(SO_4)_3 \cdot 18H_2O$ | 123.5 | Use 25 ml. of 5 *N* $H_2SO_4$ |
| Chromium (ic) | $CrCl_3 \cdot 6H_2O$ | 51.2 | Use 50 ml. of 5 *N* HCl |
| | $Cr(NO_3)_3 \cdot 9H_2O$ | 77.0 | Use 50 ml. of 5 *N* $HNO_3$ |
| | $Cr_2(SO_4)_3 \cdot 18H_2O$ | 68.9 | Use 50 ml. of 5 *N* $H_2SO_4$ |
| (ate) | $K_2CrO_4$ | 37.3 | |
| | $K_2Cr_2O_7$ | 28.3 | |
| Cobalt | $CoCl_2 \cdot 6H_2O$ | 40.4 | Use 25 ml. of 5 *N* HCl |
| | $Co(NO_3)_2 \cdot 6H_2O$ | 49.4 | Use 25 ml. of 5 *N* $HNO_3$ |
| | $CoSO_4 \cdot 7H_2O$ | 47.7 | Use 25 ml. of 5 *N* $H_2SO_4$ |
| Nickel | $NiCl_2 \cdot 6H_2O$ | 40.5 | Use 25 ml. of 5 *N* HCl |
| | $Ni(NO_3)_2 \cdot 6H_2O$ | 49.5 | Use 25 ml. of 5 *N* $HNO_3$ |
| | $NiSO_4 \cdot 6H_2O$ | 44.8 | Use 25 ml. of 5 *N* $H_2SO_4$ |

METALS (Continued)

| Metal | Formula of Dry Salt | Grams of Salt per Liter of Soln. | Special Precautions in Preparing the Soln. |
|---|---|---|---|
| Manganese (ous) | $MnCl_2 \cdot 4H_2O$ | 36.0 | Use 5 ml. of 5 *N* HCl |
| | $Mn(NO_3)_2 \cdot 6H_2O$ | 52.3 | Use 5 ml. of 5 *N* $HNO_3$ |
| | $MnSO_4 \cdot 2H_2O$ | 34.0 | Use 5 ml. of 5 *N* $H_2SO_4$ |
| (permanganate) | $KMnO_4$ | 28.8 | |
| (manganate) | $K_2MnO_4$ | | Place 28.8 g. of $KMnO_4$ and 125 g. of KOH in a liter crucible, add 100 ml. of $H_2O$, cover with a watch glass and boil gently until decomposition to $K_2MnO_4$ is complete. Dissolve in 500 ml. of $H_2O$ and dilute to 1 liter. |
| Zinc | $ZnCl_2$ | 20.8 | |
| | $Zn(NO_3)_2$ | 29.0 | |
| | $ZnSO_4 \cdot 7H_2O$ | 44.0 | |
| Barium | $BaCl_2 \cdot 2H_2O$ | 17.8 | |
| | $Ba(NO_3)_2$ | 19.0 | |
| Strontium | $SrCl_2 \cdot 6H_2O$ | 30.4 | |
| | $Sr(NO_3)_2$ | 24.2 | |
| Calcium | $CaCl_2 \cdot 2H_2O$ | 36.7 | |
| | $Ca(NO_3)_2 \cdot 4H_2O$ | 58.9 | |
| Magnesium | $MgCl_2 \cdot 6H_2O$ | 83.6 | Use 5 ml. of 5 *N* HCl |
| | $Mg(NO_3)_2 \cdot 6H_2O$ | 105.4 | Use 5 ml. of 5 *N* $HNO_3$ |
| | $MgSO_4 \cdot 7H_2O$ | 101.4 | Use 5 ml. of 5 *N* $H_2SO_4$ |
| Sodium | NaCl | 25.4 | |
| | $NaNO_3$ | 35.2 | |
| | $Na_2SO_4$ | 30.9 | |
| Potassium | KCl | 19.1 | |
| | $KNO_3$ | 25.9 | |
| | $K_2SO_4$ | 22.3 | |

METALS (Continued)

| Metal | Formula of Dry Salt | Grams of Salt per Liter of Soln. | Special Precautions in Preparing the Soln. |
|---|---|---|---|
| Ammonium | $NH_4Cl$ | 29.7 | |
| | $NH_4NO_3$ | 44.4 | |
| | $(NH_4)_2SO_4$ | 36.1 | |

NON-METALS

| Metal | Formula of Dry Salt | Grams of Salt per Liter of Soln. | Special Precautions in Preparing the Soln. |
|---|---|---|---|
| Bromine (Bromide) | KBr | 14.9 | |
| Carbon | | | |
| (oxalate) | $K_2C_2O_4$ | 69.0 | |
| (carbonate) | $K_2CO_3$ | 115.0 | |
| Chlorine | | | |
| (chloride) | $NH_4Cl$ | 15.1 | |
| | KCl | 21.0 | |
| | NaCl | 16.5 | |
| (chlorate) | $KClO_3$ | 34.6 | |
| Iodine | | | |
| (iodide) | KI | 13.1 | |
| (iodate) | $KIO_3$ | 16.9 | |
| Nitrogen | | | |
| (nitrate) | $KNO_3$ | 72.2 | |
| | $NaNO_3$ | 60.7 | |
| Phosphorus | | | |
| (phosphate) | $(NH_4)_2HPO_4$ | 42.6 | |
| | $Na_2HPO_4 \cdot 12H_2O$ | 115.6 | |
| Sulfur | | | |
| (sulfide) | $Na_2S \cdot 9H_2O$ | 75.0 | |
| (sulfite) | $Na_2SO_3 \cdot 7H_2O$ | 79.0 | |
| (sulfate) | $(NH_4)_2SO_4$ | 41.3 | |
| | $K_2SO_4$ | 54.4 | |
| | $Na_2SO_4$ | 44.4 | |

## TABLE XII. pH EQUIVALENTS ASSUMING $pH = \log \frac{1}{[H_3O^+]}$

| pH | $[H_3O^+]$ | pOH | $[OH^-]$ | pH | $[H_3O^+]$ | pOH | $[OH^-]$ |
|---|---|---|---|---|---|---|---|
| 0 | 1 | 14.0 | $1.0 \times 10^{-14}$ | 4.00 | $1.0 \times 10^{-4}$ | 10.0 | $1.0 \times 10^{-10}$ |
| 0.25 | 0.56 | 13.75 | $1.8 \times 10^{-14}$ | 4.50 | $3.2 \times 10^{-5}$ | 9.5 | $3.2 \times 10^{-10}$ |
| 0.50 | 0.32 | 13.50 | $3.2 \times 10^{-14}$ | 5.00 | $1.0 \times 10^{-5}$ | 9.0 | $1.0 \times 10^{-9}$ |
| 0.75 | 0.18 | 13.25 | $5.6 \times 10^{-14}$ | 5.25 | $5.6 \times 10^{-6}$ | 8.75 | $1.8 \times 10^{-9}$ |
| 1.00 | 0.10 | 13.0 | $1.0 \times 10^{-13}$ | 5.50 | $3.2 \times 10^{-6}$ | 8.50 | $3.2 \times 10^{-9}$ |
| 1.25 | $5.6 \times 10^{-2}$ | 12.75 | $1.8 \times 10^{-13}$ | 5.75 | $1.8 \times 10^{-6}$ | 8.25 | $5.6 \times 10^{-9}$ |
| 1.50 | $3.2 \times 10^{-2}$ | 12.50 | $3.2 \times 10^{-13}$ | 6.00 | $1.0 \times 10^{-6}$ | 8.00 | $1.0 \times 10^{-8}$ |
| 1.75 | $1.8 \times 10^{-2}$ | 12.25 | $5.6 \times 10^{-13}$ | 6.25 | $5.6 \times 10^{-7}$ | 7.75 | $1.8 \times 10^{-8}$ |
| 2.00 | 0.01 | 12.0 | $1.0 \times 10^{-12}$ | 6.50 | $3.2 \times 10^{-7}$ | 7.50 | $3.2 \times 10^{-8}$ |
| 2.50 | $3.2 \times 10^{-3}$ | 11.5 | $3.2 \times 10^{-12}$ | 6.75 | $1.8 \times 10^{-7}$ | 7.25 | $5.6 \times 10^{-8}$ |
| 3.00 | $1.0 \times 10^{-3}$ | 11.0 | $1.0 \times 10^{-11}$ | 7.00 | $1.0 \times 10^{-7}$ | 7.00 | $1.0 \times 10^{-7}$ |
| 3.50 | $3.2 \times 10^{-4}$ | 10.5 | $3.2 \times 10^{-11}$ | | | | |

## TABLE XIII. SOME APPROXIMATE pH VALUES

| Substance | Normality | pH | $[H_3O^+]$ | Substance | Normality | pH | $[H_3O^+]$ |
|---|---|---|---|---|---|---|---|
| HCl | 1.0 | 0.1 * | 0.8 | $NH_4OH$ | 1.0 | 11.6 | $0.0_{11}24$ |
| | .1 | 1.07 | .085 | ($K = 1.75 \times 10^{-5}$) | .1 | 11.1 | $.0_{11}8$ |
| | .01 | 2.02 | .0096 | | .01 | 10.6 | $.0_{10}24$ |
| | .001 | 3.01 | $.0_{3}98$ | | .001 | 10.1 | $.0_{10}8$ |
| $HC_2H_3O_2$ | 1.0 | 2.37 | 0.0043 | $H_2SO_4$ | 0.1 | 1.2 | 0.63 |
| ($K = 1.82 \times 10^{-5}$) | .1 | 2.87 | .0014 | $H_2SO_3$ | .1 | 1.5 | .032 |
| | .01 | 3.37 | $.0_{3}43$ | $H_3PO_4$ | .1 | 1.5 | .032 |
| | .001 | 3.87 | $.0_{3}14$ | $H_2C_2O_4$ | .1 | 1.6 | .025 |
| | | | | HCOOH | .1 | 2.3 | .005 |
| NaOH | 1.0 | 14.05 | $0.0_{14}9$ | $H_2CO_3$ | .1 | 3.8 | $.0_{3}2$ |
| | .1 | 13.07 | $.0_{13}86$ | $H_2S$ | .1 | 4.1 | $.0_{4}8$ |
| | .01 | 12.12 | $.0_{12}76$ | HCN | .1 | 5.1 | $.0_{5}8$ |
| | .001 | 11.13 | $.0_{11}74$ | $H_3BO_3$ | .1 | 5.2 | $.0_{5}6$ |
| | | | | KCN | .1 | 11.0 | $.0_{10}1$ |

* $[H_3O^+][OH^-]$ is $0.59 \times 10^{-14}$ at 18°; $1.25 \times 10^{-14}$ at 25°.

Methyl orange starts to change from red to orange at pH 3.8. The change is complete at pH 4.2.

Litmus starts to change from red to blue at pH 4.6. The change is complete at pH 8.4.

Phenolphthalein starts to change from colorless to red at pH 8.3. The change is complete at pH 9.0.

## TABLE XIV. THE SIMPLER RADICALS

### A. The Common Positive Radicals

| Symbol | Valence Number | Symbol | Valence Number |
|---|---|---|---|
| Ag | 1 | Fe(ic) | 3 |
| $Ag(NH_3)_2$ | 1 | Al | 3 |
| Pb | 2 | Cr | 3 |
| $Hg_2$(ous) | 2 | Mn | 2 |
| Hg(ic) | 2 | Co | 2 |
| Bi | 3 | $Co(NH_3)_6$ | 2 |
| Cu(ous) | 1 | Ni | 2 |
| Cu(ic) | 2 | $Ni(NH_3)_6$ | 2 |
| $Cu(NH_3)_4$ | 2 | Zn | 2 |
| Cd | 2 | $Zn(NH_3)_4$ | 2 |
| $Cd(NH_3)_4$ | 2 | Ba | 2 |
| As(ous) | 3 | Sr | 2 |
| As(ic) | 5 | Ca | 2 |
| Sb(ous) | 3 | Mg | 2 |
| Sb(ic) | 5 | K | 1 |
| Sn(ous) | 2 | Na | 1 |
| Sn(ic) | 4 | $NH_4$ | 1 |
| Fe(ous) | 2 | | |

### B. The Common Negative Radicals

| Name | Symbol | Valence Number | Name | Symbol | Valence Number |
|---|---|---|---|---|---|
| Acetate | $C_2H_3O_2$ | 1 | Manganate | $MnO_4$ | 2 |
| Aluminate | $Al(OH)_4$ | 1 | Nitrate | $NO_3$ | 1 |
| Arsenate | $AsO_4$ | 3 | Nitrite | $NO_2$ | 1 |
| Arsenite | $AsO_3$ | 3 | Oxide | O | 2 |
| Borate | $BO_3$ | 3 | Oxalate | $C_2O_4$ | 2 |
| Bromide | Br | 1 | Permanganate | $MnO_4$ | 1 |
| Chlorate | $ClO_3$ | 1 | Peroxide | $O_2$ | 2 |
| Chloride | Cl | 1 | Persulfate | $S_2O_8$ | 2 |
| Chromate | $CrO_4$ | 2 | Phosphate | $PO_4$ | 3 |
| Chromite | $Cr(OH)_4$ | 1 | Plumbite | $Pb(OH)_3$ | 1 |
| Cyanide | CN | 1 | Stannate | $Sn(OH)_5$ | 1 |
| Dichromate | $Cr_2O_7$ | 2 | Stannite | $Sn(OH)_3$ | 1 |
| Ferricyanide | $Fe(CN)_6$ | 3 | Sulfate | $SO_4$ | 2 |
| Ferrocyanide | $Fe(CN)_6$ | 4 | Sulfide | S | 2 |
| Hydroxyl | OH | 1 | Sulfite | $SO_3$ | 2 |
| Iodate | $IO_3$ | 1 | Thiocyanate | CNS | 1 |
| Iodide | I | 1 | Zincate | $Zn(OH)_3$ | 1 |

## TABLE XV. SOLUBILITIES AND SOLUBILITY PRODUCTS

In the following table some of the values are known with a fairly high degree of accuracy, others only approximately. In general, for substances of higher solubility, the value in grams per liter has been determined directly and the other quantities calculated from this. For substances of lower solubility, the solubility product has been determined under particular conditions and the other values calculated from this. In the latter case the solubility values are ideal numbers based on the assumption that water is an inert solvent. The formulas for converting molar solubility to solubility product and vice versa for different types of compounds are based on the assumption that in these dilute solutions the compounds are practically completely dissociated into the simple ions.

I. For compounds of the formula, $AB$, the molar solubility, $S_{AB}$, of the salt equals the concentration of each ion; therefore $L_{AB} = (S_{AB})^2$ and $S_{AB} = \sqrt{L_{AB}}$.

II. For compounds of the formula $A_2B$, the molar solubility $S_{A_2B}$ equals the concentration of $B$ ion, but only half the concentration of $A$ ion; therefore

$$L_{A_2B} = (2S_{A_2B})^2(S_{A_2B}) = 4(S_{A_2B})^3 \quad \text{and} \quad S_{A_2B} = \sqrt[3]{\frac{L_{A_2B}}{4}}$$

(for compounds of the formula $AB_2$ the same relation holds between $L$ and $S$ as for $A_2B$).

III. For compounds of the formula $A_2B_3$, the molar solubility $S_{A_2B_3}$ equals half the concentration of $A$ ion and one-third the concentration of $B$ ion; therefore,

$$L_{A_2B_3} = (2S_{A_2B_3})^2(3S_{A_2B_3})^3 = 108(S_{A_2B_3})^5 \quad \text{and} \quad S_{A_2B_3} = \sqrt[5]{\frac{L_{A_2B_3}}{108}}$$

| Compound | Grams per Liter | Moles per Liter | Solubility Product |
|---|---|---|---|
| $Al(OH)_3$ | $3.3 \times 10^{-7}$ | $4.2 \times 10^{-9}$ | $8.5 \times 10^{-33}$ |
| $BaCO_3$ | $2 \times 10^{-2}$ | $1.0 \times 10^{-4}$ | $1 \times 10^{-8}$ |
| $BaC_2O_4$ | $8.6 \times 10^{-2}$ | $3.8 \times 10^{-4}$ | $1.4 \times 10^{-7}$ |
| $BaCrO_4$ | $3.5 \times 10^{-3}$ | $1.4 \times 10^{-5}$ | $2 \times 10^{-10}$ |
| $BaSO_4$ | $2.3 \times 10^{-3}$ | $1.0 \times 10^{-5}$ | $1 \times 10^{-10}$ |
| $Bi_2S_3$ | $1.7 \times 10^{-16}$ | $3.1 \times 10^{-19}$ | $3.2 \times 10^{-91}$ |
| $CaCO_3$ | $1.3 \times 10^{-2}$ | $1.3 \times 10^{-4}$ | $1.7 \times 10^{-8}$ |
| $CaC_2O_4$ | $6.4 \times 10^{-3}$ | $5.0 \times 10^{-5}$ | $2.5 \times 10^{-9}$ |
| $CaSO_4$ | $2.02 \times 10^{0}$ | $1.49 \times 10^{-2}$ | $2.2 \times 10^{-4}$ |
| $CdC_2O_4$ | $3.4 \times 10^{-2}$ | $1.7 \times 10^{-4}$ | $2.9 \times 10^{-8}$ |
| $Cd(OH)_2$ | $2.6 \times 10^{-4}$ | $1.8 \times 10^{-6}$ | $2.2 \times 10^{-17}$ |
| $CdS$ | $1 \times 10^{-12}$ | $7.1 \times 10^{-15}$ | $5.1 \times 10^{-29}$ |
| $Co(OH)_2$ | $2.3 \times 10^{-4}$ | $2.5 \times 10^{-6}$ | $6.0 \times 10^{-17}$ |
| $CoS$ | $3.9 \times 10^{-12}$ | $4.3 \times 10^{-14}$ | $1.9 \times 10^{-27}$ |
| $Cr(OH)_3$ | $3.3 \times 10^{-6}$ | $3.2 \times 10^{-8}$ | $2.9 \times 10^{-29}$ |
| $Cu(OH)_2$ | $2.7 \times 10^{-5}$ | $2.8 \times 10^{-7}$ | $8.5 \times 10^{-20}$ |
| $CuS$ | $1 \times 10^{-19}$ | $1.1 \times 10^{-21}$ | $1.2 \times 10^{-42}$ |
| $Fe(OH)_2$ | $4 \times 10^{-5}$ | $4.5 \times 10^{-7}$ | $3.6 \times 10^{-19}$ |
| $Fe(OH)_3$ | $1.6 \times 10^{-8}$ | $1.5 \times 10^{-10}$ | $1.3 \times 10^{-38}$ |
| $FeS$ | $5.4 \times 10^{-8}$ | $6.1 \times 10^{-10}$ | $3.7 \times 10^{-19}$ |

TABLE XV. SOLUBILITIES AND SOLUBILITY PRODUCTS (Continued)

| Compound | Grams per Liter | Moles per Liter | Solubility Product |
|---|---|---|---|
| $PbBr_2$ | $8.4 \times 10^{0}$ | $2.3 \times 10^{-2}$ | $4.8 \times 10^{-5}$ |
| $PbCO_3$ | $1.3 \times 10^{-3}$ | $5.0 \times 10^{-6}$ | $2.5 \times 10^{-11}$ |
| $PbC_2O_4$ | $1.5 \times 10^{-3}$ | $5.0 \times 10^{-6}$ | $2.5 \times 10^{-11}$ |
| $PbCl_2$ | $9.7 \times 10^{0}$ | $3.5 \times 10^{-2}$ | $1.7 \times 10^{-4}$ |
| $PbCrO_4$ | $4.3 \times 10^{-5}$ | $1.3 \times 10^{-7}$ | $1.8 \times 10^{-14}$ |
| $PbI_2$ | $6 \times 10^{-1}$ | $1.3 \times 10^{-3}$ | $8.5 \times 10^{-9}$ |
| $Pb(OH)_2$ | $1.4 \times 10^{-4}$ | $5.9 \times 10^{-7}$ | $8.3 \times 10^{-19}$ |
| $PbS$ | $4.3 \times 10^{-12}$ | $1.8 \times 10^{-14}$ | $3.4 \times 10^{-28}$ |
| $PbSO_4$ | $3.9 \times 10^{-2}$ | $1.3 \times 10^{-4}$ | $1.7 \times 10^{-8}$ |
| $MgCO_3$ | $4.8 \times 10^{-1}$ | $5.1 \times 10^{-3}$ | $2.6 \times 10^{-5}$ |
| $MgC_2O_4$ | $3.0 \times 10^{-1}$ | $2.7 \times 10^{-3}$ | $7.3 \times 10^{-6}$ |
| $Mg(OH)_2$ | $2.3 \times 10^{-2}$ | $4 \times 10^{-4}$ | $3 \times 10^{-10}$ |
| $Mn(OH)_2$ | $4.4 \times 10^{-3}$ | $5.0 \times 10^{-5}$ | $5.1 \times 10^{-13}$ |
| $MnS$ | $2.3 \times 10^{-6}$ | $2.6 \times 10^{-8}$ | $7.0 \times 10^{-16}$ |
| $HgI_2$ | $4.5 \times 10^{-4}$ | $1 \times 10^{-6}$ | $4 \times 10^{-18}$ |
| $HgS$ | $7.4 \times 10^{-25}$ | $3.2 \times 10^{-27}$ | $1.0 \times 10^{-53}$ |
| $Ni(OH)_2$ | $1.8 \times 10^{-4}$ | $1.9 \times 10^{-6}$ | $2.7 \times 10^{-17}$ |
| $NiS$ | $3 \times 10^{-12}$ | $3.3 \times 10^{-14}$ | $1.1 \times 10^{-27}$ |
| $AgBr$ | $1.1 \times 10^{-4}$ | $5.8 \times 10^{-7}$ | $3.4 \times 10^{-13}$ |
| $Ag_2C_2O_4$ | $3.3 \times 10^{-2}$ | $1.1 \times 10^{-4}$ | $5.3 \times 10^{-12}$ |
| $AgCl$ | $1.5 \times 10^{-3}$ | $1 \times 10^{-5}$ | $1 \times 10^{-10}$ |
| $Ag_2CrO_4$ | $2.6 \times 10^{-2}$ | $8.0 \times 10^{-5}$ | $2 \times 10^{-12}$ |
| $AgI$ | $3.7 \times 10^{-6}$ | $1.6 \times 10^{-8}$ | $2.6 \times 10^{-16}$ |
| $Ag_2S$ | $5.7 \times 10^{-16}$ | $2.3 \times 10^{-18}$ | $4.8 \times 10^{-53}$ |
| $SrCO_3$ | $1.2 \times 10^{-2}$ | $8 \times 10^{-5}$ | $6.4 \times 10^{-9}$ |
| $SrC_2O_4$ | $4.6 \times 10^{-2}$ | $2.6 \times 10^{-4}$ | $6.8 \times 10^{-8}$ |
| $SrSO_4$ | $1.1 \times 10^{-1}$ | $6 \times 10^{-4}$ | $3.6 \times 10^{-7}$ |
| $ZnC_2O_4$ | $6.5 \times 10^{-3}$ | $4.2 \times 10^{-5}$ | $1.7 \times 10^{-9}$ |
| $Zn(OH)_2$ | $9.8 \times 10^{-5}$ | $1 \times 10^{-6}$ | $4 \times 10^{-18}$ |
| $ZnS$ | $2.2 \times 10^{-11}$ | $2.4 \times 10^{-13}$ | $5.1 \times 10^{-26}$ |

TABLE XVI. IONIZATION CONSTANTS

| Substance | Formula for Constant | Numerical Value of Constant |
|---|---|---|
| Acetic acid | $\frac{[H_3O^+] \times [C_2H_3O_2^-]}{[HC_2H_3O_2]}$ | $1.8 \times 10^{-5}$ |
| Aluminum hydroxyl ion (1OH) | $\frac{[Al^{+3}] \times [OH^-]}{[AlOH^{++}]}$ | $7 \times 10^{-10}$ |
| Ammonium hydroxide | $\frac{[NH_4^+] \times [OH^-]}{[NH_3] + [NH_4OH]}$ | $1.8 \times 10^{-5}$ |
| Arsenic acid, First step | $\frac{[H_3O^+] \times [H_2AsO_4^-]}{[H_3AsO_4]}$ | $5 \times 10^{-3}$ |
| Second step | $\frac{[H_3O^+] \times [HAsO_4^{--}]}{[H_2AsO_4^-]}$ | $4 \times 10^{-5}$ |
| Third step | $\frac{[H_3O^+] \times [AsO_4^{-3}]}{[HAsO_4^{--}]}$ | $6 \times 10^{-10}$ |
| Cadmium ammonia ion | $\frac{[Cd^{++}] \times [NH_3]^4}{[Cd(NH_3)_4^{++}]}$ | $1 \times 10^{-7}$ |
| Cadmium chloride | $\frac{[Cd^{++}] \times [Cl^-]^2}{[CdCl_2]}$ | $6.1 \times 10^{-3}$ |
| Cadmium chloride ion (1Cl) | $\frac{[Cd^{++}] \times [Cl^-]}{[CdCl^+]}$ | $4 \times 10^{-2}$ |
| Cadmium chloride ion (3Cl) | $\frac{[Cd^{++}] \times [Cl^-]^3}{[CdCl_3^-]}$ | $4 \times 10^{-3}$ |
| Cadmium cyanide ion | $\frac{[Cd^{++}] \times [CN^-]^4}{[Cd(CN)_4^{--}]}$ | $1.4 \times 10^{-17}$ |
| Carbonic acid, First step | $\frac{[H_3O^+] \times [HCO_3^-]}{[H_2CO_3]}$ | $3 \times 10^{-7}$ |
| Second step | $\frac{[H_3O^+] \times [CO_3^{--}]}{[HCO_3^-]}$ | $5.3 \times 10^{-11}$ |
| Chloric acid | $\frac{[H_3O^+] \times [ClO_3^-]}{[HClO_3]}$ | Strong electrolyte |

TABLE XVI. IONIZATION CONSTANTS (Continued)

| Substance | Formula for Constant | Numerical Value of Constant |
|---|---|---|
| Chromic acid, First step | $\frac{[H_3O^+] \times [HCrO_4^-]}{[H_2CrO_4]}$ | Strong electrolyte |
| Second step | $\frac{[H_3O^+] \times [CrO_4^{--}]}{[HCrO_4^-]}$ | $6 \times 10^{-7}$ |
| Chromic hydroxyl ion (1OH) | $\frac{[Cr^{+3}] \times [OH^-]}{[CrOH^{++}]}$ | $6 \times 10^{-11}$ |
| Cupric ammonia ion | $\frac{[Cu^{++}] \times [NH_3]^4}{[Cu(NH_3)_4^{++}]}$ | $4.5 \times 10^{-14}$ |
| Cuprocyanide ion | $\frac{[Cu^+] \times [CN^-]^3}{[Cu(CN)_3^{--}]}$ | $5 \times 10^{-28}$ |
| Ferric chloride | $\frac{[Fe^{+3}] \times [Cl^-]^3}{[FeCl_3]}$ | 2.22 |
| Ferric chloride ion (1Cl) | $\frac{[Fe^{+3}] \times [Cl^-]}{[FeCl^{++}]}$ | $3 \times 10^{-2}$ |
| Ferric chloride ion (2Cl) | $\frac{[Fe^{+3}] \times [Cl^-]^2}{[FeCl_2^+]}$ | 0.222 |
| Ferric hydroxyl ion (1OH) | $\frac{[Fe^{+3}] \times [OH^-]}{[FeOH^{++}]}$ | $2.5 \times 10^{-12}$ |
| Hydrobromic acid | $\frac{[H_3O^+] \times [Br^-]}{[HBr]}$ | Strong electrolyte |
| Hydrochloric acid | $\frac{[H_3O^+] \times [Cl^-]}{[HCl]}$ | Strong electrolyte |
| Hydrocyanic acid | $\frac{[H_3O^+] \times [CN^-]}{[HCN]}$ | $7 \times 10^{-10}$ |
| Hydrogen sulfide, First step | $\frac{[H_3O^+] \times [HS^-]}{[H_2S]}$ | $9 \times 10^{-8}$ |
| Second step | $\frac{[H_3O^+] \times [S^{--}]}{[HS^-]}$ | $1.2 \times 10^{-15}$ |

TABLE XVI. IONIZATION CONSTANTS (Continued)

| Substance | Formula for Constant | Numerical Value of Constant |
|---|---|---|
| Hydriodic acid | $\frac{[H_3O^+] \times [I^-]}{[HI]}$ | Strong electrolyte |
| Lead chloride ion | $\frac{[Pb^{++}] \times [Cl^-]}{[PbCl^+]}$ | 0.08 |
| Mercuric chloride | $\frac{[Hg^{++}] \times [Cl^-]^2}{HgCl_2}$ | $6 \times 10^{-15}$ |
| Mercuric chloride ion | $\frac{[HgCl_2] \times [Cl^-]^2}{[HgCl_4^{--}]}$ | $1 \times 10^{-2}$ |
| Mercuric iodide ion | $\frac{[Hg^{++}] \times [I^-]^4}{[HgI_4^{--}]}$ | $5 \times 10^{-32}$ |
| Mercuric thiocyanate ion | $\frac{[Hg^{++}] \times [CNS^-]^4}{[Hg(CNS)_4^{--}]}$ | $1 \times 10^{-22}$ |
| Nitric acid | $\frac{[H_3O^+] \times [NO_3^-]}{[HNO_3]}$ | Strong electrolyte |
| Oxalic acid, First step | $\frac{[H_3O^+] \times [HC_2O_4^-]}{[H_2C_2O_4]}$ | $3.8 \times 10^{-2}$ |
| Second step | $\frac{[H_3O^+] \times [C_2O_4^{--}]}{[HC_2O_4^-]}$ | $4.9 \times 10^{-5}$ |
| Phosphoric acid, First step | $\frac{[H_3O^+] \times [H_2PO_4^-]}{[H_3PO_4]}$ | $1.1 \times 10^{-2}$ |
| Second step | $\frac{[H_3O^+] \times [HPO_4^{--}]}{[H_2PO_4^-]}$ | $2 \times 10^{-7}$ |
| Third step | $\frac{[H_3O^+] \times [PO_4^{-3}]}{[HPO_4^{--}]}$ | $3.6 \times 10^{-13}$ |
| Silver ammonia ion | $\frac{[Ag^+] \times [NH_3]^2}{[Ag(NH_3)_2^+]}$ | $6.8 \times 10^{-8}$ |
| Silver cyanide ion | $\frac{[Ag^+] \times [CN^-]^2}{[Ag(CN)_2^-]}$ | $1 \times 10^{-21}$ |

TABLE XVI. IONIZATION CONSTANTS (Continued)

| Substance | Formula for Constant | Numerical Value of Constant |
|---|---|---|
| Silver thiosulfate ion | $\frac{[Ag^+] \times [S_2O_3^{--}]^2}{[Ag(S_2O_3)_2^{-3}]}$ | $1 \times 10^{-13}$ |
| Sulfuric acid, First step | $\frac{[H_3O^+] \times [HSO_4^-]}{[H_2SO_4]}$ | Strong electrolyte |
| Second step | $\frac{[H_3O^+] \times [SO_4^{--}]}{[HSO_4^-]}$ | $3 \times 10^{-2}$ |
| Sulfurous acid, First step | $\frac{[H_3O^+] \times [HSO_3^-]}{[H_2SO_3]}$ | $1.7 \times 10^{-2}$ |
| Second step | $\frac{[H_3O^+] \times [SO_3^{--}]}{[HSO_3^-]}$ | $5 \times 10^{-6}$ |
| Zinc ammonia ion | $\frac{[Zn^{++}] \times [NH_3]^4}{[Zn(NH_3)_4^{++}]}$ | $2.6 \times 10^{-10}$ |
| Zinc hydroxyl ion (1OH) | $\frac{[Zn^{++}] \times [OH^-]}{[ZnOH^+]}$ | $2.45 \times 10^{-10}$ |

## REDUCTION POTENTIALS

A consideration of the facts developed in connection with the ion-electron method of balancing oxidation-reduction equations leads to the idea that the strength of a reducing agent corresponds to the readiness with which it loses electrons. This quantity can be measured in terms of the electromotive force set up in a cell in which one element is the reducing agent in question and the other is a standard oxidizing agent. The different potentials when different reducing agents are studied correspond to differences in the strength of the various reducing agents. In the same way, different oxidizing agents may be compared with a standard reducing agent and the different potentials taken as measurements of the various strengths of the oxidizing agents. The standard used in these measurements, and arbitrarily assigned a zero value in the tables, is the hydrogen electrode. This consists of a strip of platinized platinum saturated with hydrogen, dipping into a molar solution of hydrochloric acid, arranged to maintain an atmosphere of hydrogen at normal pressure in contact with the solution, and kept at a temperature of 25°C. In this system it will be noted that hydrogen as a reducing agent may be oxidized to hydrogen ion, or hydrogen ion as an oxidizing agent may be reduced to hydrogen. Therefore this system may serve both as a standard reducing agent and as a standard oxidizing agent. Thus stronger oxidizing agents will become positive electrodes and stronger reducing agents will become negative as compared with the hydrogen electrode when connected with it to form a cell (see Fig. 1, p. 22).

The potential of an oxidant depends in part on the concentration of the product to which it is reduced. Therefore, to set up standard values it is necessary to fix the concentrations of these materials. When the reagent and product are both soluble, the concentrations of both should be made $M$; if either is relatively insoluble, the solution should be saturated with respect to that substance and $M$ with respect to the other. Thus the potential assigned a free metal in the oxidation-reduction series is that of the free metal in contact with a molar solution of its positive ion. Since in each of these cases the solution contains both an oxidant and a reductant, either of which may become operative under proper conditions, it is evident that the series of reducing agents with their products of oxidation is identical with the series of oxidizing agents with their products of reduction, the "strong oxidizing agents—weak reducing agents" forming one end of the list and the "weak oxidizing agents—strong reducing agents" the other end.

**Notes on Table XVII.** 1. Because of the intimate relation of oxidation and reduction to each other, a reduction series is just the reverse of an oxidation series. In the reduction series, the strong reductants are put at the top of the list, and the weak reductants at the bottom, the order indicating the relative strength of the reagents (in systems in equilibrium, so far as possible, and under standard conditions). If the equations for the reactions were written in the reverse order ($K^+ + e^- = K(s)$, $Fe^{+3} + e^- = Fe^{++}$, etc.), the sign of the potential would be reversed, and the list would become an oxidation series, with the weak oxidants at the top and the strong oxidants at the bottom.

2. There is much confusion in the literature concerning the sign to be used with respect to the potentials. The measurement actually made is the E.M.F. of a system, and from this the potential of one of the electrodes is calculated by assuming a definite value for the other as a reference electrode. The basis of the values assigned is the potential of the hydrogen electrode, which is arbitrarily called zero. Since the electropositive character of a metal represents the readiness with which an atom loses an electron and becomes positively charged, the plus sign has been attached to the potentials of those systems in which the reductant loses electrons more readily than does the hydrogen in the hydrogen electrode, and the minus sign has been attached to the potentials of those systems in which the reductant loses electrons less readily than does the hydrogen in the hydrogen electrode. The opposite convention is fre-

TABLE XVII. REDUCTION POTENTIALS

| Reagent | Potential | Reaction |
|---|---|---|
| K | +2.924 | $K(s)$ * $= K^+ + e^-$ |
| Ca | +2.76 | $Ca(s) = Ca^{++} + 2e^-$ |
| Mg | +1.55 | $Mg(s) = Mg^{++} + 2e^-$ |
| Zn | +1.25 | $Zn(s) + 2OH^- = ZnO(s) + H_2O + 2e^-$ |
| Mn | +1.0 | $Mn(s) = Mn^{++} + 2e^-$ |
| Cu | +0.89 | $Cu(s) + SH^- + OH^- = CuS(s) + H_2O + 2e^-$ |
| H | +0.83 | $H_2(g) + 2OH^- = 2H_2O + 2e^-$ |
| Hg | +0.77 | $Hg(l) + SH^- + OH^- = HgS(s) + H_2O + 2e^-$ |
| Zn | +0.76 | $Zn(s) = Zn^{++} + 2e^-$ |
| Ag | +0.67 | $2Ag(s) + SH^- + OH^- = Ag_2S(s) + H_2O + 2e^-$ |
| Pb | +0.578 | $Pb(s) + 2OH^- = PbO(s\ red) + H_2O + 2e^-$ |
| Pb | +0.575 | $Pb(s) + 2OH^- = PbO(s\ yellow) + H_2O + 2e^-$ |
| Cr | +0.56 | $Cr(s) = Cr^{++} + 2e^-$ |
| $S^{--}$ | +0.55 | $S^{--} = S(s) + 2e^-$ |
| Ag | +0.51 | $Ag(s) + 2CN^- = Ag(CN)_2^- + e^-$ |
| Fe | +0.44 | $Fe(s) = Fe^{++} + 2e^-$ |
| Cr | +0.4 | $Cr^{++} = Cr^{+3} + e^-$ |
| Cd | +0.4 | $Cd(s) = Cd^{++} + 2e^-$ |
| Cu | +0.34 | $2Cu(s) + 2OH^- = Cu_2O(s) + H_2O + 2e^-$ |
| Pb | +0.34 | $Pb(s) + SO_4^{--} = PbSO_4 + 2e^-$ |
| Tl | +0.33 | $Tl(s) = Tl^+ + e^-$ |
| Pb | +0.31 | $Pb(s) + 2I^- = PbI_2 + 2e^-$ |
| Co | +0.29 | $Co(s) = Co^{++} + 2e^-$ |
| Cu | +0.26 | $Cu(s) + H_2S(g) = CuS + 2H^+ + 2e^-$ |
| Pb | +0.26 | $Pb(s) + 2Cl^- = PbCl_2 + 2e^-$ |
| Ni | +0.23 | $Ni(s) = Ni^{++} + 2e^-$ |
| $VSO_4$ | +0.2 | $2VSO_4 + 2H_2O = (VO)_2SO_4 + 4H^+ + SO_4^{--} + 2e^-$ |
| Ag | +0.15 | $Ag(s) + I^- = AgI(s) + e^-$ |
| Sn | +0.13 | $Sn(s) = Sn^{++} + 2e^-$ |
| Pb | +0.12 | $Pb(s) = Pb^{++} + 2e^-$ |
| Fe | +0.04 | $Fe(s) = Fe^{+3} + 3e^-$ |
| Ag | +0.04 | $2Ag(s) + H_2S(g) = Ag_2S + 2H^+ + 2e^-$ |
| H | ±0.00 | $H_2 = 2H^+ + 2e^-$ |
| $Ti^{+3}$ | −0.04 | $Ti^{+3} + 2SO_4^{--} = Ti(SO_4)_2 + e^-$ |
| Pb | −0.07 | $Pb(s) + H_2S(g) = PbS(s) + 2H^+ + 2e^-$ |
| Ag | −0.07 | $Ag(s) + Br^- = AgBr + e^-$ |
| Sb | −0.1 | $Sb(s) = Sb^{+3} + 3e^-$ |
| $Sn^{++}$ | −0.13 | $Sn^{++} = Sn^{+4} + 2e^-$ |
| Cu | −0.13 | $Cu(s) + Cl^- = CuCl(s) + e^-$ |
| Sb | −0.144 | $2Sb(s) + 3H_2O = Sb_2O_3(s) + 6H^+ + 6e^-$ |
| Bi | −0.15 | $Bi(s) + Cl^- + H_2O = BiOCl + 2H^+ + 3e^-$ |
| $Cu^+$ | −0.17 | $Cu^+ = Cu^{++} + e^-$ |
| Bi | −0.2 | $Bi(s) = Bi^{+3} + 3e^-$ |

* s = solid, l = liquid, g = gas.

TABLE XVII. REDUCTION POTENTIALS (Continued)

| Reagent | Potential | Reaction |
|---|---|---|
| Sb | −0.21 | $Sb(s) + H_2O = SbO^+ + 2H^+ + 3e^-$ |
| Ag | −0.22 | $Ag(s) + Cl^- = AgCl + e^-$ |
| As | −0.23 | $2As(s) + 3H_2O = As_2O_3(s) + 6H^+ + 6e^-$ |
| $Hg_2Cl_2$ | −0.24 | $Hg_2Cl_2(s) + 2Cl^- = 2HgCl_2 + 2e^-$ |
| PbO | −0.27 | $PbO(s) + 2OH^- = PbO_2 + H_2O + 2e^-$ |
| Hg | −0.280 * | $2Hg + 2Cl^- = Hg_2Cl_2(s) + 2e^-$ |
| As | −0.3 | $As(s) = As^{+3} + 3e^-$ |
| Hg | −0.333 † | $2Hg + 2Cl^- = Hg_2Cl_2(s) + 2e^-$ |
| Cu | −0.34 | $Cu(s) = Cu^{++} + 2e^-$ |
| Ag | −0.38 | $Ag(s) + 2NH_3 = Ag(NH_3)_2^+ + e^-$ |
| $OH^-$ | −0.41 | $4OH^- = O_2(g) + 2H_2O + 4e^-$ |
| $CuCl_2^-$ | −0.45 | $CuCl_2^- = Cu^{++} + 2Cl^- + e^-$ |
| $K_4Fe(CN)_6$ | −0.489 | $K_4Fe(CN)_6 = K_3Fe(CN)_6 + K^+ + e^-$ |
| Ag | −0.50 | $2Ag(s) + CO_3^{--} = Ag_2CO_3(s) + 2e^-$ |
| $H_3AsO_3$ | −0.50 | $H_3AsO_3 + H_2O = H_3AsO_4 + 2H^+ + 2e^-$ |
| Cu | −0.52 | $Cu(s) = Cu^+ + e^-$ |
| $I^-$ | −0.53 | $2I^- = I_2 + 2e^-$ |
| $MnO_4^{--}$ | −0.66 | $MnO_4^{--} = MnO_4^- + e^-$ |
| $Fe^{++}$ | −0.75 | $Fe^{++} = Fe^{+3} + e^-$ |
| $H_2O_2$ | −0.80 | $H_2O_2 = O_2(g) + 2H^+ + 2e^-$ |
| Hg | −0.80 | $2Hg(l) = Hg_2^{++} + 2e^-$ |
| Ag | −0.80 | $Ag(s) = Ag^+ + e^-$ |
| Pd | −0.82 | $Pd(s) = Pd^{++} + 2e^-$ |
| $OH^-$ | −0.84 | $2OH^- = H_2O_2 + 2e^-$ |
| Hg | −0.86 | $Hg(l) = Hg^{++} + 2e^-$ |
| $Hg_2^{++}$ | −0.90 | $Hg_2^{++} = 2Hg^{++} + 2e^-$ |
| $VOSO_4$ | −0.92 | $VOSO_4 + 2H_2O = HVO_3 + SO_4^{--} + 3H^+ + e^-$ |
| NO | −0.95 | $NO + 2H_2O = NO_3^- + 4H^+ + 3e^-$ |
| $Br^-$ | −1.06 | $2Br^- = Br_2 + 2e^-$ |
| $I_2$ | −1.20 | $I_2(s) + 6H_2O = 2IO_3^- + 12H^+ + 10e^-$ |
| Au | −1.3 | $Au(s) = Au^{+3} + 3e^-$ |
| $Cr^{+3}$ | −1.3 | $Cr^{+3} + 4H_2O = HCrO_4^- + 7H^+ + 3e^-$ |
| $Mn^{++}$ | −1.33 | $Mn^{++} + 2H_2O = MnO_2(s) + 4H^+ + 2e^-$ |
| $Cl^-$ | −1.36 | $2Cl^- = Cl_2(g) + 2e^-$ |
| $Cl^-$ | −1.44 | $Cl^- + 3H_2O = ClO_3^- + 6H^+ + 6e^-$ |
| Au | −1.5 | $Au = Au^+ + e^-$ |
| $Ce^{+3}$ | −1.5 | $Ce^{+3} = Ce^{+4} + e^-$ |
| $Mn^{++}$ | −1.52 | $Mn^{++} + 4H_2O = MnO_4^- + 8H^+ + 5e^-$ |
| $MnO_2$ | −1.63 | $MnO_2(s) + 2H_2O = MnO_4^- + 4H^+ + 3e^-$ |
| $H_2O$ | −1.66 | $2H_2O = H_2O_2 + 2H^+ + 2e^-$ |
| $PbSO_4$ | −1.68 | $PbSO_4(s) + 2H_2O = PbO_2(s) + 4H^+ + SO_4^{--} + 2e^-$ |
| $Co^{++}$ | −1.8 | $Co^{++} = Co^{+3} + e^-$ |
| $O_2$ | −1.9 | $O_2(g) + H_2O = O_3 + 2H^+ + 2e^-$ |
| $F^-$ | −1.9 | $2F^- = F_2 + 2e^-$ |

* Normal calomel electrode ($Cl^- = N$).

† Decinormal calomel electrode ($Cl^- = 0.1\ N$).

quently adopted; therefore it is necessary to know the approximate character of the system being studied in order to avoid error in the use of data found in the literature.

3. The potential $E$ of an electrochemical reaction is given by the equation:

$$E = E_0 - \frac{0.059}{N} \log_{10} \frac{(A_P)^x}{(A_R)^y}$$

$E_0$ = potential under standard conditions.
$N$ = number of electrons in the equation for the reaction.
$A_P$ = activities of the products.
$A_R$ = activities of the reactants.

$x$ and $y$ are the corresponding coefficients in the electrochemical equation.

4. The effect of change in the ratio of concentrations of products to concentrations of reactants is shown in a number of cases in the table. Thus, the reducing power of Hg in contact with $M$ $Hg^{++}$, is represented by a potential of $-0.80$. By making the solution 0.1 $M$ with respect to $Cl^-$, and saturated with respect to $Hg_2Cl_2$, the reducing power of the Hg is raised to $-0.333$ volt; and by substituting $M$ $Cl^-$ for 0.1 $M$ $Cl^-$, the potential is raised still higher to $-0.280$ volt. By lowering the concentration of mercury ion still further through the use of $M$ $SH^-$ and $M$ $OH^-$ (the $Hg^{++}$ precipitating as HgS), the potential is raised to $+0.77$, which indicates a reducing power for Hg of the same order as Zn° in contact with $M$ $Zn^{++}$.

In the same way, if one compares the reducing power of Ag (or the oxidizing power of $Ag^+$) in solutions containing $M$ $Ag^+$ ($E = -0.80$), $M$ $Cl^-$ ($E = -0.22$), $M$ $I^-$ ($E = +0.15$), and $M$ $CN^-$ ($E = +0.51$), it becomes evident that there are chemical means available by which the ordinary powers of reagents may be profoundly modified.

5. By proper modification of conditions, it is possible to make reactions effective which might not be thought feasible on the basis of the data in Table XVII. Thus, in using $CuSO_4$ as a reagent to oxidize $I^-$ to $I_2$ in the test for $I^-$, it is assumed that the significant reaction is: $2Cu^{++} + 2I^- = 2Cu^+ + I_2$. According to the table, the potential of the reaction, $Cu^+ = Cu^{++} + e^-$, is $-0.17$ volt, while that of the reaction, $2I^- = I_2 + 2\,e^-$, is $-0.53$ volt. This would indicate that the reverse reaction might be expected to occur, namely, the oxidation of $Cu^+$ to $Cu^{++}$ by $I_2$. But the insolubility of the cuprous salt, or the readiness of formation of a complex anion, makes it possible to use this reaction effectively in the qualitative detection of $I^-$.

6. On the other hand, reactions which might be expected to occur readily, may involve an indirect mechanism such that the data of the table do not apply. The potential of the reaction, $Fe = Fe^{+3} + 3e^-(+0.04)$, would suggest that HCl might oxidize Fe to $Fe^{+3}$; but the potential of the reaction, $Fe^{++}$

$= Fe^{+3} + e^-(-0.75)$, indicates that the conversion to $Fe^{+3}$ would be more difficult if the formation of $Fe^{++}$ is an intermediate stage.

Also, the displacement reactions among the metals above hydrogen in the list do not take place readily because of the necessary presence of $H_2O$ and its ions as complicating factors.

7. Three types of problems are commonly solved by the aid of the data on standard oxidation potentials and the equation given above.

(1) How completely will $Ag^+$ be removed from a solution by precipitation as AgCl if the solution is $M$ with respect to $Cl^-$ and the potential of the silver cathode in the solution is $-0.22$ volt?

Since the potential of the silver cathode in contact with $M$ $Ag^+$ is $-0.80$ volt and the potential rises 0.059 volt for each tenfold decrease in concentration of $Ag^+$ the concentration of $Ag^+$ in the solution in question will be $1 \times 10^{-\frac{0.80-0.22}{0.059}}$ $M$.

$$\frac{0.80 - 0.22}{0.059} = 9.83$$

$$[Ag^+] = 1 \times 10^{-9.83} = 1.48 \times 10^{-10}$$

(It should be noted that this does not represent the total solubility of AgCl under this condition since a significant amount will be in solution in the form of $AgCl_2^-$ and $AgCl_3^{--}$.)

(2) From data such as are used in the first problem the solubility products of various insoluble compounds may be calculated. Thus, if the solution is saturated with respect to AgCl and $[Ag^+] = 1.48 \times 10^{-10}$ and $[Cl^-] = 1$,

$$L_{AgCl} = 1 \times 1.48 \times 10^{-10} = 1.48 \times 10^{-10}$$

(3) How completely will $KMnO_4$ oxidize $Fe^{++}$ to $Fe^{+3}$ if the two are mixed in equivalent proportions in a solution in which the concentration of hydrogen ion is kept molar?

When the reaction is half completed $[Fe^{++}] = [Fe^{+3}]$, $[Mn^{++}] = [MnO_4^-]$, and the potentials of the two systems will be the normal electrode values, $-0.75$ volt and $-1.52$ volt, respectively. Applying the general equation, at any stage in the reaction

$$E_{Fe^{+3}/Fe^{++}} = -0.75 - \frac{0.059}{1} \log \frac{[Fe^{+3}]}{[Fe^{++}]}$$

and

$$E_{MnO_4^-/Mn^{++}} = -1.52 - \frac{0.059}{5} \log \frac{[MnO_4^-]}{[Mn^{++}]}$$

At equilibrium the two potentials become equal; therefore,

$$-0.75 - \frac{0.059}{1} \log \frac{[Fe^{+3}]}{[Fe^{++}]} = -1.52 - \frac{0.059}{5} \log \frac{[MnO_4^-]}{[Mn^{++}]}.$$

## TABLE XVIII. TABLE OF SOLUBILITIES

The numbers represent ranges of solubility at room temperature as follows:

1—soluble (more than 50 g. per liter)
2—moderately soluble (10–50 g. per liter)
3—slightly soluble (1–10 g. per liter)
4—moderately insoluble (0.01–1 g. per liter)
5—insoluble (less than 0.01 g. per liter)

The letters refer to the solvent action of acids as follows:

a—soluble in acids generally, even acetic acid
b—soluble in strong acids but not in acetic acid
c—soluble in strong oxidizing acids ($HNO_3$, $HCl + HNO_3$, etc.), but not in hydrochloric acid
d—relatively insoluble in acids
h—requires free acid to prevent hydrolysis

Blank spaces indicate that the quantitative data are uncertain or that the compounds are rare or do not exist

| | Arsenate | Arsenite | Bromide | Carbonate | Chlorate | Chloride | Chromate | Ferricyanide | Ferrocyanide | Iodate | Iodide | Nitrate | Oxalate | Oxide (hydroxide) | Phosphate | Sulfate | Sulfide | Sulfite |
|---|---|---|---|---|---|---|---|---|---|---|---|---|---|---|---|---|---|---|
| Silver | 5b | 4b | 5d | 4a | 1 | 5d | 4b | 4d | 3d | 4b | 5d | 1 | 4b | 4a | 5b | 3b | 5c | 4b |
| Lead | 5b | 4b | 3d | 5a | 1 | 2b | 5b | 4b | 5d | 4d | 4c | 1h | 5b | 4a | 5b | 4d | 5b | 4b |
| Mercurous | 4b | 4b | 5c | 4b | | 5c | 3b | | | 4 | 5c | 1h | 5b | 5b | 5c | 4c | | |
| Mercuric | 5b | 5b | 3c | 5b | 1 | 2 | 3b | | | 4 | 5c | 1h | 5b | 5a | 5b | 2h | 5c | |
| Cupric | 5b | 5b | 1 | 4a | 1 | 1 | 2b | 5d | 5d | 3 | | 1 | 4b | 5a | 5b | 1 | 5c | |
| Bismuth | 5b | | 1h | 5b | 1 | 1h | 4b | 5d | 5d | 4 | 4b | 1h | 4b | 5b | 5b | 1h | 5c | |
| Cadmium | | | 1 | 4a | 1 | 1 | | 5 | 5 | 3 | 1 | 1 | 4b | 5a | 5b | 1 | 5b | 3b |
| Antimonous | 5b | 5b | 1h | | | 1h | | | | | 3b | 1h | | 4b | | 1h | 5b | |
| Stannous | | | 1h | | | 1h | | | 4 | | 3b | | | 5b | | 1h | 5b | |
| Stannic | 5b | | 1h | | | 1h | | | 4 | | 2b | | | 5b | 5b | 1h | 5b | |
| Aluminum | 5b | | 1h | | 1 | 1h | | | | | 1h | 1h | 4b | 5b | 5b | 1h | | |
| Chromium | 4b | | 1h | | 1 | 1h | 4b | | | | 1h | 1h | 3 | 5b | 5b | 1h | | |
| Ferrous | | | 1 | 4b | | 1 | | 5d | 5d | | 1 | | 4b | 4b | 4b | 1 | 5b | 4b |
| Ferric | 5b | 4b | 1h | | | 1h | 1 | 1 | 5d | | | 1h | 1 | 5b | 5b | 1h | 5b | |
| Cobalt | 5b | 5b | 1 | 5a | | 1 | 4b | 5d | 5d | 3 | 1 | 1 | 5b | 5b | 5b | 1 | 5c | 4b |
| Nickel | 5b | 5b | 1 | 4a | | 1 | 4b | 5d | 5d | | 1 | 1 | 5b | 5b | 5b | 1 | 5c | 4b |
| Manganese | 4b | 4b | 1 | 4a | | 1 | | 5d | 5 | | 1 | 1 | 4b | 5a | 5b | 1 | 5a | |
| Zinc | 5b | | 1 | 4a | | 1 | 3b | 5d | 5d | 3 | 1 | 1 | 5b | 5a | 5b | 1 | 5b | |
| Barium | 4b | | 1 | 4a | | 1 | 5b | | 3 | 4d | 1 | 1 | 4b | 2a | 5b | 5d | 2a | 4b |
| Strontium | 3b | 3b | 1 | 4a | | 1 | 3b | | 1 | | 1 | 1 | 4b | 3a | 5b | 4d | | 4b |
| Calcium | 4b | | 1 | 4a | | 1 | 3b | | 1 | | 1 | 1 | 5b | 3a | 4b | 3d | 3a | 4b |
| Magnesium | 4b | 1 | 1 | 4a | 1 | 1 | 1 | 1 | 1 | 1 | 1 | 1 | 4b | 5a | 4b | 1 | | 2b |
| Potassium | 1 | 1 | 1 | 1 | 1 | 1 | 1 | 1 | 1 | 1 | 1 | 1 | 1 | 1 | 1 | 1 | 1 | 1 |
| Sodium | 1 | 1 | 1 | 1 | 1 | 1 | 1 | 1 | 1 | 1 | 1 | 1 | 2 | 1 | 1 | 1 | 1 | 1 |
| Ammonium | 1 | 1 | 1 | 1 | 1 | 1 | 1 | 1 | 1 | 2 | 1 | 1 | 2 | 1 | 1 | 1 | 1 | 1 |

Since the reagents were mixed in equivalent amounts, at equilibrium $\frac{[Fe^{+3}]}{[Fe^{++}]}$ $= \frac{[Mn^{++}]}{[MnO_4^-]}$ and the expression

$$\frac{-0.059}{5} \log \frac{[MnO_4^-]}{[Mn^{++}]} \text{ may be written } \frac{+0.059}{5} \log \frac{[Fe^{+3}]}{[Fe^{++}]}$$

Rearranging

$$1.52 - 0.75 = \frac{0.059}{1} \log \frac{[Fe^{+3}]}{[Fe^{++}]} + \frac{0.059}{5} \log \frac{[Fe^{+3}]}{[Fe^{++}]}$$

Whence

$$\log \frac{[Fe^{+3}]}{[Fe^{++}]} = 0.77 \times \frac{5}{6 \times 0.059} = 10.9$$

In the experiment in question it would be expected, therefore, that the $Fe^{++}$ would be oxidized until the $[Fe^{+3}] = 1 \times 10^{10.9} \times [Fe^{++}]$, the concentration of $MnO_4^-$ being correspondingly lowered until $[Mn^{++}] = 1 \times 10^{10.9} \times [MnO_4^-]$.

8. The data in this table have been taken chiefly from International Critical Tables, Landolt and Börnstein, 4th and 5th editions, and the article by Gerke in *Chemical Reviews*, **1,** 377 (1924–5).

TABLE XIX COLORED IONS

(Moderately dilute solutions)

| *Ion* | *Color* |
|---|---|
| $Cu^{++}$ | Blue |
| $Cu(NH_3)_4^{++}$ | Deep blue |
| $FeCl^{++}$ | Yellow |
| $FeOH^{++}$ | Red-brown |
| $Cr^{+++}$ | Blue-violet |
| $CrCl^{++}$ | Green |
| $CrOH^{++}$ | Green |
| $Cr_2O_7^{--}$ | Orange |
| $CrO_4^{--}$ | Yellow |
| $Co^{++}$ | Light red |
| $Co(NH_3)_6^{++}$ | Red |
| $Ni^{++}$ | Green |
| $Ni(NH_3)_6^{++}$ | Blue |
| $MnO_4^-$ | Purple |
| $MnO_4^{--}$ | Dark green |

TABLE XX COLORED FLAMES

(Pt-wire test in Bunsen flame)

| *Metal* | *Color* |
|---|---|
| Cu | Green |
| Ba | Green |
| Sr | Crimson |
| Ca | Brick red |
| Na | Yellow |
| K | Violet |
| $(NH_4)_2Cr_2O_7$ | Violet |

## SOME MATHEMATICAL RELATIONS

*Significant Figures.* In scientific measurement very little of the data is exact. In fact, only those numbers which can be counted directly may be regarded as completely accurate, and even then there is the possibility of error in the counting process. For quantities which have to be measured, such as the weight of a sample, the volume of reagent being added, or the rate at which a reaction is taking place, there will always be experimental errors involving the accuracy of calibration of the measuring device and the effect of conditions under which the measurement is made. Depending on the magnitude of these errors in relation to that of the quantity being measured, the accuracy of the measurement may be expressed in terms of "percentage error." For measurements which can be made with fairly high accuracy, this may be as low as 0.1%, or one part in a thousand. In a very few cases the error may be as small as one part in a million. However much of the data involve uncertainties of considerably larger magnitude. Thus, in qualitative analysis where small quantities of reagent are being added from small graduates or with dropper tubes, the accuracy of adjustment of conditions even with reasonable care is probably in the order of 20% error.

In carrying out calculations with the data of experiments, it is possible to waste considerable time by expressing the results with a larger number of digits than is justified by the accuracy of the data. Thus, if there is probable inaccuracy in the original data of one part in a hundred, there is no need for more digits in the answer than will be required to maintain this accuracy. If the limit of error is assumed to be one part in a hundred, then an answer involving three significant figures will be more than adequate; and if the first figure is fairly large (7, 8, or 9), even two figures will be sufficient.

*Two Useful Approximations.* (1) The sum or difference of two quantities, one of which is much larger than the other, may be replaced by the larger of the two. Expressed mathematically, $a \pm x = x$ if $x$ is small as compared with $a$.

Examples:

(*a*) In calculating the concentration of $OH^-$ in a solution containing both $NH_4Cl$ and $NH_4OH$, the concentration of $NH_4^+$ supplied by the $NH_4Cl$ will be enough larger than that from the $NH_4OH$ so that it is unnecessary to add the latter.

(*b*) In calculating the extent of dissociation of acetic acid in an ordinary solution, the concentration of undissociated acetic acid may be taken as equal to the total concentration of the acetic acid since the extent of dissociation will be quite small.

(2) If a factor in a given multiplication is approximately equal to 1, it may be called 1 and dropped. In mathematical form, $ax = x$ if $a$ is approximately 1.

If $a$ lies between the limits of 0.99 and 1.01, the error thus introduced will not be greater than 1%.

*The exponential form of handling very small or very large numbers.* Such quantities as 185,000 and 0.00467 are frequently written as $1.85 \times 10^5$ or $4.67 \times 10^{-3}$, and sometimes condensed still more to the form $10^{5.267}$ or $10^{-2.669}$. In the form $1.85 \times 10^5$ the positive exponent of the base, 10, indicates how many places the decimal point has been moved to the left to yield the number 1.85. In $4.67 \times 10^{-3}$, the negative exponent shows how many places the decimal point has been moved to the right to give 4.67. Certain other identities should be familiar to the student. For example:

$$a^n = \frac{1}{a^{-n}}, \quad a^{-n} = \frac{1}{a^n}, \quad a\frac{1}{n} = \sqrt[n]{a}, \quad \sqrt{a^2n} = a\sqrt{n},$$

$$a^m \times a^n = a^{m+n}, \quad \frac{a^m}{a^n} = a^{m-n}$$

The student should note that the reciprocal of $1.45 \times 10^3$ is $\frac{1}{1.45 \times 10^3}$ or $\frac{10^{-3}}{1.45}$, and not $1.45 \times 10^{-3}$. However, when the number is converted completely to the exponential form, $1.45 \times 10^3 = 10^{3.161}$, then the reciprocal of this may be written as $10^{-3.161}$.

*Solving a Quadratic Equation.* If one has a simple quadratic equation to deal with it may be converted to the general form $ax^2 + bx + c = 0$, in which $a$, $b$, and $c$ have known numerical values. The general formula for solving this equation is the following:

$$x = \frac{-b \pm \sqrt{b^2 - 4ac}}{2a}$$

However, if this formula has been forgotten, or one is not sure of certain of the signs, it is possible to use the method of "completing the square" to obtain the solution. In this case the equation is converted to the form $ax^2 + bx = -c$; then by dividing the coefficients by $a$, this is changed to $x^2 + \frac{b}{a}x = -\frac{c}{a}$. To complete the square on the left it is necessary to add $\left(\frac{b}{2a}\right)^2$ to this side and, to balance this, the same amount is added to the right side. The equation thus becomes $x^2 + \frac{b_x}{a} + \left(\frac{b}{2a}\right)^2 = \left(\frac{b}{2a}\right)^2 - \frac{c}{a}$. Extracting the square root on both sides yields the following:

$$x + \frac{b}{2a} = \sqrt{\left(\frac{b}{2a}\right)^2 - \frac{c}{a}}, \quad \text{or} \quad x = \sqrt{\left(\frac{b}{2a}\right)^2 - \frac{c}{a}} - \frac{b}{2a}$$

Since $a$, $b$, and $c$ have definite numerical values, the indicated numerical operations will give the value of $x$. In solving such a problem since $\sqrt{x^2} = \pm x$, two answers may be obtained which will satisfy the equation mathematically. If one is negative and the other positive, only the positive answer will be correct if $x$ is a measurable quantity. On the other hand, if both answers are positive it may be necessary to examine the data of the experiment to choose between them.

Sometimes the necessity of solving a quadratic equation may be avoided by manipulating the data in such a way as to have a ratio of "perfect squares." Then by extracting the square root the problem is reduced to one involving only the first powers. Thus such an equation as $(a + x)^2 = cx^2$ may be changed to the form $\frac{(a + x)^2}{x^2} = c$ and $\frac{a + x}{x} = \sqrt{c}$.

*Ratios and Fractions.* The combination of two ratios into a proportion—$A:B::C:D$—is equivalent to stating that the two fractions $\frac{A}{B}$ and $\frac{C}{D}$ are equal. If the quantities $A$ and $B$ are both multiplied (or divided) by the same quantity, this does not change either the ratio or the value of the fraction.

$$A:B::AX:BX, \quad \frac{A}{B} = \frac{AX}{BX}, \text{ etc.}$$

Occasionally one may be given the sum of two quantities and their ratio to each other and wish to calculate the numerical values of the two quantities. If $A + B = N$, and $A:B::2:7$, calculate the values of $A$ and $B$ in terms of $N$. If $A:B::2:7$, then $A:A + B::2:2 + 7$, and $B:A + B::7:2 + 7$. $\therefore A = \frac{2N}{9}$ and $B = \frac{7N}{9}$.

Another problem sometimes encountered is to combine two (or more) ratios involving two items each, but with one item in common, into a single ratio. Given $A:B::2:5$, and $B:C::7:3$ to form a single ratio $A:B:C::$. The first two items may be taken directly from the first ratio $A:B::2:5$. But the second ratio must then be manipulated in such a way as to change the 7 to a 5 without changing the value of the ratio. This is done by multiplying both the 7 and the 3 by the same quantity $\frac{5}{7}$. This yields $B:C = 5:\frac{15}{7}$. The combined ratio thus becomes $A:B:C::2:5:\frac{15}{7}$. If desired, this ratio could be changed to one involving only whole numbers by multiplying each quantity by 7, thus obtaining $A:B:C::14:35:15$. From such a ratio one may calculate that $\frac{A}{A + B + C} = \frac{14}{14 + 35 + 15}$, $\frac{B}{A + B + C} = \frac{35}{14 + 35 + 15}$, and $\frac{C}{A + B + C} = \frac{15}{14 + 35 + 15}$.

## USE OF LOGARITHMS

Any number may be expressed in terms of 10 by use of an exponent showing the power to which the base must be raised to yield that number. This exponent is called the logarithm (commonly abbreviated to log) of the number. Certain numbers are related to the base in such simple fashion that the logarithm may be determined by inspection. For example: $10 = 10^1$, $100 = 10^2$, $1000 = 10^3$, etc., and $0.1 = 10^{-1}$, $0.01 = 10^{-2}$, $0.001 = 10^{-3}$, etc. Thus the corresponding logarithms of 10, 100, and 1000 are 1, 2, and 3, and of 0.1, 0.01, and 0.001 are $-1$, $-2$ and $-3$. All other numbers may be converted to the product of two quantities, one of which will lie between 1 and 10 while the other is one of those numbers whose logarithm can be obtained by inspection. Thus $425 = 4.25 \times 100$ and $0.00378 = 3.78 \times 0.001$. The logarithm of the original numbers will be the sum of the logarithms of these two numbers.

To find the logarithm of the number between 1 and 10 it is necessary to consult a table of logarithms where these values are given. Such a table consists of a series of eleven main columns, headed respectively by No. (or N) and the numbers 0, 1, 2, 3, 4, 5, 6, 7, 8, 9. Depending on whether this is a 3-place, 4-place, or 5-place (etc.) table, the number in the first column will contain 1, 2, or 3 digits, and the numbers in the other columns will contan 3, 4, or 5 digits. Thus a 3-place table gives logarithms of numbers with two significant figures, a 4-place table covers three significant figures and a 5-place table covers four significant figures. Usually a set of "proportional parts" at the side of the regular logarithms permits one to approximate the next significant figure.

In using a table of logarithms it is necessary to remember that the number you are actually looking up lies between 1 and 10 and that the logarithm lies between 0 and 1. For the number, therefore, a decimal point lies after the first digit in the numbers column and the decimal point is understood to precede the logarithm. Using the 3-place table, to find the logarithm of 45, one converts this to the form $10 \times 4.5$, sets down the logarithm of 10 as 1, by inspection, and then consults the table. Run down the first column to 4, then follow this line across to the column headed 5. Here is the number 653. The logarithm of 4.5 is 0.653. The logarithm of 45 is the sum of the two quantities $1 + 0.653$. Thus $45 = 10^{1.653}$. If the number contained 3 digits, such as 455, this would be converted to $100 \times 4.55$, the logarithm for 100 being 2, and the logarithm for 4.55 lying between those for 4.5 and 4.6, i.e., between 0.653 and 0.663. As an approximate value, the logarithm of 4.55 would lie halfway between these two figures and would be taken as 0.658. Thus the logarithm of 455 as determined by a 3-place table would be 2.658.

Logarithms are particularly useful to simplify calculations involving multiplication or division where numbers containing several digits are involved, or in finding powers or extracting roots of such numbers. To multiply numbers together, find their logarithms, add these, and then consult the table to find what number would have this sum as a logarithm. To divide one number by another, subtract the logarithm of the second from the first and use this difference as the logarithm of the answer. To find the power of a number multiply the logarithm of the number by the indicated power and take the result as the logarithm of the desired quantity. To extract a root of a given number divide the logarithm of the number by the root number and look up the number which would have this as its logarithm.

THREE-PLACE LOG TABLE

| | 0 | 1 | 2 | 3 | 4 | 5 | 6 | 7 | 8 | 9 |
|---|---|---|---|---|---|---|---|---|---|---|
| 1 | 000 | 041 | 079 | 114 | 146 | 176 | 204 | 230 | 255 | 279 |
| 2 | 301 | 322 | 342 | 362 | 380 | 398 | 415 | 431 | 447 | 462 |
| 3 | 477 | 491 | 505 | 519 | 531 | 544 | 556 | 568 | 580 | 591 |
| 4 | 602 | 613 | 623 | 633 | 643 | 653 | 663 | 672 | 681 | 690 |
| 5 | 699 | 708 | 716 | 724 | 732 | 740 | 748 | 756 | 763 | 771 |
| 6 | 778 | 785 | 792 | 799 | 806 | 813 | 820 | 826 | 833 | 839 |
| 7 | 845 | 851 | 857 | 863 | 869 | 875 | 881 | 886 | 892 | 898 |
| 8 | 903 | 908 | 914 | 919 | 924 | 929 | 934 | 940 | 944 | 949 |
| 9 | 954 | 959 | 964 | 968 | 973 | 978 | 982 | 987 | 991 | 996 |
| 10 | 000 | 004 | 009 | 013 | 017 | 021 | 025 | 029 | 033 | 037 |

In carrying out these operations by the use of logarithms the answers obtained are seldom exact. Instead they are usually approximations whose accuracy is determined by the number of places in the table. Thus a 3-place table is accurate to two significant figures, a 4-place table to three significant figures and a 5-place table to 4 figures. Example: To multiply 425 by 683:

(*a*) Using a 3-place table:

log of 425 = 2.628
log of 683 = 2.835

sum = 5.463

0.463 is the logarithm of 2.9, therefore 425 × 683 = (approximately) $2.9 \times 10^5$.

(*b*) Using a 4-place table (see p. 332):

log of 425 = 2.6284
log of 683 = 2.8344

sum = 5.4628

0.4628 is the log of a number lying between 2.90 and 2.91. Using the proportional parts this is approximately 2.903. Therefore, the product may be written $2.903 \times 10^5$.

(*c*) Using a 5-place table (chemistry handbook) the corresponding data are:

log of 425 = 2.62839
log of 683 = 2.83442

sum = 5.46281

0.46281 is the log of a number lying between 2.902 and 2.903. It may be approximated as 2.9027. The product would then be written $2.9027 \times 10^5$.

By actual multiplication the product is found to be 290,275. However, it is to be noted that such numbers as 425 and 683, if obtained by experimental measurement, usually involve some rounding off so far as the last digit is concerned. Therefore, there will be an uncertainty in their product which justifies carrying only three significant figures in the answer. To insure this number of significant figures, the common practice is to carry the operation to the fourth place and then round this off to the next higher or lower digit in the third place according to whether it is larger or smaller than 5. On that basis the last three values calculated above—$2.903 \times 10^5$, $2.9027 \times 10^5$, and 290275—would all be rounded off to $2.90 \times 10^5$.

Problem: To calculate $(425)^4$, using a 4-place table:

log of 425 = 2.6284
$4 \times 2.6284 = 10.5136$
0.5136 is the log of 3.263
$(425)^4 = 3.263 \times 10^{10}$ *Ans.*

Problem: To calculate $\sqrt[3]{425}$:

log of 425 = 2.6284
$2.6384 \div 3 = 0.8761$
0.8761 is the log of 7.519
$\sqrt[3]{425} = 7.519$ *Ans.*

*The p-System of Handling Small Numbers.* In calculations involving ionization constants and solubility products, the numbers are usually very small.

Thus, the ionization constant of ammonium hydroxide is $1.8 \times 10^{-5}$, and the solubility product of lead chromate is $1.7 \times 10^{-14}$. The corresponding logarithms are commonly written $5.26 - 10$ and $6.23 - 20$, or $\bar{5}.26$, $\overline{14}.23$. To simplify the stating of these logarithms it is common practice to carry out the addition of the two parts of such logarithms, change the sign, and call them pK, pL, etc. In this system the quantities $\bar{5}.26$ and $\overline{14}.23$ would be changed to 4.74 and 13.77 and referred to as the pK of $NH_4OH$ and the pL of $PbCrO_4$. In similar fashion a concentration of hydrogen or chloride ion of $1 \times 10^{-6}$ would be referred to as a pH or $pCl^-$ of 6.

In calculations involving multiplying, dividing, and finding roots or powers of these small numbers the p-values are somewhat simpler to use than ordinary logarithms. With ordinary logarithms it must be kept in mind that the part to the left of the decimal point is negative while that to the right is positive and the operations must be carried out on these two parts separately. with p-values no such distinction exists. Two problems will serve to illustrate this case.

(*a*) To multiply $2.5 \times 10^{-4}$ by $5.7 \times 10^{-6}$.

Using common logarithms:

$$\begin{aligned} \text{log of } 2.5 \times 10^{-4} &= \bar{4}.40 \\ \text{log of } 5.7 \times 10^{-6} &= \bar{6}.76 \\ \hline \text{sum} &= \bar{9}.16 \end{aligned}$$

In this case the sum of $-4$ and $-6$ is $-10$, but the sum of 0.40 and 0.76 is 1.16; therefore, the $-10$ is changed to $-9$ by the addition of the 1. $\bar{9}.16$ is the log of $1.45 \times 10^{-9}$.

Using p-values:

$$\begin{aligned} \text{p-value of } 2.5 \times 10^{-4} &= 3.60 \\ \text{p-value of } 5.7 \times 10^{-6} &= 5.24 \\ \hline \text{sum} &= 8.84 \end{aligned}$$

The product may be expressed as $10^{-8.84}$, or the p-value may be changed to the usual logarithm $\bar{9}.16$ and the answer given as $1.45 \times 10^{-9}$.

(*b*) To extract the cube root of $2.5 \times 10^{-4}$.

Using common logarithms:

$$\text{log of } 2.5 \times 10^{-4} = \bar{4}.40$$

To extract the cube root it is necessary to convert the $-4$ to a quantity which is a whole multiple of 3, such as $-6$. To offset this change it is necessary to add 2 to the positive part of the logarithm, making the total $\overline{6} + 2.40$. Dividing by 3 gives $\overline{2}.80$ as the logarithm of the answer, which is $6.3 \times 10^{-2}$.

Using p-value of $2.5 \times 10^{-4} = 3.60$:

$3.60 \div 3 = 1.20$

The cube root of $2.5 \times 10^{-4}$ may be expressed as $10^{-1.2}$ or the p-value may be changed to the usual form of logarithm, $\overline{2}.80$, and the answer given as $6.3 \times 10^{-2}$.

# LOGARITHMS

# TABLE XXI. FOUR-PLACE LOGARITHM TABLES

| | LOGARITHMS | | | | | | | | | | Proportional Parts | | | | | | | | |
|---|---|---|---|---|---|---|---|---|---|---|---|---|---|---|---|---|---|---|---|
| No. | 0 | 1 | 2 | 3 | 4 | 5 | 6 | 7 | 8 | 9 | 1 | 2 | 3 | 4 | 5 | 6 | 7 | 8 | 9 |
| 10 | 0000 | 0043 | 0086 | 0128 | 0170 | 0212 | 0253 | 0294 | 0334 | 0374 | 4 | 8 | 12 | 17 | 21 | 25 | 29 | 33 | 37 |
| 11 | 0414 | 0453 | 0492 | 0531 | 0569 | 0607 | 0645 | 0682 | 0719 | 0755 | 4 | 8 | 11 | 15 | 19 | 23 | 26 | 30 | 34 |
| 12 | 0792 | 0828 | 0864 | 0899 | 0934 | 0969 | 1004 | 1038 | 1072 | 1106 | 3 | 7 | 10 | 14 | 17 | 21 | 24 | 28 | 31 |
| 13 | 1139 | 1173 | 1206 | 1239 | 1271 | 1303 | 1335 | 1367 | 1399 | 1430 | 3 | 6 | 10 | 13 | 16 | 19 | 23 | 26 | 29 |
| 14 | 1461 | 1492 | 1523 | 1553 | 1584 | 1614 | 1644 | 1673 | 1703 | 1732 | 3 | 6 | 9 | 12 | 15 | 18 | 21 | 24 | 27 |
| 15 | 1761 | 1790 | 1818 | 1847 | 1875 | 1903 | 1931 | 1959 | 1987 | 2014 | 3 | 6 | 8 | 11 | 14 | 17 | 20 | 22 | 25 |
| 16 | 2041 | 2068 | 2095 | 2122 | 2148 | 2175 | 2201 | 2227 | 2253 | 2279 | 3 | 5 | 8 | 11 | 13 | 16 | 18 | 21 | 24 |
| 17 | 2304 | 2330 | 2355 | 2380 | 2405 | 2430 | 2455 | 2480 | 2504 | 2529 | 2 | 5 | 7 | 10 | 12 | 15 | 17 | 20 | 22 |
| 18 | 2553 | 2577 | 2601 | 2625 | 2648 | 2672 | 2695 | 2718 | 2742 | 2765 | 2 | 5 | 7 | 9 | 12 | 14 | 16 | 19 | 21 |
| 19 | 2788 | 2810 | 2833 | 2856 | 2878 | 2900 | 2923 | 2945 | 2967 | 2989 | 2 | 4 | 7 | 9 | 11 | 13 | 16 | 18 | 20 |
| 20 | 3010 | 3032 | 3054 | 3075 | 3096 | 3118 | 3139 | 3160 | 3181 | 3201 | 2 | 4 | 6 | 8 | 11 | 13 | 15 | 17 | 19 |
| 21 | 3222 | 3243 | 3263 | 3284 | 3304 | 3324 | 3345 | 3365 | 3385 | 3404 | 2 | 4 | 6 | 8 | 10 | 12 | 14 | 16 | 18 |
| 22 | 3424 | 3444 | 3464 | 3483 | 3502 | 3522 | 3541 | 3560 | 3579 | 3598 | 2 | 4 | 6 | 8 | 10 | 12 | 14 | 15 | 17 |
| 23 | 3617 | 3636 | 3655 | 3674 | 3692 | 3711 | 3729 | 3747 | 3766 | 3784 | 2 | 4 | 6 | 7 | 9 | 11 | 13 | 15 | 17 |
| 24 | 3802 | 3820 | 3838 | 3856 | 3874 | 3892 | 3909 | 3927 | 3945 | 3962 | 2 | 4 | 5 | 7 | 9 | 11 | 12 | 14 | 16 |
| 25 | 3979 | 3997 | 4014 | 4031 | 4048 | 4065 | 4082 | 4099 | 4116 | 4133 | 2 | 3 | 5 | 7 | 9 | 10 | 12 | 14 | 15 |
| 26 | 4150 | 4166 | 4183 | 4200 | 4216 | 4232 | 4249 | 4265 | 4281 | 4298 | 3 | 3 | 5 | 7 | 8 | 10 | 11 | 13 | 15 |
| 27 | 4314 | 4330 | 4346 | 4362 | 4378 | 4393 | 4409 | 4425 | 4440 | 4456 | 2 | 3 | 5 | 6 | 8 | 9 | 11 | 13 | 14 |
| 28 | 4472 | 4487 | 4502 | 4518 | 4533 | 4548 | 4564 | 4579 | 4594 | 4609 | 2 | 3 | 5 | 6 | 8 | 9 | 11 | 12 | 14 |
| 29 | 4624 | 4639 | 4654 | 4669 | 4683 | 4698 | 4713 | 4728 | 4742 | 4757 | 1 | 3 | 4 | 6 | 7 | 9 | 10 | 12 | 13 |
| 30 | 4771 | 4786 | 4800 | 4814 | 4829 | 4843 | 4857 | 4871 | 4886 | 4900 | 1 | 3 | 4 | 6 | 7 | 9 | 10 | 11 | 13 |
| 31 | 4914 | 4928 | 4942 | 4955 | 4969 | 4983 | 4997 | 5011 | 5024 | 5038 | 1 | 3 | 4 | 6 | 7 | 8 | 10 | 11 | 12 |
| 32 | 5051 | 5065 | 5079 | 5092 | 5105 | 5119 | 5132 | 5145 | 5159 | 5172 | 1 | 3 | 4 | 5 | 7 | 8 | 9 | 11 | 12 |
| 33 | 5185 | 5198 | 5211 | 5224 | 5237 | 5250 | 5263 | 5276 | 5289 | 5302 | 1 | 3 | 4 | 5 | 6 | 8 | 9 | 10 | 12 |
| 34 | 5315 | 5328 | 5340 | 5353 | 5366 | 5378 | 5391 | 5403 | 5416 | 5428 | 1 | 3 | 4 | 5 | 6 | 8 | 9 | 10 | 11 |
| 35 | 5441 | 5453 | 5465 | 5478 | 5490 | 5502 | 5514 | 5527 | 5539 | 5551 | 1 | 2 | 4 | 5 | 6 | 7 | 9 | 10 | 11 |
| 36 | 5563 | 5575 | 5587 | 5599 | 5611 | 5623 | 5635 | 5647 | 5658 | 5670 | 1 | 2 | 4 | 5 | 6 | 7 | 8 | 10 | 11 |
| 37 | 5682 | 5694 | 5705 | 5717 | 5729 | 5740 | 5752 | 5763 | 5775 | 5786 | 1 | 2 | 3 | 5 | 6 | 7 | 8 | 9 | 10 |
| 38 | 5798 | 5809 | 5821 | 5832 | 5843 | 5855 | 5866 | 5877 | 5888 | 5899 | 1 | 2 | 3 | 5 | 6 | 7 | 8 | 9 | 10 |
| 39 | 5911 | 5922 | 5933 | 5944 | 5955 | 5966 | 5977 | 5988 | 5999 | 6010 | 1 | 2 | 3 | 4 | 5 | 7 | 8 | 9 | 10 |
| 40 | 6021 | 6031 | 6042 | 6053 | 6064 | 6075 | 6085 | 6096 | 6107 | 6117 | 1 | 2 | 3 | 4 | 5 | 6 | 8 | 9 | 10 |
| 41 | 6128 | 6138 | 6149 | 6160 | 6170 | 6180 | 6191 | 6201 | 6212 | 6222 | 1 | 2 | 3 | 4 | 5 | 6 | 7 | 8 | 9 |
| 42 | 6232 | 6243 | 6253 | 6263 | 6274 | 6284 | 6294 | 6304 | 6314 | 6325 | 1 | 2 | 3 | 4 | 5 | 6 | 7 | 8 | 9 |
| 43 | 6335 | 6345 | 6355 | 6365 | 6375 | 6385 | 6395 | 6405 | 6415 | 6425 | 1 | 2 | 3 | 4 | 5 | 6 | 7 | 8 | 9 |
| 44 | 6435 | 6444 | 6454 | 6464 | 6474 | 6484 | 6493 | 6503 | 6513 | 6522 | 1 | 2 | 3 | 4 | 5 | 6 | 7 | 8 | 9 |
| 45 | 6532 | 6542 | 6551 | 6561 | 6571 | 6580 | 6590 | 6599 | 6609 | 6618 | 1 | 2 | 3 | 4 | 5 | 6 | 7 | 8 | 9 |
| 46 | 6628 | 6637 | 6646 | 6656 | 6665 | 6675 | 6684 | 6693 | 6702 | 6712 | 1 | 2 | 3 | 4 | 5 | 6 | 7 | 7 | 8 |
| 47 | 6721 | 6730 | 6739 | 6749 | 6758 | 6767 | 6776 | 6785 | 6794 | 6803 | 1 | 2 | 3 | 4 | 5 | 5 | 6 | 7 | 8 |
| 48 | 6812 | 6821 | 6830 | 6839 | 6848 | 6857 | 6866 | 6875 | 6884 | 6893 | 1 | 2 | 3 | 4 | 4 | 5 | 6 | 7 | 8 |
| 49 | 6902 | 6911 | 6920 | 6928 | 6937 | 6946 | 6955 | 6964 | 6972 | 6981 | 1 | 2 | 3 | 4 | 4 | 5 | 6 | 7 | 8 |
| 50 | 6990 | 6998 | 7007 | 7016 | 7024 | 7033 | 7042 | 7050 | 7059 | 7067 | 1 | 2 | 3 | 3 | 4 | 5 | 6 | 7 | 8 |
| 51 | 7076 | 7084 | 7093 | 7101 | 7110 | 7118 | 7126 | 7135 | 7143 | 7152 | 1 | 2 | 3 | 3 | 4 | 5 | 6 | 7 | 8 |
| 52 | 7160 | 7168 | 7177 | 7185 | 7193 | 7202 | 7210 | 7218 | 7226 | 7235 | 1 | 2 | 2 | 3 | 4 | 5 | 6 | 7 | 7 |
| 53 | 7243 | 7251 | 7259 | 7267 | 7275 | 7284 | 7292 | 7300 | 7308 | 7316 | 1 | 2 | 2 | 3 | 4 | 5 | 6 | 6 | 7 |
| 54 | 7324 | 7332 | 7340 | 7348 | 7356 | 7364 | 7372 | 7380 | 7388 | 7396 | 1 | 2 | 2 | 3 | 4 | 5 | 6 | 6 | 7 |
| No. | 0 | 1 | 2 | 3 | 4 | 5 | 6 | 7 | 8 | 9 | 1 | 2 | 3 | 4 | 5 | 6 | 7 | 8 | 9 |

## TABLE XXI. FOUR-PLACE LOGARITHM TABLES (Continued)

| No. | LOGARITHMS 0 | 1 | 2 | 3 | 4 | 5 | 6 | 7 | 8 | 9 | Proportional Parts 1 | 2 | 3 | 4 | 5 | 6 | 7 | 8 | 9 |
|---|---|---|---|---|---|---|---|---|---|---|---|---|---|---|---|---|---|---|---|
| 55 | 7404 | 7412 | 7419 | 7427 | 7435 | 7443 | 7451 | 7459 | 7466 | 7474 | 1 | 2 | 2 | 3 | 4 | 5 | 5 | 6 | 7 |
| 56 | 7482 | 7490 | 7497 | 7505 | 7513 | 7520 | 7528 | 7536 | 7543 | 7551 | 1 | 2 | 2 | 3 | 4 | 5 | 5 | 6 | 7 |
| 57 | 7559 | 7566 | 7574 | 7582 | 7589 | 7597 | 7604 | 7612 | 7619 | 7627 | 1 | 2 | 2 | 3 | 4 | 5 | 5 | 6 | 7 |
| 58 | 7634 | 7642 | 7649 | 7657 | 7664 | 7672 | 7679 | 7686 | 7694 | 7701 | 1 | 1 | 2 | 3 | 4 | 4 | 5 | 6 | 7 |
| 59 | 7709 | 7716 | 7723 | 7731 | 7738 | 7745 | 7752 | 7760 | 7767 | 7774 | 1 | 1 | 2 | 3 | 4 | 4 | 5 | 6 | 7 |
| 60 | 7782 | 7789 | 7796 | 7803 | 7810 | 7818 | 7825 | 7832 | 7839 | 7846 | 1 | 1 | 2 | 3 | 4 | 4 | 5 | 6 | 6 |
| 61 | 7853 | 7860 | 7868 | 7875 | 7882 | 7889 | 7896 | 7903 | 7910 | 7917 | 1 | 1 | 2 | 3 | 4 | 4 | 5 | 6 | 6 |
| 62 | 7924 | 7931 | 7938 | 7945 | 7952 | 7959 | 7966 | 7973 | 7980 | 7987 | 1 | 1 | 2 | 3 | 3 | 4 | 5 | 6 | 6 |
| 63 | 7993 | 8000 | 8007 | 8014 | 8021 | 8028 | 8035 | 8041 | 8048 | 8055 | 1 | 1 | 2 | 3 | 3 | 4 | 5 | 5 | 6 |
| 64 | 8062 | 8069 | 8075 | 8082 | 8089 | 8096 | 8102 | 8109 | 8116 | 8122 | 1 | 1 | 2 | 3 | 3 | 4 | 5 | 5 | 6 |
| 65 | 8129 | 8136 | 8142 | 8149 | 8156 | 8162 | 8169 | 8176 | 8182 | 8189 | 1 | 1 | 2 | 3 | 3 | 4 | 5 | 5 | 6 |
| 66 | 8195 | 8202 | 8209 | 8215 | 8222 | 8228 | 8235 | 8241 | 8248 | 8254 | 1 | 1 | 2 | 3 | 3 | 4 | 5 | 5 | 6 |
| 67 | 8261 | 8267 | 8274 | 8280 | 8287 | 8293 | 8299 | 8306 | 8312 | 8319 | 1 | 1 | 2 | 3 | 3 | 4 | 5 | 5 | 6 |
| 68 | 8325 | 8331 | 8338 | 8344 | 8351 | 8357 | 8363 | 8370 | 8376 | 8382 | 1 | 1 | 2 | 3 | 3 | 4 | 4 | 5 | 6 |
| 69 | 8388 | 8395 | 8401 | 8407 | 8414 | 8420 | 8426 | 8432 | 8439 | 8445 | 1 | 1 | 2 | 2 | 3 | 4 | 4 | 5 | 6 |
| 70 | 8451 | 8457 | 8463 | 8470 | 8476 | 8482 | 8488 | 8494 | 8500 | 8506 | 1 | 1 | 2 | 2 | 3 | 4 | 4 | 5 | 6 |
| 71 | 8513 | 8519 | 8525 | 8531 | 8537 | 8543 | 8549 | 8555 | 8561 | 8567 | 1 | 1 | 2 | 2 | 3 | 4 | 4 | 5 | 5 |
| 72 | 8573 | 8579 | 8585 | 8591 | 8597 | 8603 | 8609 | 8615 | 8621 | 8627 | 1 | 1 | 2 | 2 | 3 | 4 | 4 | 5 | 5 |
| 73 | 8633 | 8639 | 8645 | 8651 | 8657 | 8663 | 8669 | 8675 | 8681 | 8686 | 1 | 1 | 2 | 2 | 3 | 4 | 4 | 5 | 5 |
| 74 | 8692 | 8698 | 8704 | 8710 | 8716 | 8722 | 8727 | 8733 | 8739 | 8745 | 1 | 1 | 2 | 2 | 3 | 4 | 4 | 5 | 5 |
| 75 | 8751 | 8756 | 8762 | 8768 | 8774 | 8779 | 8785 | 8791 | 8797 | 8802 | 1 | 1 | 2 | 2 | 3 | 3 | 4 | 5 | 5 |
| 76 | 8808 | 8814 | 8820 | 8825 | 8831 | 8837 | 8842 | 8848 | 8854 | 8859 | 1 | 1 | 2 | 2 | 3 | 3 | 4 | 5 | 5 |
| 77 | 8865 | 8871 | 8876 | 8882 | 8887 | 8893 | 8899 | 8904 | 8910 | 8915 | 1 | 1 | 2 | 2 | 3 | 3 | 4 | 4 | 5 |
| 78 | 8921 | 8927 | 8932 | 8938 | 8943 | 8949 | 8954 | 8960 | 8965 | 8971 | 1 | 1 | 2 | 2 | 3 | 3 | 4 | 4 | 5 |
| 79 | 8976 | 8982 | 8987 | 8993 | 8998 | 9004 | 9009 | 9015 | 9020 | 9025 | 1 | 1 | 2 | 2 | 3 | 3 | 4 | 4 | 5 |
| 80 | 9031 | 9036 | 9042 | 9047 | 9053 | 9058 | 9063 | 9069 | 9074 | 9079 | 1 | 1 | 2 | 2 | 3 | 3 | 4 | 4 | 5 |
| 81 | 9085 | 9090 | 9096 | 9101 | 9106 | 9112 | 9117 | 9122 | 9128 | 9133 | 1 | 1 | 2 | 2 | 3 | 3 | 4 | 4 | 5 |
| 82 | 9138 | 9143 | 9149 | 9154 | 9159 | 9165 | 9170 | 9175 | 9180 | 9186 | 1 | 1 | 2 | 2 | 3 | 3 | 4 | 4 | 5 |
| 83 | 9191 | 9196 | 9201 | 9206 | 9212 | 9217 | 9222 | 9227 | 9232 | 9238 | 1 | 1 | 2 | 2 | 3 | 3 | 4 | 4 | 5 |
| 84 | 9243 | 9248 | 9253 | 9258 | 9263 | 9269 | 9274 | 9279 | 9284 | 9289 | 1 | 1 | 2 | 2 | 3 | 3 | 4 | 4 | 5 |
| 85 | 9294 | 9299 | 9304 | 9309 | 9315 | 9320 | 9325 | 9330 | 9335 | 9340 | 1 | 1 | 2 | 2 | 3 | 3 | 4 | 4 | 5 |
| 86 | 9345 | 9350 | 9355 | 9360 | 9365 | 9370 | 9375 | 9380 | 9385 | 9390 | 1 | 1 | 2 | 2 | 3 | 3 | 4 | 4 | 5 |
| 87 | 9395 | 9400 | 9405 | 9410 | 9415 | 9420 | 9425 | 9430 | 9435 | 9440 | 0 | 1 | 1 | 2 | 2 | 3 | 3 | 4 | 4 |
| 88 | 9445 | 9450 | 9455 | 9460 | 9465 | 9469 | 9474 | 9479 | 9484 | 9489 | 0 | 1 | 1 | 2 | 2 | 3 | 3 | 4 | 4 |
| 89 | 9494 | 9499 | 9504 | 9509 | 9513 | 9518 | 9523 | 9528 | 9533 | 9538 | 0 | 1 | 1 | 2 | 2 | 3 | 3 | 4 | 4 |
| 90 | 9542 | 9547 | 9552 | 9557 | 9562 | 9566 | 9571 | 9576 | 9581 | 9586 | 0 | 1 | 1 | 2 | 2 | 3 | 3 | 4 | 4 |
| 91 | 9590 | 9595 | 9600 | 9605 | 9609 | 9614 | 9619 | 9624 | 9628 | 9633 | 0 | 1 | 1 | 2 | 2 | 3 | 3 | 4 | 4 |
| 92 | 9638 | 9643 | 9647 | 9652 | 9657 | 9661 | 9666 | 9671 | 9675 | 9680 | 0 | 1 | 1 | 2 | 2 | 3 | 3 | 4 | 4 |
| 93 | 9685 | 9689 | 9694 | 9699 | 9703 | 9708 | 9713 | 9717 | 9722 | 9727 | 0 | 1 | 1 | 2 | 2 | 3 | 3 | 4 | 4 |
| 94 | 9731 | 9736 | 9741 | 9745 | 9750 | 9754 | 9759 | 9763 | 9768 | 9773 | 0 | 1 | 1 | 2 | 2 | 3 | 3 | 4 | 4 |
| 95 | 9777 | 9782 | 9786 | 9791 | 9795 | 9800 | 9805 | 9809 | 9814 | 9818 | 0 | 1 | 1 | 2 | 2 | 3 | 3 | 4 | 4 |
| 96 | 9823 | 9827 | 9832 | 9836 | 9841 | 9845 | 9850 | 9854 | 9859 | 9863 | 0 | 1 | 1 | 2 | 2 | 3 | 3 | 4 | 4 |
| 97 | 9868 | 9872 | 9877 | 9881 | 9886 | 9890 | 9894 | 9899 | 9903 | 9908 | 0 | 1 | 1 | 2 | 2 | 3 | 3 | 4 | 4 |
| 98 | 9912 | 9917 | 9921 | 9926 | 9930 | 9934 | 9939 | 9943 | 9948 | 9952 | 0 | 1 | 1 | 2 | 2 | 3 | 3 | 4 | 4 |
| 99 | 9956 | 9961 | 9965 | 9969 | 9974 | 9978 | 9983 | 9987 | 9991 | 9996 | 0 | 1 | 1 | 2 | 2 | 3 | 3 | 3 | 4 |
| No. | 0 | 1 | 2 | 3 | 4 | 5 | 6 | 7 | 8 | 9 | 1 | 2 | 3 | 4 | 5 | 6 | 7 | 8 | 9 |

# Index

E.M.F. Series

| | |
|---|---|
| K | $H_2$ |
| Ca | Sb |
| Mg | Bi |
| Mn | As |
| Zn | Cu |
| Cr | Ag |
| Fe | Hg |
| Cd | Au |
| Co | |
| Ni | |
| Sn | |
| Pb | |
| $H_2$ | |